HUMPHREY WELCH • GORD(

The World Checklist
of Conifers

Gordon Haddow

Published by Landsman's Bookshop Ltd.
On behalf of The World Conifer Datapool

Preface

The compilers have taken all possible care to ensure accuracy, but it is obvious that in a work of this kind , undertaken by individuals at their own inclination and expense over a period of years, that errors and omissions are inevitable. The Checklist is believed to be the most complete and authoritative listing of its kind ever to have been published. Nevertheless the data on which it is based can only be the information in the possession of the World Conifer Data Pool, and no responsibility is accepted by the compilers or the publishers.

It is also obvious that where any shortcoming is found, the only remedy is for the finder to acquaint us with the true facts for incorporation in a later Edition. In the meantime we apologise and invite correspondence to this end.

In the compilation of a list of this kind, just as perfection is unattainable, so also is completeness. This is because botany itself is an on-going science and also because horticulturists continue to produce marketable novelties that they describe as "new named garden varieties" ('Cultivars', to the cognoscenti). And in this profitable way of enriching our gardens and landscapes they meet the problem of publicising their wares.

In this problem, an early appearance in a widely-circulated medium must have considerable value. WCDP intend to follow up the World Checklist by publishing Supplements at intervals, pending the production of an amended Edition. We shall be happy to include particulars of any novelty, provided that it has a *prima face* that will enrich our gardens and not merely lengthen the long lists of cultivars with which we already have to struggle, and provided also that we are supplied with as much data to put on record as is known or can be obtained. Important are the names of the individuals and their addresses, the places and the dates involved in (i) the origination (i.e. the finding or raising) of the plant, (2) in its naming, (3) in its introduction to the trade. And, most important of all, (4) details of the first known appearance of the name in print. And, of course, a practical man' s description of the plant and how it differs from those we have already.

We would be pleased to be on nurserymen's mailing lists for catalogues, but rarely is a catalogue "blurb" adequate as the sort of description that is required for record purposes . This calls for a delineation in sufficient detail not only to describe the plant, but also to distinguish it from other, similar plants already in cultivation.

Introduction

The World Checklist of Conifers contains about 10,000 names, old and new, each with one or more lines of relevant data. It is intended to be a practical working tool for horticulturists, especially as an aid to answering the following questions that at present bedevil the world of cultivated conifers.

We have a conifer - What is its name?
We know the name - Have we the right plant?

The authors of the book *Manual of Cultivated Conifers* (Den Ouden and Boom) published in 1965 claimed (although not with complete success) to have included the names of all the cultivars published since 1753, making that book a useful standby for everyone concerned with this important group of plants. Unfortunately the surviving author died soon after the book's appearance, and since then there has been little, if any, systematic work done in this field save by one or two private conifer enthusiasts. So for 27 years no updated checklist has been published, although the proliferation of new conifer cultivars throughout the world since 1965 has given rise to a much-felt need for one.

The *World Checklist of Conifers* is an attempt to meet that need.

The layout follows the arrangement used in nursery catalogues from time immemorial, and every device is used to make the Checklist "user-friendly". Italics distinguish between botanical and horticultural names and Bold type is used to pick out the accredited from illegitimate, obsolete, undocumented and 'other' names. Hundreds of synonyms and cross-references are included, together with references to widely available conifer manuals for further information.

The Checklist is based on the World Conifer Data Pool records that Humphrey Welch has been building up since 1965, working alone until joined recently by Gordon Haddow. Wherever possible it follows such parts of the International Conifer Register as have so far been published, and hopefully it will form a useful basis for future work on that erudite undertaking. But a checklist is not the same as a register --- they are very different in appearance, they are used by different people and they serve different purposes. So both are required. But as the Royal Horticultural Society was appointed International Registration Authority for this group in 1964, yet only three Parts (out of a possible ten) have so far been published, the World Checklist will probably have to serve as a useful and authoritative stand-by for some years to come. In addition to valuable help from the present Registrar, John Lewis, WCDP has had the support of the Horticultural Trades Association (U.K.), the Royal Boskoop Horticultural Society (Holland), the Conifer Society of Australia and the American Conifer Society (including in this last case a substantial donation which is here gratefully acknowledged), and also much help from members of WCDP and a host of other helpers world-wide, too numerous to mention. To all who have helped in any way we here express the debt of gratitude due to them from all users of this book, with a special vote of thanks to June Haddow for tackling all this tricky typing.

All botanical names and author citations follow the currently accepted classification. In cases still under dispute amongst botanists, the authority here followed is stated. No taxonomic changes are here proposed.

The *Cultivated Code* (ICNCP), including (where considered relevant) changes proposed in a revision of the Code now under discussion, has been followed except that inadequate information in some cases has compelled the rounding of a few corners. So, for instance, "First valid publication" sometimes must be read "First appearance in print known to WCDP". And where a plant first recorded as a cultivar (as was the case with many of the early names) was drawn into the infra-specific jungle but has found its way out again, the logical principle "Once a cultivar, always a cultivar" has been accepted. And since the Code (Art. 47) states that the cultivar name remains unchanged when the botanical name is changed, it is usually the first known use of the basionym that is recorded, this being the only event of any present-day horticultural significance. Other cases may be found where the practical convenience of users of the Checklist has been given priority over an academic approach.

No claim is made that the list is exhaustive. Names raised a century or more ago by long-since-dead authors, (oftimes for a single tree, never seen or heard of since) on the one hand and the names being lavished nowadays by irresponsible persons on untried novelties on the other are not included. Otherwise, most names found "in the literature" are listed as are also names known by WCDP to be in current use in the trade or listed in important conifer collections or nursery catalogues, or which have been culled from other reliable sources, including extensive correspondence.

The data having been brought together from such a variety of sources, it varies widely in completeness, (and possibly, in a few cases, in accuracy). Limitations of space preclude full bibliographical case-histories or diagnostic descriptions. Where the information is available, a basic description is given and also whatever data is available to provide the vital connection between the name first used for a plant (i.e. the basionym), the coiner of that name and the plant to which the name rightly and exclusively belongs. Fuller information, available to enquirers, is available in most cases on WCDP files, to which the Checklist serves as a sort of index.

The data has been verified wherever possible, but this is put out as a 'Preliminary' edition so that all entries may be critically examined. Doubtless much additional data will be brought to our notice, additional names will need to be added and mistakes corrected. Our dependence on world-wide help in this work is obvious and we invite contributions, great or small.

What of the Future.

It must be evident that the price at which this Checklist is being distributed represents only a fraction of the cost of assembling the data over the 25 years spent in its compilation, let alone the cost of the actual production. This puts each user of the book who is interested in conifers and in the appearance of an up-graded edition 'on the spot'. So, hopefully, every reader possessed of information that he could contribute for the general benefit will do just that. This obligation should be particularly felt by anyone conscious of having knowledge unique to himself that will perish for ever when he passes on unless he relieves his conscience in time. But even 'scraps' of knowledge, if reliable, help to build up the whole picture so are equally of value.

How soon it appears, and how great the improvement possible in a revised edition will largely depend on the response to our appeal in the preceding paragraph. As new material accumulates we intend issuing Supplements at intervals. These will be sent free to those who have responded to our plea for help. Nurserymen and those who introduce 'novelties' need to realise that the only way to protect the new introduction and the name chosen for it and to prevent future confusion (or worse) in the trade is to publicise it as widely as possible **before any distribution of the plant or use of the name is commenced.**. Information supplied to WCDP will ensure world-wide publicity in the next Supplement or Edition.

The World Conifer Data Pool is a non-institutional group aimed at providing a central collection-centre for data relating to cultivated conifers world-wide and to hold, as a service to horticulture, a *corpus* of information available to everyone who can make use of it, including any registration authority. It must be obvious that such an on-going, global objective cannot be left indefinitely to a group of enthusiasts, so widespread thought should be given to how the continuation of such an important service can be put onto a permanent basis. Consideration is being given to the possible formation of an Educational Trust. Anybody, or any Body, interested in developing this or any feasible alternative scheme is invited to let us know at the address below.

The World Conifer Data Pool,
"Treetops"
Buzzacott Lane,   Humphrey Welch
Combe Martin,
Devon EX34 0NL, U.K.   Tel: 0271 883761   Gordon Haddow

Using the Checklist

The general layout will be familiar to anyone who has ever used a nurseryman' catalogue.

Typography

Valid (i.e. "correct") names of species in Column One are printed in ***Bold Italics***

All other botanical names are printed in *Italics*.

Cultivar names in Column One that have been verified by WCDP are printed in **Bold** type.

Cultivar names considered to be obsolete, illegitimate or not verified by WCDP are printed in Roman type.

The use of Columns

COLUMN ONE The scientific name of the plant . This always consists of (or at .least must commence with) two Latin words, either spelled out or represented by hyphens. The first is the name of the Genus (i.e. the "generic" name, here always printed in Capitals). Each of the 43 Genera has its own Chapter and they are listed alphabetically through the book. *(Abies, Araucaria, Athrotaxis* etc., through to *Widdringtonia.).*

The second word is the Specific name (epithet). These two Latin words together are the name of the species. Every plant except a hybrid must 'belong' to one particular species. The species are listed in alphabetical order within each Genus. (Note that the singular and plural of the word species are spelled the same).

Where a plant is in a minor botanical category below 'species' (hence the term "infra-specific"), or is a cultivated garden variety (usually abbreviated to **cultivar** or **cv.**.) the two Latin words are replaced by hyphens to save space and a third element is added to the name. If the variation is botanically recognised it will be printed in italics and the abbreviations "sub-species", "var." or "f" will have been used. If it is a cultivar it will be printed within single quote-marks and with Initial Capitals. All such trinomials are listed alphabetically following the relevant species name. (Note that the alphabetical order of cultivar names consisting of more than one word is determined by regarding each such name as a single English word.).

So, **by opening the book at the right Genus and then searching for the required species,** any plant whose full name is known can be readily found. Numerous cross references have been included to help in other cases.

The name of the plant is followed (outside the 'quotes') by the name of its coiner, technically the 'author' of or the 'authority' for the name. This of importance for removal of doubt where two authors have used the same name for two different plants. If the author's name is not known to WCDP it will have been replaced by "Hort. . ."., an abbreviation of a Latin word meaning 'of gardens' or 'of gardeners'.

One editorial problem due to our lack of global omniscience has been to decide when to use Bold type to differentiate between names fully authenticated by WCDP and other names. Some names in the latter group are obsolete or illegitimate, but a large number would have had this recognition had we been better informed. We apologise for any such case, which shall be corrected as soon as we are made aware of the facts.

Another matter of great difficulty has been ascertaining the legitimacy of some cultivar names consisting of or containing Latin or Latin-form names. Such names in recognised use before 1st January 1959 may be retained, provided the new typography is used, but any name introduced since that date is illegitimate and **must be replaced.** . But despite the rule, such names are still being introduced for conifers (and by people who must know better), so there are many names in use whose acceptability rests on the date of their publication. This is a matter of fact, not opinion, so such names can only be tentatively allocated here, pending evidence of their 'date of birth'. Here again, we rely on world-wide help. Persons with any responsibility for any illegitimate name should accept immediate responsibility for rectifying the situation by proposing an acceptable name. WCDP will offer advice if requested and will publicise any such name change if notified thereof with a brief explanation of the circumstances.

COLUMN TWO The Date   This is the date of the "first valid publication" of a name where this is known. Otherwise it is. the date of the first use of the name in the trade known to WCDP. Where this is a dated nurseryman's catalogue that vital **first appearance** might have been in an earlier catalogue which we have not seen (or the credit might be due to an altogether different firm). We have very limited access to early catalogues, so an offer of help from anyone with access to a good collection (in any country, including U.K.) would be very welcome

COLUMN THREE Identification of the plant with the name   The only facts that are beyond dispute are what is known as the **Protologue** of the name. This is defined as "Everything associated with the name at its first publication, i.e. diagnosis, description, illustrations, references, synonymy, geographical data, citation of specimens, discussion and comments".

Full diagnostic descriptions are seldom available and are precluded by lack of space. Of greater value are the names and addresses, the places and the dates surrounding the origination. --- its finding, selection or raising --- of: the coiner of the name, of: the introducer to the trade and of the first appearance in print or in a dated nursery catalogue and of the first good published description or picture.

NIC means that the plant is either "Not in cultivation", (i.e. no living specimen is recorded by WCDP) or is "Not in circulation" (i.e. No current source of supply is known). In the absence of evidence to the contrary, we have used the symbol arbitrarily for introductions earlier than 1900.

Botanical terms are avoided so far as possible and words used both with an every-day, gardeners' meaning and also as a botanical term are used in the former sense unless the latter is clear from the context. No reference is made to plant production rights or patents.

COLUMN FOUR   This column is used in two ways. For species it is used for the probable height in metres of a maturing tree in cultivation and its hardiness under favourable conditions, under the U.S.D.A. scale. Both these figures can only be approximations.

In other cases it is used to gives coded references to the following readily available conifer manuals as sources of further information, case by case.

B	Den Ouden and Boom	*Manual of Cultivated Conifers*. (1965) .
C	A. Carlisle	*Guide to the named varieties of Scots fir*. In "Forestry" Vol. 31 (1958).
D	Dallimore and Jackson	Handbook of Coniferae. (Editions 1923 to 1966).
G	D.M. van Gelderen and J.R.P. van Hoey-Smith. *Conifers*. (1967).	
H	M. Hornibrook	*Dwarf and Slow-growing Conifers*. Editions 1923 and 1939).
K	G. Krussmann	*Die Nadelgeholze* (Editions 1955, 1960, 1979). *Handbuch der Nadelgeholze*. (German, editions 1972, and 1983) *Manual of Cultivated Conifers*. English translation.
N	W.N. Valavanis	*Japanese Five-needle Pines*. (1976). (1985)
R	K. Rushforth	*Conifers*. (1987).
S	J.C. Swartley	*The Cultivated Hemlocks*. (1984).
W1	Humphrey Welch	*Dwarf Conifers*. (1966).
W2		*Manual of Dwarf Conifers*. (1979).
W3		*The Conifer Manual*, Vol. 1. (1991).

COLUMN FIVE   This column is limited by the space available to a broad indication of the country or area of origin. Due to recent political changes some names, may be obsolete.

A B I E S Miller (1766) Fir, Silver fir

Pinaceae

The nomenclature of the Silver Firs is not straightforward. For many years, until 1768, they were included in the Genus *Pinus*. Even then it was a long time before the *Abies* were clearly separated from other genera. Later still, several important writers reversed the accepted use of *Abies* for the Firs and *Picea* for the Spruces, and this has caused a great deal of confusion. The genus is remarkably undiversified. As a result of this the species are difficult to recognise and there have been many suggested changes of rank and position, and the disputes continue. To help meet the resulting complicated situation numerous cross-references are listed.

ABIES abies (L.) Borbas   1902 Now known as *PICEA abies*.

ABIES acicularis Maximowicz
                               1868 Now known as *PICEA bicolor*.

ABIES acutissima Knight & Perry
                               1850 Now known as *PICEA glauca*.

ABIES ajanensis Lindley and Gordon
                               1850 Now known as *PICEA jezoensis*.

ABIES alba (1) Michaud   1810 Now known as *PICEA glauca*.

ABIES alba (2) Miller   1759 Silver Fir, European Silver Fir. Formerly known as *ABIES pectinata*. Less ornamental than some species.   40-50m,Z6   Europe

- - var. *acutifolia* Turrill   1925 Now known as *ABIES borisii-regis*. (per Liu, 1971).

- - var. *alpina* Svoboda   1964 No longer distinguished within the species. (per Liu, 1971).

- - **'Apennina'** Svoboda   1953 A listed name. No further information.

- - **'Aurea'** Nelson   1866 Some leaves yellow, others green. Unstable.   B,K,W3   U.K.

- - 'Aureovariegata' Sénéclauze
                               1868 Not distinct from 'Aurea'.   France

- - 'Auricoma' Carrière   1867 Not distinct from 'Aurea'.   France

- - 'Bad Wildungen' Horstmann
                               1978 In "Naamslijst . . .".   Germany

- - 'Baldensis' Zuccarini ex Nyman
                               1878 Not now distinguished within the species. (per Int. Con. Register. 1987).

- - **'Barabit's Spreader'** Hort. Hungary.
                               1980 Dwarf spreading. O. Barabits, Sopron, Hungary.

- - **'Brevifolia'** Carrière   1867 Dwarf, leaves short and broad.O. Sénéclauze Nurs, Bourg Argental, Loires (1861). NIC.   B,D,H,K   France

- - var. *bulgarica* Svoboda   1960 Now known as *ABIES* x *borisii-regis*.

- - var. *calabrica* Svoboda   1964 Now known as *ABIES nebrodensis*.

- - 'Candicans' Masters   1892 A selection with whitish foliage. No longer identifiable.   Europe

- - 'Cinerea' Baumann   1835 A selection with greyish foliage.

- - **'Columnaris'** Carrière   1859 Columnar, numerous short branches. O. Found in a forest on Mount Pila. NIC.   B,D,K,W3   France

- - **'Compacta'** Parsons   1887 Descriptively named but now seldom seen. O. Parsons Nurs, Flushing, N.Y.   B,D,G,H,K,W2 U.S.A.

- - 'Elegans' Carrière   1867 A dwarf, bushy plant. NIC.   B,K   France

- - 'Fastigiata' Carrière	1855	A fastigiate tree. I. Sénéclauze Nurs, Bourg Argental, Loires (1846). O. Found in the forests of Grande Chartreuse. NIC.	B,K,R,W3	France
- - 'Flabellata' Beissner	1910	Named for a tree found in a forest near Erlangen. NIC.	B,K	Germany
- - *folliis variegata* Loudon	1838	See 'Variegata'.		U.K.
- - 'Gelbunt' G. Horstmann	1978	In "Nameslist . . .". An unacceptable listed name for a weak growing tree with yellowish foliage.		Germany
- - 'Glauca' Knight & Perry	1850	Now known as *PICEA glauca* 'Coerulea'.		
- - 'Globosa' Hort. Amer.	1986	An illegit. listed name.		U.S.A.
- - **'Green Spiral'** Welch	1979	A pendulous tree with spiralling branches. O. Secrest Arboretum, Wooster, Ohio, (Not = 'Tortuosa').	K,W2	U.S.A.
- - 'Irramosa' Moreillon	1896	Named for a tree found in the forest of Chaumont. NIC.	B,K	Switzerl.
- -'**King's Dwarf**' Hort. Anglia	1983	A listed name for a dense conical plant. I. King and Paton Nurs, Sandyhills by Dalbeattie.		Scotland
- - 'Leioclada' Steven	1838	A confused name. Now listed under *ABIES nordmanniana*. (per Int. Con. Register. 1987). NIC.		Russia
- - 'Massonii' Beissner	1884	Leaves spreading radially as in *ABIES pinsapo*. NIC.	B,K	Germany
- - 'Metensis' Sénéclauze	1846	Named for a fastigiate tree at Metz. NIC.		France
- - 'Microcarpa' Nelson	1866	"Cones small". No longer identifiable.	B,K	U.K.
- - 'Microphylla' Carrière	1867	A congested dwarf form with small buds and leaves. NIC.	B,D,H,K,W3	France
- - 'Minima' Knight & Perry	1850	Now known as *PICEA glauca* 'Minima'.		
- - 'Minor' Masters	1892	No longer identifiable. NIC.		U.K.
- - **'Mlada Boleslaw'** Hort. Germany	1984	Dwarf bush. I. Horstmann Nurs, Schneverdingen, Germany. (1992).		Hungary
- - 'Nana' (1) Knight & Perry	1850	No longer identifiable. NIC.	B,W2	U.K.
- - 'Nana' (2) Loudon	1838	Now listed under *PICEA glauca*.		U.K.
- - 'Nana Compacta' Hort.		A listed name. (Probably = "Compacta").		
- - f. *parsonii* Mattfeld	1925	Not now distinguished within the species.		
- - **'Pendula'** Knight & Perry	1850	Narrowly columnar. O. Godefroy, Ville d'Avray (1835). Probably several clones in cultivation.	B,D,G,H,W2	France
- - **'Pendula Gracilis'** Sénéclauze	1868	Longer branches than last. O. Found by M. Massé.	B,K,W2	France
- - 'Podolica' Beissner	1909	NIC.		
- - 'Polonica' Svoboda	1953	NIC.		
- - 'Prostrata' Hort ex Gordon	1858	A synonym of 'Nana'. NIC.		
- - 'Pumila' Beissner	1889	A name of uncertain application. NIC.		Germany
- - **'Pygmy'** Linssen	1990	A globose dwarf of unrecorded origin.		
- - **'Pyramidalis'** Lawson	1851	Columnar, ageing to conical. Dense, erect branches.	B,D,G,K,W3	U.K.

- - 'Recurva' Sénéclauze   1868   A mere curiosity. Found in a forest on Mount Pila. NIC.   B,K   France

- - **'Scarabantia'** Hort. Germany
     1980   Dwarf bush. **I.** Horstmann Nurs, Schneverdingen, Germany. (1992).   Hungary

- - **'Schwarzwald'** G.Horstmann
     1983   In "Nameslist . . .". A dense, short leaved form raised from a witch's broom found at Badenweiler in Schwarzwald.   Germany

- - 'Spinescens' Beck   1895   NIC.

- - 'Stricta' Carrière   1867   Conical, broader than 'Pyramidalis'; thick branches, less erect. NIC.   France

- - 'Tenuifolia' Loudon   1842   In "Encyclopaedia of Trees".O. Smith of Ayr. NIC.   B,K   Scotland

- - 'Tenuiorifolia' Beissner   1891   A mere curiosity. Named for a tree found in a park at Worlitz, NIC.   B,K   Germany

- - **'Tortuosa'** (Lawson) Booth
     1838   Dwarf with irregularly twisted branches and leaves. **O. J.** Booth & Sons, Flottbeck Nurs, Hamburg. (NOT = 'Green Spiral').   B,D,H,K,W2   Germany

- - 'Umbraculifera' Sénéclauze
     1868   Named for a tree found near the Loire river. NIC.   B,K   France

- - 'Variegata' Forbes   1839   Named for a tree at Woburn with a slight variegation. NIC.   B,K   U.K.

- - 'Virgata' Caspary   1883   Snakelike branches. Named for a tree seen in 1879. NIC.   B,D,K,W3   Czechoslo.

ABIES albertiana A. Murray
     1863   Now known as *TSUGA heterophylla.*

ABIES alcockiana Veitch   1861   Now known as *PICEA bicolor.*

ABIES alpestris Bruegger   1887   Now known as *PICEA abies.*

ABIES amabilis (1) Pardé   1906   Now known as *ABIES concolor* var. *lowiana.*

ABIES amabilis (2) (Douglas) Forbes
     1839   Red Fir, Pacific Silver Fir.   25-35m,Z6   Canada/U.S.A.

- - 'Blijdenstein' Hort.   Superfluous name for 'Spreading Star'.

- - **'Compacta'** Hornibrook   1923   A compact dwarf form, apt to become tree-like in time. **O.** S.B. Parsons Nurs, Flushing, N.Y. NIC.   B,D,G,H,K   U.S.A.

- - var. *magnifica* Lavallee   1877   Now known as *ABIES magnifica.*

- - 'Procumbens' Hort. Anglia
     1964   A superfluous illegit. name for 'Spreading Star'.

- - **'Spreading Star'** Den Ouden/Boom
     1965   A magnificent spreading specimen. **O.** Blijdenstein Pinetum, Hilversum. Probably a cultivariant.   B,K,R,W1   Holland

ABIES americana (1) K. Koch
     1873   Now known as *PICEA mariana.*

ABIES americana (2) Miller   1768   Now known as *TSUGA canadensis.*

ABIES apollinis (1) Link   1841   Now known as *ABIES cephalonica* var. *apollinis.*

ABIES apollinis (2) Bornmueller
     1899   Now known as *ABIES* x *bornmuelleriana.*

ABIES araragi Siebold   1830   Now known as *TSUGA sieboldii.*

ABIES araucana Poiret   1804 Now known as *ARAUCARIA araucana*.

ABIES arctica (1) Cunningham ex Gordon
                      1858 Now known as *PICEA mariana*.

ABIES arctica (2) A. Murray
                      1867 Now known as *PICEA glauca*.

ABIES arizonica Merriam   1896 Now known as *ABIES lasiocarpa* var. *arizonica*.

- - *f. compacta* (Beissner) Rehder
                      1919 See *ABIES lasiocarpa* f. *compacta*.   H

ABIES x arnoldiana Nitzelius
                      1969 A natural hybrid; *ABIES koreana* x *ABIES veitchii*. **O.**
                            Gothernberg Botanic Garden (1953).   K   Sweden

- - 'Graciosa' Krüssmann   1970 An illegit. name. Clone with grey-yellow-brown cones.   K   Germany

- - **'Poulsen'** Hort. Denmark 1983 A controlled repeat of the same hybrid.**O** Poulsen Nurs.   G,K   Denmark

- - 'Violet' Krüssmann   1972 An unacceptable name. A clone with brown-violet cones.   K   Germany

ABIES aromatica Rafinesque
                      1832 Now known as *ABIES balsamea*.

ABIES atlantica Lindley ex Gordon
                      1858 Now known as *CEDRUS atlantica*.

ABIES baboriensis (1) Cosson
                      1861 Not now distinguished from *ABIES numidica*.

ABIES baboriensis (2) Morley
                      1878 Now known as *ABIES pinsapo*.

ABIES baldensis Nyman   1878 Now known as *ABIES alba*.

ABIES balsamea (L.) Miller
                      1768 Balsam Fir (*balsamifera*).   15m,Z3   Canada/U.S.A.

- - 'Albicans' Sénéclauze 1868 A weak growing form with young leaves quite white at first.
                            O. Sénéclauze Nurs, Bourg Argental, Loires. NIC.   B,K   France

- - 'Albida' Meyer   1924 Possibly same as previous entry. NIC.   Germany

- - 'Andover' Reg'd. Arn. Arb.
                      1959 Probably merely a damaged plant. NIC.   K,W2   U.S.A.

- - 'Angusta' Rehder   1928 Narrowly conical. ('Angustata'). NIC.   B,K   U.S.A.

- - 'Argentea' R. Smith   1864 Foliage dense, of a glaucous-whitish tint. NIC.   B,K   U.K.

- - 'Argenteovariegata' Schelle
                      1909 Superfluous name for 'Variegata'.

- - 'Argentifolia' Sudworth 1927 Superfluous name for 'Argentea'.

- - 'Ben Blackburn' Hort. Amer.
                      1972 Reported from Gotelli collection, South Orange, N.J.

- - var. *brachylepis* Willkommen
                      1875 Reportedly similar to *ABIES* x *phanerolepis*. NIC.   Balkans

- - 'Coerulea' Carrière   1867 A colour form. NIC. ('Caerulea').   B,K,W3   Sporadic

- - 'Coerulescens' Sénéclauze
                      1868 Silvery blue leaves. O. Sénéclauze Nurs. NIC.   B,K   France

- - **'Columnaris'** Frahm 1936 Vigorous; columnar.**O.** Frahm Nurs, Elmshorn.   B,K   Germany

- - 'Compacta' Meyer   1914 NIC.

- - 'Compacta Nana' Hort. France   An illegit. listed name for an unidentified clone.

- - **'Cree's Blue'** Hort. Amer.
                       1991 L. L.C. Cree, Colebrook, New Hudson.   W3

- - 'Denudata' Pépin   1860 Peculiar branching. O. Cochet Nurs, Suynes. NIC.   B,K   France

- - 'Elegans' Sénéclauze   1868 Leaves arranged spirally or recurved. NIC.   B,K   France

- - 'Fastigiata' H.J. van de Laar
                       1986 In "Naamlijst . . .". NOM.   Holland

- - *foliis variegatis* Knight & Perry
                       1850 See 'Variegata'.

- - var. *fraseri* Spach   1842 Now known as *ABIES fraseri*.

- - 'Glauca' Beissner   1899 Probably not distinct from 'Coerulescens'. NIC.

- - 'Globosa' (1) Beissner   1884 A clone no longer identifiable. NIC.   W3   Germany

- - 'Globosa' (2) Hort. Amer. 1986 A mistake for *ABIES lasiocarpa* 'Green Globe'.

- - 'Globosa Nana' Hort.   An illegit. name. Indistinguishable from 'Globosa' (1).

- - 'Hemispherica' Sudworth   1927 Superfluous synonym for 'Globosa'.

- - f. *hudsonia* Jacques   1829 A botanical designation covering all the low-growing
                           cultivars in this species.   B,D,H,K

- - **'Hudsonia'** Welch   1966 A clone of f.*hudsonia* in cultivation.   R,W1   Widespread

- - 'Krause' Hort. Amer.   1972 Globose dwarf; congested foliage. L. J.W. Spingarn, Baldwin,
                           L.Is., N.Y.   U.S.A.

- - 'Le Feber' Hort. Holland 1993 Dwarf plant with yellow-green leaves tinged brown in winter.
                           O. Le Feber Nurs. I. K.A. Koemans, Boskoop.

- - 'Longifolia' Lawson   1836 Strong growing, branches ascending, leaves long and narrow.
                           O. J. Booth and Sons, Flottbeck Nurs, Hamburg. NIC.   B,K   Germany

- - 'Lutescens' Schwerin   1903 Leaves at first straw-coloured. Named for a tree found in the
                           Trial Gardens at Diedorf. NIC.   B,K   Germany

- - var *macrocarpa* Sargent 1892 No longer distinguished within the species.   B,D,K   U.S.A.

- - 'Marginata' Beissner   1894 Yellowish young leaves. O. Schröder, Moscow. NIC.   B,K   Russia

- - **'Nana'** Nelson   1866 A dwarf, globose bush, a clone of f. *hudsonia*.   B,D,G,H,K,R Canada

- - 'Nana Globosa' Hort.   1965 A synonym of 'Nana'. (per Den Ouden/Boom).   B

- - 'Nudicaulis' Carrière   1867 A monstrous form. O. A. Leroy, Angers. NIC.   B,K   France

- - 'Paucifolia' Sudworth   1927 Superfluous name for 'Nudicaulis'.

- - **'Pedersen's Globe'** L.C. Hatch
                       1985 In "Reference Guide". NOM.   U.S.A.

- - var. *phanerolepis* Fernald
                       1909 Now known as *ABIES* x *phanerolepis* (Fernald) Liu.   B,D,K,W3   Canada

- - **'Piccolo'** Hort. Germany 1987 A globose dwarf form. O. and I. Erwin Carstens Nurs, Varel.

- - **'Prostrata'** Knight & Perry
                       1850 Prostrate clone of f. *hudsonia*; foliage pectinate.   B,H,K,W3   U.K.

- - 'Pyramidalis' Hort. Europe.   A superfluous synonym for 'Columnaris'.

- - **'Quintin Spreader'** Hort. Canada
  1986 L. E A Cope. "Native . . . Conifers . . . ". NOM.   Canada

- - 'Variegata' Carrière   1855 Leaves with a whitish variegation. NIC.   B,D,K   France

- - **'Verkade's Prostrate'** Verkade
  1984 In "Nurs. Cat". Slow growing spreading form, foliage dark
  green. Annual growth 25-30cm. **O. and I.** Verkade Nurs,
  Lincoln Park, N.J.   W3   U.S.A.

- - 'Versicolor' Sudworth   1927 A superfluous name for 'Variegata'.

ABIES batavorum Siebold   Now known as *CUNNINGHAMIA lanceolata*.

ABIES beissneriana Rehder & Wilson
  1914 Now known as *ABIES chensiensis* var. *ernestii*.

ABIES beshanzuensis M. H. Wu
  1976 Chekiang Fir, Beshuan Fir. A recently described species not
  yet in western cultivation.   10-15m,Z7 China

ABIES bicolor Maximowicz 1866 Now known as *PICEA bicolor*.

ABIES bifida Siebold and Zuccarini
  1842 No longer distinguished from *ABIES firma*.

ABIES bifolia Murray   1863 No longer distinguished from *ABIES lasiocarpa*.

ABIES x *borisii-regis* Mattfeld
  1925 King Boris Fir. Thought by some to be a natural hybrid:
  ABIES alba x *ABIES cephalonica*, but it has its own
  distribution area.   25m,Z5   Balkans

ABIES x *bornmuelleriana* Mattfeld
  1925 Bornmueller Fir. By some thought to be a hybrid: *ABIES
  cephalonica* x *ABIES nordmanniana*.   25m,Z5   Turkey

- - **'Archer'** Int. Con. Reg.   1991 Dwarf low spreading plant. **O. and I.** Kenwith Nurs,
  Bideford, Devon. (1991).

- - var. *leioclada* Steven   1838 A much confused epithet. Of no present value.

ABIES brachyphylla (Maxim.) Parlatore
  1868 Now known as *ABIES homolepis.*.

ABIES brachytyla Franchet 1899 Now known as *PICEA brachytyla*.

ABIES bracteata (D.Don) Poiteau
  1845 Bristlecone Fir, Santa Lucia Fir.   25m,Z7   Calif.

ABIES bridgesii Kellogg   1863 Now known as *TSUGA heterophylla*.

ABIES brunoniana Knight & Perry
  1850 Now known as *TSUGA dumosa*.

ABIES californica Hort. ex Steudel
  1840 Now known as *PSEUDOTSUGA menziesii*.

ABIES campylocarpa A. Murray
  1860 Now known as *ABIES magnifica*.

ABIES canadensis (1) Michaud
  1803 Now known as *TSUGA canadensis*.

ABIES canadensis (2) Miller
  1768 Now known as *PICEA glauca*.

ABIES candicans Endlicher 1847 See *ABIES concolor* 'Candicans'.

ABIES caroliniana (Engelmann) Chapman
        1883 Now known as *TSUGA caroliniana.*

ABIES cedrus Poiret   1805 Now known as *CEDRUS libani.*

ABIES cephalonica Loudon 1838 Greek Fir.   30m,Z6   Greece

- - 'Acicularis' Sénéclauze   1868 Leaves very fine. O. Raised on the Sénéclauze Nurs, in 1867.
        NIC.   B,K   France

- - var. *apollinis* (Link) Beissner
        1887 Now known as var. *graeca* (per Silba, 1984).   D,G,K

- - var. *arcadica* Henkel & Hochstetter
        1865 No longer distinguished within the species.   D,K

- - **'Aurea'** Carrière   1867 Young leaves golden-yellow. O. Sénéclauze Nurs, Bourg
        Argental, Loires.   B,K,W3   France

- - 'Aureovariegata' Beissner 1891 Not distinct from 'Aurea'.   Austria

- - 'Barabit's Gold   1992 A listed name for a selection with yellow foliage. O. Barabit.   Hungary

- - var. ***graeca*** (Fraas) Liu   1971 Apollo Fir. Formerly known as var. *apollinis*.   30m,Z6   Greece

- - 'Latifolia' Carrière   1867 Leaves large, spreading. NIC.   B,K   France

- - **'Meyer's Dwarf'** Den Ouden/Boom
        1965 A popular dwarf form, lacking a leader. ('Nana').   B,G,K,R,W1   Holland

- - 'Nana' Meyer   1963 Now known as 'Meyer's Dwarf'.

- - var. *panachaica* Henkel & Hochstetter
        1865 No longer distinguished within the species.

- - var. *parnassica* Henkel & Hochstetter
        1865 No longer distinguished within the species.

- - var. *pyramidalis* Zedebaur
        1907 Conical. No longer identifiable.

- - var. *reginae-ameliae* Heldreich
        1860 No longer distinguished within the species.

- - **'Robusta'** Carrière   1867 A very vigorous form. O. No record. (c. 1845).   B,K,W3   France

- - 'Rubiginosa' Carrière   1867 A form with the young foliage dark red. NIC.   B,K   France

- - 'Submutica' Bailly   1888 A minor variant with peculiar cones. NIC.   B,K   France

ABIES chayuensis Cheng et Fu
        1978 See "Flora Reipublica Popularis Sinicae 7". (1978).   20m,Z6   Tibet

ABIES chengii Rushforth   1987 A little-known species near to *ABIES fargesii*.   15m,Z6   Yunnan

ABIES chensiensis Van Teighem
        1891 Shensi Fir.   15-20m,Z6   China

- - var. ***ernestii*** (Rehder) Liu 1971 Chien-Lu Fir. A widely distributed form with minor
        differences in foliage and cones.   W

- - sub sp. ***salouenensis*** (Borderes-Rey & Gaussen) Rushforth
        1987 A recently described geographical variant.   Tibet

- -sub sp.*yulongxueshanensis* Rushforth
        1987 A recently described geographical variant.   China

ABIES chiloensis Carrière   1867 Now known as *ABIES spectabilis.*

ABIES chilrowensis Henkel & Hochstetter
        1865 Now included in *ABIES firma.*

ABIES chinensis Franchet   1899 Now known as *TSUGA chinensis.*

ABIES cilicica (Antoine & Kotschy) Carrière
        1855 Cilician Fir.   20-30m,Z6   Mediterranea

- - sub sp. *isaurica* Coode & Cullen
        1965 No longer distinguished within the species.   R

- - var. *leioclada* Gordon   1858 A confused epithet, of no present day value. NIC.

ABIES cinerea Borkhausen   Now known as *PICEA abies.*

ABIES clanbrassiliana Lawson
        1836 Now known as *PICEA abies* 'Clanbrassiliana'.

ABIES coahuilensis (Johnston) Martinez
        1963 Now usually listed as *ABIES durangensis* var. *coahuilensis.*   K   Mexico

ABIES coerulea Forbes   1839 Now known as *PICEA glauca* var. *coerulea.*

ABIES coerulescens Hort. ex C.Koch
        Now known as *PICEA rubens.*

ABIES communis Lawson   1836 Now known as *PICEA abies.*

ABIES concolor (Gordon) Lindley ex Hildebrand
        1861 Colorado White Fir.   25-50m,Z3   U.S.A.

- - 'Albospica' Schwerin   1920 Whitish foliage. No longer distinguishable. NIC.   B,K,W3

- - 'Angustata' Sudworth   1927 Name only. NIC.

- - **'Archer's Dwarf'** G. Haddow
        1982 In "Nurs. Cat". A conical dwarf plant with powder blue
               congested foliage. O. J.W. Archer of Farnham, Surrey. I.
               Kenwith Castle Nurs, Bideford, Devon.   G,W3   U.K.

- - f. *argentea* Niemetz   1903 Foliage white. Similar seedlings turn up.   B,K   Sporadic

- - 'Atroviolacea' Hort.   A superfluous synonym for 'Violacea'.

- - **'Aurea'** Beissner   1906 Young leaves yellow turning to silvery-grey. O. Ansorge
               Nurs, Flottbeck, Hamburg.   B,D,K,W3   Germany

- - 'Biella' Hort. Hungary   A listed name for a slow-growing clone with very good blue
               colour. ('Bella').

- - 'Brevifolia' Beissner   1907 Leaves short, stout. O. Ansorge Nurs, Flottbeck, Hamburg.
               NIC.   B,D,K   Germany

- - 'Butzii' Schwerin   1922 Named for a tree with peculiar foliage in a Kaliningrad Park
               by Butz (c. 1900). NIC.   B,K   Russia

- - **'Candicans'** Viguie & Gaussen
        1929 A clone of f. *argentea*. O. Arboretum les Barres, Nogent sur
               Vernisson.   D,K,R,W3   France

- - 'Clarence' Hort. Amer.   1970 A listed name.

- - **'Compacta'** Hornibrook   1939 A dwarf, irregular, compact shrub; leaves stout, straight or
               falcate. ('Violacea Compacta', 'Glauca Compacta').   B,D,G,H,K   U.K.

- - var. *concolor*   The typical or mountain form, as distinct from the coastal var.
               lowiana.   B,K

- - **'Conica'** Slavin 1932 Compact, conical. **O.**A.D. Slavin. Found in the Durand Eastman Park, Rochester. — B,D,H,K,W — U.S.A.

- - **'Creamy'** Int. Con. Reg. 1991 Reg'd. by G. Haddow. A dwarf globose form of var *lowiana*. New foliage cream. **O.** and **I.** Kenwith Nurs, Bideford, Devon. — U.K.

- - **'Elkins's Weeper'** Welch 1979 Pendulous; dark green foliage. **L.** J.W. Spingarn, Baldwin, L. Is., N.Y. **O.** Raised from seed by H. Elkins. — W2 — U.S.A.

- - **'Fagerhult'** G.Horstmann 1978 In "Nameslist". A slow-growing pendulous/prostrate form. **O.** Found by Tage Lundell on Fagerhult Nurs. (1933). **I.** to U.K. as 'Pendula Fagerhult' by Wansdyke Nurs. Devizes. (1977). — K,W3 — Sweden

- - **'Falcata'** Niemetz 1905 Leaves sickle-shape. **O.** Niemetz, Temesvár. NIC. — B,K — Hungary

- - **'Fastigiata'** Charguerand 1889 Columnar. **O.** Thibault & Keteleer Nurs, Sceaux, Paris. — B,K — France

- - **'Gable's Weeping'** Reg'd Arn. Arb. 1970 Dwarf, pendulous. Reg'd. by J.B. Gable, Stewartstown, PA, **I.** Watnong Nurs, Morris Plains, N.Y. — G,W2 — U.S.A.

- - 'Glauca' Silva-Tarouca 1924 Now used loosely for any glaucous selection.

- - 'Glauca Compacta' Hornibrook 1923 Name changed by Hornibrook to 'Compacta' in ed. 2 (1939). — W — U.K.

- - 'Glauca Nana' Hort. A superfluous name for 'Compacta'.

- - 'Glenmore' R.E. More 1960 In "The Green Thumb" **O.** The Glenmore Arb., Buffalo Park, Colarado. — U.S.A.

- - 'Globosa' Niemetz 1905 Dwarf; globose. **O.** Raised by Niemetz, Temesvár. NIC. — B,D,H,K,W2 — Hungary

- - 'Green Globe' Welch 1979 Now listed under *ABIES lasiocarpa*.

- - 'Hexe' G. Horstmann 1977 Dwarf, wider than high, leaves grey-blue. **O.** Horstmann Nurs. Schneverdingen. An acceptable cultivar name is required. — Germany

- - **'Hillier's Dwarf'** G. Haddow 1986 In "Nurs. Cat". Found as a witch's broom by Sir H.G. Hillier. Very dwarf and spreading. **I.** Kenwith Castle Nurs, Bideford, Devon. — U.K.

- - 'Horstmann's Igel' See 'Igel'. The name 'Horstmann's' is unacceptable, being already in use in the genus. (See Art. 50 of I.C.N.C.P.).

- - **'Husky Pup'** Reg'd. Arn. Arb. 1975 Dwarf, irregular; leaves dark green. **O.** N. Sizoo, Seattle, Washington. — W3 — U.S.A.

- - **'Igel'** Reuter 1984 In "Amer. Conif. Soc. Bull 1". A very slow-growing seedling. from var. *lowii*. (1959), near to *ABIES grandis*. **O.** Horstmann Nurs. Schneverdingen. — W3 — Germany

- - var. *lasiocarpa* Beissner 1887 Now known as var. *lowiana*.

- - 'Lareta' Hort. Amer. 1993 In "Nurs. Cat". Suncrest Gardens, Mt. Holly Springs, PA. without description.

- - 'Little Globe' Hort. Amer. 1984 A listed name. (See *ABIES lasiocarpa* 'Green Globe').

- - 'Longleaf' Hort. Amer. An unacceptable listed name.

- - var. **lowiana** (Gordon) Lemmon 1862 Californian White Fir. The coastal form differing from the type in the foliage and bark. Intermediate examples occur. — B,K,W3 — U.S.A

- - **'Masonic Broom'** J.W. Spingarn
    1978 In "Nurs. Cat." A flat-topped bush with curved, blue leaves. L. Hillside Gardens, Lehighton, PA (1970), as 'Mason Broom'. O. Ed. Rezek.   W3

- - 'Nana' Hort.   A loose name in use for any slow-growing selection.

- - 'Nana Horstmann' Hort. Germany
    1978 An illegit. listed name for a conical form with short blue-grey leaves.

- - 'Nana Ludemann' Hort. Germany
    1978 An illegit. listed name for a dense bush with blue-grey leaves.

- - 'Olcott' Hort. Amer.   Reported from Morton Arboretum, Lisle, Ill.

- - 'Pendens' Carrière   1890 Pendulous example of var. *lowiana* found by Carrière as a street tree in Paris. Not now identifiable.   B,K   France

- - 'Pendula' Simon-Louis   1896 Pendulous form of var. *concolor*. Not now identifiable.   B,D,H,K,W3   France

- - 'Pendula Fagerhult'   1977 A mistake for 'Fagerhult'.

- - **'Piggelmee'** H.J. van de Laar
    1971 In "Dendroflora 8". Dwarf form originating from a witch's broom on 'Candicans'. I. H.J. Draijer Nurs, Heemstede, ('Pigglemee', 'Pigomy').   G,K,R,W2   Holland

- - **'Pineola Dwarf'** Hort. Amer.   A slow-growing upright form but hardly a dwarf. I. Don Smith, Watnong Nurs, Morris Plains, N.J.   U.S.A.

- - 'Purpurea' Sudworth   1927 Probably a superfluous name for 'Violacea'.

- - 'Pyramidalis' (1) Lawson   1851 Sentinel silver Fir. A clone no longer identifiable.   U.K.

- - 'Pyramidalis' (2) Krüssmann
    1979 Named for a tree found in Whitnal Park, Chicago. An illegit. name if raised since lst Jan. 1959.   K,W3

- - 'Recurva' (1) Sénéclauze   1868 Named for a tree found on Mount Pila. NIC.   France

- - 'Recurva' (2) Beissner   1900 A form with young leaves recurved. O. F.J. Grootendorst & Sons Nurs, Boskoop. NIC.   B,K   Holland

- - 'Schrammii' Schwerin   1913 Named for a tree found in a park near Rostock. NIC.   B,K   Germany

- - 'Select Blue' Hort. Amer. 1983 L. Vermeulen Nurs, N.J. A selection with glaucous-blue foliage. The name is unacceptable under ICNCP, Recommendation 31.A (g).   U.S.A.

- - 'Silver Blue' Hort. Amer.   A listed name. Unacceptable under ICNCP Recommendation 31.A (g) of the "Cultivar Code".

- - 'Varia' Sudworth   1927 No longer identifiable.

- - 'Variegata' Beissner   1891 A variegated form of var. *lowiana*. O. Lobkowitz Nurs, Eisenberg. NIC.   B,K   Czechoslo.

- - **'Violacea'** Murray   1875 A descriptively named colour form. Similar seedlings turn up and other names are used. NIC.   B,D,G,K,W3

- - 'Violacea Compacta' Beissner
    1891 Probably indistinguishable from 'Glauca Compacta'. NIC.   Germany

- - 'Violacea Fastigiata' Beissner
    1909 A fastigiate selection from seed of 'Violacea' (Other names were used). NIC.   Austria

- - **'Violacea'** (Prostrate) Hort.   This is a cultivariant of 'Violacea'. In no sense is it a separate clone needing a different cultivar name.   W

- - **'Wattezii'** Wattez   1900   A colour selection with very pale cream leaves afterwards grey-green. **O. D.** Wattez Nurs, at Bussum.   B,D,G,K,W3   Holland

- - **'Wattezii'** (Prostrate) Hort.   Grafted side branches do not remain prostrate for long. See note under 'Violacea' (Prostrate).   G,K,R,W2

- - **'Winter Gold'** Krüssmann   1979   A clone that is a rather insipid yellow-green in summer, turning a bright gold in winter. **O.** Horstmann Nurs, Schneverdingen.   G,K,W3   Germany

- - 'Wustemeyer' Wittboldt-Muller   1991   A dense plant with blue foliage.   Germany

ABIES cupressoides Poiret   Now known as *PILGERODENDRON uviferum.*

ABIES curvifolia Salisbury   Now known as *TSUGA canadensis.*

ABIES dammari Poiret   Now known as *AGATHIS dammari.*

ABIES davidiana Franchet   Now known as *KETELEERIA davidiana.*

ABIES decidua Wallich   Now known as *TSUGA dumosa.*

ABIES delavayi (Van Tieghem) Franchet   1899   Delavay Fir.   10-15m,Z8   China etc.

This fir, gives its name to what is called the "Delavayi Complex", this being a group of allied firs widely distributed throughout Asia, the best classification of which is still a matter of debate amongst botanists. Liu (1971), Silba (1984) and Rushforth (1987) suggest different classifications. Fortunately, they do all use the same vernacular names: Delavay, Forrest, Faber, Faxon, Farges, George and Sutchuensis. The nomenclature here follows Rushforth, (1987). The garden forms are listed under *ABIES delavayi.*

	Liu (1971)	Silba (1984)	Rushforth (1987)
Delavay Fir	*Abies delavayi* Franchet var. *delavayi.*	*Abies delavayi* Franchet var. *delavayi.*	*Abies delavayi* Franchet
Forrest Fir	*Abies delavayi* Franchet var. *smithii* (Vig. et Gauss.) Liu.	*Abies delavayi* Franchet var. *smithii.* var. *forrestii* pro syn.	*Abies forrestii* C. Coltman-Rogers. var. *smithii* pro syn.
George Fir	*Abies delavayi* Franchet var. *georgei* (Orr) Melville.	*Abies delavayi* Franchet var. *georgei* (Orr) Melville	*Abies georgei* Orr. Seldom grown true in UK.
Faber Fir	Not distinguished within the species.	Not distinguished within the species.	*Abies fabri* (Masters) Craib.
Farges Fir	*Abies fargesii* Franchet var. *fargesii.*	*Abies fargesii* Franchet.	*Abies fargesii* Franchet.
Faxon Fir	*Abies fargesii* Franchet var. *faxoniana.* (Rehd. et Wils.) Liu	Not distinguished within the species.	Not distinguished within the species.
Sutchuensis Fir	*Abies delavayi* Franchet var. *delavayi.*	Not distinguished from *Abies fargesii.*	Not distinguished from *Abies fargesii.*

- - 'Buchanan' Hort. Anglia   1987   A dwarf seedling form originating at Hilliers Nurs, in a similar way to 'Major Neishe' but a more upright plant with leaves generally more radial on the shoots. Description from Mother plant in Royal Edinburgh Botanic Garden

.- - 'Headfort'	See *ABIES fargesii*.		
- -' Major Neishe' Rushforth			
	1987 Another dwarf only putting on some height after forty years. O. Hillier Nurs, Winchester.		U.K.
- - 'Nana' Hillier	1970 An illegit name. Hillier Cat. 1970. See 'Buchanan' and 'Major Neishe'.		
- - var. *fabri*	Not now distinguished within the species by some authorities. But see *ABIES fabri*.		
- - var. *fargesii*	Farges Fir. Now recognised as a species, *ABIES fargesii*. (per Rushforth, 1987).		
- - var. *faxoniana* Jackson	1932 Not now distinguished within *ABIES delavayi* (per Rushforth, 1987).		
- - var. *forrestii* Jackson	1932 "Forrest Fir". Now generally known as *ABIES delavayi* var. *smithii*. But by some authorities treated as a species *ABIES forrestii* (per Rushforth, 1987).		
- - var. **georgei** (Orr) Melville			
	1958 "George fir". By some authorities now treated as a species *ABIES georgei* (per Rushforth, 1987).		
- - var. **motuoensis** Cheng et Fu			
	1978 In "Flora Reipublica Popularis Sinicae. Vol. 7".		China
- - var. *smithii* (Viguie & Gaussen) Liu			
	1971 Forrest Fir. Here listed under *ABIES forrestii*.		
ABIES densa Griffith	1851 Sikkim Fir. By some listed as *ABIES spectabilis* var. *densa*.	15-20m,Z7	India
ABIES denticulata Michaux	1903 Now known as *PICEA mariana*.		
ABIES deodara Standish & Noble			
	1852 Now known as *CEDRUS deodara*.		
ABIES diversifolia Maximowicz			
	1868 Now known as *TSUGA diversifolia*.		
ABIES douglasii Lindley	1833 Now known as *PSEUDOTSUGA menziesii*.		
ABIES drummondii Gordon	1858 Now known as *PSEUDOTSUGA menziesii*.		
ABIES dumosa (D. Don) Loudon			
	1838 Now known as *TSUGA dumosa*.		
ABIES durangensis Martinez			
	1942 Durango Fir.	20-40m,Z7	Mexico
- - var. **coahuilensis** (Johnston) Martinez			
	1963 Coahuila Fir.	20-40m,Z7	Mexico
ABIES elegans Smith of Ayr ex Knight and Smith			
	1850 Now known as *PICEA abies* 'Elegans'.		
ABIES engelmannii Parry	1863 Now known as *PICEA engelmannii*.		
ABIES equi-trojanii Ascherson & Sintensis			
	1883 Trojan Fir. Now usually listed as *ABIES cephalonica* var. *graeca*.	Z5	Turkey
ABIES eremita C. Koch	Now known as *PICEA abies* 'Eremita'.		
ABIES ernestii Rehder	1939 Now known as *ABIES chensiensis* var. *ernestii*.		
ABIES erythrocarpa Nyman	Now known as *PICEA abies*.		

ABIES excelsa Poiret 1805 Now known as *PICEA abies*, along with its cultivars.

ABIES excelsior Franco 1949 Now known as *ABIES grandis*.

ABIES faberi (Masters) Craib
    1919 Faber Fir. (per Rushforth, 1987).   15m,Z6   China

- - sub sp. **minensis** (Borderes-Rey & Gaussen) Rushforth
    1987 A vigorous local variant of *ABIES faberi* (per Rushforth, 1987).

ABIES falcata Rafinesque 1832 Now known as *PICEA sitchensis*.

ABIES fanjinshanensis Huang, Tu & Fu
    A recently described species, not in European cultivation.   China

ABIES fargesii Franchet 1899 Farges Fir.   15m,Z5   China

- - var. *faxoniana* (Rehder & Wilson) Liu
    1971 Faxon fir. Not now distinguished within the species (per Rushforth, 1987).

- - **'Headfort'** H.G. Hillier 1964 A dwarf slow-growing form found at Headfort, Co.Meath. ('Herdford' Hort. U.S.A.).   Ireland

- - var. *sutchuenensis* Franchet
    1899 Not now distinguished within the species (per Rushforth, 1987).

ABIES faxoniana Rehder & Wilson
    1914 Now merged in *ABIES fargesii*. (per Rushforth, 1987).

ABIES ferreana Borderes-Rey & Gaussen
    1947 Not now distinguished within *ABIES forrestii* (per Rushforth, 1987).

ABIES finedonensis Gordon 1862 Now known as *PICEA abies* 'Finedonensis'.

ABIES firma Siebold. & Zuccarini
    1842 Momi Fir.   25m,Z7   Japan

- - 'Bedgebury' Hort. Germany
    1986 A listed name. Possibly a hybrid: *ABIES firmc* x *ABIES homolepis*.

- - var. *bifida* Siebold & Zuccarini
    1879 No longer distinguished withi· ⸱he species.

- - var. *momi* Siebold & Zuccarini No longer distinguished within the species.

- - 'Pendula' Hort. Amer.   An illegit. listed name.

- - 'Sol' Hort. Amer.   1993 In "Nurs. Cat". Suncrest Gardens, Mt. Holly Springs, PA. without description.

- - 'Tardina' Mitchell   1972 Named for a tree at Borde Hill, Sussex. Note that unless and until such a tree has been propagated it is, technically, not a cultivar.   U.K.

- - f. *tardiva* Silva Tarouca 1913 A listed name. Probably =*ABIES homolepis*.   Germany

- - 'Variegata' Hort. Japan 1959 A name reported from Japan (per Uehara).

ABIES forrestii Coltman-Rogers ex Craib
    1932 Forrest fir. Now known as *ABIES delavayi* var. *smithii*.

- - var. *smithii* Viguie & Gaussen A variety with stout, hairy shoots. Widely mis-labelled as *ABIES georgii*.   R   Tibet

ABIES fortunei Masters   Now known as *KETELEERIA fortunei*.

ABIES fraseri (Pursch) Poiret
     1817 Fraser Fir. A species closely related to *ABIES balsamea*.   15m, Z4   U.S.A./Canada

- - var. *brachyphylla* Maximowicz
     1866 Now known as *ABIES homolepis*.

- - 'Cline's Dwarf'   See 'Kline's Nest'.

- - 'Coerulea' Hort. ex Carrière
     1867 Vigorous spreading bush. NIC. ('Caerulea').   France

- - 'Compacta' Bailey   1933 Name only. NIC.   U.S.A.

- - 'Glauca' Hort. ex Carrière
     1867 A synonym of 'Coerulea'.   France

- - 'Horizontalis' Hort. Amer.   An illegit. listed name.   U.S.A.

- - var. *hudsonia* Knight & Perry
     1850 Mistake for *ABIES balsamea* var. *hudsonia*. *(hudsonica.)*

- - **'Kline's Nest'** Hort. Amer.
     1972 A low, spreading bush; short dark green leaves. L. Raraflora
     Nurs, Feasterville, PA (Cline's Dwarf, Klein's Dwarf).   W3   U.S.A.

- - 'Nana' Hort. ex Gordon   1850 A synonym of var. *hudsonia*.

- - 'Pendula' Hort. Amer.   1985 An illegit. name. L. Coenosium Gar, Aurora, OR.

- - f. *prostrata* Rehder   1928 A botanical designation of doubtful value. Such plants are
     probably all cultivariants.   B   U.S.A.

- - **'Prostrata'** Reg. A.A.N.   1950 An example of f. *prostrata*. Reg'd by Seth L. Kelsey, E.
     Boxford, Mass. O. The same (1916).   B,D,H,K,W2   U.S.A.

- - 'Verkades Prostrate'   1980 Dwarf prostrate spreading plant. O. Verkade Nurs.   U.S.A.

ABIES gamblei Hickel   1929 Gamble Fir. A tree possibly now extinct in the wild.   Z7   India

ABIES georgei Orr   1933 George Fir.   China

- - var. **smithii** (Viguie & Gaussen) Cheng & Fu
     1975 Forrest Fir.

ABIES gigantea Smith ex Carrière
     1867 Now known as *PICEA abies*.

ABIES glehnii (Fr. Schmidt) Masters
     1868 Now known as *PICEA glehnii*.

ABIES gmelinii Ruprecht   1845 Now known as *LARIX gmelinii*.

ABIES gordoniana Carrière   1867 Now known as *ABIES grandis*.

ABIES gracilis Komarov   1901 Now known as *ABIES nephrolepis*.

ABIES grandis (1) Hooker   1840 Now known as *ABIES amabilis*.

ABIES grandis (2) (Douglas) Lindley
     1833 Grand Fir, Vancouver Fir.   30-60m, Z2   U.S.A.

- - **'Aurea'** Hesse ex Beissner
     1891 Leaves golden-yellow.O. Hesse Nurs, Weener-on-Ems,
     (1891).   B,D,K,W3   Germany

- - 'Aurifolia' Dallimore & Jackson
     1923 Indistinguishable from 'Aurea'.   U.K.

- - **'Compacta'** (1) Parsons　1887　In "Nurs. Cat". Dwarf, globose, densely branched. **O.** Parsons
and Sons, Flushing, N.Y. About 1885.　　　　　　　　　　　　U.S.A.

- - 'Compacta' (2) Hort. ex Beissner
　　　　　　　　1891　Possibly the same. A low-growing bush with habit similar to
ABIES balsamea 'Hudsonia'. **O.** Hesse Nurs, Weener-on-Ems,
(c 1891). Seldom offered true in the trade.　　　B,D,H,K,W3　　Germany

- - var. *concolor* A. Murray　1875　Now known as *ABIES concolor.*

- - 'Crassa' Dallimore & Jackson
　　　　　　　　1923　A compact clone, no longer identifiable.　　　　　　　U.S.A.

- - var. *densiflora* Engelmann
　　　　　　　　1878　Now known as *ABIES amabilis.*

- - **'Johnson'** Matthews　　1942　In "Journal of Forestry". The Johnson fir. A slow-growing,
narrowly pyramidal tree. Similar seedlings turn up.　　W3　　U.S.A.

- - var. *lowiana* Hoopes　1868　Now known as *ABIES concolor* var. *lowiana.*

- - 'Nana' Zedebauer　　1907　Probably a superfluous synonym for 'Compacta'.

- - f. *oregona* Hort. ex Fitschen
　　　　　　　　1930　Not now distinguished within the species.

- - **'Pendula'** Späth　　1896　Strongly pendulous. **O.** Späth Nurs, Berlin.　　B,D,H,K,W3　　Germany

ABIES gregoryana Low ex Gordon
　　　　　　　　1862　Now known as *PICEA abies* 'Gregoryana'.

ABIES griffithiana Gordon　1858　Now known as *LARIX griffithii.*

ABIES guatamalensis Rehder
　　　　　　　　1939　Guatamalan Fir.　　　　　　　20-30m　　Guatamala

- - var. *tacanensis* Martinez　1963　Not now distinguished within the species.

ABIES heterophylla Rafinesque
　　　　　　　　1830　Now known as *TSUGA heterophylla.*

- - var. *jaliscana* Martinez　1948　No longer distinguished within the species.

ABIES hickelii Flous & Gaussen
　　　　　　　　1932　Hickel Fir.　　　　　　　30m,Z8　　Mexico

- - var. *macrocarpa* Martinez
　　　　　　　　1942　No longer distinguished within the species.

ABIES holophylla Maximowicz
　　　　　　　　1866　Manchurian Fir, Needle Fir.　　　　15m,Z5　　China, Kore

ABIES homolepis Siebold and Zuccarini
　　　　　　　　1842　Nikko Fir. Formerly known as *ABIES brachyphylla.*　25m, Z5　　Japan

- - 'Malahide' Krüssmann　1979　A dwarf plant discovered at Malahide Castle. NIC.　K　　Ireland

- - 'Molenhill' Hort. Holland　1993　Dwarf conical plant with regularly tiered branches. Leaves
typical of the species but much shorter. About 1m high in
twenty five years. **O.** and **I.** Konijn Nurs, Ederveen.

- - 'Nana' Hort. Germany　　1990　An illegit. listed name. **L.** zu Jeddeloh Nurs, Oldenburg,
Germany.

- - **'Prostrata'** Hort.　　　Of various authors. All are cultivariants. **L.** Vermeulen &
Sons Nurs, Neshanic Sta, N.J. (1970).　　G,W3　　U.S.A.

- - 'Scottae' Mcfarlane　1932　Dwarf; discovered in a garden at Media, Penn .('Scottiae').
NIC.　　　　　　　B,D,H,K,W　　U.S.A.

- - **'Shelter Island'** Int. Con. Reg.
  1981 Semi-prostrate; irregular; yellow-green. Reg'd. by F. Crowe, San Diego, Cal. **O.** The same (1975). NIC. W3 U.S.A.

- - var. *tokniae* Carrière 1855 Now known as *ABIES sachalinensis.*

- - 'Tomomi' Bobbink & Atkins
  1909 In "Nurs. Cat". A plant with a peculiar habit. NIC. B,D,K,R U.S.A.

- - var. *umbellata* (Mayr) Wilson
  1916 Now listed as *ABIES* x *umbellata.* B,D,K,R

- - 'Variegated' Hort. Amer. 1991 **L.** "Mitsch Coenosium Notes 5". A plant with a scattered white variegation.

ABIES hookeriana A. Murray
  1855 Now known as *TSUGA mertensiana.*

ABIES iidaensis Kusaka 1952 Now listed under *ABIES* x *umbellata.*

ABIES x *insignis* Bailly 1890 A hybrid: *ABIES pinsapo* x *ABIES nordmanniana.* **O.** Renault Nurs, Bulgneville, (1850). 30m,Z6 France

- - 'Andréana' Mottet 1902 **O.** Moser Nurs, Versailles, (1878). NIC. B,K,R France

- - 'Beissneriana' Mottet 1902 **O.** Moser Nurs, Versailles, (1878). NIC. B,K,R France

- - 'Kentiana' Mottet 1902 **O.** Moser Nurs, Versailles, (1878). NIC. B,K,R France

- - 'Mastersiana' Mottet 1902 **O.** Moser Nurs, Versailles, (1878). NIC. B,K,R France

- - **'Pendula'** Amaral Franco
  1950 **O.** Found by Franco in Sierra de Sinatra. NIC. B,D,K,R Portugal

- - 'Speciosa' (Bailly) Rehder
  1890 Possibly a hybrid with the above parentage reversed. **O.** Croux Nurs, Sceaux, Paris (1871). NIC. B,D,K,R France

ABIES intermedia (1) Hort. Now usually listed as *ABIES pindrow* 'Intermedia'.

ABIES intermedia (2) Fulling
  1936 Now known as *ABIES* x *phanerolepis.*

ABIES inverta R. Smith ex Gordon
  1862 Now known as *PICEA abies* 'Inverta'.

ABIES japonica (1) Rovelli 1913 Now known as *PSEUDOTSUGA japonica.*

ABIES japonica (2) Parsons ex Sargent
  1893 Now known as *ABIES veitchii.*

ABIES jezoensis (1) Siebold & Zuccarini
  1842 Now known as *PICEA jezoensis.*

ABIES jezoensis (2) Lindley ex Paxton
  1850 Now known as *KETELEERIA fortunei.*

ABIES kaempferi (1) (Lambert) Lindley
  1833 Now known as *LARIX kaempferi.*

ABIES kaempferi (2) Lindley
  1854 Now known as *PSEUDOLARIX amabilis.*

ABIES kamtschatica Ruprecht
  1845 Now known as *LARIX gmelini.*

ABIES kansuensis Borderes-Rey & Gaussen
  1944 Now known as *ABIES fargesii* var. *sutchuensis.*

ABIES kawakamii (Hayata) Ito
        1909 Taiwan Fir, Kawakami Fir.   15m, Z6   Taiwan Is.

ABIES khutrow Royle   1839 Now known as *PICEA smithiana.*

ABIES koreana Wilson   1920 Korean Fir.   10m, Z6   Korea

- - **'Aurea'** Hort. Amer.   1977 Globe and bushy as a young plant later developing a leader. Short leaves which are golden yellow becoming dull by autumn. **O.** Lohbrunner Nurs, Victoria, B.C. (1956).   G,R,W3   Canada

- - **'Blaue Zwo'** Hort. Germany
        1984 Slow-growing, upright tree, blue-grey foliage and cones. **O.** Wustemeyer Nurs, Schermbeck, (1970). **I.** The same.   Germany

- - **'Blauer Dragoner'** Hort. Germany
        1990 A listed name for a dense, compact form with blue leaves. **O.** K. Wittboldt-Muller Nurs, Verden-Eitze.   Germany

- - 'Blauer Eskimo' Hort. Germany
        1990 A listed name for a very hardy blue dwarf, low spreading, blue-grey leaves. **O.** K. Wittboldt-Muller Nurs, Verden-Eitze.   Germany

- - **'Blauer Pfiff'** Krüssmann
        1979 Blue grey, slow-growing, globose, eventually upright. **O.** Raised by K. Wittboldt-Muller Nurs, Verden-Eitze, from treated seed.   K,W3   Germany

- - 'Blue Hit' Hort. Anglia   An unnecessary and undesirable translation of 'Blauer Pfiff'.

- - **'Blue Magic'** Hort. Germany
        1990 Small dwarf; the best blue of the Wittboldt-Muller plants. It is considered to be a better blue than 'Blauer Pfiff'. **O.** K. Wittboldt-Muller Nurs, Verden-Eitze.   Germany

- - **'Blue Standard'** Krüssmann
        1979 Growth slow, free coning; cones deep violet. **I.** Jeddeloh Nurs, Oldenburg, **O.** The same. (1962).   K,W3   Germany

- - 'Brevifolia' Krüssmann   1979 An illegit. name. Slow, growth open, cones small. **O.** Jeddeloh Nurs, Oldenburg, (1965).   K   Germany

- - 'Cis' Hort. Holland   1989 Dwarf bush, very dark green leaves. **O.** Roelvink Nurs, Groningen, Holland.

- - 'Compacta' Hort.   Now known as 'Compact Dwarf'.

- - **'Compact Dwarf'** Ouden/Boom
        1965 Low bush, seldom cones. **O.** Found in Blijdenstein Pinetum, Hilversum. ('Compacta', 'Compacta Nana').   B,G,K,W   Holland
- - 'Dark Hill' Hort. Germany 1990 A listed name. **O.** K. Wittboldt- Muller Nurs, Verden-Eitze.

- - 'Eisregen' Hort. Germany
        1990 **O.** K. Wittboldt-Muller Nurs, Verden-Eitze.

- - **'Flava'** Browicz   1956 A local variant with green cones ripening to yellowish-brown. **O.** Kornik Arb. (1933).   B,K   Poland

- - 'Fliegender Untertasse' Hort. Germany
        1991 Dwarf prostrate plant, rather open for the first five years but later filling out to produce quite a tight plant in maturity. **O.** K. Wittboldt-Muller Nurs, Verden-Eitze.

- - 'Frosty' Hort. Holland   1990 Upright, conical, slow-growing plant with up curled leaves which seems reliably to keep it's habit. **L.** Libo Nurs, Baexam, Holland.

.- - 'Gait' Hort. Holland   1990 Dwarf very narrow, almost fastigiate. **O.** Roelvink Nurs, Groningen, Holland.

- - 'Gelbbunt' Hort. Germany
           1978 Leaves partly yellow or yellow-green. **L.** Horstmann in "Nurs. Cat".

- - 'Golden Dream' Hort. Germany
           1988 Dwarf prostrate plant. Gold in winter. **O.** K.Wittboldt-Muller Nurs, Verden-Eitze.   Germany

- - 'Golden Glow' Hort. Holland
           1990 **L.** L. Konijn & Co., Lunteren, (Ederveen), Holland.

- - **'Golden Wonder'** Hort. Germany
           1990 Flat growing, pale gold in winter and spring. **O.** K. Wittboldt-Muller Nurs, Verden-Eitze. **I.** K. Wezelenburg, Hazerwoude, Holland.

- - 'Goldherz' Hort. Holland   1992 Reported from Pinetum "De Belfen", Vorden.

- - 'Green Carpet' Hort. Holland
           1990 Report from Trompenburg Arboretum. **O.** Konijn & Co. Nurs, Reeuwijk.   Holland

- - 'Grüne Spinne' Hort. Germany
           1990 A listed name. **O.** K.Wittboldt-Muller Nurs, Verden-Eitze.

- - 'Hexenbesen Wustemeyer' Hort. Amer.
           1984 Now known as 'Silberkugel'. (Silver Globe). In "Amer. Conif. Soc. Bull. **1**".

- - 'Hexenbesen Horstmann' 1986 See 'Silverperl'.

- - **'Horstmann'** G. Horstmann
           1986 Dwarf conical bush with dark green leaves. Annual leader growth up to 10 cm per year. Probably very dwarf on own roots. **O.** and **I.** Horstmann Nurs, Schneverdingen. (Formerly listed as 'Hexenbesen Horstman' (1983)).

- - 'Horstmann's Silberlocke' and 'Horstmann's Silver'
           Redundant names for 'Silberlocke'.   K,R

- - **'Inverlieth'** G. Haddow 1985 Low-growing much wider than high, eventual small tree. Very free coning. Original plant in Royal Edinburgh Botanic Garden. Original unrecorded.

- - 'Lippetal' Wustemeyer 1989 Dwarf form. **O.** Wustemeyer Nurs, Schermbeck.   Germany

- - 'Luminetta' Hort. Holland 1990 Bushy plant with pale cream leaves. **O.** and **I.** L. Konign & Co., Lunteren, (Ederveen). (Originally known as 'Lutea').

- - 'Lutea' Hort. Holland   1977 An illegit. name which has been changed to 'Luminetta'.

- - 'Mondschein' Hort. Europe
           1984 A listed name.

- - 'Nadelkissen' Hort. Germany
           1990 K. Wittboldt-Muller Nurs, Verden-Eitze.   Germany

- - 'Nana' (1) H.G. Hillier 1964 In "Dwarf Conifers". A mistake for 'Compact Dwarf'.

- - 'Nana' (2) Hort.   An invalid name loosely used for several clones.   W

- - 'Nanaimo' Hort. Amer. 1991 Listed name for compact, early fruiting selection, with violet purple cones.

- - **'Nisbet'** G. Haddow   1983 In "Nurs. Cat". A very slow-growing, conical bush, free coning, leaves dull green. **L.** Kenwith Castle Nurs, Bideford, Devon. **O.** A selected seedling by A.H. Nisbet of Gosport. **I.** Don Hatch Nurs, Honiton, Devon.

- - **'Piccolo'** Welch   1979   Slow-growing; seldom forming a leader with pendulous branches and branchlets, short dark green leaves. ('Picolo').**O.** Konijn Nurs, Ederveen.   G,K,W3   Holland

- - **'Pinocchio'** Hort. Germany
     1981   Dwarf globose bush. **I.** E. Carsten Nurs, Varel.

- - **'Pompon'** Welch   1990   A mistake; the accepted name is 'Silberkugel'.

- - 'Procumbens' Hort. Germany   An illegit. name. Now known as 'Taija'.

- - 'Prostrata' Hort.   An illegit. name for the following and similar selections.

- - **'Prostrate Beauty'** Den Ouden/Boom
     1965   Irregular, widespreading; early coning form, lacking a leader. **O.** Arnold Arboretum, Jamaica Plain, Mass.   B,W3   U.S.A.

- - **'Schneverdingen'** Hort. Germany
     1987   Dwarf globose bush. Listed by G. Horstmann, Schneverdingen.

- - f. *sikokiana* Nakai ex Viguie and Gaussen
     1929   Now listed under *ABIES veitchii*.   B,K

- - **'Silberglanz'** Hort. Germany
     1986   **O.** Dierks Nurs, Oldenburg, Germany. Silver recurved foliage.

- - **'Silberkugel'** Wustemeyer 1986   In "Nurs. Cat". Formerly listed as 'Hexenbesen Wustemeyer No. 1'. (Per Reuter in "Amer. Conif. Soc. Bull. **1**"). Dwarf globe shaped bush.   Germany

- - 'Silberlade' Hort. Germany
     1986   L. H.J. van de Laar in "Naamlijst . . .". Not distinguishable from 'Silverlocke'. NIC.   Germany

- - **'Silberlocke'** Krüssmann   1979   ('Silver Curls'). L. G. Horstmann Nurs, Schneverdingen (1978). Small tree with recurved leaves, exposing the silvery underside.   G.W3   Germany

- - 'Silbermavers' Hort. Holland
     1989   A listed name for a very dwarf silver-blue globe. ('Silver Mavers').

- - **'Silberperl'** Hort. Germany
     1986   Dwarf, cushion shaped much wider than high congested branch system covered with small leaves, many of which show the silver undersides. **L.** G. Horstmann, Schneverdingen, (formerly listed as 'Hexenbesen Horstmann' No.1).

- - **'Silberreif'** Hachmann   1982   In "Nurs. Cat". **O.** and **I.** Hachmann Nurs, Barmstedt in Holstein. Silver recurved leaves. Tree size clone.   Germany

- - **'Silberzwerg'** Jeddeloh   1989   In "Nurs. Cat". 1991. Dwarf globose bush.   Germany

- - 'Silver Curls' Hort. Amer.   An unnecessary and undesirable translation of 'Silberlocke'.

- - 'Silver Mavers' Hort. Holland
     1993   Reported by J.R.P. van Hoey Smith, Rotterdam.

- - **'Silver Show'** H.J. Grootendorst
     1977   In "Dendroflora **13-14**". A slow-growing, spreading plant with leaves curled, exposing the white undersides. **O.** and **I.** K. Wittboldt-Muller, Verden-Eitze, Bremen (1970).   K,W3   Germany

- - **'Starker's Dwarf'** Welch
     1979   A dwarf plant, at first squat, later becoming conical. Cones early. Named for Carl Starker, Jennings Lodge, OR. **O.** Unrecorded, probably Canada.   W3   Canada

- - 'Stolwijk No. 2' Hort. Holland
  1985 Dwarf globose bush, short dark green leaves. **O.** and **I.**
  Stolwijk Nursery.

- - **'Taiga'** Hachmann   1984 Dense, slow, flat-growing; dark green, blue cones. **O.** and **I.**
  Hachmann Nurs, Barmstedt-in-Holstein. (At first distributed
  as 'Procumbens').   Germany

- - 'Tundra' Hort. Holland   1986 Dwarf low spreading. **O.** and **I.** Korner Nursery.

- - 'Verdener Dom'   **O.** K. Wittboldt-Muller Nurs, Verden-Eitze.   Germany

- - 'Waldgreuze' Hort. Germany   A hybrid *ABIES koreana* x *ABIES lasiocarpa.* **O.** K.
  Wittboldt-Muller Nurs, Verden-Eitze.

- - 'Wustemeyer' Int. Con. Reg.
  1987 Now to be 'Silberkugel'.

- - 'Zwergform Wustemeyer' Hort. Germany
  1984 An unsatisfactory listed name. **O.** A seedling raised by W.
  Wustemeyer of Schermbeck.

ABIES lanceolata (1) Desfontaines
  1822 Now known as *CUNNINGHAMIA lanceolata.*

ABIES lanceolata (2) Poiret 1805 Now known as *CUNNINGHAMIA lanceolata.*

ABIES lasiocarpa (1) Auct. 1855 Now known as *ABIES concolor* var. *lowiana.*

ABIES lasiocarpa (2) Lindley & Gordon
  1850 Now known as *ABIES grandis.*

ABIES lasiocarpa (3) (Hooker) Nuttall
  1849 Subalpine Fir, Rocky Mountain Fir.   25m,Z2   Rocky Mts.

- - 'Alba' Hort. France   1972 (Name illegit?) L. Renault Nurs, Gorron.   France

- - 'Alpina' Schelle   1909 A shrubby form of var. *arizonica.* NIC.   Germany

- - **'Argentea'** Henkel   1901 A clone of var. *arizonica* with conspicuously silvery leaves.
  Introduced from the wild.   B,K   U.S.A.

- - var. *arizonica* (Merriam) Lemmon
  1898 Corkbark Fir. Differs in its much bluer foliage, smaller cones
  and thick, corky bark.   15m   U.S.A.

- - 'Arizonica Argentea' André
  1901 A superfluous name for 'Argentea'.

- - **'Arizonica Compacta'** Welch
  1979 A popular dwarf form, with silvery-blue foliage. **O.** J.Boer
  Gz, Boskoop. c. 1927 (= 'Compacta' of Hornibrook 1939).   B,G,H,W3   Holland

- - 'Arizonica Glauca' De Vilmorin
  1906 Indistinguishable from 'Argentea'.

- - 'Arizonica Pendula' Schelle
  1909 A pendulous clone of var. *arizonica.* NIC.   Germany

- - 'Beissneri' Hornibrook   1923 **O.** Hesse Nurs, Weener on Ems, NIC.   B,D,H,K,W2   Germany

- - 'Coerulescens' Fröbel ex Beissner
  1891 **O.** Fröbel Nurs, Zurich. NIC.   B,K   Switzerl.

- - f. *compacta* (Beissner) Rehder
  1919 A compact form of var. *lasiocarpa.* **O.** Raised by Ordnung
  Nurs, Eisenberg, and probably lost to cultivation.   D,H,K   Czechoslo.

- - 'Compacta' Beissner   1900   A clone of var. *arizonica*. The name being 'occupied' is unavailable for re-use. See 'Arizonica Compacta'.   H,K

- - 'Compacta Glauca' Hort.   An illegit. superfluous name. for 'Arizonica Compacta' ('Glauca Compacta').

- - 'Compacta Prostrata' Hort. Amer.   An illegit. name. O. Paul Palomino.

- - **'Conica'** Hornibrook   1923   A slow growing conical form with grey-green leaves. O. Raised in the Arnold Arboretum from seeds sent by Dr. C. Parry from Colorado in 1873.   B,H,K,W3   U.S.A.

- - 'Day Creek' Hort. Amer.   1984   A listed name.

- - **'Duflon'** Hort. Amer.   1976   An extremely slow-growing form found by E.H. Lohbrunner in the garden of Mr. & Mrs. Duflon of Seattle, Washington. (1954).   W3   U.S.A.

- - 'Elaine' Hort. Anglia   1988   A slow growing, narrowly conical form with short, soft, pale grey-blue leaves. O. and I. H.J. Welch, Combe Martin, Devon. Named for his wife.

- - 'Flat Top' Hort. Amer.   1985   An unsatisfactory listed name. See article 31A(f) of ICNCP.

- - 'Glauca' (1) P. de Vilmorin   1906   Indistinguishable from 'Argentea'.   France

- - 'Glauca' (2) Hort. Germany   1972   An illegit. name. L. Jeddeloh Nurs, Oldenburg.

- - 'Globe' Hort.   A mistake for the following entry.

- - **'Green Globe'** Welch   1979   Listed wrongly under *ABIES concolor*. I. Verkade Nurs, Wayne, N.J.   W3   U.S.A.

- - 'Hexenbesen' Hort. Amer.   1990   An unsatisfactory listed name. L. Coenosium Gardens "Nurs. Cat". 1990 Supplement.

- - **'Kenwith Blue'** Int. Con. Reg.   1978   In "Nurs. Cat". Kenwith Castle Nurs, Bideford, Devon. Upright small tree blue-grey foliage. O. Don Hatch Nurs, Honiton, Devon.   U.K.

- - 'King's Blue' Hort. Anglia   A listed name. Possibly the same as 'Kenwith Blue'.

- - 'Logan Pass' G. Horstmann   1976   In "Nurs. Cat". Very small blue dwarf form.

- - 'Lopalpun' Hort. Amer.   1985   A listed name for an extremely dwarf, bun forming plant.

- - **'Mulligan's Dwarf'** Welch   1979   Conical dwarf, leaves short, dark green.   W3   U.S.A.

- - 'Nana' Noble   1951   A clone of var. *lasiocarpa* found in the Cascades by James Noble of California in 1935. Conical dwarf. Leaves short, dark green.   U.S.A.

- - 'Pendula' Beissner   1909   A strongly pendulous clone of var. *lasiocarpa* raised by Ordnung Nurs, Eisenberg. Doubtless other such variants have turned up since.   B,K,W3   Czechoslo.

- - **'Roger Watson'** Welch   1979   Named for the owner of a small conical tree with grey foliage in Taunton, Somerset. I. Wansdyke Nurs, Devizes, Wilts.   W2   U.K.

ABIES laxa C. Koch   Now known as *PICEA glauca*.

ABIES ledebourii Ruprecht   Now known as *LARIX russica*.

ABIES leioclada Stevens ex Gordon
        1858 Now known as *ABIES cilicica* var. *leioclada*.

ABIES lemoniana Booth ex Gordon
        1858 Now known as *PICEA abies*.

ABIES leptolepis Siebold & Zuccarini
        1842 Now known as *LARIX kaempferi*.

ABIES likiangensis Franchet
        1899 Now known as *PICEA likiangensis*.

ABIES lowiana Murray   1863 Now known as *ABIES concolor* var. *lowiana*. *(lowii)*.

ABIES macrocarpa Vasey   1876 Now known as *PSEUDOTSUGA menziesii*.

ABIES magnifica A. Murray			
1863 Californian Red Fir, Great Red Fir and other names.	30m, Z6	U.S.A.	
- - 'Argentea' Schelle 1909 Probably indistinguishable from 'Glauca'. NIC.	B,D,K	Germany	
- - 'Cyanea' Sudworth 1897 Superfluous name for 'Glauca'.			
- - **'Glauca'** Beissner 1891 Leaves conspicuously glaucous.	B,D,K	Sporadic	
- - 'Hexenbesen' Horstmann 1986 In "Nurs. Cat". Very dwarf plant with short bluish incurved leaves. Suitable name required.		Germany	
- - 'Nana' H.G.Hillier 1964 A dwarf conical plant. First recorded from the Gotelli collection at South Orange, N.J.	G,K	U.S.A.	
- - 'Prostrata' Beissner 1904 Probably a cultivariant. NIC. O. Jurrissen Nurs, Bussum. Also listed as 'Glauca Prostrata'.	B,D,K,W2	Holland	
- - 'Shasta Prostrate' Hort. Now known as *ABIES* x *shastensis*. 'Shasta Prostrate'.		U.S.A.	
- - var. *shastensis* Lemmon 1890 Now known as *ABIES* x *shastensis*. Mount Shasta Fir.	B,K	U.S.A.	
- - f. *xanthocarpa* Lemmon 1890 A local form with small golden-yellow cones.	B,D,K	U.S.A	

ABIES mariana Miller   1768 Now known as *PICEA mariana*.

ABIES mariesii Masters 1897 Maries' Fir.	25m,Z6	Japan

- - var. *kawakami* Hayata   1908 Now known as *ABIES kawakami*.

ABIES marocana Trabut 1906 Moroccan Fir. Now known as *ABIES pinsapo* var. *marocana* (Per Silba, 1984).	Z7	Morocco

ABIES mayriana Miyabe & Kudo
        1920 Now known as *ABIES sachalinensis* var. *mayriana*.

ABIES menziesii (1) Lindley 1833 Now known as *PICEA sitchensis*.

ABIES menziesii (2) Engelmann
        1862 Now known as *PICEA pungens*.

ABIES menziesii (3) Franchet et Savatier
        1875 Now known as *PICEA jezoensis*.

ABIES menziesii (4) Mirbel   Now Known as *PSEUDOTSUGA menziesii*.

ABIES merkiana Fischen   1959 Now known as *PICEA sitchensis*.

ABIES mertensiana (1) (Bongard) Lindley & Gordon
        1850 Now known as *TSUGA mertensiana*.

ABIES mertensiana (2) Gordon
        1858 Now known as *TSUGA heterophylla*.

ABIES mexicana Martinez   1942 Mexican Fir. Not *ABIES vejari* var. *mexicana* (per Rushforth
  1987).   Z7   Mexico

ABIES microcarpa (Poiret) Lindley & Gordon
  1850 Now known as *LARIX laricina*.

ABIES microphylla Rafinesque
  1832 Now known as *TSUGA heterophylla*.

ABIES microspermae Lindley
  1861 Now known as *PICEA jezoensis*.

ABIES miniata Knight ex Gordon
  1882 Now known as *PICEA abies* 'Eremita'.

ABIES minuta Poiret   Now known as *PICEA rubens*.

ABIES momi Siebold   1830 Not now distinguished from *ABIES firma*.

ABIES montana Nyman   1878 Now known as *PICEA abies*.

ABIES morinda (Lawson) Wenderoth
  1851 Now known as *PICEA smithiana*.

ABIES mucronata (1) Rafinesque
  1832 Now known as *PSEUDOTSUGA menziesii*.

ABIES mucronata (2) Endlicher
  1847 Now known as *PICEA abies*.

ABIES nebrodensis (Lojacono-Pojero) Mattei
  1908 Sicilian Fir. Now nearly extinct in the wild.   15m,Z5   Sicily

ABIES nephrolepis (1) (Trautvetter) Maximowiczii
  1866 Eastern Siberian Fir, Klinghan Fir.   15m,Z3   China

ABIES nephrolepis (2) Hakai
  1914 Now known as *ABIES koreana*.

- - f. ***chlorocarpa*** Wilson   1920 Cones green before ripening. NIC.   B,D,K   China

- - 'Elegans' Schelle   1909 A compact form with bright green leaves.   B   Germany

ABIES nigra Aiton, Poiret, and others
                     Now known as *PICEA mariana*.

ABIES nobilis (D. Don) Lindley
  1833 Noble Fir. Now known as *ABIES procera*.

- - var. *magnifica* Nelson   1866 Now known as *ABIES* x *shastensis*.

ABIES nordmanniana (Steven) Spach
  1842 Caucasian Fir.   35m,Z5   Caucasus

- - 'Albospicata' Beissner   1898 Leaves on young branchlets white-tipped. **O.** Gebbers,
                     Wiesenberg. NIC.   B,K   Germany

- - "Ambrolauri"   1984 Name used for seedlings from a provenance in Central
                     Caucasus. L. Kordes Nurs, Bilsen. Not a clone.   Russia

- - **'Aurea'** Beissner   1891 Leaves golden-yellow.   B,D,K,W3   Germany

- - 'Aurea Nana' Hort.   1961 Now known as 'Golden Spreader'.

- - 'Aureospica' Beissner   1891 Green leaves, tipped golden-yellow. **O.** Hesse, Weener-on-
                     Ems. ('Aureospicata'). NIC.   B,K,W3   Germany

- - 'Aureovariegata' Schwerin

  1903 Leaves irregularly variegated or completely yellow. **O.**
      Ganghofer, Diedorf, Augsburg. NIC.   B,K   Germany

- - 'Barabit's Compact' H.J. van de Laar

  1990 In "Dendroflora 27". A broad, spreading, dwarf form;
      compact at first. **O.** M. Barabits, Sopron. **I.** M.M. Bömer,
      Zundert, Holland.   Hungary

- - 'Barabit's Gold'   1992 A listed name. No further information.

- - **'Brandt'** H.J. Hohman 1970 In Kingsville "Nurs. Cat", Kingsville, MD. A low spreader.   U.S.A.

- - 'Brevifolia' Carrière 1867 A dwarf form with peculiar leaves and erratic habit. NIC. B,H,K France

- - 'Broom' F. Bergman 1970 An illegit.listed name for a witch's broom introduced by
      Raraflora Nurs, Feasterville, PA.   U.S.A.

- - 'Coerulescens' Beissner 1891 An unidentifiable form. NIC.   B   Germany

- - 'Compacta' Den Ouden/Boom

  1965 Superfluous name for 'Nana Compacta'. **O.** Sénéclauze 1868. B,K   France

- - **'Emerald Pearl'** H.J. van de Laar

  1990 In "Dendroflora 27". A dense conical bush; leaves flat, long,
      dark green. Possibly a hybrid with *ABIES procera.* **O.** Libo
      Nurs, Baexem.   Holland

- - var. *equi-trojani* Ascherson & Sintensis

  1883 Now known as *ABIES cephalonica* var. *graeca.*   D

- - 'Erecta' Beissner 1907 Named for a fastigiate tree found by F. Pittet, Lausanne. NIC. B,K Switzerl.

- - 'Glauca' Beissner 1891 Glaucous seedlings appear from time to time.   B,K Sporadic

- - **'Gold Spear'** Hort. 1987 A listed name. No further information.

- - **'Golden Spreader'** Den Ouden/Boom

  1965 A dwarf, forming a spreading plant with golden-yellow
      foliage. **O.** Seedling on the S.N. Schoots' Nurs, Culemborg
      near Boskoop. **I.** L. Konijn & Co. Nurs,Reeuwijk. (1961). B,G,K,W3 Holland

- - 'Horizontalis' Carrière 1887 NIC. A compact form with horizontal habit. **O.** Nursery at
      Voudrey - Evrard, Misacours (Vosges).   B,K   France

- - **'Jakobsen'** G. Horstmann 1991 In "Nameslist".Very small dwarf with mid green leaves. **O.**
      and **I.** Arne Jacobsen, Denmark.   Denmark

- - **'Jensen'** Den Ouden/Boom

  1965 A strong-growing, pendulous tree; leaves short. **O.** Asger
      M.Jensen Nurs, Holmstrip.   B,K,W3 Denmark

- - f. *macrolepis* Viguie & Gaussen

  1929 A variant with large leaves and cones. NIC.   B,K

- - 'Munsterland' Hort. Germany Dwarf wider than high. **O.** and **I.** Eschrich Nursery.

- - 'Nana Compacta' Sénéclauze

  1868 A dwarf, compact conical bush with branches erect. Found
      by A. Sénéclauze as a seedling in 1867. NIC.   France

- - **'Pendula'** Young 1874 This form re-appears from time to time. See also 'Jensen'. **O.**
      Youngs Nurs, Milford, Surrey.   B,H,K,W3 U.K.

- - **'Procumbens'** Browicz & Bugala

  1958 A low, spreading plant reported from Körnickie Arboretum
      (1934). Probably a cultivariant.   B,K,W3 Poland

- - 'Prostrata' Hort. Amer. An illegit. listed name. Probably as preceding entry.   U.S.A.

- - 'Refracta' Carrière   1867 Named for an unidentifiable plant on the nursery. **O.**
Sénéclauze Nurs, (1866). NIC.   B,K   France

- - **'Robusta'** Carrière   1867 Named for a strong-growing tree on the nursery. **O.**
Sénéclauze Nurs, (1866). NIC.   B,K   France

- - var. *speciosa* Bailly   1890 Now listed as a cultivar under *ABIES* x *insignis*.

- - 'Tortifolia' Bailey   1923 Named for a curious tree with some leaves twisted owned by
Mrs W.B. Cuttery, Oakdale, L.I., N.Y. NIC.   B,D,K   U.S.A.

ABIES novae-angliae C. Koch   Now known as *PICEA mariana.*

ABIES nukiangensis Cheng & Fu
    1978 In "Flora Reipublicae Popularis Sinicae, 7". Possibly only a
sub sp. of *ABIES delavayi* (per Rushforth, 1987).

ABIES numidica de Lannoy ex Carrière
    1866 Algerian Fir.   20m,Z6   Algeria

- - 'Aurea' Viguie & Gaussen
    1929 Leaves yellow. NIC.   France

- - 'Drath' Hort. Germany   A listed name. No further information.

- - **'Glauca'** Beissner   1900 A glaucous tree. **O.** Probably a 6m high tree reported from
the Arboretum des Barres, Logent-sur-Venisson (per Pardé,
1906).   B,K   France

- - **'Glauca Pendula'** H.G.Hillier
    1970 In "Conifer Conf. List". NOM. Probably the same as
'Pendula'.

- - **'Lawrenceville'** (1) J. Vermeulen
    1972 In "Nurs. Cat". A conical tree with silvery-blue foliage. **O.** A
tree at Skylands Arboretum, Ringwood, N.J., raised from seed
collected in Lawrenceville, N.J.   U.S.A.

- - 'Lawrenceville' (2) Krüssmann
    1979 Dwarf form, foliage pale green. **I.** Jeddeloh Nurs. (1969). **O.**
Raised from a witch's broom.   K   U.S.A.

- - 'Nana' Hort. Germany   1980 An illegit. listed name for a dwarf with blue-green leaves. **L.**
zu Jeddeloh Nurs, Oldenburg, Germany.

- - **'Pendula'** H.G. Hillier   1971 In "Conifer Conf. List". An illegit. name for a dwarf form that
unless stem-trained, becomes an untidy bush.   G,K   France

- - 'Zwergform' Hort. Germany
    1978 An unacceptable listed name.

ABIES oaxacana Martinez   1948 No longer distingished from *ABIES hickelii,* (per Rushforth,
1987).   30m,Z8   Mexico

ABIES obliqua Bongard ex Gordon
    1862 Now known as *PSEUDOTSUGA menziesii.*

ABIES obovata (1) Ledebour
    1838 Now known as *PICEA obovata.*

ABIES omorika Nyman   1881 Now known as *PICEA omorika.*

ABIES orientalis (Linnaeus) Poiret
    1805 Now known as *PICEA orientalis.*

ABIES Pardéi Gaussen   1929 Thought by some to be a hybrid, with *ABIES numidica* as one
parent. **O.** Found by Pardé, in the Arboretum des Barres,
1912.   France

ABIES parlatorei Hort. ex Liu
1971 Now known as *PICEA pungens*.

ABIES parryana Hort. ex Liu
1971 Now known as *PICEA pungens*.

ABIES pattoniana Jeffrey ex A. Murray
1853 Now known as *TSUGA mertensiana*.

ABIES pattonii Jeffrey ex Gordon
1862 Now known as *TSUGA mertensiana*.

ABIES pectinata (1) Gilbert
1792 Now known as *PICEA abies*.

ABIES pectinata (2) Poiret   1804 Now known as *TSUGA canadensis*.

ABIES pectinata (3) De Candolle
1805 Now known as *ABIES alba*.

ABIES pendula Griffith ex Gordon
1862 Now known as *PICEA smithiana*.

ABIES x *phanerolepis* Fernald, emend Liu
1971 A hybrid: *ABIES balsamea* x *ABIES fraseri*.

ABIES picea (1)Miller   1768 Now known as *PICEA abies*.

ABIES picea (2) Lindley   1838 Now known as *ABIES alba*.

ABIES pichta Forbes   1939 Now merged with *ABIES sibirica*.

ABIES pindrow (Lambert) Royle			
1836 Pindrow Fir.		30m,Z7	Himalayas
- - 'Aureovariegata' Sénéclauze			
1868 See 'Variegata'.			France
- - 'Brevifolia' Dallimore and Jackson			
1923 Now known as *ABIES gamblei* (per Rushforth, 1987).		B,D,K,W3	Himalayas
- - 'Intermedia' Elwes & Henry			
1909 Named for a tree found at Eastnor Castle, Herefordshire, (1872). Possibly a hybrid with *ABIES spectabilis* .NIC.		B,D,K,W3	U.K.
- - 'Variegata' Carrière	1867 A variety with leaves striped or edged in a golden-yellow. O. Raised from seed on the Sénéclauze Nurs, Bourg Argental, Loires.	B	France
ABIES pinsapo Boissier	1838 Spanish Fir, Hedgehog Fir.	20m,Z7	Spain
- - 'Argentea' Nelson	1866 Leaves and young shoots partly yellow, straw or creamy-white. NIC.	B,K	U.K.
- - **'Aurea'** Sénéclauze	1868 Seldom more than a low shrub, leaves flushed yellow. O. Sénéclauze Nurs, Bourg Argental, Loires.	B,G,K,W2	France
- - var. *baborensis* Cosson	1861 Now merged in *ABIES numidica*.		
- - 'Barbara's Dwarf' Hort. Amer.	A listed name. No further information.		
- - 'Clarke' Reg'd. A.A.N.	1949 In "Woody Plant Register, List No.1". Extremely dwarf. O. W.B. Clarke Nurs, San José, Cal. (1935).	B,K,W3	U.S.A.
- - var. *concolor* Lavallee	1877 In "Arboretum Segrezianum". NIC.		
- - 'Delbert's Dwarf' Hort. Amer.	A listed name. No further information.		

- - **'Fastigiata'** Sénéclauze	1868	A dense, columnar form with short leaves. **O.** Sénéclauze Nurs, Bourg-Argental, Loires. NIC.	B,K	France
- - *folliis variegatis* Lawson	1850	Now known as 'Variegata'.		
- - **'Glauca'** Carrière	1867	Leaves glaucous and primrose. Widely planted. **O.** Defosse and Thuiller, Orleans.	B,D,G,K,W3	France
- - 'Hamondii' Veitch	1881	A widespreading plant; probably a cultivariant. NIC. ('Hammondii' is incorrect).	B,H,K	U.K.
- - var. *hispanica* Christ	1865	No longer distinguished within the species. (per Int. Con. Reg., 1987).		
- - **'Horstmann'** G. Horstmann	1978	In "Nurs. Cat". A dense dwarf form, blue-grey leaves. **O.** and **I.** G. Horstmann, Schneverdingen. ('Horstmann's Nana').	K,W3	Germany
- - 'Horstmann's Nana' Hort.	1984	An illegit. name . A mistake for the previous item.		
- - **'Kelleriis'** Krüssmann	1979	A very strong-growing, hardy selection with blue leaves. **O.** Poulsen Nurs, Kelleriis. (1920).	G,K,W3	Denmark
- - 'Kilmacurragh'	1962	Reported from the De Belten Pinetum, Vorden.		Holland
- - var. *marocana* (Trabut) Ceballos & Bolanos	1928	Moroccan Fir. A geographical form found in the mountains south of Tetuan.	12-15m,Z7	Morocco
- - 'Nana' A.A.N.	1987	See 'Clarke'.		
- - 'Nana Glauca' Hort. Germany	1976	**L.** M.G. Eiselt in "Nadelgehölze." Ed.4.		
- - **'Pendula'** Beissner	1891	A more or less pendulous form. NIC.	B,D,K	Germany
- - 'Pygmaea' Sénéclauze	1868	A very dwarf, conical shrub. **O.** Sénéclauze Nurs, Bourg Argental, Loires. NIC.	B,W2	France
- - 'Pyramidalis Glauca' Hort. France	1972	An illegit. listed name.		France
- - 'Pyramidata' Carrière	1867	A dwarf, conical tree with ascending leaves. NIC.	B,H,K	France
- - 'Quicksilver' Hort. Anglia	1984	Dwarf, silver grey colour. **I.** Don Hatch Nurs, Honiton, Devon, England.		
- - 'San Diego Creeper' Int. Con. Reg.	1981	Reg'd by F. J. Crowe, San Diego, Cal. A totally procumbent plant. NIC.	W3	U.S.A.
- - var. *tazaotana* Cozar ex Huguet del Wilar	1954	Tazaotan Fir. A geographical form from Tazaot.	30-50m,Z7	Morocco
- - 'Weeping Blue' Hort. Amer.	1984	An illegit. name.		
ABIES polita Siebold & Zuccarini	1842	Now known as *PICEA polita*.		
ABIES procera Rehder	1940	Noble Fir (Formerly known as *ABIES nobilis*).	40m,Z5	U.S.A.
- - **'Argentea'** Freundenburg	1886	Leaves bluish-white, shining silvery. NIC.	B,K	
- - 'Argentea Nellemann' Hort. Anglia	1987	An illegit. listed name for a form similar to but more vigorous than 'Blaue Hexe'.		
- - 'Argentea Wattezii' Hort.	1901	Superfluous name for 'Wattezii'.		

- - 'Aurea' (1) Reg. A.A.N. 1948 In "Woody Plant Register, List No. 1." Regd. by Sherwood
Nurs, Portland. OR. A form with bright golden-yellow
foliage. **O.** The same (1933). Now generally known as
'Sherwoodii' in the trade.   U.S.A.

- - 'Aurea' (2) Hort. 1987 A clone with sulphur-yellow foliage. (See Rushforth, 1987).   R

- - **'Blaue Hexe'** Krüssmann
     1979 A broad, dense, flat globose bush. **O.** and **I.** Propagated from
a witch's broom by C.D. Boehlje Nurs, Westerstede. (1965).   G,K,W3   Holland

- - 'Compacta' Dallimore 1932 In "Conifers in Cultivation". NOM. A mistake for 'Prostrata'
(1).

- - 'Franken' Hort. Holland 1993 A listed name.

- - **'Glauca'** Ravenscroft 1863 In "Pinet. Brit". The Blue Fir. See the following note.   B,D,G,K,W3   U.K.

Glaucous and intermediate forms turn up in the seed-beds. The name should be restricted to clones of outstanding
colour, propagated vegetatively.

- - 'Glauca Nobel' Hort. Anglia
     1983 A mistake for 'Noble's Dwarf'. (as is 'Nana Nobel').

- - 'Glauca Prostrata' (1) H.G. Hillier
     1928 A low bush with spreading branches and glaucous leaves. **O.**
Hilliers' Shroner Wood Nurs, before 1890.   B,H,K,W2,W3U.K.

- - 'Glauca Prostrata' (2) Hort.   See the following note.

This name is now widely used for cultivariants (ie. plants with a low, spreading habit and no leader), individually
produced by the use of side shoots for propagation. Note: Such are not a clone in the biological sense and are apt to
develop a leader and become arboreal, making nonsense of the word "Prostrate" and to save disappointment it is safer
to offer such plants as 'Glauca' adding the words *Prostrate form* not part of the name but as a 'trade description' of
each actual plant.

- - 'Glaucifolia' Sudworth 1897 Superfluous name for 'Glauca'.

- - **'Jeddeloh'** Krüssmann 1979 A dwarf form similar to 'Blaue Hexe', but the foliage is a
greenish-blue. **O.** From a witch's broom at Jeddeloh Nurs.   K,W3   Germany

- - **'La Graciosa'** Hort. Amer.
     1988 A compact prostrate plant. **I.** Evans Farm Nurs, Oregon City,
OR. **O.** A seedling raised at Drakes Crossing Nurs.   W3

- - **'Mount Hood'** Hort. Amer.
     1989 Iseli Nurs, Boring, OR. Golden procumbent form.   U.S.A.

- - **'Nobel'** Krüssmann 1979 Now to be 'Noble's Dwarf'.   K

- - **'Noble's Dwarf'** Welch 1991 A slow growing plant with a leader and blue foliage. **O.**
James Noble Collection, Golden Gate Park, San Francisco.
The spelling 'Nobel' is incorrect.   W3   U.S.A.

- - 'Procumbens' Hort. Germany
     1979 An illegit. name for plants of the 'Glauca Prostrata' type. In
cultivation but propagated from a less colourful, grey-green
clone.

- - 'Prostrata' (1) Edwin Hillier
     1890 Named for a grafted plant of a weak side branch which
remained prostrate at one time in th Hillier Nurs,
Winchester.   H,K   U.K.

- - **'Prostrata'** (2) Hort.   A name widely in use for cultivariants of this species.

- - 'Robusta' Beissner 1891 A robust clone with unusually large leaves. NIC.   B,D,K   Germany

- - 'Robustifolia' Sudworth 1927 Superfluous name for 'Robusta'.

- - **'Sherwoodii'** Hort. Amer.

        1948 Reg'd. as 'Aurea' but 'Sherwoodii' is now in general usage in the trade. **O.** Sherwood Nurs, Portland, OR, (1933).   B,K,W3   U.S.A.

ABIES pseudomenziesii Wenderoth

        1851 Now known as *PICEA sitchensis.*

ABIES pumila Hort. ex Gordon

        1858 Now known as *PICEA abies* 'Pumila'.

ABIES pungens Parry   1863 Now known as *PICEA engelmanii.*

ABIES recurvata Masters   1906 Min Fir.   30m, Z6   China

- - var. **ernestii** Rehder   1949 By some authorities listed under *ABIES chensiensis.*

ABIES religiosa (1) (Humboldt, Bonpland & Kunth). Schlechtendal

        1830 Sacred Fir.   30m, Z8   Mexico

ABIES religiosa (2) Parlatore

        1868 Now known as *ABIES guatamalensis.*

ABIES religiosa (3) Hooker Arnott

        1841 Now known as *SEQUOIA sempervirens.*

- - var. *glaucescens* (Gordon) Carrière

        1867 No longer distinguished within the species.   B,K   Mexico

- - var. *hirtella* (Humboldt, Bonpland & Kunth) Carrière

        1867 No longer distinguished within the species.

ABIES rolii Borderes-Rey & Gaussen

        1948 Not now distinguished within *ABIES forrestii* (per Rushforth, 1987).   K

ABIES romania Loudon ex Steudel

        1841 Now known as *PINUS nigra* var. *caramanica.*

ABIES rubra Poiret   1805 Now known as *PICEA rubens.*

ABIES sachalinensis Fr. (Schmidt) Masters

        1879 Sakhalin Fir.   15m, Z5   Japan

- - var. *corticosa* Tatewaki   1935 No longer distinguished within the species.

- - var. **mayriana** Miyabe & Kudo

        1919 A minor variant with smooth bark and peculiar cones. Mayr fir.   B,D,K,W3   Japan

- - var. *nemorensis* Mayr   1890 Not now distinguished within the species by most authorities.   B,D,K

ABIES sacra David   1875 Now known as *KETELEERIA davidiana.*

ABIES saluenensis Borderes & Gaussen

        Now known as *ABIES chensiensis.*

ABIES schrenkiana (Fisher) Lindley & Gordon

        1850 Now known as *PICEA schrenkiana.*

ABIES semenovii Fedschenko   Tienshan Fir. A little known species, near to *ABIES sibirica.*   30-50m,Z2   Asia

ABIES x shastensis (Lemmon) emend Liu

        1971 Shasta Fir. A hybrid: *ABIES magnifica* x *ABIES procera.*   W3

- - **'Shasta Prostrate'** Hort. Amer.

        1986 A stable prostrate plant of a good blue colour. **O.** Girard Nurs, Geneva, OH.   W3   U.S.A.

ABIES sibirica Ledebour   1833 Siberian Fir.   10-15m, Z2-5   Siberia

- - 'Alba' Carrière   1855 Named for a tree with leaves light green, whitish beneath,
                                found in N. Russia, 1853. NIC.   B,K   Russia

- - var. *araucarioides* Viguie & Gaussen
                                1929 No longer distinguished within the species.

- - 'Candelabrum' Schröder   1894 Named for a tree in Moscow with many erect stems. NIC.   B   Russia

- - **'Columnaris'** Beissner   1914 No longer identifiable.   Germany

- - 'Compacta Glauca' Beissner
                                1908 Named for a dense dwarf plant found in the forest nursery at
                                Crenzow. NIC.   B,H   Germany

- - var. *conica* Beissner   1914 No longer distinguished within the species.   Czechoslo.

- - 'Elegans' Beissner   1891 A compact form with peculiar foliage. **O.** Lobkowitz Nurs,
                                Eisenberg. NIC.   B   Czechoslo.

- - 'Glauca' Schröder   1894 Leaves curved, glaucous. Possibly a hybrid.**O.** Schröder,
                                Petrowskaya Acad., Moscow. NIC.   B   Russia

- - var. *gracilis* Patschke   1913 Now known as *ABIES nephrolepis*.

- - var. *hybrida* Beissner   1914 No longer distinguished within the species.

- - var. *longifolia* Beissner   1914 No longer distinguished within the species.

- - 'Maritima' Beissner   1914 No longer distinquished within the species.

- - 'Monstrosa' Schröder   1894 Named for a plant with short tufted, twisted branches and
                                leaves, found by Schröder, in the Petrowskaya Acad.,
                                Moscow. NIC.   B,H   Russia

- - var. *nephrolepis* Trautvetter
                                1859 Now known as *ABIES nephrolepis*.

- - 'Parvula' Schröder   1894 A slow-growing plant found by Schröder, in the Petrowskaya
                                Acad., Moscow. NIC.   B   Russia

- - 'Pendula' Schröder   1894 A strongly pendulous form. **O.** Regel and Kesselring Nurs,
                                (1881). NIC.   B,H,K   Russia

- - 'Pumila' Schröder   1894 Named for a dwarf shrub, lacking a leader, raised by
                                Schröder, at the Petrowskaya Acad., Moscow. NIC.   B,H   Russia

- - 'Pyramidalis' Schröder   1894 Named for a tree with branches ascending, raised by
                                Schröder, at the Petrowskaya Acad., Moscow. NIC.   B   Russia

- - var. *semenovii* (Fedtschenko) Liu
                                1971 Tienshen Fir. A minor variant, not accepted by some
                                authorities.   Asia

- - 'Variegata' Nelson   1866 A form with leaves on some branches yellowish-white that has
                                turned up more than once. NIC.   B

- - var *viridis* Beissner   1914 No longer recognised within the species.

ABIES sikokiana (Nakai) Kusaka
                                1954 Shikiku Fir. Now known as *ABIES veitchii* var. *sikokiana*.   Japan

ABIES spectabilis (D. Don) Spach
                                1824 Himalayan Fir; Webb Fir.   15-20m, Z6

- - 'Affinis' Carrière   1867 Leaves bluish-white beneath. NIC.   B,D

- - var. *brevifolia* (Henry) Rehder
                                1919 Not distinguished within the species by some authorities.   B,K,W3   Himalayas

- - var. *densa* (Griffith) Silba
          1984 A geographical variant, forming a much larger tree.

- - 'Intermedia' Henry
          Here listed under *ABIES pindrow*. Possibly a hybrid with that species.

ABIES spinulosa Griffith	1847 Now known as *PICEA spinulosa*.			
ABIES squamata Masters	1906 Flaky Fir.		50m,Z5	China

ABIES standishiana C. Koch
          1878 Now known as *PSEUDOTSUGA menziesii*.

ABIES sub-alpina Engelmann
          1876 Now known as *ABIES lasiocarpa*.

ABIES sub-arctica Nyman   1878 Now known as *PICEA abies*.

ABIES sutchuenensis Rehder & Wilson
          1914 Now merged with *ABIES fargesii* by some authorities. (Per Rushforth, 1987).

ABIES tacanensis Lundell   1940 Now merged in *ABIES guatamalensis*.   Mexico

ABIES taxifolia (1) Desfontaines
          1804 Now known as *ABIES alba*.

ABIES taxifolia (2) Poiret   1804 Now known as *PSEUDOTSUGA menziesii*.

ABIES taxifolia (3) Jeffrey ex Gordon
          1858 Now known as *TSUGA heterophylla*.

ABIES taxifolia (4) Rafinesque
          1829 Now known as *TSUGA canadensis*.

ABIES tazaotana S. Cozar   1947 Now known as *ABIES pinsapo* var. *tazaotana* (per Silba, 1984).

ABIES thunbergii Thunberg ex Gordon
          1875 Now known as *PICEA smithiana*.

ABIES torano Siebold   1830 Now known as *PICEA polita*.

ABIES tsuga Siebold & Zuccarini
          1842 Now known as *TSUGA sieboldii*.

ABIES x **umbellata** Mayr emend Liu
          1971 A hybrid: *ABIES firma* x *ABIES homolepis*.

- - f. *fusijanensis* Hayashi   1969 Not now distinguished within the species.

ABIES umbilicata Mayr   1894 See *ABIES* x *umbellata*.

ABIES x **vasconcellosiana** Franco
          1946 A hybrid: *ABIES pindrow* x *ABIES pinsapo*. **O.** found by Franco in Pena Park, Sintra.   B,K   Portugal

- - 'Amaral Franco' Meyer   1961 Named for a tree in Pena Park, Sintra NIC.   B,K,W3   Portugal

ABIES veitchii Lindley   1861 Veitch Fir.   15-20m, Z3   Japan

- - 'Glauca' Hort. Germany   1968 An illegit. name for a selection with bluish-green needles.

- -' Hedergott' Wustemeyer   1986 Very dwarf low spreading bush, very short leaves with under side silvery. **O.** and **I.** Wustemeyer.   Germany

- - 'Heine' Wustemeyer   1991 Dwarf spreading form, longer lighter green leaves than 'Hedergott'. Branchlet growth up to 5 cm per year. **O.** and **I.** Wustemeyer.   Germany

- - 'Minima' Hort. Germany   1991   An illegit. name. **O.** Found by the Backhus Nursery. **I.** zu Jeddeloh. In "Nurs. Cat". 1991.

- - var. *nikkoensis* Mayr   1890   No longer distinguished within the species.   B,D,K   Japan

- - var. *olivacea* Shirasawa   1913   Green cones. No longer distinguished within the species.   B,D,K   Japan

- - 'Pendula' (1) Jeddeloh   1991   An illegit. listed name. Jeddeloh Catalogue. New name required. (1970).

- - 'Pendula (2) Hachmann   Slow growing pendulous form. An illegit. name. **O.** Hachmann Nurs, Barmstedt in Holstein.   Germany

- - var. ***sikokiana*** (Nakai) Kusaka
     1954   Shikoku Fir. Not in European cultivation.   W3   Japan

ABIES vejari Martinez   1942   Vejar Fir.   20m, Z6   Mexico

- - var. *macrocarpa* Martinez
     1948   No longer distinguished within the species.   W

- - var. ***mexicana*** (Martinez) Liu
     1972   Mexican Fir. A geographical variety; showing minor variations in foliage and fruit. (per Rushforth, 1987).   K,W3   Mexico

- - 'Serpent' Int. Con. Reg.   1985   Reg'd by F.J. Crowe, San Diego, Cal. (1975). **O.** The same.   W3   U.S.A.

ABIES venusta (Douglas) K. Koch
     1872   Now known as *ABIES bracteata.*

ABIES* x *vilmorinii Masters 1901   A hybrid: *ABIES pinsapo* x *ABIES cephalonica.* **O.** M. de Vilmorin, Verrieres-les-Buisson near Paris in 1867.   B,K   France

ABIES vulgaris Wenderoth   1851   Now known as *PICEA abies.*

ABIES webbiana (1) Lindley
     1833   Now known as *ABIES spectabilis.*

ABIES webbiana (2) Of some authors
     Refers to *ABIES firma.*

ABIES williamsonii Newberry
     1857   Now known as *TSUGA mertensiana.*

ABIES yuana Borderes-Rey & Gaussen
     1987   A variant of *ABIES forrestii,* (per Rushforth, 1987).

ABIES yuanbaoshanensis Lu & Fu
     1987   A recently described species.   China

ABIES yunnanensis Franchet
     1899   Now known as *TSUGA yunnanensis.*

ABIES ziyuanensis Fu & Mo   A newly described species not yet in western cultivation.   China

ACMOPYLE Pilger (1903)

Podocarpaceae

A small genus of small evergreen trees allied to *Podocarpus* and *Dacrydium*. Neither of the species is hardy in Europe, and no cultivars have been recorded.

ACMOPYLE alba Buchholz 1949 May be synonymous with *ARAUCARIA pancheri*. (per Rushforth, 1987).

ACMOPYLE pancheri (Brongniart & Grisebach) Pilger.
               1903 New Caledonian Acmopyle.   5-20m,Z9   New Caledonia

ACMOPYLE sahniana Buchholz & Gray
               1947 Fijian Acmopyle.   3-5m,Z9   Fiji

ACTINOSTROBUS Miguel & Lehmann (1845)

Cupressaceae

A small genus of evergreen shrubs allied to *Callitris*. Native to Western Australia and not hardy in Europe.

ACTINOSTROBUS acuminatus Parlatore
               1862 Moore river Cypress-Pine. A small, usually conical shrub.   3m,Z9   W. Australia

ACTINOSTROBUS arenarius Gardner
               1964 See *ACTINOSTROBUS pyramidalis* var. *arenarius*. (per
                     Silba, 1984).   Z9   W. Australia

·*ACTINOSTROBUS pyramidalis* Miguel & Lehmann
               1845 King George Cypress-Pine. A narrowly conical shrub.   1-4m,Z9   W. Australia

- - var. *arenarius* (C.Gardner) Silba.
               1984 Bruce Rock Cypress Pine. A geographical variant.   Z9   W. Australia

AGATHIS Salisbury (1807)

Araucariaceae

A genus of tall trees containing upwards of a dozen species from New Zealand, Australia, Indonesia and the Malay peninsula, of which only one species is even marginally hardy in U.K. No cultivars are recorded.

AGATHIS australis (Lambert) Steudel
               1841 Kauri Pine.   40-50m,Z9   N.Z.

AMENTOTAXUS Pilger (1916)

Taxaceae

A genus of three or four species, all confined to S.E. Asia. None of which is hardy in Europe.

ARAUCARIA Jussieu (1789)

Araucariaceae

A genus of about 18 species of tall trees from Australia, New Zealand, Indonesia and S. America of which only *ARAUCARIA araucana* is hardy in Europe, although *ARAUCARIA heterophylla* is widely grown under greenhouse culture as a decorative plant. The genus was formerly listed under the names *EUTACTA* and also *COLYMBEA* and has suffered from numerous name changes. Here the taxonomy follows the International Conifer Register 1987. In the heyday of its early popularity numerous seedlings with foliar or colour differences were selected and named. Gordon (1875) wrote "such differences are only retained while the plants are young". This may explain why none, if any, of these clones has survived in cultivation today.

ARAUCARIA angustifolia (Bertolini) Kuntze
1893 Parana Pine; Candelabra Pine. Formerly listed under *COLYMBEA*.	30m,Z7	S. America

- - 'Elegans' Lawson
1852 Clone with narrow leaves, NIC. Formerly listed under *ARAUCARIA brasiliensis*.	B,K	

- - 'Ridolfiana' Gordon
1858 Vigorous mountain form with large leaves. **O.** Count Ridolfi. NIC. Formerly listed under *ARAUCARIA brasiliensis*.	B,K	

- - 'Saviana' Parlatore
1868 Clone with narrow leaves. Formerly listed under *ARAUCARIA brasiliensis*.	B,D,K	

ARAUCARIA araucana (Molina) K Koch
1873 The Monkey-puzzle tree. Formerly listed as *ARAUCARIA imbricata*.	20-35m, Z7	S. America

- - 'Andenzwerg' Krussmann
1979 Dwarf. **O.** Raised from seed collected in the Andes by H. Neulen, Heligoland.	K	Germany

- - 'Angustifolia' Dallimore & Jackson
1948 Branches and leaves long, slender. NIC. Formerly listed under *ARAUCARIA brasiliensis*.	B,D,K	U.K.

- - 'Aurea' Dallimore & Jackson
1923 Golden form raised by Taylor of Castle Kennedy, Stranraer, Scotland in 1855 with golden yellow leaves.	B,K	U.K.

- - 'Aurea Variegata' Carrière
1867 Foliage striped pale yellow and branchlets slender. NIC.		

- - 'Aureovariegata' Barron
1875 A form with golden yellow leaves raised by A. Fowler at Castle Kennedy, Stranraer, in 1855.		

- - 'Auslese' G. Horstmann
1983 A hardy selection made by Horstmann and raised from seed from S.W. Argentina.		Germany

- - 'Densa' Carrière
1867 Leaves short and dense. NIC. Formerly listed under *COLYMBIA imbricata*.	B,K	France

- - 'Denudata' Carrière   1867   Branching sparse. NIC. **O**. A. Leroy Nurs, Angers. NIC. Formerly listed under *COLYMBEA imbricata*.   B,K   France

- - 'Distans' Carrière   1867   Tree of open habit. NIC. Formerly listed under *COLYMBEA imbricata*.   B,K   France

- - 'Kurt Sachs' Krussmann   1979   A very hardy clone, long grown in the Hamburg area.   K   Germany

- - 'Platifolia' Nicholson   1901   Leaves broad. **O**. and **I**. A. Leroy Nurs, Angers. NIC. Formerly listed under *ARAUCARIA imbricata*.   B,K   France

- - 'Striata' ('Stricta') Carrière

    1867   Foliage striped yellow. **O**. A. Leroy Nurs, Angers. NIC. Formerly listed under *COLYMBEA imbricata*.   B,K   France

- - 'Variegata' (1) Gordon   1858   **O**. and **I**. Glendinning Nurs, Turnham Green, near London. NIC. Formerly listed under *ARAUCARIA imbricata*.   B,K   U.K.

- - 'Variegata' (2) Hort. ex Carrière

    1867   A superfluous name for 'Striata'.

- - 'Virgata' Schwerin   1927   A superfluous name for 'Denudata'.

ARAUCARIA balansae Brongniart & Grisebach

    1868   Now known as *ARAUCARIA subulata*.   New Caledonia

ARAUCARIA beccarii Warburg

    1900   Now known as *ARAUCARIA cunninghamii* var. *papuana*.   New Guinea

ARAUCARIA bernieri Buchholz

    1949   Not hardy in cool temperate regions.   40-50m   New Caledonia

ARAUCARIA bidwillii Hooker

    1843   Bunya-Bunja. Not hardy in cool temperate regions. *(bidwilliana)*   50m,Z9   Australia

ARAUCARIA biramulata Buchholz

    1949   Not hardy in cool temperate regions.   30m   New Caledonia

ARAUCARIA brasiliana R. Richard

    1812   Now known as *ARAUCARIA augustifolia (brasiliensis)*.

- - 'Gracilis' Carrière   1855   Now known as *ARAUCARIA angustifolia* 'Elegans'.

ARAUCARIA chilensis (Lamarck) Mirbel

    1825   Now known as *ARAUCARIA araucana*.

ARAUCARIA columnaris (Forster) Hooker

    1852   Cook Pine. Not hardy in cool temperate regions.   60m,Z9   New Caledonia

ARAUCARIA cookii R.Brown ex Lindley

    1841   Now known as *ARAUCARIA columnaris*.

ARAUCARIA cunninghamii Sweet

    1827   Hoop Pine, Moreton Bay pine.   50-60m,Z9   Australia

- - **'Glauca'** (Antoine) Endlicher

    1847   Foliage glaucous. **I**. Loddiges Nurs, Hackney near London.   B,K,D   U.K.

- - 'Longifolia' Antoine   1840   Habit robust; leaves long. NIC.   B,K

- - var. **papuana** Lauterbach 1913   New Guinea Hoop Pine.   25-50m   New Guinea

- - 'Pendula' Carrière   1867   Branches pendulous. NIC. Formerly listed under *EUTACTA cunninghamii*.   B,K   France

- - 'Taxifolia' Carrière   1867   Foliage very dense. NIC. Formerly listed under *EUTACTA cunninghamii*.   B,K   France

ARAUCARIA dioica Stellfeld
1944 Now known as *ARAUCARIA angustifolia.*

ARAUCARIA dombeyi A. Richard
1812 Now known as *ARAUCARIA araucana.*.

ARAUCARIA elegans (1) C. Moore
1895 Probable a synonym of *ARAUCARIA angustifolia* 'Elegans'. (per Rushforth, 1987).

ARAUCARIA elegans (2) Hort.
1895 A mistake for *ARAUCARIA subulata.*   U.K.

ARAUCARIA excelsa R. Brown in Aiton
1813 Now known as *ARAUCARIA heterophylla*. (But see Silba, 1984).

ARAUCARIA goldieana (1) Hort. Now known as *ARAUCARIA heterophylla* 'Robusta'.   U.K.

ARAUCARIA goldieana (2) Moore
1877 Now listed under *ARAUCARIA rulei.*   U.K.

ARAUCARIA heterophylla (Salisbury) Franco
1952 The Norfolk Island Pine. Formerly known as *ARAUCARIA*
      excelsa..   50-60m   Australia etc.

- - **'Albospica'** Seneclauze   1868 Silvery variegation. NIC. Formerly listed under *EUTACTA*
      excelsa.   B,D,K   France

- - 'Aurea Variegata' Carrière
1867 Sport from 'Glauca'; shoots and leaves streaked yellow.
      Formerly listed under *ARAUCARIA excelsa.*   B,K   Australia

- - 'Compacta' Baur   1891 In "Gartenflora". Compact habit. NIC. Formerly listed under
      ARAUCARIA excelsa.   B,K

- - **'Glauca'** Carrière   1855 Leaves glaucous green. Formerly listed under *ARAUCARIA*
      excelsa.   B,K   France

- - **'Gracilis'** Dallimore & Jackson
1923 Growth very compact. NIC. Formerly listed under
      ARAUCARIA excelsa.   B,D,K   U.K.

- - 'Joseph Napoleon Bauman' Madeleine
1873 In "Revue Horticole". Indistinguishable from 'Glauca'.

- - 'Leopoldii' Dallimore & Jackson
1923 Compact, glaucous. NIC.   B,D,K   U.K.

- - 'Monstrosa' Carrière   1867 Peculiarities of foliage. Formerly listed under *EUTACTA*
      excelsa.   B,K   France

- - 'Muelleri' Dallimore & Jackson
1923 A vigorous clone. NIC. Formerly listed under *EUTACTA*
      excelsa.   B,D,K   U.K.

- - 'Pendula' Hort. Amer.   1972 An illegit. listed name.

- - 'Robusta' Veitch   1881 Vigorous clone; dark green. NIC.   B,K   U.K.

- - 'Silver Star' Bailey & Raffill
1914 Superfluous name for 'Albospica'. NIC.   D

- - 'Speciosissima' Carrière   1874 In "Revue Horticole". Foliage peculiarity. NIC. O. Rougier,
      at Chauviere near Paris.   B,K   France

- - 'Variegata' Gordon   1875 A mistake for 'Aurea Variegata'.

- - 'Variegata Alba' Carrière 1867 A mistake for 'Albospica'.

- - 'Virgata' Schwerin   1906 Branching sparse. NIC **O**. Found in a garden at Palermo, Sicily.   B,D,K   Sicily

ARAUCARIA humboltensis Buchholz
        1949 Not hardy in cool temperate regions.   10-15m   New Caledonia

ARAUCARIA hunsteinii K. Schumacher & Hollrung
        1899   80m   New Guinea

ARAUCARIA imbricata Pavon
        1797 Now known as *ARAUCARIA araucana*.

ARAUCARIA intermedia R. Brown ex Vieillard
        1861 Now known as *ARAUCARIA columnaris*.

ARAUCARIA klinkii Lauterbach ex Engler
        1913 Now known as *ARAUCARIA hunsteinii*.

ARAUCARIA laubenfelsii Corbasson
        1968 Not hardy in cool temperate regions.   10-30m   New Caledonia

ARAUCARIA luxurians (Brongniart & Grisebach) De Laubenfels ex Gaussen
        1970 Not hardy in cool temperate regions.   30m   New Caledonia

ARAUCARIA montana Brongniart & Grisebach
        1871 Not hardy in cool temperate regions.   10-40m   New Caledonia

ARAUCARIA muelleri (Carrière) Brongniart & Grisebach
        1871 Not hardy in cool temperate regions.   10-25m   New Caledonia

ARAUCARIA nemorosa De Laubenfels
        1969 Not hardy in cool temperate zones.   15m

ARAUCARIA niepratschii Baumann ex Pynaert
        1905 Now known as *ARAUCARIA rulei*.

ARAUCARIA ribbiana Hort.   Superfluous name for *ARAUCARIA angustifolia* 'Ridolfiana'.

ARAUCARIA rulei Mueller ex Lindley
        1860 Not hardy in cool temperate regions.   20-50m   New Caledonia

- - 'Elegans' Nicholson   1884 Leaves small, branches closely whorled. NIC.   B,K   U.K.

- - 'Goldieana' (Moore) Masters
        1892 Neat habit; leaves small. NIC.   B,D,K   U.K.

- - 'Intermedia' Dallimore & Jackson
        1923 Foliage intermediate between *ARAUCARIA rulei* and *ARAUCARIA columnaris*.   D,K   U.K.

- - 'Polymorpha' Carrière   1866 Peculiarity of foliage. NIC. Formerly listed under *EUTACTA rulei*.   B,K   France

ARAUCARIA schmidii De Laubenfels
        1969 Not hardy in cool temperate regions.   20-30m   New Caledonia

ARAUCARIA schumanniana Lauterbach ex Engler
        1913 Now known as *ARAUCARIA hunsteinii*.

ARAUCARIA scopulorum De Laubenfels
        1969 Not hardy in cool temperate regions.   5-20m   New Caledonia

ARAUCARIA subulata Vieillard
        1861 Formerly known as *ARAUCARIA balansae*.   50m   New Caledonia

ARAUCARIA vangaertii Hort.   Superfluous name for *ARAUCARIA rulei*.

ATHROTAXIS D. Don (1839)

Taxodiaceae

A genus of two or three closely-related species of tall trees from Tasmania, related to *Cryptomeria.* They make interesting specimen trees in even a small garden, being very slow-growing in cultivation. No cultivars are reported.

ATHROTAXIS cupressoides D. Don
        1839 Smooth Tasmanian Cedar.   6-15m,Z8   Tasmania

ATHROTAXIS doniana Henkel & Hochstetter
        1865 Now known as *ATHROTAXIS laxifolia.*

ATHROTAXIS laxifolia Hooker
        1843 Summit or yellow-twig Athrotaxis.   12-20m,Z7   Tasmania

ATHROTAXIS selaginoides D. Don
        1839 King William Pine; Longleaf Athrotaxis.   30m,Z8   Tasmania

AUSTROCEDRUS Florin & Boutelje (1954)

Cupressaceae

A monotypic genus separated from *Libocedrus* in 1954, a change that has not been accepted by all botanists. (See Silba, 1984).

AUSTROCEDRUS chilensis (D. Don) Florin & Boutelje
        1954 Chilean Incense Cedar.   15m,Z8   Chile

- - **'Argentea'** Seneclauze   1868 A clone with whitish foliage. **O.** From seed on Seneclauze
                                  Nurs, Bourg Argental, Loires.   W3   France

- - **'Viridis'** Hort. ex Carrière
        1867 Clone in cultivation lacking white stomata. It may represent a
                variant of botanical significance. (per Rushforth, 1987).   D,W3   France

- - 'Viridis Compacta' Seneclauze
        1868 Compact clone. **O.** Seneclauze Nurs, Bourg Argental, Loires.
                NIC.   W2   France

AUSTROTAXUS Compton (1922)

Taxaceae

A monotypic genus, resembling *Podocarpus* in the foliage and *Taxus* in the fruit; a native of New Caledonia and therefore not hardy in cool temperate regions. No cultivars are recorded.

AUSTROTAXUS spicata Compton
        1922 New Caledonian Yew.   5-25m,Z10   New Caledonia

CALLITRIS Ventenat (1808)

Cupressaceae

A genus of 14 species of trees or shrubs, all native to Australia, New Caledonia or Tasmania, and none hardy in cool temperate regions.

CALOCEDRUS Kurz (1873)

Cupressaceae

A genus of 3 species, for many years included in *Libocedrus*, and at one time in *Heyderia*.

CALOCEDRUS decurrens (Torreya) Florin
1956 Incense Cedar.   20-60m,Z5   U.S.A.

- - **'Aureovariegata'** Beissner
1904 Bold yellow variegation. Commonly planted. ('Variegata Aurea').   B,D,G,K,W3   Germany

- - **'Berrima Gold'** Hort Australia.
1986 Foliage at first orange; later, yellow-green. L. Hillier & Son Nurs, Winchester (1987). **O.** A seedling found by Claude Crowe of Berrima Bridge Nurs, N.S.W., but not introduced by them in Australia.   R   Australia

- - 'Burwanda Gold' Hort. Holland
1991 A listed name. Information required.

- - 'Columnaris' Beissner
1884 Columnar clone no longer identifiable. No need for all columnar plants in cultivation ('Fastigiata').   B,D,K,W3   Sporadic

- - 'Compacta' (1) Beissner 1891 Dense, globose shape, similar to a globose *Thuja*. NIC.   B,D,G,K,W2   Germany

- - 'Compacta' (2) SENSU Welch
1966 Now accepted as being the clone 'Depressa'.   W2

- - **'Depressa'** Scott ex Gordon
1975 Globose dwarf bronzing in winter. **O.** Scott's Nurs, Merriott, Somerset.   G,R,W2   U.K.

- - 'Fastigiata' H.G. Hillier 1971 In "Hilliers Manual", see 'Columnaris'.

- - **'Glauca'** Beissner 1884 Conspicuously glaucous. Similar plants turn up.   B,D,K,W3   Sporadic

- - 'Greenspire' Hort. Amer. 1986 A listed name; possibly superfluous to 'Columnaris'.   U.S.A.

- - 'Horizontalis' Beissner 1909 Branches more or less horizontal. **I.** Spaeth Nurs, Berlin (1891). No longer identifiable.   B,K   Germany

- - **'Intricata'** H.G. Hillier 1964 Conical congested dwarf. **O.** Raised from seed by J.R. Noble of San Francisco. **I.** A.H. Nisbet of Gosport, Hants.   B,G,K,R,W2   U.K.

- - 'Nana' Dallimore & Jackson
1923 A name of no clear application; useful now only as a group name.

- - **'Pillar'** Hort. Holland   1968   I. L. Konijn and Co., Nurs., then of Reeuwijk, in "Sortimentslijst" (1970). **O.** Unrecorded. NIC. ('Pilaris' is incorrect).

- - 'Pygmaea' Hort. Holland   1968   An illegit. name. **O.** Same as last item.

- - **'Riet'** H.G. Hillier   1971   **O.** Raised from a witch's broom found by J.R.P. van Hoey-Smith during an International Dendrological Society visit and named in honour of Mrs. van Hoey-Smith.   G,W3   California

- - 'Variegata' Hort. Anglia   1968   See 'Aureovariegata'.

CALOCEDRUS formosana (Florin) Florin
1956   Taiwan Incense Cedar.   Z8   Taiwan

CALOCEDRUS macrolepis Kurz
1873   Chinese Incense Cedar.   30m, Z8   China

- - var. *formosana* Florin (Cheng)
1978   See CALOCEDRUS formosana.

CATHAYA Chun & Kuang (1958)

Pinaceae

A monotypic genus described in 1955 which is something of a botanical curiosity, having foliage that is similar to *CEDRUS* and *LARIX* but in other respects an affinity with *ABIES, PICEA, PSEUDOTSUGA* and *TSUGA* separately; the same year. A suggestion (per Silba 1984) that it be included within *TSUGA* has not been widely accepted by botanists.

CATHAYA argyrophylla Chun & Kuang
O. Discovered 1955.   20m,Z7   China

CATHAYA nanchuanensis Chun & Kuang
1955   **O.** Discovered by Yang 1955, but it is probably the same as last.   China

CEDRUS Trew (1757)

Pinaceae

A group of tall trees found in four widely separated areas in Africa and Asia, but all so similar that botanists have long disagreed as to how many species to recognise, and which of the groups to regard as being only a variety. Here, because of the widespread geographical dispersal, the four populations are listed as separate species.

CEDRUS africana A.Murray
1867 See *CEDRUS atlantica*.

CEDRUS atlantica Manetti
1844 Atlantic or Mount Atlas Cedar. It is by some authorities regarded as *CEDRUS libani* var. *atlantica*, under which name some of the names listed here may be found. 40m, Z6 Morocco

- - 'Albospica' Seneclauze 1868 Broad, conical tree; young foliage white. NIC. ('Albospicata'). B,K,W3 France

- - 'Argentea' (Renou) A. Murray
1867 Indistinguishable from 'Glauca'. U.K.

- - **'Argentea Fastigiata'** Narrowly fastigiate; foliage grey. L. Hillier Nurs, Winchester. (1958, or earlier?). B,D,K U.K.

- - 'Arneson's Dwarf' Hort. Amer.
1985 A listed name. Information required. U.S.A.

- - **'Aurea'** Kent 1900 Golden-yellow; leaves short. O. Boskoop? B,D,G,K,R,W3 Holland

- - 'Aurea Prostrata' Hort. Holland
1987 An illegit. name. L. Esveld Nurs. NOM. Holland

- - 'Aurea Robusta' Den Ouden
1937 Golden-yellow; more vigorous than 'Aurea'. I. Den Ouden Nurs, Boskoop, (1932). B,K,W3 Holland

- - 'Aureovariegata' Seneclauze
1868 A superfluous synonym of 'Variegata'.

- - **'Cheltenham'** D. Sampson
1990 In "Nurs. Cat". A glaucous clone with widespreading pendent branches. I. Cedar Lodge Nurs, New Plymouth. N.Z.

- - 'Cinerea' Seneclauze 1868 Vigorous; silvery-blue. I. Seneclauze Nurs, Bourg Argental, Loires. ('Cinerascens') NIC. France

- - 'Columnaris' Otin 1889 Indistinguishable from 'Fastigiata'. NIC. ('Columnaris Erecta'). B,K France

- - 'Compact Gem' Hort. Holland
1993 A listed name.

- - 'Compacta' Hort.Amer. An illegit. listed name.

- - 'Contorta' Hort. 1985 A mistake for *CEDRUS deodara* 'Raywood's Contorted'.

- - f. *fastigiata* (Carrière) Rehder
1949. A botanical designation covering all forms with unusually fastigiate habit. Such are commonly listed as next item. Sporadic

- - **'Fastigiata'** Carrière 1890 Narrowly conical habit, leaves erect. Probably more than one clone is now in cultivation under this name. O. Lalande, Nantes. B,D,K,W3 France

- - 'Fastigiata Glauca' Hort. France
1972 An illegit. listed name. L. Renault Freres, Gorron. France

- - **'Fez'** Hort. Anglia 1985 Reported from Windsor Great Park, Berks. O. Found by M. Mason, Talbot Manor, Fincham, Kings Lynn. W3 U.K.

- - f. *glauca* Beissner — A botanical designation covering all forms with glaucous blue foliage. Such are usually listed as the next item. — Germany

- - **'Glauca'** Carrière — 1867 Blue Atlas Cedar. Probably several clones are in cultivation. Inferior colour forms often arise from seed. — B,D,K,R,W3 — France

- - 'Glauca Aurea' Hort. N.Z. — 1992 An illegit. listed name for a tree, with a yellow dusting over the blue foliage.

- - 'Glauca Fastigiata' Hort. Amer. — 1972 An illegit. name for a blue form with fastigate branches. **O.** Wells Nurs, Mount Vernon, WA.

- - 'Glauca Horizontalis' Krussmann — 1979 An illegit. name for a tree in the Jardin Botanique, Nantes. NIC. — K — France

- - 'Glauca Hoyt' Hort. Amer. An illegit. and uncertain name.

- - **'Glauca Pendula'** Paillet ex Beissner — 1900 A descriptive name for a tree raised on the Paillet Nurs, Châtenay. — B,D,G,K,R,W3 — France

- - 'Glauca Pendula Contorta' Hort. France — 1976 An illegit. name. Possibly the same as 'Pendula Contorta'. — France

- - 'Glauca Pyramidalis' Hort. Germany — 1988 An illegit. name. L. Bruns Nurs, Bad Zwischenau. — Germany

- - **'Morocco'** J. Iseli — 1986 In "Nurs. Cat". Conical; long dark-green needles. **I.** Iseli Nurs, Boring, OR. U.S.A. **O.** Wm Goddard, Floravista Gardens, Victoria, B.C. — W3 — Canada

- - **'Mount Saint. Catherine'** Don Teese — 1985 In "Conif. Soc. Australia Newsletter 1". A diminutive bun; foliage green. **I.** P. Taverna, Crafers, S. Australia. **O.** The same. From a witch's broom found in 1977. See also 'Taverna'. — W3 — Australia

- - 'Nana' Den Ouden — 1949 Dwarf and slow-growing forms appear as seedlings and are virtually indistinguishable from similar variants of *CEDRUS libani*, so the name should not be used.

- - 'Nivea' Hort. ex Carrière — 1867 A clone of f. *glauca*, no longer identifiable.

- - 'Pendula' Moreau ex Carrière — 1875 Weeping Atlas Cedar. **O.** Moreau Nurs, Fontenay-aux-Roses, near Paris. — B,G,K,W3 — France

- - 'Pendula Contorta' Hort. France — An illegit. name. No further information,.

- - 'Pendula Glauca' Hort. France — See 'Glauca Pendula' .

- - 'Pyramidalis' Paillet — 1889 Indistinguishable from 'Fastigiata'. **O.** Paillet Nurs, Châtenay, Near Paris. — B,K — France

- - 'Raywood's Contorted' Hort. — See *CEDRUS deodara* 'Raywood's Contorted'.

- - 'Robusta Green' Hort. Germany — 1984 An illegit. name. A hardy selection. L. Hachmann Nurs, Barmstedt-in-Holstein. — Germany

- - **'Rustic'** Monrovia — 1962 In "Nurs. Cat". Habit irregular; foliage blue. L. Monrovia Nurs, Azusa, Calif. ('Rustica', 'Glauca Rustic'). — B,K,W3 — U.S.A.

- - 'Saint Catherine' Hort. Australia — A mistake for 'Mount Saint Catherine'.

CEDRUS ATLANTICA

- - 'Sander's Blue Weeper' Hort. Amer.
A listed name. No further information.

- - 'Silberspitz' G. Horstmann
1992 In "Nurs. Cat". Plant with silvery white tips. **O.** and **I.** Horstmann Nurs, Schneverdingen.

- - **'Silver Dust'** L. Sampson
1988 In Cedar Lodge "Nurs Cat". A silvery white. **O.** Raised from seed by Ian Gordon on a farm near Taihope.   N.Z.

- - **'Taverna'** Welch
1992 A diminutive bun; foliage grey. **O.** Witch's broom found by Peter Taverna at Crafers, (1977) on the same tree as 'Mount Saint Catherine' but it makes a less healthy plant.   W3   S. Australia

- - 'Uwe' Hort. Germany
1966 A slow growing form with pale light-blue foliage raised from a witch's broom found by G. Horstmann and named for his son.

- - 'Variegata' Carrière
1867 Irregularly variegated. **O.** Seneclauze Nurs, Bourg Argental, Loires. NIC.   B,K   France

- - 'Viridis' Seneclauze
1868 Not now distinguished within the species. NIC.

- - 'Wilkman' Hort. Amer.
1984 Vigorous; rich green colour. **L.** Iseli Nurs, Boring, OR. (Wilkman's Green??).   W3

CEDRUS brevifolia (Hooker f.) Henry
1908 Cyprian Cedar. Leaves mainly smaller than in the other species, but it is not a dwarf. It is by some authorities regarded as *CEDRUS libani* var *brevifolia*, under which varietal name some of the names listed here may be found.   15-20m,Z7   Cyprus

- - **'Bergman'** Iseli
1985 In "Nurs. Cat". A dwarf with growth irregular. Small leaves; dark green. ('Bergmani' 'Bergmann').   W3   U.S.A.

- - 'Compacta' (1) Dallimore & Jackson
1966 Dense bush. Possibly the result of a side-graft.   D,K,W2   U.K.

- - 'Compacta' (2) Hort. Anglia
1964 See 'Hillier Compact'.   B,K   U.K.

- - **'Epstein'** New name
1979 The name 'Epsteinianum' used by Welch in 1979 is illegit. Very slow-growing, growth irregular; foliage dark green. **O.** From seed by H. Epstein, Larchmont, N.Y.   W2   U.S.A.

- - 'Gracilis' Seneclauze
1868 Slender, pendulous habit. **O.** From seed on Seneclauze Nurs, Bourg Argental, Loires. NIC.   France

- - **'Hillier Compact'** Den Ouden/Boom
1965 Dense bush. **O.** Found in garden of J.W. Archer. Formerly illegitimately listed as 'Compacta'.   B,K,W3   U.K.

- - 'Horizon' Den Ouden/Boom
1965 Prostrate: probably a cultivariant. **O.** Found by Sir Harold Hillier in his garden. (Formerly listed as 'Horizontalis').   B,K,W2   U.K.

- - 'Horizontalis' (1) Hort. Anglia   See 'Horizon'.   D

- - 'Horizontalis' (2) Hort. Amer.   An illegit. name. Probably a cultivariant.

- - **'Kenwith'** Int.Con.Reg.
1992 In "Nurs. Cat". 1986. Upright growing very dwarf. Leaves near branch ends are larch-like. **O.** and **I.** Kenwith Nurs, Bideford, Devon.   U.K.

- - 'Rosemoor' Hort. Anglia
1983 Named for a tree at Rosemoor, Torrington with contorted branches. **L.** Kenwith Castle Nurs, Bideford, Devon.

- - 'Treveron' Hort.Canada
1984 **L.** Iseli Nurs, Boring, OR. U.S.A. (1984). **O.** Wm. Goddard, Floravista Gardens, Victoria, B.C.   Canada

CEDRUS deodara (Roxburgh) G. Don
          1830 Deodar; Deodar Cedar.   35m, Z6   Himalayas.

This species had long been known to vary considerably from seed, and of recent years selections of particularly graceful pendulous habit, and colour forms ranging from golden-yellow, white and glaucous-blue have been made. Some of these, especially the paler shades are not reliably hardy, but several recently named clones, raised from known provenances have proved to be very winter hardy indeed.

- - 'Albospica' Annesley   1899   Young shoots white. Other spellings are found. ('Albospicata').   B,D,G,K,R,W U.K.

- - 'Argentea' Nelson   1866 Leaves long, silvery blue.   B,D,K,R   France

- - 'Argenteovariegata' de Vos   1887 See 'Variegata'.   France

- - 'Aurea' Nelson   1866 Foliage golden-yellow fading to greenish-yellow. Original clone no longer identifiable.   B,D,G,K,R,W U.K.

- - 'Aurea Pendula' Hort. Amer.   1966 An illegit. name for a strongly pendulous form. L.. Raraflora Nurs, Feasterville, PA.   W3   U.S.A.

- - 'Aurea Wells' Hort. Amer.   1972 Now to be 'Well's Golden'.   W3

- - 'Bewley's Variegated' Hort. Australia   1991 A form with a white variegation. O. Bill Bewley, Warrimoo, N.S.W. Seldom offered in the trade.

- - **'Blue Dwarf'** H.J. van de Laar   1983 In "Dendroflora 20:" Compact, globose; short, grey-blue leaves. O. Raised from seed by G. Huizer, Boskoop, (1965).   Holland.

- - **'Blue Snake'** H.J. van de Laar   1990 In "Dendroflora 27". Upright tree with elegant twisted habit and good blue-grey colour. O. P. Vergeldt, Lottum, (1962).   Holland

- - 'Blue Triumph' Hort. Holland   1993 A listed name.

- - 'Bold Dwarf'   1990 A mistake for 'Blue Dwarf'.   W3

- - 'Clarke' Den Ouden/Boom   1965 O. W. B. Clarke Nurs, San Jose, Cal. (1928, as 'Compacta').   B,W3   U.S.A.

- - 'Compacta' Carrière   1867 A clone not now identifiable in cultivation.   B,D,K,W2   France

- - 'Contorta' Hort.   A mistake for 'Raywood's Contorted'.   W3

- - 'Crassifolia' (1) Knight   1850 See CEDRUS deodara 'Robusta'. NIC.

- - 'Crassifolia' (2) Carrière   1855 Compact conical habit. NIC.   B,K   France

- - **'Cream Puff'** G.Bentham   1981 In "Dwarf Conifer Notes 2". Compact, globose; creamy-white. O. Wm. Goddard Nurs, Flora-vista Gardens, Victoria, B.C. Not hardy in U.K.   W3   Canada

- - **'Deep Cove'** G. Bentham   1981 In "Dwarf Conifer Notes 2". Conical tree; foliage deep green; young growth white. O. Wm Goddard Nurs, Flora-vista Gardens, Victoria, B.C.   W3   Canada

- - **'Descancio Dwarf'** Mitsch   1977 In "Nurs. Cat". A compact clone, semi-weeping. ('Descanso Dwarf', 'Derancio Dwarf').   U.S.A.

- - 'Droop Tip' Hort. Amer.   1985 A listed name. No further information.

- - 'Ed. Lohbrunner' Hort. Amer.   A listed name. No further information.   U.S.A.

- - **'Eisregen'** Krussmann   1983 A hardy clone in the "Paktia" group. **I.** Jeddeloh Nurs, Oldenburg.   K,W3   Germany

- - **'Eiswinter'** Krussmann   1983 A hardy clone in the "Paktia" group. **I.** Jeddeloh Nurs, Oldenburg.   K,W3   Germany

- - **'Emerald Spreader'** Hort.Amer.
1985 A low, spreading plant; bright, mid-green. **O.** Harold Wells of Mt. Vernon, WA. **L.** Iseli Nurs, Boring, OR. (Formerly distributed as 'Well's Prostrate' and as 'Viridis Prostrata').   W3   U.S.A.

- - 'Erecta' Cripps ex Gordon
1875 A clone with an upright and silvery habit. **O. and I.** Cripps Nurs, Tunbridge Wells, Kent. NIC.   B,D,K   U.K.

- - 'Fastigiata' Carrière   1867 **O.** Named for a tree found by Dr Turrel in a garden near Toulouse. Now probably more than one clone in cultivation.   B,K,W2   France

- - **'Feelin Blue'** H.J. van de Laar
1987 In "Dendroflora 24". Dwarf, spreading; foliage grey-blue. **O.** H.C. Trimp & Sons Nurs, Boskoop.   Holland

- - 'Flava' Carrière   1867 A chlorotic tree, foliage yellow or whitish, seen in a garden in Angers. NIC.   B,K   France

- - 'Fontinalis' Beissner   1884 A regularly conical tree. NIC.   B,K   Germany

- - 'Gigantea' Hort.   See 'Robusta'.

- - 'Glauca' Schelle   1909 A clone with foliage bluish-green to silvery-grey; not now distinguishable. The name is loosely used for any clone in this colour group.   B,K,W2   Germany

- - 'Glauca Pendula' Hort. Anglia.
1988 A listed name. Possibly a mistake for *CEDRUS atlantica* 'Glauca Pendula'.

- - **'Gold Cone'** G. Bentham
1981 In "Dwarf Conifer Notes 2". A vigorous, narrowly conical clone; strongly pendulous branches; foliage yellowish.**O.** Wm Goddard Nurs, Flora-vista Gardens, Victoria, B.C.   W3   Canada

- - 'Gold Gowa' Hort. Holland
1992 A listed name.

- - **'Golden Horizon'** H.J. van de Laar
1975 In "Dendroflora 11-12". Large spreading bush; golden yellow foliage. **O. and I.** Gebr. van Vliet Nurs, Boskoop.   G,K,R   Holland

- - 'Golden Jubilee' H.J. van de Laar
1986 **L.** In "Naamlijst . . .". NOM.

- - 'Gold Mound' Hort. Amer.
1986 Broad-conical plant, young foliage bright golden-yellow. **O.** Wm Goddard, Flora-vista Gardens, Victoria, B.C.   G,W3   Canada

- - 'Gold Rush' Hort. Amer.   1986 Broad cone, foliage bright gold. **O.** Wm. Goddard Nurs, Flora-vista Gardens, Victoria, B.C.   Canada

- - 'Gold Strike' Iseli   1986 In "Nurs. Cat". Broadly conical; golden yellow. **I.** Iseli Nurs, Boring, OR, U.S.A. (1982). **O.** Wm Goddard, Flora-vista Gardens, Victoria, B.C.   W3   Canada

- - 'Gracilis' Seneclauze   1868 A clone with slender shoots. NIC.   K   France

- - **'Harvest Gold'** Hort. Amer.

1989 A listed name for a yellow plant with the colour slightly more intense than Aurea. L. Coenosium Gardens, Aurora, OR.

- - **'Hesse'** Hesse ex Meyer

1963 In "Plant Explorations 1963". Very dwarf and dense. O. H. A. Hesse Nurs, Weener-on-Ems.   B,K,W2   Germany

- - **'Hibernal'** R.L. Fincham

1983 In "Nurs. Cat". A bluish hardy form from seed. O. Coenosium Gardens, then of Lehighton, PA.   U.S.A.

- - **'Hollandia'** Hort. Amer. 1989 A listed name for a dwarf form, stronger than 'Pygmaea' and less blue. L. Coenosium Gardens, Aurora, OR., U.S.A.

- - **'Ibridio'** Hort. Germany

1990 A supposed hybrid with CEDRUS atlantica var glauca. L. Jeddeloh Nurs, Oldenburg.

- - **'Karl Fuchs'** Krussmann

1979 A hardy clone with silvery foliage. O. It is one of the "Paktia" seedlings. Raised by G. Horstmann Nurs, Schneverdingen.   G,K,W3   Germany

- - 'Kashmir' Reg'd. Arn. Arb.

1968 Reg'd. by Dr. J. F. Styer, Concordville, PA. O. The same. (1934). Of normal habit, it is outstandingly winter-hardy.   K,W3   U.S.A.

- - 'Kingsville' Hort. Amer. 1986 A listed name. L. E.A. Cope. "Native. . . Conifers . . .". NOM.   U.S.A.

- - **'Klondyke'** G. Bentham 1981 In "Dwarf Conifer Notes 2". Broad, conical; chartreuse with yellow stems. O. Wm Goddard Nurs, Flora-vista Gardens, Victoria, B.C.   W3   Canada

- - **'Lime Glow'** Reg'd. Arn Arb.

1980 Congested dwarf; growth irregular, foliage yellow-green. Reg'd. by J.D. Vertrees. O. Found by A.J. Teese, Yamina Rare Plants Nurs, Monbulk, Victoria, in the Dandegong Ranges, Victoria, (1970).   G,W3   Australia

- - **'Limelight'** Iseli 1985 In "Nurs. Cat". Conical, pendulous: lime-white, fading to pale green. L. Iseli Nurs., Boring, OR. O. Wm Goddard Nurs, Flora-vista Gardens, Victoria, B.C.   W3   Canada

- - 'Lohbrunner's Weeper' Hort. Amer.

O. Wm Goddard Nurs, Flora-vista Gardens, Victoria, B.C.   Canada

- - 'MacPenny's Seedling' Hort. Anglia

1993 A listed name. NOM.

- - 'Maxima Pendula' Hort. Amer.

1966 An illegit. name. L. Raraflora Nurs, Feasterville, PA. NOM.   U.S.A.

- - **'Mountain Beauty'** P.C. Nitschke

1989 In "Conif. Soc. Australia Newsletter 5". A dwarf, spreading form, greyish foliage. O. A witch's broom found by Gordon Wilton in the Blue Mountains, west of Sydney. I. Milton Nurs, Wentworth Falls, N.S.W. (1985).

- - 'Mutabilis' Beissner 1984 Regularly conical. NIC.   B,K   Germany

- - **'Mylor'** Don Teese 1985 In "Amer. Conif. Soc. Bull 2". Stiff upright bush; dull yellow foliage. O. A witch's broom found at Mylor, S. Australia. I. Drue Wholesale Nurs, Berry. (See 'Warrakilla').   W3   Australia

- - **'Nana'** Hornibrook 1939 O. Named for a tree in the Royal Botanical Gardens, Kew. (1934), and still in cultivation.   B,H,K,W2   U.K.

- - 'Nana Aurea' Hort. Anglia

1988 An illegit. name. A slow-growing form that retains a golden colour throughout the year.   U.K.

- - 'Nivea' Annesley	1899 Named for a pendulous tree with leaves snow-white found at Castlewellan.	B,K	Ireland
- - 'Nugget' Hort. Amer.	1981 A listed name. **O.** Wm Goddard Nurs, Flora-vista Gardens, Victoria, B.C.		Canada
- - 'Paktia' Krussmann	1979 A group name for several hardy clones raised from seed collected by K. Fuchs in Paktia Provence.	K,W2	Afghanistan
- - 'Pendula' (1) Beissner	1900 Prostrate unless leader-trained. See 'Prostrata'. NIC. Neither use of the name 'Pendula' relates to a now-identifiable clone, so it should not be used save in a collective sense.	B,D,G,H	Germany
- - 'Pendula' (2) Krussmann	1983 Habit almost columnar, branches pendulous. **O.** Found by Moreau in Fontenay-aux-Roses near Paris. NIC.	B,K,W2	France
- - **'Polar Winter'** Krussmann	1983 A hardy clone of the "Paktia" group of hardy forms raised from seed.	K,W3	Germany
- - 'Procumbens' Hort. France	1972 An illegit. listed name. Dwarf, procumbent, short leaves.		
- - 'Prostrata' (1) Nelson	1866 Habit prostrate, lacking a leader. NIC. (See note under 'Pendula' (2)). Similar plants arise in cultivation.	B,D,H,K	U.K.
- - 'Prostrata' (2) H.G. Hillier	1964 An illegit. name for a pot-grown plant seen by Sir Harold Hillier in W.B. Archer's garden.		U.K.
- - 'Prostrate Beauty' Hort. Amer.	1985 A listed name. See 'Prostrata' (1).		
- - 'Pygmaea' Gotelli	1960 In "Amer. Hort. Mag". **O.** An unnamed seedling found by James Noble in 1943 and willed to Wm. Gotelli in 1958. See next item.		
- - **'Pygmy'** Den Ouden/Boom	1965 Diminutive bush. Formerly listed as 'Pygmaea'.	B,G,K,R,W2	U.S.A.
- - 'Raraflora Gold Prostrate' Hort. Amer.	1986 L. E. A. Cope "Native . . . Conifers . . . ".NOM.		U.S.A.
- - **'Raywood's Contorted'** Don Teese	1985 In "Amer. Conif. Soc. Bull. **2**". (incorrectly under *CEDRUS atlantica*). A dwarf form of unusual branching habit. **I.** P. C. Nitschke, Hahndorf, S. Australia. **O.** Raised from seed by Quinton Wollaston of Raywood Nurs, Delamere, (1978).	W3	S. Australia
- - 'Raywood's Prostrate Dwarf' Hort. Tasmania	1990 A listed name for a vigorous ground cover plant; needles are blue.		
- - **'Repandens'** Hort. Amer.	Description as 'Prostrata'. **I.** Clarke Nurs, San Jose, Cal.	B,K,W	U.S.A.
- - 'Repens' Hort. Amer.	1986 Growth low and spreading. L. E. A. Cope "Native . . . Conifers . . . ".		U.S.A.
- - **'Robusta'** Lawson	1852 A vigorous clone; leaves long and glaucous-blue. NIC.	B,D,G,K,R,W3	U.K.
- - 'Robusta Glauca' Hort.	An illegit. name.		France
- -'Sander's Blue' Hort. Amer.	A graceful tree with bright blue, pendulous foliage. L. Iseli Nurs, Boring, OR. (1986). **O.** ?	W3	U.S.A.
- - **'Scott'** Don Teese	1985 In "Amer. Conif. Soc. Bull. **2**". Graceful prostrate habit; foliage pale blue-green. **O.** Witch's broom found by Peter Taverna, Upper Sturt, S. Australia (1977). **I.** Drue Wholesale Nurs, Berry, N.S.W.	W3	S. Australia

- - **'Shalimar'** G. L. Koller   1982   In "Arnoldia **42** (4)". A very hardy clone from mountain seed. Soft needles on long pendulous branches.   W3   U.S.A.

- - **'Sharp's Golden Weeping'** Hort. Amer.
       1984   A pendulous clone with yellow foliage. L. Iseli Nurs, Boring, OR. **O.** Sharp ?   U.S.A.

- - **'Silver Mist'** G.Bentham
       1981   In "Dwarf Conifer Notes 2". A mounded bush of creamy-white foliage. **O.** Wm Goddard Nurs, Flora-vista Gardens, Victoria, B.C. Not hardy in U.K.   W3   Canada

- - **'Snow Sprite'** G.Bentham
       1981   In "Dwarf Conifer Notes 2". A small white mounded bush. **O.** Wm Goddard Nurs, Flora-vista Gardens, Victoria, B.C. Not hardy in U.K.   W3   Canada

- - 'Tenuifolium' Knight & Perry
       1850   NOM. Indistinguishable from 'Viridis'. NIC.   B,K   U.K.

- - 'Tristis' Carrière   1855   A clone with short branches. NIC.   B,K   France

- - 'Uncinata' Zederbour   1907   Clone with irregular habit and peculiar foliage. NIC.   B,K   Germany

- - 'Variegata' Carrière   1867   Clone with an unstable white variegation. NIC.   B,K   France

- - 'Variegata Alba' Seneclauze
       1868   A delicate plant almost wholly white. NIC.   B,K   France

- - 'Variegated' Hort. Australia
       1989   In "Conif. Soc. Australia Newsletter 5". An unsatisfactory name for a clone with yellow patches throughout the tree. **O.** A seedling found by John Emery at Gerringong, N.S.W. NIC. See also 'Bewley's Variegated'.

- - 'Veronica' H.J. van de Laar
       1986   In "Naamlijst . . .". NOM.   Germany?

- - 'Verticillata' de Vos   1887   Branchlets almost whorled. Reported from Arboretum La Maulevrie, Angers.   B,D,K,W3   France

- - **'Verticillata Glauca'** R. Smith
       1867   Columnar, of open habit; glaucous green. Still listed.   B,K   Holland

- - 'Victoria' Hort. Amer.   1984   Narrowly conical, dense; bluish green. L. Iseli Nurs, Boring, OR. U.S.A. **O.** Wm Goddard Nurs, Flora-vista Gardens, Victoria, B.C.   W3   Canada

- - **'Vink's Golden'** Hort. Tasmania
       1985   A slow-growing, conical, bright golden plant from a witch's broom with branches somewhat pendulous. **I.** Ron Radford, Cedar Lodge Nurs, Tasmania.

- - **'Viridis'** Lawson   1852   Clone with vivid green foliage and foliar peculiarities. The name has been used for other clones with green foliage.   B,D,K,W   France

- - 'Viridis Prostrata' Hort. Amer.
       1966   An illegit. name. L. Iseli Nurs, Boring, OR. Now to be 'Emerald Spreader'. **O.** Harold W. Wells Nurs, Mt. Vernon, Washington, U.S.A.   W

- - 'Warrakilla' Hort. Australia
       1987   Slow-growing bun-shape; tight blue foliage. **I.** P C Nitschke, Hahndorf, S. Australia. **O.** The same, found as a witch's broom on a property named "Warrakilla" at Mylor.The name 'Mylor' is now in general use in the trade.   W3   S. Australia

- - **'Waverly Ridge'** Don Teese
      1985 In "Amer. Conif. Soc. Bull. **2**". Dwarf, horizontal habit with compact yellowish foliage **I**. P C Nitschke, Hahndorf, S. Australia. **O**. Witch's broom found by Peter Taverna on Waverly Ridge Road, Crafers. (1979).   W3   S. Australia

- - **'Well's Golden'** Hort. Amer.
      1978 Broad, irregular cone; foliage dense, bright golden-yellow. **L**. Mitsch Nurs, Aurora, OR. **O**. Seedling on Wells Nurs, Mt. Vernon, Washington.   W3   U.S.A.

- - **'White Imp'** Hort. Amer.
      1982 Dwarf; foliage white. **L**. Iseli Nurs, Boring, OR. U.S.A. **O**. Wm Goddard Nurs, Flora-vista Gardens, Victoria, B.C. Not hardy in U.K.   W3   Canada

- - **'Wiesemannii'** P. Moll   1936 In "Nurs. Cat". Slow-growing, compact; foliage dense, bluish-green. **O**. P. Moll Nurs, Heisterbacherott.   B,K,W3   Germany

CEDRUS intermedia Seneclauze
      1868 Probably a hybrid: *CEDRUS deodara* and *CEDRUS libani*. NIC.

CEDRUS libani A. Richards
      1823 Cedar of LeBánón. (*libanensis, liBánótica*).   40m, Z7   Asia

- - 'Argentea' Hort. Anglia   1858 Not distinguishable from 'Glauca'.

- - **'Aurea'** Seneclauze   1868 Slow-growing; foliage yellow over a greenish ground.   B,D,K,R,W3   France

- - 'Aurea Prostrata' Hort. Amer.   Name changed to 'Golden Dwarf'.   D,K,R

- - 'Aurea Variegata' Hort. Amer.
      1967 An illegit. name. **L**. Raraflora Nurs, Feasterville, PA. NOM. See 'Gold Tip'.   U.S.A.

- - **'Beacon Hill'** Hort. Amer.
      1981 A listed name. **O**. Wm Goddard Nurs, Flora-vista Gardens, Victoria, B.C.   Canada

- - var. *brevifolia* (Hooker f.) Henry & Elwes
      1908 Now known as *CEDRUS brevifolia* by most authorities.

- - 'Candelabrum' Carrière   1859 Named for a peculiar tree at Limon. NIC.   B   France

- - 'Columnaris' Hort. Holland
      1993 An illegit. listed name.

- - **'Comte de Dijon'** Barbier
      1908 In "Nurs. Cat". A dwarf form. **O**. Barbier Nurs, Orleans.   B,D,G,H,K,W3 France

- - 'Conica Nana' Hort. Holland
      1993 An illegit. name. See 'Nana Pyramidata'.

- - 'Decidua' Seneclauze ex Carrière
      1867 Bush with deciduous habit. **O**. Seneclauze Nurs, Bourg Argental, Loires, NIC.   B,D,K   France

- - 'Denudata' Carrière   1856 Irregularly branched. **O**. Jacquement-Bonneford Nurs.   B,K   France

- - var. *deodara* (Roxburgh) Hooker f.
      1854 Now known as *CEDRUS deodara*.

- - f. *fusiformis* Carrière   1859 Cones of unusual shape. NIC.   B,K   France

- - 'Glauca' Carrière   1855 A compact, glaucous form.   B,D,K,W   France

- - 'Glauca Pendula' Hort. Amer.   An illegit. listed name.

- - 'Golden Dwarf' Den Ouden/Boom
| | | | |
1965 Low-growing; foliage golden-yellow. Probably a cultivariant.(= 'Aurea Prostrata' Hort.).   B,K,R,W   U.K.?

- - 'Gold Tip' (1) Welch   1979 A seedling descriptively named by F.W. Bergman; with bright yellow tips on the young foliage.   W2   U.S.A.

- - 'Gold Tip' (2) Hort. Australia
1990 Possibly the same as last. If a different clone, a new name must be found.   G,W3

- - 'Green Knight' Hort. Amer.
1981 Very dwarf; growth irregular; foliage very dense hiding the shoot. Prone to sun scorch. L. (= 'Minuta' Hort.).   W3   U.S.A.

- - 'Green Prince' Hort. Amer.   Similar to 'Green Knight', but faster growing.   U.S.A.

- - 'Heemstede' H.J. van de Laar
1986 In "Naamlijst . . . ". NOM.   W3   Holland

- - f. *microcarpa* Carrière   1859 No longer distinguished within the species.   B,K   France

- - 'Minuta' Hort. Amer.   An illegit. name. Now to be known as 'Green Knight'.   U.S.A.

- - 'Multicaulis' Seneclauze   1868 Dwarf conical bush; many-stemmed. O. Audibert Nurs, Tonelle, NIC.   B,K   France

- - 'Nana' Loudon   1838 Now only of value as a group name for all the dwarf forms now in cultivation, including the following:

- - 'Nana Pyramidata' Carrière
1855 O. Seneclauze Nurs, Bourg Argental, Loires, NIC.   B,H,K,W   France

- - 'Pendula' Knight & Perry
1850 Pendulous; leaves long.   B,D,G,H,K,W   U.K.

- - 'Purdue Hardy' Int. Con. Reg.
1988 A hardy clone from collected seed. Reg'd. D. L. Schuder of Purdue University, West Lafayette. IN. I. the Indiana Assoc., of Nurserymen, West Lafayette, IN.   U.S.A.

- - 'Sargentii' Hornibrook   1923 Dwarf, pendulous. O. Arnold Arboretum, Jamaica Plain, Mass. (c. 1910) as 'Pendula Sargentii'. but the shorter name is now in general use.   B,D,G,H,K,W   U.S.A.

- - var. *stenocoma* (Schwarz) Davis
1949 Geographical form from the Cilician Taurus. Discovered in S. W. Anatolia in 1938.   B,K,W   Turkey

- - 'Stricta' Carrière   1859 Named for a tree found in a garden near Auck. NIC.   B,D,K   France

- - 'Taurus' H.J. van de Laar
1988 In "Dendroflora 25". A dwarf raised from seed by A.A.M. Vergeer, Boskoop.   Holland

- - 'Tortuosa' Henry   1908 Named for a curious tree in a garden at Dulwich, London. (1903). NIC.   B,D,K   U.K.

- - 'Viridis' Carrière   1867 Ascending; dark glossy green foliage. NIC.   B,K   France

- - 'Wormleybury' Hort. Anglia
1970 Listed Hillier in "Conif. Conf. Names List". NOM.

CEDRUS liBánótica Link   1831 Now known as *CEDRUS libani. (libanitica).*

CEPHALOTAXUS Siebold and Zuccarini ex Endlicher (1842)

Cephalotaxaceae

The Plum Yews are a group of shrubs or small trees all from Eastern Asia which give botanists a problem, since the foliage is similar to the yews but the reproductive parts resemble *TORREYA*, and the fruit is a plum-like drupe. All are useful garden plants because of their tolerance of shade. The differences are slight, so some authorities merge several species. Earlier writers mix up the names to a most confusing extent.

CEPHALOTAXUS coriacea Hort. ex Knight & Perry
1850 (in synonymy) Now known as *CEPHALOTAXUS harringtonia* var. *drupacea*.

CEPHALOTAXUS drupaceae Siebold & Zuccarini
1846 Now known as *CEPHALOTAXUS harringtonia* var. *drupacea*..

- - var. *harringtonia* (Forbes) Pilger
1903 Now known as *CEPHALOTAXUS harringtonia*.

- - var. *pedunculata* Miguel 1867 Now known as *CEPHALOTAXUS harringtonia*.

CEPHALOTAXUS fortunei Hooker f.
1850 Chinese Plum Yew. (*fortuni* is now regarded as incorrect) · 10-15m, Z7 · Asia

- - var. *alpina* Li
1953 Found at high altitudes in N.W. Yunnan & Sikiang. Not now distinguished within the species by some authorities (per Silba, 1984). · D,K,R

- - 'Brevifolia' Dallimore & Jackson
1948 Leaves shorter than normal. · B,D,K · U.K.

- - var. *concolor* Franchet 1899 Leaves white below. No longer recognised within the species. · B,D,K,R · Szechuan.

- - **'Grandis'** Hillier
1928 In "Nurs. Cat". A beautiful selection with exceptionally long leaves. (female). · B,K,R,W3 · U.K.

- - 'Lion's Plume' Blackburn 1972 Reported from Willowwood Arboretum, Rutgers University, Gladstone, N.J. · W3 · Japan

- - 'Longifolia' Dallimore & Jackson
1948 A form with unusually long leaves. · B,D,K,R · Japan

- - 'Pendula' Nelson
1866 A form with pendulous branches. NIC. · B,K · U.K.

- - **'Prostrate Spreader'** Den Ouden/Boom
1965 Possibly a superfluous name for the following. · B,K,R,W2 · U.K.

- - **'Prostrata'** Hillier
1964 Low growing, wide-spreading shrub. Probably a cultivariant. O. Hilliers Nurs, Winchester, U.K. (1914). · B,K,W3 · U.K.

- - 'Robusta' Carrière 1867 Vigorous; larger than normal in all parts. NIC. · B,K · France

CEPHALOTAXUS griffithii Hooker f.
1888 Griffith Plum Yew. A little-known species close to *CEPHALOTAXUS harringtonia*. · 15m, Z9 · India

CEPHALOTAXUS hainanensis Li
1953 Hainan Plum Yew. A species close to *CEPHALOTAXUS harringtonia*.

CEPHALOTAXUS harringtonia (Knight ex Forbes) K.Koch
1873 Plum Yew. (At one time listed as *TAXUS harringtonia*). · 10m,Z6 · Asia (E)

- - var. *coraiana* Koidzumi 1930 Not now distinguished within the species.

- - var. **drupacea** (Siebold & Zuccarini)
1930 Japanese Plum Yew. Formerly listed as *CEPHALOTAXUS drupacea* and also as *CEPHALOTAXUS pedunculata*. · B,D,K,R,W2 · Japan

- - **'Duke Gardens'** Int. Con. Reg.
  1977 A low spreading bush with dark green foliage. **I.** Robert F. Doren, of the U.S. Nat. Arb. **O.** R.D. Fillimore at the Sarah P. Duke Gardens, Durham, NC. (1958). W3 U.S.A.

- - **'Fastigiata'** (Carrière) Schneider
  1913 A more or less fastigiate plant. Somewhat unstable. B,D,G,H,K,W Hort. Japan

- - **'Fastigiata Aurea'** de Vos
  1874 Mutation with leaves margined yellow. NIC. B Holland

- - **'Fastigiata Aureovariegata'** Hort. ex Beissner
  1891 A delicate, gold-coloured plant. NIC. H Germany

- - **'Gimborn's Pillow'** H.J.van de Laar
  1987 In "Dendroflora 24". Spreading shrub with long, dark green leaves. **I.** L.Konijn & Co., Ederveen. **O.** Found as a seedling in the Arboretum von Gimborn. Holland

- - **'Glauca'** Nelson 1866 Leaves glaucous. NIC. B U.K.

- - **'Globosa'** Rehder & Wilson
  1914 See 'Sphaeralis'

- - **'Gnome'** Hillier 1971 In "Manual of Trees & Shrubs". Flat-topped shrub with radial leaves. **O.** Hillier & Sons Nurs, Winchester, from mutation on 'Fastigiata'. W2 U.K.

- - var. **koreana** (Nakai) Rehder
  1941 A geographical variant forming only a low bush. B,D,K,R,W Korea

- - **'Korean Gold'** B. Klinger
  1984 In "A.A.B.G.A. Bull". A fastigiate plant with young leaves wholly yellow.**I.** B. Yinger, Brookside Gardens, Wheaten, MD, (1977). **O.** Hort. Japan. W3

- - **'Lad'** Barabits 1965 A variety raised from seed. Hungary

- - var. **nana** (Nakai) Rehder
  1941 A shrubby local variant, prone to suckering. B,D,H,R,W Japan Is.

- - **'Nana Compacta'** Fischen in Beissner
  1930 L. Froebel Nurs. Probably the same as previous item. NIC. B,H,W Germany

- - **'Ogon Chosen Maki'** Hort. Japan
  Japanese name for 'Korean Gold'.

- - **'Prostrata'** Hillier ex Hornibrook
  1923 A prostrate form, probably a cultivariant. **O.** Hillier & Son Nurs, Winchester. (1920). B,D,H,K,R,W U.K.

- - var. **sinencis** (Masters) Schneider
  1913 A shrub. NIC. B,W China

- - **'Sphaeralis'** (Masters) Schneider
  1913 A globose shrub, leaves sickle-shaped. B,D,K

CEPHALOTAXUS koreana Nakai Now listed under *CEPHALOTAXUS harringtonia*.

CEPHALOTAXUS lanceolata K. M. Feng
  1975 A little known species, near *CEPHALOTAXUS fortunei*. Yunnan

CEPHALOTAXUS mannii Hooker f. ex Hooker
  1886 Mann Plum-Yew. Another little known species from Northern Burma and Yunnan. Asia

CEPHALOTAXUS oliveri Masters
  1898 Oliver Plum Yew. Shrub with flat, rigid branches. China

CEPHALOTAXUS pedunculata Siebold & Zuccarini
              1846 Now known as *CEPHALOTAXUS harringtonia* var.
                     drupacea.

- - var. *fastigata* Carrière   1867 Now known as *CEPHALOTAXUS harringtonia* 'Fastigata'.

CEPHALOTAXUS sinensis (Rehder & Wilson) Li
              1953 Chinese Plum Yew. A species close to *CEPHALOTAXUS*
                     harringtonia.   5m, Z7   China

- - var. *globosa* (Rehder & Wilson) Li   D,K

- - var. *latifolia* Cheng & L. K. Fu
              1975 A variant having broader leaves.   R

CEPHALOTAXUS wilsoniana Hayata
              1914 Taiwan Plum Yew. Now merged in *CEPHALOTAXUS*
                     harringtonia by some authorities (per Silba, 1984).   20m, Z9   Taiwan

CHAMAECYPARIS Spach (1842) False Cypress

Cupressaceae

The false Cypresses were for many years included in the genus *Cupressus*. Even today some botanists question the need for this separation and a few conservative Nurserymen still ignore it. There are seven species, but of these three are very variable and have given rise to a ridiculous flood of selected seedlings and mutations, many of which are so similar to others as to be just not worth perpetuating. Unfortunately this flow still continues. Very great restraint should now be exercised in introducing fresh forms that will add more names to our listings but no more beauty to our gardens. *Chamaecyparis* x *Cupressocyparis* and *Cupressus* are regarded as one cultivar class by the International Registration Authority. This means that no cultivar name can be re-used anywhere within this group.

CHAMAECYPARIS boursieri (1) Carrière
        1867 Now known as *CHAMAECYPARIS lawsoniana*.

CHAMAECYPARIS boursieri (2) Decaisne
        1854 Now known as *JUNIPERUS occidentalis*.

CHAMAECYPARIS formosensis Matsumara			
1901 Taiwan Cypress.		15-60m,Z8	Taiwan
CHAMAECYPARIS funebris Endlicher			
1847 Chinese Weeping Cypress, Mourning Cypress. Formerly known and by some authorities still regarded as *CUPRESSUS funebris*. (per Rushforth, 1987).		2m,Z8	China
- - 'Aurea' Hort. Australia See *CUPRESSUS torulosa* 'Gold Spangle'.			
- - 'Gracilis' Carrière 1867 Form with all parts elongated. NIC.		B,K	France
- - 'Viridis' Sénéclauze 1868 Graceful tree; vivid green foliage. NIC.		B,K	France

CHAMAECYPARIS henryae Li
        1962 Not now distinguished from *CHAMAECYPARIS thyoides*.
        (per Silba, 1984).

CHAMAECYPARIS lawsoniana (Murray) Parlatore			
1864 Lawson Cypress, Port Orford Cypress.		40m,Z6	U.S.A.
- - 'Alba Keessen' Hort. France			
1972 An illegit. name. See 'Erecta Alba'.		W3	France

White or creamy-white mutations or seedlings arise but rarely turn out to be worth perpetuating. Early writers coined and copied names for plants they did not know and there was professional jealousy, so the many early names using the prefixes *alba, albo* and *argentea* form a tangle almost impossible to unravel with certainty. But since many of the clones have been lost sight of for a century or more it would be best to restrict production to those clones whose value has ensured their continued popularity (and the use of "bold" type here). Any worthwhile novelties in this group should be registered under new clonal names.

- - 'Alba Nana' R.Smith 1867 (In synonymy). Now known as 'Nana Albospica'.		B,H,W	
- - 'Alba Pendula' Hort. ex Beissner			
1891 See 'Pendula Alba'.			
- - 'Alba-spica' (1) R. Smith 1867 The Speckled Lawson Cypress. Densely and regularly mottled with silvery specks. NIC.		B,D,K,W3	U.K.
- - 'Alba Spica' (2) Young ex Lawson			
1875 ("Young's variety"). Free-growing bright green clone thickly speckled all over with white leaves in Spring and summer. O. Young's Nurs, Milford, Surrey.		B,K	U.K.
- - 'Alba-spica Nana' R. Smith			
1867 Dwarf, compact plant, the brightest of the white-tipped varieties. It is of continental origin. Now known as 'Nana Albospica', following Hornibrook.		B,H,W	Europe
- - 'Alba-spica Variegata' R. Smith			
1867 Now known as 'Argenteovariegata'.			

- - 'Alba Variegata' Gordon   1875 "The Silver Variegated Lawson Cypress". Branchlets and leaves are interspersed with a silvery whiteness. **O.** Lawson's Nurs, Edinburgh.   B,K,W   Scotland

- - 'Albomaculata' Masters   1896 Exhibited at Roy. Hort. Soc. Conference. NOM. Possibly indistinguishable from 'Albo Variegata'.   U.K.

- - 'Albo-picta' Masters   1896 Clone with speckled white variegation. Indistinguishable from Alba-spica (1). NIC.   U.K.

- - 'Albo-spica'   The spellings Alba- and Albo- were not distinguished by some early writers so some uncertainty about several old names is inevitable.

- - 'Albo-spicata' Hort. ex Beissner
                 1909 A now unidentifiable clone with white foliage.   Germany

- - **'Albo-variegata'** Veitch   1881 Compact, conical to rounded bush, foliage deep green, profusely spotted & blotched with white. **O.** Veitch, Combe Wood Nurs.   B,G,K,R,W2 U.K.

- - 'Albrechii' Hort. Anglia   1959 In "Nurs. Cat". A conical tree; foliage light green. Notcutt's Nurs, Woodridge, Suffolk ('Albechii. but 'Olbrichii' is not the same).

- - 'Allonii' Hort. Anglia   1963 Narrow cone: foliage grey-green. **L.** Jackmans & Son. In "Nurs. Cat". 1963 but not later issues. Probably a mistake for 'Alumii'.

- - **'Alumigold'** P. de Vogel   1961 In "Dendroflora 4". Sport from 'Alumii'. Young growth clear yellow, older foliage blue-green; broadly conical. **O.** Maks Nurs, Dedemsvaart. I. (1966) (Spelling varies).   G,K,W   Holland

- - **'Alumii'** Beissner   1891 A well known cultivar with blue-grey foliage. **O.** Uncertain: it possibly is a mutation on 'Erecta Glauca'. (All other spellings are illegit. either alone or in comination with a descriptive name).).   B,G,K,R,W U.K?

- - 'Alumii Magnifica' Krüssmann
                 1979 An illegit. name. Slim, upright habit. The same colour as 'Columnaris'.   G,K,W   France

- - 'Alumii Nana Compacta' Krüssmann
                 1979 An illegit. name. A spreading form with the colour of 'Alumii'. **I.** Minier Nurs, Angers.   K,W   France

- - 'Annesleyana' Hort. Ireland
                 1985 Reported from Castlewellan Nat. Arboretum, Co. Down.   Ireland

- - f. *argentea* (Gordon) Beissner
                 1887 A botanical designation covering all forms with silvery-grey glaucous foliage.

- - 'Argentea' (1) Lawson ex Gordon
                 1862 Description transferred to 'Alba Variegata' in 1875.   D,W3   U.K.

- - **'Argentea'** (2) R. Smith   1867 "The Silvery Lawson Cypress". Drooping silvery-glaucous foliage. **O.** James Smith and Son, Darley Dale Nurs, Matlock. NIC. See 'Greycoat'.   B,K   U.K.

- - 'Argentea Compacta' Hort. N.Z.
                 1970 An illegit. name for a conical dwarf form with creamy-white foliage. **L.** South Taranaki Nurs, Hawera.   N.Z.

- - 'Argentea Nana' Hort. Anglia
                 1964 An illegit. listed name of no clear application.

- - 'Argentea Nova' Schelle   1909 Bright silvery-grey foliage. No longer identifiable.

- - 'Argentea Smith' Den Ouden/Boom
  1865 Leaves silvery-grey. A superfluous and illegit. name for
  'Argentea' (2). See 'Greycoat'.   U.K.

- - 'Argentea Superba' Hort. N.Z.
  1987 An illegit. listed name. L. South Taranaki Nurs, Hawera.

- - 'Argentea Waterer' Hort. Anglia
  1864 Leaves silver-grey on upperside; spreading. O. Anthony
  Waterer Nurs, Knaphill, Surrey. NIC.   B   U.K.

- - **'Argenteovariegata'** Fraser
  1875 Another robust form. Foliage blotched with bright creamy-
  white variegation. Still one of the best forms. O. Lawson's
  Nurs, Edinburgh.   B,G,K,W   Scotland

- - **'Argenteovariegata Nova'** De Vos
  1887 A variegated form resistant to sun-scorch. O. C. G.
  Overeijnder Nurs, Boskoop.   B,G,K,W   Holland

- - 'Armstrongii' Hort. N.Z.
  An illegit. name. L. Blue Mountain Nurs, Tapanui, W.
  Otago. Indistinguishable from 'Aureovariegata'.   W   N.Z.

- - **'Ashton Gold'** Krüssmann
  1979 Chrome-yellow foliage; upright habit. I. Jan Spek Nurs,
  Boskoop, Holland. O. Possibly from Ireland.   K,W   Ireland

- - **'Atrovirens'** Hort. ex Beissner
  1891 Broadly conical, dense, glossy dark-green foliage.   B,K

- - **'Aurea'** (1) Waterer ex Gordon
  1862 Graceful tree; small, conical shoots and leaves of golden
  colour. O. J. Waterer Nurs, Bagshot, Surrey.   B,D,G,K,W   U.K.

- - 'Aurea' (2) Hort.
  An unsatisfactory name loosely used for any golden form.

- - **'Aurea Densa'** Hornibrook
  1939 Popular golden dwarf form. O. and I. W.H. Rogers, Red
  Lodge Nurs, Eastleigh, Hants, (1930).   B,D,G,H,K,W   U.K.

- - 'Aurea Kelleriis' Hort.
  Now known as 'Kelleriis Gold'.

- - **'Aurea Nova'** Van der Elst.
  1895 In "Nurs. Cat" Leaves greenish-yellow, becoming yellow,
  ultimately dark green, conical. L. Tottenham Nurs,
  Dedemsvaart, (before 1893). NIC.   B,K   Holland

- - 'Aurea Rogersii' Hort.
  A mistake for 'Minima Aurea'.

- - 'Aurea Romana' Hort. Holland   A mistake for 'Romana'.   G

- - 'Aurea Variegata' R. Smith
  1867 See 'Aureovariegata'.

- - 'Aureospica' Jurissen ex Beissner
  1891 Conical, young leaves golden-yellow, older ones green. L. Jac
  Jurissen Nurs, Naarden, (1887). NIC. ('Aureospicata').   B,K   Holland

- - **'Aureovariegata'** Waterer ex Sénéclauze
  1868 Large rounded bush or tree; bold golden-yellow variegation.
  O. J. Waterer Nurs, Bagshot, Surrey. A large specimen at
  "Nymans", Handcross, Surrey was blown down in one of the
  recent disastrous autumn gales in U.K, but many other
  specimens still in cultivation.   B,D,K,W   U.K.

- - 'Aurescens' Hort. Holland
  1968 An illegit. name. L. J. Konign Nurs, in "Sortimentslijst".

- - **'Azurea'** D. Wyman   1962 In "American Nurseryman 1". A blue sport from 'Alumii' with extremely blue foliage in large sprays.   W3   U.S.A.

- - 'Backhouse Silver' Hort.   A commercial synonym for 'Pygmaea Argentea'.   W

- - 'Backhousiana' Hort. Anglia.
  1969 In "Planters' Handbook No. **30**", but not later issues. Conical, dense, fine grey-green foliage. L. Geo Jackman Nurs, Woking, Surrey.

- - 'Bagshot Blue' Hort. Holland
  1976 L. A Pannebacker's Nurs, Hazerwoude, Holland.

- - **'Barabit's Globe'** Barabits
  1965 Forms a large globose,- later conical -bush with bluish-green spreading foliage. New name to replace illegit. names 'Globus', 'Glauca Globus' etc. **O.** Raised by E. Barabits at Sopron Botanic Garden, (1952).   G,W3   Hungary

- - 'Barker' Hort. N.Z.   1970 A listed name. L. South Taranaki Nurs, Hawera, N.Z.

- - 'Barry's Bright' Hort. N.Z.
  A listed name for a mutation on 'Columnaris', with large cream patches that die out. **O.** as next item.

- - **'Barry's Silver'** Hort. N.Z.
  1990 A listed name for a mutation on 'Silver Queen'. Silvery foliage shaded creamy-green. **O.** Roly Barry, South Taranaki Nurs, Hawera, N.Z.   W3

- - 'Barry's White' Hort. N.Z.   See 'Barry's Silver'.

- - 'B.D. Edginton' Hort. N.Z.
  1963 In "Nurs. Cat". Golden yellow; conical. Duncan & Davies.

- - 'Beissneriana' P. Smith ex Beissner
  1891 Conical; bright bluish-green foliage. **I.** P. Smith Nurs, Bergedorf. NIC.   B,K   Germany

- - 'Billwoodiana' Dallimore & Jackson
  1948 Branchlets pendulous. NIC.   B,D,K   U.K.

- - **'Bleu Nantais'** Renault   1971 Reg'd at the Museum National d'Histoire Naturelle. A blue sport from 'Ellwoodii' with silvery juvenile foliage. **O.** and **I.** Renault Nurs, Gorron. Sometimes wrongly anglicised to 'Blue Nantais' ('Bleu de Nantes', 'Bleu de Doulon').   G,K,R,W3   France

- - **'Blom'** Den Ouden   1949 A sport of 'Alumii' forming a dense column with blue foliage. **I.** Adr. Blom Nurs, Boskoop, (1942). **O.** The same (c. 1930). ('Erecta Blom' is incorrect).   B,D,K,W3   Holland

- - **'Blue Gem'** N.R. Barry   1970 A blue sport from 'Ellwoodii' with soft, juvenile foliage. **O.** Roly Barry, South Taranaki Nurs, Hawera, (1961).   R,W   N.Z.

- - **'Blue Gown'** Den Ouden/Boom
  1965 A conical tree with glaucous-blue foliage. **O.** J. Hogger Nurs, Felbridge, E. Grinstead, Sussex (1935). ('Hogger's Blue Gown', 'Hoggeri').   B,K,W3   U.K.

- - **'Blue Jacket'** W. Dallimore in Chittenden.
  In "Nurs. Cat". Conical tree; foliage bluish-green above, bluish-white below. **I.** Young's Nurs, Milford, Surrey. (='Milford Blue Jacket'; NON 'Milfordensis').   B,G,K,W3   U.K.

- - 'Blue Nantais' Hort. Anglia   See 'Bleu Nantais'.

- - 'Blue Plume' Den Ouden/Boom
      1965 A name raised by Dr. Boom to replace the (probably illegit.) name 'Plumosa Glauca' for a tree found at Isola Madre, Lago Maggiore. Assuming the latter name was illegit.   B,K,W   Italy

- - 'Blue Ribbon' Hort.   See 'Dart's Blue Ribbon'.

- - **'Blue Surprise'** P.J. de Vogel
      1968 In "Dendroflora 5". Conical tree with blue-grey juvenile foliage. O. Raised from seed, by P. J. de Beer, Tilburg.   G,K,R,W2   Holland

- - 'Blue Weeper' Hort. N.Z. 1986 Wide-spreading habit; blue, pendulous foliage.

- - **'Boeri'** Den Ouden   1937 Columnar; foliage yellow to yellow-green. I. Jan de Boer and Son Nurs, Boskoop.   B,K   Holland

- - **'Booth'** Den Ouden/Boom
      1965 Bluish colour, rounded, upright tree. L. M. Koster & Sons Nurs. ('Glauca Booth').   B,K   Holland

- - 'Bowleri' Webster   1896 Close growing, pendulous. ('Smith's Weeping', 'Pendula Bowleri'). I. J. Smith and Sons, Darley Dale Nurs, Matlock, Derbyshire.   B,D,K   U.K.

- - 'Boy Blue' Hort. Anglia   1987 A listed name for a blue-grey dwarf form similar to Minima Glauca. L. Kenwith Castle Nurs, Bideford, Devon.   U.K.

- - 'Brabant'   A listed name.

- - **'Bregeon'** H.J.van de Laar
      1989 In "Naamlijst . . . ". NOM. O. and I. H. Bregeon, (1988).   Switzerl.

- - 'Brilliance' Hort. N.Z.   1992 Listed name for a compact conical, golden-yellow clone.

- - 'Brilliantissima' Hort. Holland
      1989 Reported from National Botanic Gardens. Dublin.

- - **'Broomhill Gold'** Krüssmann
      1979 A columnar clone with erect branching: a good yellow in summer fading to greenish-yellow. O. A sport on 'Erecta Viridis'. Stewarts Nurs, Wimborne, Dorset (1972). I. The same, (1979).   K,W3   U.K.

- - **'Bruinii'** Den Ouden   1937 Conical; foliage glaucous, sharp to touch. O. W. de Bruin Nurs, Boskoop, (c. 1930).   B,K   Holland

- - 'Buckland Gold' Hort. Anglia
      1988 Similar in shape to 'Broomhill Gold but a far better winter colour. L. The Don Hatch Nurs, Honiton, (1991).

- - 'Casuarinifolia' Hort. ex Beissner
      1891 Branchlets partly fan-shaped, partly contorted, whitish beneath. O. Seedling at Lobkowitz Nurs, Eisenberg, NIC.   B,D,K   Czechosl.

- - 'Casuarinifolia Aureovariegata' Beissner
      1904 Similar to previous but leaves yellow variegated. O. The same. NIC.   B,K   Czechosl.

- - **'Caudata'** Hornibrook   1934 In "Gard. Chron". Dwarf, conical; foliage irregular and bearing tufts. O. Goudkade Bros. Nurs, Boskoop.   B,G,H,K,W   Holland

- - 'Chantry Gold' Hort. Anglia
      1985 Broadly conical and slow-growing with deep gold colour, orange at tips. I. Don Hatch, Chantry Nurs, Honiton, Devon. O. Seedling from 'Yellow Transparent'.   U.K.

- - **'Chilworth Silver'** Hillier

1971 In "Hillier's Manual". Silvery-blue foliage; upright, dense bush. A mutation from 'Ellwoodii' (Not as K). **O.** Hillier and Sons Nurs, Winchester, Hants. (='Nyewoods' Hort.).   G,K,R,W2,   U.K.

- - **'Chingii'** Hort. N.Z.

1949 Dense, golden pendulous foliage. **L.** Duncan & Davies Nurs, New Plymouth, (1963). **O.** Seedling raised on Millichamp & Sons Nurs, Ashburton, N.Z. and named for an employee. ('Chinii').   W3

- - **'Clean Leaf'** H.J. van de Laar

1986 In "Naamlijst . . . ". **O.** and **I.** J. van de Veldon, Bakelse Brug (Helmond).   Holland

- - 'Coerulea' Gordon

1875 Compact; foliage bluish-green, shaded grey. **O.** A. van Leeuwen Nurs, Boskoop, (1860). NIC.   B,K   Holland

- - 'Coerulea Erecta' Schelle   1909 Similar to previous item but more erect. NIC.   B,K   Germany

- - 'Coerulescens' Carrière

1873 Glaucous, dwarf, globose. **O.** Thibault & Keteleer Nurs, Sceaux, Paris, NIC.   B   France

- - **'Columnaris'** Spek ex Den Ouden

1949 Narrowly conical; foliage dense, regular, grey appearance. **O.** J Spek Nurs, Boskoop, ('Columnaris Glauca').   B,D,G,K,W   Holland

- - 'Columnaris Aurea' Hort.   An illegit. name. See 'Golden Spire'.   W

- - 'Columnaris Glauca' Hort. See 'Columnaris'.

- - **'Compacta'** R. Smith

1867 Similar to but more vigorous than 'Minima'. Still in cultivation. ('Compacta Nana').   B,H,K,W   Holland

- - 'Compacta Elegans' De Vos

1887 Habit similar to *THUJA orientalis* 'Compact'. NIC.   Holland

- - 'Compacta Nova' Hort. ex Beissner

1891 Light green foliage; dwarf, conical, compact. NIC.   B,H,K   Germany

- - 'Conica' Hornibrook

1939 A mistake by Hornibrook for 'Fragrans Conica' Beissner (1891). Now known as 'Wisselii'.

- - 'Cooperi' Lombarts

1906 In "Nurs. Cat". Conical tree, glaucous foliage. **I.** Lombarts Nurs, Zundert. NIC.   B,K   Holland

- - 'Cream Crackers' Hort. Anglia

1983 A listed name. In "Nurs. Cat". **I.** Kelvin Lawrence Nurs, Farnham, Surrey. NOM.

- - 'Crispa' Coninck

1889 In "Nurs. Cat". Conical; monstrous. **O.** J. Coninck, Tottenham Nurs, Zundert, NIC.   B,K   Holland

- - 'Cristata' Hort. ex Beissner

1909 Branchlets with 'cockscomb-shape tips'. **O.** Tottenham Nurs, Dedemsvaart, (1888). NIC.   B,K   Holland

- - **'Croftway'** Krüssmann   1983 Dark green with new growth-tips white. **O.** No record, but before 1972. ('Crostway').   K,W   Europe?

- - 'Croftway Green' Hort.   See 'Croftway'.   W

- - 'Cypress Grove' Hort. Ireland

1989 Reported from the National Botanic Garden, Dublin, Ireland.

- - **'Darleyensis'** J. Smith

1874 In "Nurs. Cat". ('Smith's New Silver' pro syn.). Conical form with silvery foliage. **O.** J. Smith Nurs, Darley Dale, Matlock. (Not to be confused with 'Smithii' which is a mistake for 'Lutea Smithii'). ('Darcensis').   B,G,K   U.K.

- - **'Dart's Blue Ribbon'** Hort. Holland
1989 A listed name for a selection very difficult to distinguish from
'Grayswood Pillar'. L. Darthuizer Nurs. Leersum, Holland.   G,W

- - **'Dart's Globe'** Hort. Holland
1986 L. H.J. van de Laar in "Naamlijst. . . ". O. and I. Darthuiser
Nurs, Leersum, Holland.

- - 'Dawn Gem' Hort.   A listed name.   Germany

- - **'Delorme'** H.J. Grootendorst
1969 In "Dendroflora 6". A broadly conical form with uniformly
green foliage. I. Minier Nurs, Angers, (1965).   K,W   France

- - **'Densa'** R. Smith   1875 L. R. Smith Nurs, Worcester. NOM. NIC.   U.K.

- - **'Densa Aurea'** Hort. Amer.   A listed name. Possibly a mistake for 'Aurea Densa'.

- - **'Depkenii'** Beissner   1906 Slender conical habit; foliage yellow-white to green in winter.
O. S.W.Depken Nurs, Obernerland, near Bremen (1901).   B,K   Germany

- - 'Derbyshire Dwarf' Hornibrook
1939 L. James Smith, Darley Dale Nurs, Matlock. A dwarf,
globose shrub. NIC.   B,K   U.K.

- - 'Derbyshire Weeping' Hort. Anglia
1987 In "Nurs. Cat". Weasdale Nurseries, Kirkby Stephen,
Cumbria. Possibly not in cultivation.

- - 'Dik's Weeping' H.J. van de Laar
1986 In "Naamlijst . . . ". NOM.   G

- - **'Doone Valley'** Int. Con. Reg.
1981 An alleged cross between 'Fletcheri' and 'Wisselii' raised by
J.W. Archer, Bagshot, Surrey.   W   U.K.

- - **'Dore de Croux'** Krüssmann
1979 Narrowly conical golden form. I. L. Konijn Nurs. then of
Reeuwijk, Holland, in "Sortimentslijst". (1968). O. Croux
Nurs, Versailles. ('Dore de Crouy' is incorrect).   K   France

- - **'Dow's Gem'** Den Ouden/Boom
1965 Large spreading bush, lacking a leader; dark green foliage. O.
Seedling at Dow's Nurs, Oakdean, Cal. (='Dow's Variety' and
'Noble's Variety' Hort.).   B,K,W   U.S.A.

- - **'Drummondii'** Den Ouden
1949 A slow-growing pillar shaped tree; leaves dark green, glossy.
NIC. O. Unrecorded.   B,G,K

- - **'Duncanii'** R.E. Harrison
1959 Large, flat-topped, spreading bush with thread-like glaucous
foliage. O. Duncan & Davies Nurs, New Plymouth,
(1953/54).   B,K,R,W   N.Z.

- - 'Duperoux' Hort. France   See 'New Duperoux'.

- - **'Dutch Gold'**   1986 Conical tree with soft, elegant, golden foliage throughout
year. I. Fred Barcock, Bury St. Edmunds, Suffolk. O. Said to
have originated in Holland.   W   U.K.

- - 'Dwarf Blue' Hort. Anglia
1992 See 'Pick's Dwarf Blue'.

- - **'Eclipse'** G. Haddow   1987 In "Nurs. Cat". An upright blue form with much yellow-gold
variegation. I. Kenwith Nurs, Bideford, Devon. O. Seedling
from 'Columnaris' by Mr Andréw Cassells of Markinch, Fife,
(1978).   U.K.

- - **'Elegant Pearl'** H.J. van de Laar
                1986 In "Naamlijst . . . ". NOM. **O.** Not known.

- - **'Elegantissima'**(1) R. Smith
                1872 Both foliage and shoots are a brilliant yellow, at it's best in
                        winter. **O.** Wm. Barron and Sons Nurs, Borrowash, Derby.
                        Not as K.   B,K,W3   U.K.
- - 'Elegantissima' (2) Hillier
                1928 In "Nurs. Cat". A large shrub/small tree with creamy-yellow
                        shoots, graceful; silver-grey leaves in large drooping sprays.
                        O. and **I.** Hillier & Sons Nurs, Winchester.   W3   U.K.

- - 'Elegantissima Variegata' Sénéclauze
                1868 A vigorous clone; foliage blue-green with white tips. NIC.   France

- - **'Elfin'** Hort. Anglia   Very similar to 'Gnome' but paler in colour. Low growing
                        dwarf plant wider than high with bright mid-green foliage. **O.**
                        Raised or found by W.B. Archer at an unrecorded location. **I.**
                        Kenwith Nurs, Bideford, Devon,(1986).

- - **'Ellwoodii'** Hornibrook   1929 Popular narrowly upright tree with a fastigiate branch system
                        and glaucous blue-green, semi-juvenile foliage. Widely sold
                        as a "dwarf conifer"! **O.** A seedling raised at Swanmore Park,
                        Bishop's Waltham, U.K. and named for the head gardener.   B,D,G,H,K,Wl U.K.

    'Ellwoodii' is incorrectly used in a cultivar name in combination with terms such as Aurea, Aureovariegata,
Compacta, Glauca, Gnome, Gold, Kestonensis, Nana, Pillar, Pygmy, Variegata. All such names are illegitimate.
Either the word stands alone (e.g. 'Gnome', 'Kestonensis') or the legitimate prefix 'Ellwood's' should be used. See also
the Note following the entry for 'Fletcheri'.

- - 'Ellwoodii Aurea' Hort.   Now to be 'Ellwood's Gold'.

- - 'Ellwoodii Compacta' Hort.   A name of uncertain application. See Note following entry for
                        'Fletcheri'.

- - **'Ellwoodii Glauca'** Krüssmann
                1979 An illegit. name for a colour mutant, coarser and less hardy.
                        ('Ellwood's Glauca' is also illegit.).   K   Germany

- - 'Ellwoodii Nana' Hort   A mistake for 'Ellwood's Pygmy'.

- - **'Ellwood's Empire'** H.J. van de Laar
                1986 In "Naamlijst . . . ". NOM.

- - 'Ellwood's Gnome'   A mistake for 'Gnome'.

- - **'Ellwood's Gold'** R.S. Corley
                1968 In "Gard. Chron". A golden mutation from 'Ellwoodii'. Outer
                        foliage golden, inner foliage a yellow-green. **O.** A.P. Hillier
                        Nurs.   G,K,R,W   U.K.

- - 'Ellwood's Gold Pillar' Hort. Anglia
                1990 Dwarf, globose to conical plant with juvenile foliage. A better
                        gold colour than 'Ellwood's Gold' and much slower growing.
                        Occurred as a sport on 'Ellwood's Pillar'. **O.** and **I.** Evergreen
                        Nurs, Leighton Buzzard, Beds.

- - **'Ellwood's Nymph'** G. Haddow
                1983 In "Nurs. Cat". Kenwith Nurs, Bideford, Devon. A
                        diminutive, globose bush tightly packed, with soft grey-green
                        juvenile leaves. **O.** and **I.** Douglas Loundes, MacPennys
                        Nurs, Branscore, Dorset. Originally introduced and sold as
                        'MacPenny's Gnome'.   U.K.

- - **'Ellwood's Pillar'** H.J. Grootendorst
                1977 In "Dendroflora **13-14**". Columnar form perhaps a mutation
                        of 'Ellwoodii'. **I.** Kromhout & Zonen, Hazerwoude, (1977).
                        O. Said to have originated in U.S.A.   G,K,W   Holland

- - **'Ellwood's Pygmy'** Welch
  1964 In "Nurs. Cat". A low, spreading plant. L. Wansdyke Nurs,
  Devizes, Wilts. See Note under entry for 'Fletcheri'.   B,K,R,W   U.K.

- - 'Ellwood's Splashed' Hort. Holland
  1993 A listed name.

- - 'Ellwood's Variegated' Hort. Anglia
  A probable mistake for 'Silver Threads'.

- - **'Ellwood's White'** Den Ouden/Boom
  1965 Slow-growing mutation from 'Ellwoodii' with a clear-white
  variegation.   B,G,K,R,W   U.K.

- - 'Emerald' Hort.   An unacceptable listed name (per I.C.N.C.P., Art. 31A,g.).

- - 'Emerald Green' Hort. Ireland
  1985 An unacceptable name. (I.C.N.C.P. Art. 31A (g). Reported
  from J.F. Kennedy Park, Co. Wexford.

- - 'Epacrioides' Ordnung ex Beissner
  1904 Ascending; foliage epacris-like. O. Ordnung Nurs, Eisenburg.
  NIC.   B,K   Czechosl.

- - 'Erecta' R. Smith   1867 Clone no longer identifiable, so name now useful only in a
  collective sense.   B,D,G,K,R,W

- - **'Erecta Alba'** Beissner   1891 Conical tree with tips of branchlets white. I. J. Keessen &
  Son, Terra Nova Nurs, Aalsmeer, (1882).   B,K,W   Holland

- - **'Erecta Argenteovariegata'** De Vos
  1876 Leaves green, variegated white; a sport of 'Erecta Viridis'. O.
  Koster Nurs, Boskoop, (1874).   B,K,W2   Holland

- - **'Erecta Aurea'** De Vos   1876 Conical, slow-growing; golden-yellow foliage. Wind tender.   B,G,H,K,W2   Holland

- - 'Erecta Aureospica' De Vos
  1876 Dense erect habit; growth-tips yellow. L. Overeijnder Nurs,
  Boskoop, (1884) NIC.   B,K   Holland

- - 'Erecta Blom' Hort.   See 'Blom'.

- - 'Erecta Coerulea Glauca' Schelle
  1909 L. H.A. Hesse Nurs, Weener-on-Ems. NIC.   Germany

- - **'Erecta Filiformis'** Beissner
  1896 A small tree with bright green, thread-like foliage on many
  stiff, erect brs. O. Neumänn, Waldorf, (Sachsen) (1896).
  ('Filiformis Erecta').   B,G,K,W   Germany

- - 'Erecta Filiformis Compacta'
  1986 An illegit. name. L. E.A. Cope, "Native . . . Conifers". NOM.   U.S.A.

- - 'Erecta Filiformis Glauca'
  1930 A listed name. O. H.A. Hesse Nurs, Weener-on-Ems.   Germany

- - 'Erecta Glauca' R. Smith   1872 Described as "A distinct and very desirable form of 'Erecta',
  in colour a rich glaucous hue, habit erect and elegant, distinct
  from all other varieties" in 1872, but never heard of again.
  This is almost certainly the clone that mysteriously turned up
  later in Germany as 'Alumii'.   B   U.K.

- - 'Erecta Glaucescens' Siebold ex Otto
  1868 A superfluous name for 'Erecta Glauca'.   B,K   Germany

- - 'Erecta Jackman's Variety' Hort. Anglia
  1907 Now known as 'Green Pillar'. L. Geo Jackman & Son,
  Woking (1964).

- - 'Erecta Lutea' Lawson 1874 NOM. Probably a mistake for 'Erecta Aurea'. NIC.

- - **'Erecta Viridis'** R. Smith
1867 Bright-green; fastigiate. **O.** and **I.** Anthony Waterer Nurs, Knaphill, Surrey, but several clones are now in cultivation. B,G,K,W U.K.

- - 'Ericoides' Nicholson 1884 Probably a plant with juvenile foliage that eventually disappeared. Seedlings that retain their juvenile foliage unduly are not stable, because this condition is seldom permanently retained. No longer identifiable. NIC. B,D,H,K,W2 U.K.

- - 'Erica' Hort. Anglia 1975 **O.** and **I.** D.W. Hatch, Chantry Nurs, Honiton, Devon. Dwarf upright bush of juvenile grey-green leaves, coarse to the touch. W2 U.K.

- - 'Fairfield Gold' Hort. N.Z.
1970 A dense rounded slow growing bush. Bright yellow foliage. **O.** South Taranaki Nurs, Hawera.

- - 'Falcata' Ordnung ex Beissner
1904 Foliage peculiarity. **O.** Ordnung Nurs, Eisenberg, (1904). NIC. B,K Czechosl.

- - 'Fantail' Hort. Anglia 1992 Reported from Windsor Great Park, Berks.

- - **'Fascination'** H.J. van de Laar
1986 In "Naamlijst . . . ". NOM. **O.** and **I.** G.E.F. Bolwijn, Pulten, (1975). Holland

- - 'Fastigiata' Sénéclauze 1868 A narrowly conical clone. **O.** Sénéclauze Nurs, Bourg Argental, Loires, NIC. (This name is useful nowadays only as a collective or group name). France

- - **'Felix'** Felix & Dijkhuis 1941 In "Nurs. Cat". Conical; glaucous-blue foliage. **O.** Felix & Dijkhuis Nurs, Boskoop, (1937). B,K,W3 Holland

- - 'Filicifolia Pendula Nana' Krüssmann
1979 Dense conical tree. **O.** Prior to 1930. Possibly a case of misidentification. NIC. K France

- - **'Filifera'** de Vos 1887 Spreading tree with pendulous habit, rich pale-green foliage. Still in cultivation. See also 'Filiformis'. B,G,K,W3 Holland

- - 'Filifera Aurea' Hort. A listed name. Possibly a mistake for *CHAMAECYPARIS pisifera* 'Filifera Aurea'.

- - 'Filifera Glauca' De Vos 1887 In 'Handbuch ...Coniferen'. An outstanding tree with long foliage. **O.** de Vos Nurs, **I.** K. Wezelenburg, Hazerwoude, near Boskoop. Holland

- - **'Filiformis'** Fillot 1877 Tree with arching branches, grey or yellow-green foliage, and long hanging shoots. B,D,G,K,W3 Belgium

- - **'Filiformis Compacta'** Hort. ex Beissner
1891 Dwarf; globose; branchlets drooping; dark bluish-green. ('Globosa Filiformis'). B,D,G,H,K,W Germany

- - 'Filiformis Glauca' Beissner
1891 A superfluous synonym for 'Filifera Glauca'. **O.** and **I.** K. Wezelenburg, Hazerwoude, Boskoop, (1886). NIC. B,K Holland

- - 'Flava' Cripps 1867 Superfluous name for 'Flavescens'.

- - 'Flavescens' Den Ouden/Boom
1965 A new name for 'Lutea Flavescens'. Foliage pale yellow. **O.** Cripps Nurs, Tunbridge Wells, Kent. NIC. B,K U.K.

- - **'Fleckellwood'** C.R. Harrison
  1975 A variegated sport from 'Ellwoodii'; grey-green with a small
  white fleck. **I.** South Taranaki Nurs. Hawera, (1965).
  (Spelling varies but should reflect the plant's origin).   W2   N.Z.

- - 'Fleetii' Webster
  1896 Growth stiff, erect; foliage bluish-grey.NIC.   U.K.

- - **'Fletcheri'** Hornibrook
  1923 Conical; grey-green foliage tinged mauve in winter. **I.**
  Fletcher Bros. Nurs, Chertsey, Surrey. **O.** A sporting branch
  on a normal tree found in the one-time Ottershaw Nurs. near
  Chertsey, (1911).   B,D,G,H,K,W   U.K.

Several species within the *Cupressaceae* may show variability from one plant to the next in its progression from seed-leaves to 'adult' foliage and in its growth from a seedling to a mature tree. 'Hang-ups' occasionally occurring at a 'juvenile' stage have enabled selections to be made and propagated that form attractive garden plants, but this phenomenon is essentially a delay, not a fixation, and so any such plant may resume its progress towards maturity at any time, often imperceptibly at first and perhaps not until some years later. The resulting instability makes any system of giving cultivar names to plants at an intermediate stage of development of a particular clone a problem. 'The Baby' progressively becomes Tommy, Tom, Thomas and eventually Mr. Atkins as he grows up, without any change in his individuality.

This makes the coining and use of cultivar names for these infinitely graduated and more-or-less unstable states of growth very unsatisfactory.

A further problem is that the 'mental age' of tissue, as well as the appearance of the foliage varies with its position on the plant. Hornibrook first recorded that cuttings from weak shoots of 'Fletcheri' taken from near the ground formed low, rounded bushes quite different to the vigorous, upright-growing plants produced from strong cuttings taken from the top of the same mother-plant. See e.g. 'Fletcheri Nana' and 'Kestonensis' (probably) and 'Ellwoodii Pygmaea'.

Especially when propagating dwarf mutations, this phenomenon should be recognised. Careless selection of coarse growth can destroy the dwarfness and shape in two or three "cutting generations".

- - 'Fletcheri Aurea' Hort.   A mistake for 'Fletcher's Gold'. (See Somerset).

- - 'Fletcheri Nana' Hornibrook
  1939 Low, bush-shaped plants resulting from particular selection of
  cutting material. See Hornibrook 40 (1939) and the above
  Note.   B,H,K,W2   U.K.

- - 'Fletcher's Compact' Den Ouden/Boom
  1965 Slower grower than 'Fletcheri'; of upright habit. See Note
  under 'Fletcheri'.   B,K,W   Holland

- - **'Fletcher's Gold'** Hort. Holland
  1986 H.J.van de Laar in "Naamlijst . . . ". NOM. Juvenile
  yellowish foliage. **O.** Not known. (1985).   D,G   Holland

- - 'Fletcher's Gold Splash'   See 'Gold Splash'.

- - 'Fletcher's Sunburst' Hort. N.Z.   **O.** Hughes, Blue Mountain Nurs, Tapanui, W. Otago.   N.Z.

- - **'Fletcher's White'** Den Ouden/Boom
  1965 Large upright bush; creamy-white variegation.   B,D,G,K,W   N.Z.

- - 'Fletcher's Yellow Transparent' Hort.
  A mistake for 'Yellow Transparent'.

- - **'Flying Saucer'** Den Ouden/Boom
  1965 A spreading form with soft loosely appressed foliage. **O.** N.
  Th. Bosman Nurs. Boskoop (1952).   B   Holland

- - **'Forsteckensis'** Beissner
  1904 Dense, dwarf globe of moss-like foliage. **O.** A Nursery at
  Forsteck, Kiel. ('Forsteckiana' is incorrect). Not always
  offered true. But see the second Note under 'Fletcheri'.   B,D,G,H,K,W2   Germany

- - 'Forsteckensis Glauca' Hort.   A mistake for 'Tharandtensis Caesia'.

- - 'Forsteckensis Variegata' Schelle
  1909 An unstable mutation is occasionally found on 'Forsteckensis'. NIC.   B,K   Germany

- - 'Forsteckiana' Hort. ex Beissner
  1891 Spelling altered to 'Forsteckensis' in ed. **2** (1909).

- - **'Four Seasons'** H.J. van de Laar
  1986 In "Naamlijst . . . ". NOM. **O.** A. Mauritz and Sons, Bussum, Holland. **I.** G.E.F. Bolwijn, Putten.   Holland

- - 'Fragrans' Standish ex Gordon
  1875 Vigorous tree; pendulous shoots. **O.** Standish Nurs, Bagshot, Surrey. NIC.   B,K   U.K.

- - 'Fragrans Argentea' Hort. Kew ex Beissner
  1875 As last but foliage silvery-blue. NIC.   B,K   U.K.

- - 'Fragrans Conica' Hort. ex Beissner
  1891 Indistinguishable from 'Wisselii'. **O.** Gebbers Nurs, Weisenburg.   B   Germany

- - **'Fraseri'** Beissner
  1887 Dull grey-green foliage; slender columnar tree, foliage sprays in flat vertical planes. **I.** Lombart's Nurs, Zundert. ('Fraseri Glauca').   B,D,G,K,W2   Holland

- - **'Fraser's Gold'** Hort. Holland   H.J. van de Laar 1986 in "Naamlijst . . . ". NOM. **O.** No information. (1985).

- - 'Frettinghamii' Hort. Ireland
  1989 Reported from the National Botanic Garden, Dublin, Ireland.

- - 'Friesia' Uphof   1911 Sport from 'Triomf van Boskoop'. NIC.   B,K   Germany

- - 'Gail's Gold' G. Haddow   1991 In "Nurs. Cat". Very dwarf globose bush, pale yellow in summer, deeper gold in winter. **O.** Seedling raised from Lutea at Kenwith Nurs, Bideford, Devon. **I.** The same.   U.K.

- - 'Gilt Edge' Hort. Anglia   1988 Pillar shaped tree with tip foliage cream. **I.** Kenwith Nurs, Bideford, Devon. **O.** Andréw Cassells, Markinch, Fife.

- - **'Gimbornii'** Hornibrook   1939 Upright oval bush; dense glaucous blue-green foliage tinged mauve in winter. **O.** Gimborn Estate, Doorn.   B,D,G,H,K,W   Holland

- - f. *glauca* (Jaeger) Beissner
  1887 A botanical designation covering all the forms with noticeably glaucous foliage.   Sporadic

- - 'Glauca' (1) Jaeger   1865 This is the original clone now unidentifiable, so the name is useful only in a collective sense.   B,D,W   U.K.

- - 'Glauca' (2)   The word Glauca is generally, but not invariably used in the following cultivar names, but is not now acceptable in new names.

- - **'Glauca Argentea'** Hesse
  1913 A spreading, conical tree with glaucous-blue, primrose foliage. **L.** and **I.** H. A. Hesse Nurs, Weener-on-Ems, (1913). NIC.   B,K   Germany

- - 'Glauca Booth' Meyer   1963 A mistake for 'Booth'.

- - **'Glauca Elegans'** Schelle
  1909 Slender column; leaf-tips white in summer, becoming glaucous in winter; foliage coarse.   B,G,K,W3   Germany

- - 'Glauca Felix' Hort.   1941 Now known as 'Felix'.

- - 'Glauca Globus' Barabits   1965 An illegit. name. Now to be 'Barabits Globe'.   G,K,W   Hungary

- - 'Glauca Hogger' Hort. Anglia   Now known as 'Hogger'.

- - 'Glauca Kooy' Hort.   1927 Now known as 'Kooy'.

- - **'Glauca Lombartsii'** Lombarts
   1925 In "Nurs. Cat". Conical tree; bluish bloom to foliage. I.
   Lombarts Nurs, Zundert, (1929). O. The same, (1910).   B,K,W   Holland

- - 'Glauca Spek' Hort.   1949 Now known as 'Spek'.

- - 'Glauca Tarka' Hort. Hungary
   1967 Now known as 'Tarka'.

- - **'Glauca Veitch'** Veitch ex Den Ouden
   1937 Conical; foliage green, soft blue bloom. O. Reputedly raised
   in the Veitch Nurs, Combewood, (as 'Glauca').   B,K,W   U.K.

- - 'Glaucescens' Otto   1865 See 'Erecta Glaucescens'.

- - 'Globe' Hort. Holland   An unsatisfactory listed name. Now to be 'Barabit's Globe'.   G

- - **'Globosa'** De Vos   1876 Foliage bright green; broadly globose with thick, short
   branchlets. Should not be confused with 'Barabit's Globe'.   B,D,G,K,W   Europe

- - 'Globosa Filiformis' Hort.   A mistake for 'Filiformis Compacta'.

- - 'Globosa Nana' Hort.   1989 Very similar to 'Globosa' when young, but squatly conical
   eventually. Reported from National Botanic Garden, Dublin,
   Ireland. Received from M. Hornibrook, (1922).

- - 'Globus' Welch   1979 An illegit. name. Now to be 'Barabits Globe'.   W3   Hungary

- - **'Gnome'** Corley   1970 In "Gard. Chron". Dwarf; very tight, congested foliage. I.
   D.W. Hatch, Heath End Nurs, Farnham, Surrey. O. (1968)
   W.Hart, Warnham Court, Horsham, Surrey (c 1950). ('Gnom'
   'Ellwood's Gnome').   K,R,W2   U.K.

- - 'Golden Allumii' Hort.   A mistake for 'Alumigold'.

- - 'Golden Guinea' Hort. Anglia
   1983 A listed name.   U.K?

- - **'Golden King'** Wezelenburg
   1931 In "Nurs. Cat". Conical, robust; foliage golden-yellow to
   browny-yellow in winter. O. and I. Wezelenburg Nurs,
   Hazerwoude, near Boskoop.   B,G,K,W   Holland

- - 'Golden Lace' Hort. Anglia
   1983 A listed name from "The Plantsman".   U.K?

- - **'Golden Light'** Int. Con. Reg.
   1974 Conical habit; leaves lemon-yellow, turning dark bronze. O:
   R.J. Belding, Woking, Surrey.   W3   U.K.

- - **'Golden Pot'** Int. Con. Reg.
   1983 Reg'd by D.W. Hatch, Chantry Nurs, Honiton, Devon. O. M
   Newman, Old Cherry Nurs, Hadlow Down, Sussex, (1986). A
   golden sport from 'Pottenii'. (See also 'Pot of Gold').   W3   U.K.

- - **'Golden Prince'** Krüssmann
   1983 An improved 'Golden King'. Pendulous form, golden-yellow.
   O. and I. Wm. J. Hooftman Nurs, Boskoop, (1978).   K,W3   Holland

- - 'Golden Queen' Hort. Australia   Slow-growing, upright plant with good golden colour on the
   outside, fading to lime-green on the inner foliage. I. Into U.K.
   by Dr. J. Smart of Marwood Hill, Devon. ('Yellow Queen').

- - 'Golden Shower' Hort. Anglia
   1984 Reported from the Royal Botanical Gardens, Kew, U.K.

- - **'Golden Showers'** Mitsch
  1976 In "Nurs. Cat". Growth compact, branch tips drooping; branchlet stems yellow, foliage yellow variegated. **I.** D.W. Hatch, Chantry Nurs, Honiton, Devon, (1980).   U.S.A.

- - 'Golden Spangle' R.E. Harrison
  1959 A mistake for *CHAMAECYPARIS pisifera* 'Gold Spangle'.

- - 'Golden Spire' Krüssmann
  1979 Although of different origin, and so a distinct clone, this is insufficiently distinct from 'Kellerriis Gold' to justify a separate cultivar name. **I.** Bolwijn Nurs, Putten, (1972). **O.** The same.   K,W   Holland

- - 'Golden Treasure' Hort. Anglia
  1972 A listed name. No information.   France

- - **'Golden Triumph'** Krüssmann
  1979 Conical; branches erect; foliage yellow. **I.** Mauritz Nurs, Bussum, (1972).   G,K,W3   Holland

- - **'Golden Wonder'** Roy. Hort. Soc. Journ.
  1963 The deep yellow colour is maintained throughout year. **I.** Spek Nurs, Boskoop, (1963). **O.** Found as a seedling by N.T. Bosman, Boskoop, (1955).   B,G,K,W   Holland

- - **'Goldfinger'** Int. Con. Reg.
  1978 Seedling from 'Stewartii'. Similar colour but fastigiate branch system. **R.** A. Goatcher and Sons Nurs, Washington, Sussex. **O.** The same.   W   U.K.

- - **'Gold Flake'** Hort. Holland
  1968 A variegated sport from 'Ellwoodii'. **L.** Konijn Nurs, Reeuwijk. In "Sortimentslijst". NOM. ('Ellwoodii Aureovariegata').

- - 'Goldgren' Hort. Anglia   1993 A listed name. See "The Plant Finder". NOM.

- - 'Gold Lace' Hort. Anglia   1992 Reported from Windsor Great Park, Berks.

- - 'Gold Pyramid' G. Haddow
  1989 In "Nurs. Cat". **O.** and **I.** Kenwith Castle Nurs, Bideford, Devon. Sport from Chilworth Silver with yellow juvenile foliage.   U.K.

- - 'Goldspire' Hort. Anglia   1983 A narrow, slow-growing upright form with deep green thickish foliage which is tipped golden-yellow.

- - **'Gold Splash'** C.R. Harrison
  1975 Soft grey-green foliage splashed irregularly with yellow. A variegated sport from 'Fletcheri'. Best in full sun. **O.** Barry Blackman, Te Kuifi.   W3   N.Z.

- - **'Gold Star'** Hort. Holland
  1988 L. H.J. van de Laar in "Naamlijst. . . ". NOM.

- - 'Goldsworth Gold' Hort. Ireland
  1985 Reported from Mount Congreve, Co. Waterford.

- - 'Gracilis' Nelson   1866 A tall tree, with terminals drooping. **O.** Anthony Waterer Nurs, Knaphill, Surrey, NIC.   B,D,K,W   U.K.

- - 'Gracilis Aurea' Davis   1894 Similar to previous, but young leaves. yellow at first. **O.** Davis, Hillsbrough Nurs, Co. Down, NIC.   B,D,K   Ireland

- - 'Gracilis Aurea Pygmaea' Dallimore & Jackson
  1948 Dwarf form of last. NIC.   B,D,K   U.K.

- - 'Gracilis Glauca' Den Ouden
1949 Globose; foliage glaucous, coarse. **O**. Wezelenburg Nurs,
Hazerwoude, Boskoop, (1925).   B,D,K   Holland

- - 'Gracilis Nana' Hort. ex Beissner
1891 Dwarf equivalent of 'Gracilis'. NIC.   B,H,K   Germany

- - 'Gracilis Nova' Den Ouden
1949 Conical tree; foliage irregular, bluish-green. NIC.   B,K   Holland

- - 'Gracilis Pendula' Veitch   1881 Pendulous; branches slender; foliage threadlike, dark green.
O. Wm Barron, Elvaston Nurs, Barrowash, near Derby.   B,K   U.K.

- - 'Gracillima' Beissner   1884 As 'Gracilis', but finer foliage. NIC.   B,K   Germany

- - **'Grandi'** Welch   1979 Dwarf; foliage dark glaucous-green. **I**. Clarke & Co. Nurs,
San José, California, (1950). ('Grandi Nana').   B,K,W   U.S.A.

- - 'Grant's Golden' Hort. Anglia
1992 Reported from Windsor Great Park, Berks, U.K.

- - 'Grayswood Bronze' Hort. Anglia
1992 Report from Windsor Great Park, Berks.

- - **'Grayswood Feather'** Hort. Anglia
An erect tall shrub. Foliage dark green in acid soil, yellowish
in alkaline. **I**. D.W. Hatch, Chantry Nurs, Honiton, Devon,
(1982). **O**. Found at Grayswood Hill, Hazlemere, Surrey.   G,W3

- - **'Grayswood Gold'** Hort. Anglia
Semi-dwarf, columnar, deep chrome-yellow foliage. **O**. and **I**.
As last.   G,W

- - **'Grayswood Pillar'** H.G. Hillier
1971 In "Hillier's Manual". A very narrow, columnar tree. Small
grey-blue foliage, tightly packed branches. **O**. As 'Grayswood
Feather'; a mutation from 'Blue Jacket'.   W3   U.K.

- - 'Green Diamond' Hort. Holland   A mistake for *CHAMAECYPARIS obtusa* 'Green Diamond'.

- - **'Green Globe'** C.R. Harrison
1975 Dwarf, globose, with tiny dark green foliage. **I**. South
Taranaki Nurs, Hawera, N.Z. **O**. Palmers Nurs, Glen Eden,
Auckland, (1950).   G,W2   N.Z.

- - **'Green Hedger'** Jackman
1949 In "Planters' Handbook". Dense, conical; foliage bright green.
O. Jackmans Nurs, Woking, Surrey, (1939). ('Jackman's
Green Hedger' and other variations).   B,D,K,R,W   U.K.

- - 'Green Monarch'   1988 In "The Plant Finder". Name only.

- - **'Green Pillar'** Den Ouden/Boom
1965 Conical; bright-green foliage with a golden tint, **L**. Hogger's
Nurs, Felbridge, Sussex, 1960 (as 'Hogger'). **O**. The same.   B,G,K,R,W   U.K.

- - 'Green Spire' Hort. Anglia   Superfluous name for 'Green Pillar'   W3

- - **'Green Survival'** Hort. Holland
1986 **L**. H.J. van de Laar in "Naamlijst . . .". NOM. **O**. A Moritz
& Sons, Bussum, Holland. **I**. G.E.F. Bolwign, Putten,
Holland, (1975).

- - **'Green Wall'** H.J. Grootendorst
1979 In "Dendroflora 15-16" Columnar form similar to 'Green
Pillar'.   K,W   France

- - 'Greycoat' J. Lewis   1992 In "Int. Conif. Reg". A new name suggested, perhaps
posthumously, for 'Argentea' (2).

- - 'Grey Column' Hort. Holland **L.** H.J. van de Laar in "Naamlijst . . . ". (1986). NOM.

- - 'Grey Cone' G. Haddow 1982 In "Nurs. Cat". Conical; soft juvenile foliage grey-green tinted mauve in winter. **L.** Kenwith Castle Nurs, Bideford, Devon. W3 U.K.

- - 'Handcross Park' Hort.
  1987 A superfluous synonym for 'Aureovariegata'. See Aureovariegata'. G

- - 'Harkin' Den Ouden/Boom
  1965 A mistake for 'Haskin's Variety'. B,K

- - 'Harlow Car' Hort. Anglia
  1992 Report from Windsor Great Park, Berks, U.K.

- - 'Haskin's Variety' Webster
  1896 **O.** Haskin's Nurs, Branksome, Bournemouth. NIC. U.K.

- - 'Headfort' H.G. Hillier 1971 Graceful tree. Named in honour of Lord Headfort. (Headfortii). W3 Ireland

- - **'Henri Smits'** H.J. van de Laar
  1982 In "Dendroflora **19**". Open, broadly conical, main branches arching over and pendulous at tips. **O.** Smits Nurs, Boskoop. W Holland

- - **'Henry Dinger'** Hort. Holland
  1968 **L. L.** Konijn in "Sortimentslijst". NOM. **O.** and **I.** H. Dinger, Lunteren, Holland.

- - **'Hillieri'** H.G. Hillier 1928 In "Nurs. Cat". Foliage in large floppy, feathery sprays, bright pale green-yellow outside, greenish within. **I.** Hillier's Nurs, Winchester, (1910 - as *Cupressus hillieri*). **O.** The same. (1910). B,G,K,R,W3 U.K.

- - 'Hodgers Blue Gown' Hort. Anglia
  A mistake for 'Blue Gown'.

- - 'Hogan' Hort. Amer. Now known as 'Oregon Blue'. W3

- - 'Hogger' Den Ouden/Boom
  1965 Not now distinguished from 'Blue Gown'. ('Hoggeri'). B

- - 'Hogger's Gold' Hort. Anglia
  1987 A listed name. No further information.

- - 'Hogger's Green Pillar' Hort. See 'Green Pillar'.

- - 'Holden Gold' Hort. Anglia A listed name for a golden form of medium vigour. **O.** Holden Clough Nurs, Clitheroe, Lancs.

- - **'Hollandia'** Bailey 1933 Narrowly conical; flattened spray of dark green foliage. **I.** Koster Nurs, Boskoop, (1895). B,G,K,W3 Holland

- - 'Hopken's Silberstar' Hort. Germany
  See 'Silberstar'.

- - **'Howarth's Gold'** H.J. van de Laar
  1969 In "Dendroflora **6**". Narrowly conical; dense soft golden-yellow foliage. ('Howards's Gold'). G,K,W U.K.

- - **'Hughes'** Hughes 1939 In "Nurs. Cat". Similar to 'Versicolor' but foliage cream coloured. **O.** Seedling raised by Stan Hughes, Blue Mountain Nurs, Tapanui, Otago, (1930). W N.Z.

- - 'Hybrida' Hort. A mistake for *CHAMAECYPARIS lawsoniana* 'Nidiformis'.

- - **'Imbricata Pendula'** R.E. Harrison,
    1959 In "Nurs. Cat". A pendulous form with thread-leaf foliage. **O.**
    R.E. Harrison Nurs, Palmerston, N.Z.   G,W   N.Z.

- - **'Intertexta'** R. Smith   1872 Striking tree with coarse, bold, dark glaucous-green foliage.
    I. R. Smith Nurs, Worcester.   B,D,G,K,W   U.K.

- - 'Intertexta Atrovirens' Schelle
    1909 As last, but foliage dark green. NIC.   B,K   Germany

- - **'Intertexta Pendula'** Krüssmann
    1985 An illegit name. Named for a decumbent tree at Mount Usher,
    Co. Wicklow.   G,K   Ireland

- - 'Irish Gold' Hort. Holland
    1976 **L.** Darthuiser Nurs, Leersum, Holland.

- - 'Ivánc' Barabits Hort. Hungary
    1965 A listed name.

- - **'Ivonne'** H.J. van de Laar
    1981 In "Dendroflora **18**". A compact, conical, golden form. **O.** J.
    van der Nieuwendijk Nurs, Reeuwijk.   W   Holland

- - 'Jackman's Green Hedger' Hort. Anglia
    See 'Green Hedger'.

- - 'Jackman's Lutea' Hort. Anglia
    1987 An illegit. name for an unidentified golden form purchased
    from Jackman's Nurs. Not in production.

- - 'Jackman's Triumph' Hort. Anglia
    1984 Reported from Royal Botanical Gardens, Kew, (1984). NIC.

- - 'Jackman's Variety'   1967 A mistake for 'Green Pillar'.

- - **'Jolanda'** H.J. van de Laar
    1986 In "Naamlijst . . . ". NOM. **O.** and **I.** J. van den Nieuwendijk
    Nurs, Reeuwijk, (1982).   Holland

- - **'Jones'** Duncan & Davies
    1972 Bright yellow, even in partial shade. **I.** Duncan and Davies
    Nurs, New Plymouth. **O.** Raised by J.N. Anderson of Napier
    and named for F. Jones, Owner of the mother tree at Deefton.   N.Z.

- - 'Juniperina' Lawson   1875 In "Nurs. Cat". Broadly conical; foliage juniperlike. **L.**
    Lawson Nurs, Edinburgh, (1875). NIC, but seedlings that
    retain their juvenile foliage for several years turn up
    occasionally.   B,D,H,K,W   Scotland

- - 'Juniperoides' Hornibrook
    1923 A mistake for last. But see his ed. **2.**   H

- - 'Junivers Stricta' Hort. Holland
    1993 An illegit. listed name.

- - 'Juvenalis Stricta' C.R. Harrison,
    1975 A descriptively named fixed juvenile clone similar to
    'Fletcheri' in all respects save in colour. It arose as a seedling
    at Rotorua, N.I., in the 1930's and has been grown in New
    Zealand as RETINOSPORA *leptoclada* and other names. It
    has no connection with the European form 'Kestonensis'.   W3   N.Z.

- - 'Keessen' Hort.   Superfluous name for 'Erecta Alba'.

- - **'Kelleriis'** Den Ouden/Boom
    1965 Medium vigour; foliage glaucous. **I.** D. T. Poulsen Nurs,
    Kelleriis, (1938). NIC. ('Kelleriis Glauca').   B,K   Denmark

- - **'Kelleriis Gold'** H.J. Grootendorst
  1969 In "Dendroflora **6**". Hardy, upright clone; yellow-green. **O.** and **I.** As last. (1938). G,K,W Denmark

- - 'Kelleriis Lutea' Den Ouden/Boom
  1965 A mistake for 'Kelleriis Gold'. NOM. ('Kelleriis Aurea').

- - 'Keston Variety' Hort. Anglia
  1935 This plant was first catalogued as *fletcheri* Keston var., "very dwarf compact, slow-growing form making a small mound". The simpler name 'Kestonensis' soon took over in the trade and is now in general use.

- - **'Kestonensis'**
  1935 This name has been applied by several authors to several plants. It was discovered as a seedling 'Lawson' on the Reuthe Nurs, Keston, Kent, during the 1920's. It was then a compact, slow-growing plant forming a low bun. The lost stock plant was replaced by one purchased from W.H. Rogers of Red Lodge Nurs, Eastleigh, Hants. Early catalogues of that firm offer 'Kestonensis' as "A compact Ellwoodii", so what Reuthe received is uncertain. Reuthe now (private communication, 1974) regard it as a dwarf form of 'Fletcheri', producing rather squat, bushy plants, somewhat more vigorous than 'Ellwoodii'. K U.K.

- - 'Kilboggett Gold' Donard Nurs. Co.
  1972 In "Good Garden Plants". Habit as 'Alumii' but with soft-yellow foliage. **O.** and **I.** Watsons Nurs, Killiney, Co. Down, but no longer listed by them. Ireland

- - 'Killiney' H.J. Watson
  1947 In "Nurs. Cat". Watson's Nurs, Killiney, Co. Down. (As 'Killiney Variety'). An upright grower, with very dense, grey-green foliage. Ireland

- - **'Killiney Gold'** Donard Nurs. Co.
  1972 In "Good Garden Plants". Elegant, compact, yellow foliage. **O.** and **I.** Watsons Nurs, Killiney, Co. Down. K,W3 Ireland

- - **'Kilmacurragh'** Donard Nurs. Co.
  1942 In "Nurs. Cat". (As 'Kilmacurragh Variety'). Tall, columnar; foliage dark green. **O.** A tree at Kilmacurragh, Rathdrum, Co. Wicklow. B,G,K,R,W3 Ireland

- - 'Kingswood' H.J. van de Laar
  1992 A dense, conical mutation from 'Columnaris' with sulphur - yellow foliage. In "Dendroflora **29**". **O.** and **I.** J.H.J. Geilen-Timmermans, Koningsbosch, Holland

- - 'Kloosterhuis' Den Ouden
  1949 Pyramidal; leaves green, blue bloomed; open. **O.** Egb. Kloosterhuis Nurs, Veendam. B,D,K Holland

- - **'Knowefieldensis'** Beissner
  1911 A broad, spreading plant without leader. **O.** Little and Ballantyne Nurs, Carlisle. ('Knowefieldensis Glauca'). B,D,H,K,W2 U.K.

- - **'Konijn's Silver'** H.J. van de Laar
  1986 In "Naamlijst . . . ". NOM. ('Konijn'). G

- - **'Kooy'** Den Ouden/Boom
  1965 Conical; glaucous-blue markings. **O.** Kooy & Sons Nurs, Boskoop, (1925). B,G,K,W Holland

- - **'Krameri'** Beissner
  1887 Globose shrub; glossy dark-green cordlike foliage. B,D,H,K,W Germany

- - **'Krameri Variegated'** H.G. Hillier
  1971 In "Hilliers' Manual". A sport of last with cream variegated growths. An illegit. name. U.K.

- - **'Lane'** Den Ouden — 1949 — Columnar tree; thin feathery sprays of golden-yellow foliage. O. and I. Lane's Nurs, Berkhamsted, Herts, (1938). ('Lane's Aurea'; 'Lanei'). — B,G,K,R,W — U.K.

- - **'Laxa'** Hoopes — 1868 — In "The Book of Evergreen". Ascending, irregular form; stout branches. NIC. — B,K — Germany

- - **'Lemon Queen'** Hort. Anglia — 1983 — Clone with unusual, pale sulphur-coloured foliage. — W

- - **'Lennei'** Hort. Ireland — 1985 — Reported from Mount Congreave, Kilmeadon, Co. Waterford.

- - **'Leonard Ropner'** Hort. Anglia — 1970 — L. Hillier's Nurs. In "Conif. Conf. List". NOM.

- - **'Lila'** Hort. Hungary — 1992 — A listed name for a blue selection. O. M. Barabits.

- - **'Limelight'** Hort. Anglia — A squat, conical dwarf with foliage an attractive citrus-yellow. I. L. Walker Nurs, Doncaster. O. Raised by Phil Wood, an employee on that nursery.

- - **'Little Spire'** D.W. Hatch — 1972 — In "Nurs. Cat". A compact dwarf form of 'Wisselii'. I. D.W. Hatch, Chantry Nurs, Honiton, Devon. O. A seedling raised by J.W. Archer, Farnham, Hants. — G,W3 — U.K.

- - **'Lombartsii'** Lombarts — 1915 — In "Nurs. Cat". Leaves greenish-yellow, slightly bluish bloomed; vigorous, dense habit. I. Lombart's Nurs, Zundert, (1915). O. The same (1904). — B,K,W3 — Holland

- - **'Luna'** H.J. van de Laar — 1983 — In "Dendroflora 20". Dense broadly conical tree; foliage yellow with white tips, fading to grey-green; O. A. Blanken Tzn., Boskoop. — G,W — Holland

- - **'Lutea'** R. Smith — 1867 — A broadly columnar tree with golden foliage in wide sprays.. The earliest recorded "golden Lawson" and still one of the best. O. G. and W. Rollison Nurs, London. — B,D,G,K,W — U.K.

- - 'Lutea Flavescens' Cripps ex Gordon — 1875 — Superfluous name for 'Flavescens'.

- - **'Lutea Nana'** Den Ouden/Boom — 1965 — Golden-yellow dwarf form. The hardiest in this group. O. and I. W H Rogers, Red Lodge Nurs, Eastleigh, Hants, (1930). — B,D,G,K,W — U.K.

- - **'Lutea Smithii'** J. Smith — 1898 — In "Nurs. Cat". Conical tree with pale yellow foliage. O. and I. J. Smith and Son, Darley Dale Nurs, Matlock. — U.K.

- - 'Luteocompacta' Hornibrook — 1939 — Conical; leaves small, golden-yellow, green on inside of plant. I. H. den Ouden and Sons Nurs, Boskoop, (1938). O. Van Gimborn Estate, Doorn. — B,H,K — Holland

- - 'Luteogracilis' Den Ouden — 1949 — Open conical tree; leaves golden-yellow, yellow-green in winter. O. No information. — B,K — Holland

- - 'Lutescens' Van Geert — 1875 — Vigorous conical tree; bright golden-yellow. O. Van Houtte Nurs, Ghent, (1875). Indistinguishable from 'Lutea'. NIC. — B,K — Belgium

- - **'Lycopodioides'** Van der Elst — 1895 — In "Nurs. Cat". Upright tree with grey-green contorted foliage. O. Van der Elst, Tottenham Nurs, Dedemsvaart. — B,D,G,H,K,W — Holland

- - 'Lycopodioides Aurea' — A mistake. (See under *CHAMAECYPARIS obtusa*.).

- - **'Maas'** P. Lombart, 1957 In "Nurs. Cat". Resembles 'Triompf van Lombarts'; foliage finer and yellow-green. **O.** and **I.** Lombart's Nurs, Zundert.   B,G,K,W   Holland

- - 'MacPenny's Gold' Hort. Anglia
1989 Pillar shaped, broad with semi-pendulous branches and branchlets, foliage feathery and bright gold. **O.** and **I.** MacPenny's Nurs, Branscore, Dorset.

- - 'Magnifica Aurea' Hort. ex Beissner
1891 Robust, glaucous form; tips golden-yellow.   B,K   Germany

- - **'Marianne'** Hort. Holland
1986 A duplicated name for 'Jolanda'.

- - 'Marsden' New Name   1993 Listed as 'Marsdonii' in "Gar. Chron. **186**" (1979).

- - **'Masonii'** Dallimore & Jackson
1948 Conical; green, erect habit but not threadleaf foliage.   B,G,K   U.K.

- - 'Mason's Erect' Hort. Anglia   Probably a mistake for 'Filiformis Erecta'.

- - 'Mason's Orange' Hort. Anglia
1974 Reported from Grayswood Hill, Haslemere, Surrey.   U.K.

- - 'Medlar Gold' Hort. Holland
1988 **O.** and **I.** J. Lucassen, Vorden, Holland.

- - **'Melfard'** Krüssmann   1979 Lop-sided habit of growth. **I.** Gebr. Boer, Boskoop. **O.** Melfard of Denmark, (c 1937).   G,K,W   Denmark

- - **'Merrist Wood'** R.H.S. Journ.
1972 A selection of normal habit and colour but resistant to *Phytophthera*. **O.** Agric. Coll., Merrist Wood, Surrey.   W3   U.K.

- - 'Milford Blue Jacket' Dallimore and Jackson
1948 See 'Blue Jacket'.

- - 'Milfordensis' Hornibrook
1923 A dwarf, narrowly conical form with blue foliage. NIC.   B,H,K   U.K.

- - 'Mini Globus' Hort. Hungary
1986 Now to be 'Barabit's Globe'. Dwarf globe shaped plant with dark green foliage.

- - **'Minima'** R. Smith   1867 The well-known globose shrub, with yellowish-green foliage.   B,D,G,H,K,W2 U.K.

- - 'Minima Argentea' R. Smith
1872 A superfluous synonym of 'Pygmaea Argentea'? NIC.   U.K.

- - 'Minima Argenteovariegata' Beissner
1900 Variegated sports occur, but none appears to be stable. NIC.   B,K   Germany

- - **'Minima Aurea'** Hornibrook
1939 Popular, golden dwarf form softer to touch than 'Aurea Densa' and more ovoid. **O.** W.H. Rogers, Red Lodge Nurs, Eastleigh, Hants. (The name 'Minima Aurea Rogersii' has fallen into disuse).   B,G,H,K,W2   U.K.

- - 'Minima Aurea Erecta' Hort. N.Z.
An illegit. name. **L.** South Taranaki Nurs, Hawera.   N.Z.

- - **'Minima Glauca'** R. Smith
1867 A globose bush with glaucous foliage.   B,G,H,K,W2 U.K.

- - 'Minima Gracilis' Hort. Ireland
1989 Reported from the National Botanical Garden, Dublin. NIC?

- - **'Moerheimii'** Den Ouden/Boom
  - 1965 Conical tree; leaves yellow, becoming yellow-green within plant. O. Ruys Moerheim Nurs, Dedemsvaart, (1934).   B,G,K,R,W3   Holland

- - 'Monumentalis' De Vos   1875 Columnar; glaucous-blue O. C de Vos Nurs, Hazerwoude, Boskoop, (1873). NIC.   B,K   Holland

- - 'Monumentalis Aurea' Poulsen
  - 1944 An illegit name. Conical; leaves small, dull dark blue. O. Poulsen Nurs, Kelleriis.   B   Denmark

- - 'Monumentalis Glauca' Hort. ex Beissner
  - 1891 Doubtfully distinct from 'Fraseri', but has glossy leaves.   B,K   Germany

- - **'Monumentalis Nova'** Hort. ex Beissner
  - 1891 Columnar; leaves small, fine, blue-bloomed and on underside of branchlets light green.   B,G,K   Germany

- - **'Moonlight'** H.J. Watson
  - 1963 In "Nurs. Cat". Foliage light green with pale yellow growth tips. O. Watsons Nurs, Killiney. Co. Down.   K,W3   Ireland

- - 'Moonshine' Hort. Anglia   Compact plant with good yellow colour in winter. In "Nurs. Cat". Bressingham Nurs, Norfolk.

- - **'Moor Leys Gold'** Int. Con. Reg.
  - 1992 A sport from 'Fletcheri' with deep yellow foliage. O. and I. P.F. Whitehead, Moor Leys, Little Comberton, Pershore.   U.K.

- - **'Naberi'** Den Ouden   1949 Conical; foliage green with sulphur-yellow tips, paling to creamy-blue in winter. O. and I. Naber Nurs, Gouda, Boskoop, (1929).   B,G,K,W   Holland

- - **'Nana'** Pépin   1864 Differs from 'Minima' by its bluntly conical top and horizontal branchlets. O. Dauvesse Nurs, Orleans, (1861).   B,D,G,H,K,W   France

- - 'Nana Alba' Veitch   1881 Now listed as 'Nana Albospica'.   H,K,W

- - 'Nana Alba Maculata' Hort.   A clone with a whitish variegation, no longer identifiable.

- - **'Nana Albospica'** Beissner ex Hornibrook
  - 1939 A group of dwarf clones with creamy-white young shoots. ('Alba Nana', Alba-spica Nana', 'Nana Alba', 'Nana Albospicata').   B,H,K,W2   U.K.

- - 'Nana Albovariegata' Hort. ex Beissner
  - 1891 Conical; tips pendulous; foliage pale yellow-green with dirty whitish markings. NIC.   B,H,K,W   Germany

- - **'Nana Argentea'** Beissner
  - 1884 Dwarf ovoid bush; new growth silver-cream, turning grey when older. (Similar to but not = 'Pygmaea Argentea').   B,D,H,K,W   Germany

- - 'Nana Argenteovariegata' De Vos
  - 1887 Dense, pyramidal; compact but not dwarf; white tipped foliage; ('Albo-variegata Elegans', 'Nana Variegata').   B,H,K,W2   Holland

- - 'Nana Aureovariegata' Hort. Anglia
  - 1988 In "The Plant Finder". NOM, but see 'Nymans'.

- - 'Nana Compacta' Hort. ex Beissner
  - 1891 Leaves bluish-green; compact growth. NIC.   B,K   Germany

- - 'Nana Densa' Hort. France   See 'Nana'.

- - **'Nana Glauca'** Veitch   1881 Similar to 'Nana' but foliage is coarser and glaucous.   B,H,K,W   U.K.

- - 'Nana Glauca Rogersii' Hort.   See 'Rogersii'.

- - 'Nana Rogersii' Hort. — Now known as 'Rogersii'. The inclusion of the (undescriptive) word 'Nana' has been dropped in the trade because of the confusion with 'Nana Aurea Rogersii'.

- - 'Nestoides' Welch — 1979 I. J. Manton, Vancouver, B.C. Claimed to be hardier, otherwise not distinguishable from 'Tamariscifolia'. — G,K,W — Canada

- - 'New Duperoux' Hort. Holland
  1986 L. H.J.van de Laar in "Naamlijst . . . ". NOM. I. into Holland by J. Smits, Boskoop, Holland, (1982). — France

- - 'New Golden' Lombarts — 1957 Conical; loose, leaves yellow. I. Lombart's Nurs, Zundert, (1957). ('New Gold'). — B,K,W — Holland

- - 'New Silver' A.C. Mitchell
  1972 In "Conifers in British Isles". Spray-tips silvery grey-blue, down turned; tight growth, narrow crown. O. James Smith Nurs, Matlock, (1915). — W3 — U.K.

- - 'Nidifera' Hort. — A mistake. See *CHAMAECYPARIS nootkatensis* 'Nidifera'.

- - 'Nidiformis' Beissner — 1901 When young resembles 'Tamariscifolia', eventually a wide spreading shrub. O. Rovelli Nurs, Pallanza, (1890). Not to be confused with *CHAMAECYPARIS nootkatensis* 'Nidifera'. — B,G,K,R,W — Italy

- - 'Nivea' Van Geert — 1862 Foliage silvery, speckled white. O. Van Geert Nurs, Antwerp. — B,K — Belgium

- - 'Nivea Glauca' Hort. Anglia
  1984 Reported from the Royal Botanical Gardens, Kew. — U.K.

- - 'Noble's Variety' Hort. Anglia — Now known as 'Dow's Gem'.

- - 'Nova' Barabits — 1965 In "Magyar Fenyóújdonságok". — G — Hungary

- - 'Nyewood' Hort. Anglia — 1968 Now known as 'Chilworth Silver'.

- - 'Nymans' Hort. Holland — 1987 A superfluous synonym of 'Aureovariegata'. — G

- - 'Nymph' Hort. Holland — 1986 A mistake for 'Ellwood's Nymph'.

- - 'Ochroleuca' Masters — 1896 A showy variety with pale yellow leaves. — U.K.

- - 'Olbrichii' Beissner — 1904 Columnar tree, densely branched, loose bluish-green foliage. O. Fröbel Nurs, Zurich. ('Albrechii'). — B,D,G,K,W — Switzerl.

- - 'Oliver Slocock' Hort. Anglia
  1984 Reported from the Royal Botanical Gardens, Kew.

- - 'Oregon Blue' Mitsch — 1978 In "Nurs. Cat". A strong-growing, outstandingly blue selection. L. Mitsch Nurs, Aurora, OR. O. Arneson Nurs, Canby, OR. — W3 — U.S.A.

- - 'Oro' Krüssmann — 1979 Conical, with ascending twigs; foliage bright yellow; indistinguishable from 'Howarth's Gold'. I. Felix & Dijkhuis Nurs, Boskoop. O. A. & W. Hoogendorn, Boskoop. — K — Holland

- - 'Overeynderi' Hort. ex Beissner
  1891 Tips of branchlets vividly white. NIC. — B,K — Holland

- - 'Parsons' Den Ouden/Boom
  1965 Domed shrub, densely branched. Conspicuously covered with red strobili in spring. I. Hillier & Sons Nurs, Winchester, (1964). O. The same. — B,G,K,W3 — U.K.

- - 'Patula' R. Smith — 1872 Leaves dark to blackish-green in winter; narrow fanlike spray, curving outwards, broadly conical. NIC. — B,D,K,W — U.K.

- - 'Pearl Nova' Hort. Holland — An illegit. listed name.

- - **'Pelt's Blue'** Kordes   1984   Similar to 'Columnaris' but more intense blue. **I.** Kordes Nurs, Bilsen. ('Van Pelt's Blue').   G,W3   Germany

- - **'Pembury Blue'** Geo. Jackman
   1968   In "Nurs. Cat". Conical tree with silvery dove-grey/blue foliage, darker in second year. **I.** G. Jackman Nurs, Woking, Surrey. **O.** Baggesen Nurs, Kent, (c. 1965).   G,K,R,W3   U.K.

- - 'Pena Park' F.G. Meyer   1961   In "Baileya 9". Dark green foliage, broad, low, slow growing. **O.** Named for a tree in a park at Sintra.   B,K   Portugal

- - **'Pendula'** Hort. ex Beissner
   1891   A small narrowly conical tree with branches few and strongly pendulous.   B,D,G,K,W

- - 'Pendula Alba' R. Smith   1867   Graceful habit; leaves silvery-grey. **O.** Probably raised on the Wm. Paul and Son Nurs. NIC. ('Alba Pendula').   B,K   U.K.

- - 'Pendula Aurea' Schelle   1909   Pendulous greenish to yellow. NIC.   B,K   Germany

- - 'Pendula Nova' Schelle   1909   Habit similar to 'Filiformis'. NIC.   B,K

- - 'Pendula Vera' Hesse   1890   In "Nurs. Cat". A tall narrow form with mainly pendulous branches. **O.** H.A. Hesse Nurs, Weener-on-Ems. NIC.   B,D,G,K   Germany

- - **'Pick's Dwarf Blue'** Hort. Anglia
   1986   Squat globose bush with grey-blue foliage. **I.** Walker's Nurs, Doncaster, U.K.   W3

- - 'Picta Argentea' Lawson   1875   In "Nurs. Cat". L. Lawson Nurs, Edinburgh. NIC.   Scotland

- - **'Pixie'** H.J. van de Laar"   1977` In "Dendroflora 11-12". Diminutive globose bush, bluish-green. **O.** Th. Streng Nurs, Boskoop, (1975).   K,W   Holland

- - 'Plumosa' Lieb   1901   Conical; dark green; tender. **O.** Lieb Nurs, Partenit. NIC.   B,K   Russia

- - 'Plumosa Glauca' Krüssmann
   1960   Broadly columnar; leaf sprays wide and flat; deep blue-green. **O.** Orleans (before 1914). The name 'Blue Plume' proposed by Ouden/Boom, is probably superfluous.   B,K,W   France

- - 'Pot of Gold' Hort. Anglia   Superfluous name for 'Golden Pot'. Note: Plant Breeder's Rights were granted in 1982 but in view of prior circulation in the trade of this plant as 'Golden Pot' they may not be operative.   U.K.

- - **'Pottenii'** Dallimore & Jackson
   1923   A columnar tree with sea-green, soft, feathery sprays of partly juvenile foliage. ('Pottensii' and 'Pottensoi' are wrong). **O.** Potten Nurs, Cranbrook. A beautiful young tree but tends to break up as it ages.   B,D,G,K,W   U.K.

- - **'President Roosevelt'**   1945   Golden-yellow. Not now distinguishable from 'Winston Churchill'. **O.** Hogger's Nurs, Felbridge, Sussex, (c. 1945). **I.** The same.   B,K,W   U.K.

- - 'Procumbens' Hornibrook
   1939   Vigorous prostrate form; green foliage. **I.** Backhouse Nurs, York. NIC.   B,H,K,W   U.K.

- - 'Prostrata Glauca' Hort. ex Beissner
   1891   Quite prostrate form; grey-green foliage. **O.** Ordnung Nurs, Eisenberg, NIC.   B,K   Czechosl.

- - 'Pulcherrima' Beissner   1909   Now known as 'Pyramidalis Alba'.

- - 'Pulverulenta' Lieb ex Beissner
   1903   Foliage blue-green suffused golden-yellow; an ascending form. **O.** Lieb Nurs, Partenet near Alupka. NIC.   B,K   Russia

- - 'Pygmaea' Wm. Barron   1875 In "Nurs. Cat". NOM. NIC. See 'Pygmy'.

- - **'Pygmaea Argentea'** Hort. ex Beissner
1887 Dwarf globose form; green foliage with creamy-white tips
when growing well. **O.** Backhouse Nurs, York, England.
('Backhouse Silver' is a commercial synonym).   B,D,G,K,W   U.K.

- - **'Pygmy'** Geo. Jackman   1968 In "Nurs. Cat". A miniature 'Minima Glauca'.   G,W   U.K.

- - 'Pyramidalis' De Vos   1867 Slender, columnar form. **O.** P. Smith Nurs, Bergedorf,
Hamburg. NIC. (No plant has ever yet grown into a
pyramidal shape!).   B,K,W   Germany

- - **'Pyramidalis Alba'** De Vos
1887 As last but with silvery-white tips. ('Pulcherrima').   B,D,K   Holland

- - **'Pyramidalis Alba Nana'** Pynaert
1878 Compact, pyramidal form, clear white shoots. NIC.   B,K   Belgium

- - **'Pyramidalis Glauca'** Schelle
1909 Leaves blue-bloomed. NIC.   B,K   Germany

- - 'Pyramidalis Lutea' Hort. ex Beissner
1891 Leaves golden-yellow.   B,K   Germany

- - 'Pyramidalis Lutea Gracilis' Hort. ex Beissner
1891 Similar to previous but more elegant. NIC.   B,K   Germany

- - 'Queen Anne' Hort. Anglia   A listed name. Slow-growing pillar form with soft dark green
foliage. Origin unknown.

- - **'Rabbit's Gold'** Hort. Holland
1986 **L.** H.J. van de Laar in "Naamlijst . . . ". NOM. **O.** L. Konijn
Nurs, Ederveen, Holland.

- - **'Raievskyana'** Lieb.   1901 A widespreading dwarf, foliage silvery-green. **O.** Raised by
Lieb, Partenet, Crimea, from seed of 'Fragrans'. NIC.   B,H,K   Russia

- - **'Reefton'** Hort. N.Z.   1972 **L.** Duncan & Davies Nurs, New Plymouth, N.Z. Named for a
tree at Reefton, S.I., N.Z.   N.Z.

- - 'Rena' zu Jeddeloh   1990 In "Nurs. Cat". A pendulous thread-leaf form. Shoots as
CHAMAECYPARIS pisifera 'Filifera'. A good plant for a tub.   Germany

- - **'Rijnhof'** H.J. Grootendorst
1978 In "Dendroflora **15-16**". A selection near to 'Nidiformis'. **O.**
K. Van Rijn Nurs, Hazerwoude.   K,W   Holland

- - 'Robusta' Coninck   1884 In "Nurs. Cat". Columnar; leaves thick, dark green, broad. **O.**
Coninck, Tottenham Nurs, Dedemsvaart, (1874).   B,K,W   Holland

- - 'Robusta Argentea' Hort. ex Beissner
1891 A vigorous clone; Columnar; leaves greyish-blue. NIC.   B,K   Germany

- - 'Robusta Aurea' Hort. ex Beissner
1891 A broad columnar tree with leaves golden-yellow. NIC.   B,K   Germany

- - 'Robusta Glauca' (1) Hort.   A superfluous name for 'Glauca Elegans'.

- - **'Robusta Glauca'** (2) Hort. ex Beissner
1891 Coarse tree with glaucous foliage.   B,D,G,K,W   Germany

- - **'Rogersii'** Den Ouden/Boom
1965 Foliage grey-blue; dense globose habit. **L.** W.H. Rogers Nurs,
Chandler's Ford, Hants, (1930). (The names 'Nana Rogersii'
and 'Nana Glauca Rogersii' are not now used in the trade).   B,G,K,R,W   U.K.

- - 'Rogersii Aurea' Hort. Anglia   A mistake for 'Minima Aurea'.

- - 'Rogersii Nana' Hort. Anglia   A mistake for 'Rogersii'.

- - **'Romana'** H.J. van de Laar
          1986 In "Naamlijst . . . ". A fastigiate selection with yellow-green
               colour. I. Imported by Vuy k van Nes (1980), as 'Aurea
               Romana'.   G   Italy

- - **'Rosenthali'** P. Smith2H ex Beissner
          1891 Pyramidal; leaves light green; branches ascending. I. P.
               Smith, Bergedorf, Hamburg, (1884).   B,K   Germany

- - **'Royal Gold'** Int. Con. Reg.
          1975 Dense, golden-yellow foliage; upright ovoid form. R. J.
               Allan, Guernsey. I. Wansd ke Nurs, Devizes, Wilts. O.
               Found in a garden at Taunton, Somerset.   K.,W3   U.K.

- - 'Sargentea' Hort. Ireland   1989 Reported from the National Botanic Garden, Dublin. NIC.

- - 'Schneeball' Hort. Hungary
          1990 Dwarf globe shaped plant well variegated with white. O. and
               I. Barabits, Hungary. Like a variegated 'Mini Globus'.

- - **'Schongariana'** Pfitzer ex Beissner
          1909 Bloomy, dark green; spreading pyramidal; very hardy. I. Wm.
               Pfitzer Nurs, Stuttgart.   B,K   Germany

- - **'Shawii'** Hort. ex Beissner
          1891 Dwarf upright globose form; light glaucous-green foliage in
               loose sprays.   B,D,H,K   Germany

- - 'Silberfasl' Hort.   1992 Reported from Windsor Great Park, Berks, U.K.

- - **'Silberstar'** Int.Con. Reg.
          1985 A hardy, vigorous columnar tree; foliage dense: silvery-
               glaucous. O. and I. Hans Jurgen Hopken, Petersfehn, near
               Oldenburg.,(1962).   Germany

- - 'Silvania' Hort. Holland   1989 A listed name for an upright selection rather like a
               CHAMAECYPARIS obtusa form. O. M. Barabits, (1975)?

- - 'Silver Ball' Hort. Amer.   1986 Dwarf globose; foliage tips white to yellow. L. E.A. Cope.
               "Native . . . Conifers".

- - 'Silver Dome' Hort. Anglia
          1983 A listed name for a sport of 'Ellwoodii', similar to 'Chilworth
               Silver' but faster growing. O. No record.   U.K.

- - **'Silver Gem'** Krüssmann
          1979 Similar to 'Silver Queen' but better colour in Spring, and less
               winter-hardy.   K,W   France

- - **'Silver Moon'** Hort. Amer.
          1986 A listed name for a broadly conical dwarf; growing tips
               silver. L. E.A. Cope. "Native . . . Conifers".   U.S.A.

- - **'Silver Queen'** Hort. ex Beissner
          1891 Open, conical tree; sprays and leaves creamy-white when
               young also creamy-white in autumn and winter.   B,G,K,R,W   U.K.

- - **'Silver Threads'** Int. Con. Reg
          1983 Variegated sport from 'Ellwood's Gold'. I. D.W. Hatch.
               Chantry Nurs, Honiton, Devon, (1981). O. Kelvin Lawrence
               Nurs, The Malt House, Farnham, Surrey.   W3   U.K.

- - **'Silver Tip'** Hort. Holland
          1968 In "Sortimentslist". J. Konijn & Son, then of Ederveen.

- - 'Slocock' Hort. Anglia   1989 In "Nurs. Cat". Kelvin Lawrence Nurs, The Malt House,
               Farnham, Surrey. ('Slocockiana' is an illegit. name).

- - 'Smithii' (1) Dallimore & Jackson
1948 A mistake for 'Darleyensis'.

- - 'Smithii' (2) Den Ouden/Boom
1965 A mistake for 'Lutea Smithii'.

- - 'Smithii Aurea' Hort. Amer.   A mistake for 'Lutea Smithii'.

- - 'Smith's New Silver'   Now known as 'Darleyensis'.

- - **'Snow Flurry'** C.R. Harrison
1975 A mutation from Fletcheri forming a columnar plant.
Creamy-white variegation. I. South Taranaki Nurs, Hawera.   W3   N.Z.

- - **'Snow White'** Hort. Anglia   A broadly conical plant with juvenile, greyish-green foliage
white tipped for part of the year. A mutation from 'Ellwoodii'.
O. R. Murray, Allandale Nurs, Willerby, Yorks. (1983).   W3   U.K.

- - 'Somerford Spine' Hort. Anglia
1992 Reported from Windsor Great Park, Berks, U.K.

- - **'Somerset'** Scott   1967 In "Nurs. Cat". Sport from 'Fletcheri'; blue-grey juvenile
foliage tinged yellow in summer. O. Scott's Nurs, Merriott,
Som. ('Fletcheri Somerset').   W3   U.K.

- - **'Sopron'** Barabits   1965 In "Magyar Fenyóújdonságok". The name 'Glauca Sopron' is
inadmissible.   Hungary

- - **'Southern Gold' (1)** Duncan & Davies
1972 In "Nurs. Cat". Conical tree to 4.5m. foliage pendulous;
lemon-yellow. O. Ken Burns, Timaru, N.Z. (See also
following item.)   W   N.Z.

- - 'Southern Gold' (2) Krüssmann
1979 A conical tree, lateral branches nodding; foliage yellow. I.
Darthuiser Nurs, N.E. Leersum. Received from Southern
Nurs, U.K.   K   Holland

- - 'Souvenir de Leide' De Vos
1887 Light green foliage; arching branches. O. De Vos Nurs,
Hazerwoude,Boskoop. NIC.   B,K   Holland

- - **'Spek'** Den Ouden   1949 Conical tree; foliage rough, glaucous-grey. O. and I. J. Spek
Nurs, Boskoop.   B,G,K,W   Holland

- - **'Spiegelenberg'** H.J. van de Laar
1986 In "Naamlijst . . .". NOM. O. and I. A seedling raised by
M.G. Spiegelenberg, Varden, (1983).   Holland

- - 'Spiralis' Beissner   1909 Name for a conical tree with contorted stem. O. Ordnung
Nurs, Eisenburg. NIC.   B,K   Czechosl.

- - 'Spring Showers' Hort. Amer.
1985 Foliage tinged yellow. L. L.C. Hatch in "Reference Guide".

- - 'Squarrosa' Mayr   1906 Conical; juvenile, light-green foliage. NIC. Similar seedlings
turn up but outgrow their juvenility in time.   B,K   Austria

- - **'Stardust'** P. de Vogel   1966 In "Dendroflora 3". Golden-yellow foliage, suffused bronze at
tips; compact, upright plant. O. Langenburg Nurs, Boskoop,
(1965).   G,K,R,W   Holland

- - **'Stewartii'** Schelle   1920 Elegant large tree; glossy golden-yellow foliage, changing to
yellow-green in winter; O. Stewart & Son, Bournemouth,
(1900).   B,D,G,K,W   U.K.

- - 'Stilton' Hort. Anglia   1979 Dwarf dark green foliage well variegated with white. I. D.W.
Hatch, Chantry Nurs, Honiton, Devon. Origin unknown.

- - 'Stilton Cheese' Hort. Anglia
  1992 Reported from Windsor Great Park, Berks, U.K.

- - 'Stricta' (1) Gordon   1875 Erect tree, with golden blotched branches. NIC.   B,K   U.K.

- - 'Stricta' (2) Burvenich   1888 Similar to 'Erecta Viridis'. O. Waterer & Son Nurs, Bagshot, Surrey. NIC.   B,D,K   U.K.

- - **'Stricta Aurea'**Krüssmann
  1972 Broadly conical; branches erect; green with yellow tips. L. Barbier Nurs, Orleans, (before 1930). Possibly the same as 'Erecta Aureospica'.   G,K   France

- - 'Stricta Coerulea' Pardé   1906 Reported from Arboretum National des Barres, France. NOM. NIC.

- - 'Stricta Excelsa' Schelle   1909 Similar to 'Stricta' but more strong-growing. NIC.   B,K   Germany

- - 'Stricta Glauca' Den Ouden
  1949 A dense, narrowly conical tree with branches spreading blue-green foliage. It was known in Belgium before 1937. NIC.   B,K   Belgium

- - 'Stricta Viridis' De Vos   1887 Probably indistinguishable from 'Erecta Viridis'. NIC.   Holland

- - 'Suffolk Belle' Hort. Anglia
  1987 In "The Plant Finder". NOM.

- - 'Sulphurea' Schelle   1909 A clone with a yellowish sheen to the foliage. NIC.   Germany

- - 'Summerford' Hort. Anglia
  1989 In "The Plant Finder". NOM.

- - **'Summer Gold'** Hort. Anglia   A listed name.

- - 'Summer Green' Hort. Anglia
  1993 A listed name. See "The Plant Finder". NOM.

- - **'Summer Snow'** Hort. Anglia
  1965 Growth tips milky white. O. and I. Harraway's Nurs, Warminster, Wilts.   W3

- - **'Summertime'** H.J. van de Laar
  1986 In "Naamlijst . . .". NOM. O. Not known. I. G.E.F. Bolwijn, Putten, Holland.

- - 'Sunkist' Hort. Holland   1980 In "Nurs. Cat". Slow-growing pale grey-green foliage with yellow tips and yellow branch stems. Similar to 'Golden Showers' but the gold colour not as good.

- - 'Tabuliformis' H.G. Hillier
  1971 In "Hillier's Manual". Widespreading bush; overlapping, flattened sprays of green foliage. Mounding up with age.   U.K.

- - 'Tall Gold' Hort. France   1972 An unacceptable name for yet another yellow clone.

- - **'Tamariscifolia'** Hornibrook
  1923 Dome-shaped spreading bush without a leader, sea-green foliage. O. James Smith & Son, Darley Dale Nurs, Matlock, Derbyshire.   B,G,H,K,W1   U.K.

- - 'Tarka' Barabits   1967 A listed name.   Czechosl.

- - **'Temple's White'** G.Haddow
  1991 In "Nurs. Cat". Similar to 'Nana Albospica' but one quarter it's rate of growth. O. A mutation on a tree at Pencarrow in Cornwall.

- - **'Tharandtensis'** Buettner

    1931 A globose to conical dwarf: foliage green which is conspicuously blue in summer. **O.** Found in a forest at Tharandt, (1890). NIC.?   B,H,K,W   Germany

- - **'Tharandtensis Caesia'** Buettner

    1931 Like a coarse, upright form of 'Forsteckensis' with grey-green to blue-green foliage. **O.** As previous entry.   B,G,K   Germany

- - 'The Four Seasons' Hort. Anglia

    This name is unacceptable. Now to be 'Four Seasons'.

- - **'Tilford'** Hort. Anglia

    1980 Columnar; neat foliage, grey-green. **L.** Kelvin Lawrence Nurs, The Malt House, Tilford, Farnham, Surrey.

- - **'Tilgate'** (1) Reuthe

    1965 In "Nurs. Cat". Similar to 'Forsteckensis' but more vigorous. **I.** Reuthe Nurs, Keston, Kent. **O.** Tilgate Plant Research Station.   B,D,G,K,W   U.K.

- - **'Tilgate'** (2) P. de Vogel   1969 In "Dendroflora 6". The plant exhibited and illustrated in "Dendroflora" was misidentified. The picture in the book 'Conifers' is correct.

- - 'Tortuosa' Beissner   1891 Named for a tree with branches twisted and monstrous. NIC.   B,K   Germany

- - 'Toxward Gold' Hort. Anglia

    1988 In "The Plant Finder". NOM.

- - **'Treasure'** G. Bentham   1970 Upright sport of 'Ellwoodii'. Yellow-green foliage liberally variegated with pale cream. **O.** and **I.** Floravista Gardens, Vancouver, BC. (1980).   Canada

- - 'Trentham Gold' Hort. Anglia

    1980 Raised at Trentham Park, Stoke on Trent. Staffs. **I.** Bridgemere Nurs, Cheshire.

- - **'Triomf van Boskoop'** Beissner

    1898 Large conical tree; foliage glaucous-blue, in large, loose sprays. **O.** F.J. Grootendorst & Sons Nurs, Boskoop, ('Triomphe de Boskoop' and other spellings).   B,K   Holland

- - **'Triompf van Lombarts'** Lombarts

    1940 In "Nurs. Cat". Vigorous conical tree; golden-yellow foliage. **O.** Lombart's Nurs, Zundert.   B,G,K,R,W   Holland

- - **'Van der Sande'** H.J. van de Laar

    1986 In "Naamlijst . . .". NOM.   Holland

- - **'Van Eck'** Den Ouden/Boom

    1965 Conical tree; branchlet tips yellow fading from a glaucous to a yellow-green in interior of plant. **O.** and **I.** G. van Eck Nurs, Boskoop.   B,K,W   Holland

- - 'Van Oploo's White'   1992 A listed name. **O.** A van Oploo.

- - 'Van Pelt's Blue' H.J. van de Laar

    1986 In "Naamlijst . . .". NOM. See 'Pelt's Blue'.   W3   Germany

- - **'Van Tol'** Den Ouden/Boom

    1965 A cross: 'Alumii' x 'Triompf van Lombarts'; Habit as 'Alumii' but foliage yellowish. **O.** P. von Tol Mz, Boskoop.   B,K,W3   Holland

- - 'Variegata' R. Smith   1864 Branchlets tipped pale yellow and green. No longer identifiable.   U.K.

- - 'Veitch' Hort. Europe   A commercial synonym for 'Glauca Veitch'.

- - 'Ven's Yellow' Hort. Australia.
1986 A conical plant with golden foliage. **O.** and **I.** Harry van der Ven, Toolonga Nurs, Toolonga, Victoria, Australia.

- - **'Versicolor'** Coninck ex Beissner
1891 Broadly conical; foliage spotted white or bright yellow. **O.** J. Coninck, Tottenham Nurs, Dedemsvaart (c. 1882). | B,K,W3 | Holland

- - **'Viner's Gold'** Krüssmann
1979 Columnar tree; with spreading branches, foliage golden-yellow. **L.** Darthuizer Nurs, Boskoop, Holland. **O.** Waterer, Sons and Crisp Nurs, Bagshot. (n.d.). | K,W3 | U.K.

- - 'Wallis Gold' Duncan & Davies
1972 **O.** A seedling on Wallis Nurs, Dunedin. | W3 | N.Z.

- - **'Wansdyke Miniature'** Welch
1979 A truly "miniature Lawson Cypress". **I.** Wansdyke Nurs, Devizes, Wilts. ('Wansdyke Dwarf'). | W2 | U.K.

- - 'Wansdyke Silver' Hort. Holland
1986 A mistake for *THUJA occidentalis* 'Wansdyke Silver'. | Not as G

- - **'Watereri'** Hort. Ireland
1972 Small columnar tree; silvery-white foliage. **L.** Slieve Donard Nurs, Newcastle, Co. Down. ('Watereriana').

- - **'Waitomo'** Hort. N.Z.
A slow-growing sport with splashes of white on 'Duncanii'. **O.** Barry Blackman Nurs, Te Kuiti, N.Z.

- - 'Weisseana' Hort. ex Beissner
1890 Low-growing dwarf, branch-tips pendulous. **I.** W. Weiss Nurs, Komarov, Hungary. **O.** J. Hansen, Pinneburg near Hamburg. NIC. | B,H,K | Hungary

- - **'Westermannii'** Van Hulle ex Beissner
1890 Broadly conical tree; foliage in large sprays, light yellow becoming yellow-green. **O.** Jurrissen & Son Nurs, Naarden, (c. 1880). ('Westermannii Aurea'). | B,K,W3 | Holland

- - 'Westermannii Aureovariegata' Schelle
1909 Similar to last entry but golden-spotted. NIC. | B,K | Germany

- - **'White Spot'** Krüssmann
1979 Mutation on 'Monumentalis Nova', with some white or whitish variegation on young foliage. **O.** Poulsen Nurs, Kelleriis, (1943). | K,W | Denmark

- - 'White Wonder' Hort. Holland
1989 **L.** H.J. van de Laar in "Naamlijst . . .".

- - **'Winston Churchill'** Den Ouden/Boom
1965 Conical tree; foliage golden yellow. Indistinguishable from 'President Roosevelt' in maturity. **O.** Hogger's Nurs, Felbridge, Sussex. | B,G,K,R,W | U.K.

- - **'Wisselii'** Van der Wissel ex Witte
1893 Columnar tree with erect branching; dense dark green foliage. **O.** F. van der Wissel Nurs, Epe, Holland. (Indistinguishable from 'Fragrans Conica' of Beissner (1891) although of different origin). | B,D,G,K,W | Holland

- - 'Wisselii Nana' Hornibrook
1939 An unstable dwarf cultivariant of 'Wisselii'. | B,H,K,W | U.K.

- - 'Wissel's Saguaro' H.J. van de Laar
  1987 In "Dendroflora **24**". Slow-growing mutation from 'Wisselii' with a curious branch structure resembling the Giant Cactus. **O.** J.B.A. Dekker, Mijdrecht, (1962). **I.** K.A. Koemans, Boskoop.　　　　　　　　　　　　　　　　　　　　　　　Holland

- - **'Witzeliana'** Den Ouden/Boom
  1965 Narrowly columnar tree; foliage dense, dark green. **L.** Späth Nurs, Berlin, (1934). ('Witzel').　　　B,G,K,W3　　Germany

- - 'Worlei' P. Smith ex Beissner
  1891 Stiffly erect; foliage grey-green. **O.** P. Smith Nurs, Bergedorf, Hamburg, NIC.　　　　　　　　　　B,K　　　　Germany

- - 'Wyevale Silver' Hort. Anglia
  1989 Tree with dark green foliage, outer sprays with creamy-white variegation at it's best in winter. **O.** and **I.** Wyevale Nurs, Hereford.　　　　　　　　　　　　　　　　　　　　U.K.

- - 'Yellow Queen' Hort. Australia　Now known as 'Golden Queen'.

- - 'Yellow Success' Hort. Holland
  1976 L. Darthuiser Nurs, Leesum Holland. A superfluous synonym for 'Golden Queen'?

- - **'Yellow Transparent'** Den Ouden/Boom
  1965 A sport of 'Fletcheri'; foliage yellow in summer, brown in winter; **O.** H. van't Hof, Boskoop, (c. 1955).　　B,G,K,W3　　Holland

- - 'Yellow Weeping' Hort. Holland
  1993 A listed name.

- - 'Youngii' Kent in Veitch　1900 Vigorous, spreading tree, reminiscent of *CHAMAECYPARIS obtusa* 'Filicoides'. L. M. Young, Milford Nurs, Godalming, Surrey (as 'Young's variety'). See also 'Alba Spica' (2).　B,D,G,K,R　U.K.

- - 'Young's Variety'　　　　　A mistake for 'Albospica'.

- - 'Yvonne' Hort. Amer.　1980 Upright conical plant with bright golden-yellow foliage. **I.** Iseli Nurs, Boring, OR. **O.** Found by Jean Iseli and named for his daughter.

CHAMAECYPARIS x *nidifera*　　See *CHAMAECYPARIS nootkatensis* 'Nidifera'.

CHAMAECYPARIS **nootkatensis** (D.Don) Spach
  1842 Nootka Cypress. Formerly known as *THUJOPSIS borealis* and also as *CHAMAECYPARIS nutkaensis*.　　30m,Z4　　N. Amer.

- - 'Alba' Hort. Amer.　1986 An illegit. listed name. L. E.A. Cope. "Native . . . Conifers". NOM.

- - **'Argenteovariegata'** Veitch
  1881 Foliage variegated creamy-white at the tips. Unstable.　D　　　U.K.

- - **'Aurea'** Beissner
  1909 Leaves bright yellow when young, turning yellow-green with age.　　　　　　　　　　　　　　　　B,D,KR,W　Germany

- - 'Aurea Youngii' Rehder　1923 See 'Youngii' (1).

- - **'Aureovariegata'** Young ex Gordon
  1875 Foliage with patches of golden-yellow. A branch sport. **O.** M. Young, Tilford Nurs, Godalming, Surrey. (Spelling varies).　B,D,K,R,W　U.K.

- - 'Aureoviridis' Nicholson　1901 Foliage mixed yellowish-green and green. **L.** Veitch & Sons Nurs, Exeter, Devon, NIC.　　　　　　　B　　　　U.K.

- - 'Columnaris' Schelle　1909 Named for a columnar but pendulous tree in the Botanic Garden, Tubingen, near Stuttgart. NIC.　　B,K　　　Germany

- - **'Compacta'** (1) K. Koch   1873   Rounded shrub, growth dense.   B,D,G,H,K,W   Germany

- - 'Compacta' (2) Silva Tarouca
1913   A form with juvenile foliage only. (See 'Ericoides'). NIC.   Germany

- - **'Compacta Glauca'** Schelle
1909   As 'Compacta' (1) but foliage glaucous.   B,K,R,W   Germany

- - 'Compacta Pendula' Hort. Anglia
1984   Reported from the Royal Botanic Gardens, Kew.   U.K.

- - 'Compacta Viridis' Schelle
1909   Leaves light green. Indistinguishable from 'Compacta'.   B,K   Germany

- - 'Ericoides' (1) Beissner   1904   A dwarf plant with juvenile foliage found by Count von
Sághy at Kámon. It was probably unstable. NIC.   B,H,K   Hungary

- - 'Ericoides' (2) Barabits   1965   In "Magyar Fenyóújdonságok". An illegit. name for a similar
plant found in the Kámon Arboretum.   Hungary

- - **'Glauca'** Muller   1858   A common variant found in the seed-beds with foliage
glaucous.   B,D,K,W   Germany?

- - 'Glauca Aureovariegata' Hort. ex Beissner
1891   A clone descriptively named. NIC.   B,K   Germany

- - 'Glauca Compacta' Helene Bergman
1965   In "Plants & Gardens 21". An illegit. name for a compact
bush with twisted foliage. Foliage is glaucous and juvenile in
places.   U.S.A.

- - 'Glauca Vera' Beissner   1884   A compact, conical tree. NIC.   B,K   Germany

- - 'Glenmore' More   1972   A hardy selection made by R.E. More, Denver, Colorado.   U.S.A.

- - **'Gracilis'** Beissner   1891   Compact, globose dwarf; foliage dark green.   B,H,K,W2   Germany

- - **'Jubilee'** D.M. van Gelderen
1983   In "Dendroflora 20". Narrowly upright; a fast-growing clone
of the 'Pendula' type. O. Bock Nurs. (c. 1978).   W3   Canada

- - 'Lutea' Webster   1896   Named for a tree at Penrhyn Castle, Wales with yellow,
pendulous branches. NIC.   W3   U.K.

- - 'Nana' Schneider in Silva Tarouca
1913   Useful now only as a group or collective name for all the
dwarf clones.   B,K,W   Sporadic

- - 'Nidifera' Nicholson   1889   Large spreading bush; deep apple green, feathery foliage. See
Welch, 1979. ('Nidifica', 'Nidifera Compacta').   G,R,W   Italy

- - **'Nutans'** Den Ouden   1949   A glaucous, pendulous clone, O. J. Boer Wz and Son Nurs,
Boskoop.   B,K   Holland

- - **'Pendula'** Nicholson   1884   Pendulous seedlings occur and several clones are in
cultivation under this name.   B,D,G,K,W   Sporadic

- - 'Pendula Gotelli' Hort. Germany
1990   An illegit. listed name.

- - 'Pendula Variegata' Krüssmann
1979   An illegit. listed name. A pendulous clone with some white
variegation. I. Jeddeloh Nurs, Oldenburg.   K,R   Germany

- - 'Pendula Vera' Hesse   1961   An illegit. listed name. A graceful clone of its type. I. H.A
Hesse Nurs, Weener-on-Ems.   B,K   Germany

- - 'Pyramidalis' Carrière   1882   Named for a columnar but pendulous tree found on a Nursery
near Paris. NIC.   B,K   France

- - **'Tatra'** H.J. van de Laar	1973	In "Dendroflora 10"..A vigorous broadly-pyramidal tree; foliage bluish-grey. **O.** Machala Nurs, Zehusice.	K,W3	Czechosl.
- - **'Variegata'** K. Koch	1873	Clone similar to 'Argenteovariegata' but unstable. NIC.	B,G,K,R,W	Germany
- - 'Variegated Helene' Hort. Amer.	1981	A listed name. (Probably ='Glauca Compacta').L. Iseli Nurs, Boring, OR.		
- - 'Viridis' De Vos	1867	Bright green foliage. NIC.	B,K	Holland
- - 'Viridis Pendula' Beissner	1910	Named for a pendulous tree in a hotel garden at Les Avants, NIC.	B,K	Switzerl.

CHAMAECYPARIS nutkaensis Lindley & Gordon
1850 Now spelled *nootkatensis*.

CHAMAECYPARIS obtusa (Siebold & Zuccarini) Endlicher
1847 Hinoki Cypress. (Many early authors listed forms imported
from Japan under the name *RETINISPORA*).　　　　　　　20m,Z4　　　Japan

- - 'Alaska' Koemans	1992	Low growing spreading dwarf form consisting of filiform yellow variegated branchlets only. I. K.A. Koemans Nurs, Boskoop Holland. **O.** Unrecorded.		France
- - **'Albospica'** Nicholson	1884	Young shoots are pure white, turning bright green in Autumn. ('Alba Spica', 'Albospicata', etc).	B,K,R,W	Europe
- - 'Albovariegata' Beissner	1884	A white variegated tree. ('Alba-variegata', etc). NIC.	B,K	
- - 'Aonokujahiba' Onuma ex Beissner	1900	Monstrous; short, fern-like branches.	B,H,K	Hort. Japan
- - 'Argentea' Fortune ex Gordon	1862	Mixed silvery-white and green. I. From Japan by Standish & Noble Nurs, Bagshot, (c. 1860) ('Argenteovariegata').	B,K,W	Hort. Japan
- - 'Arneson's Compact' Hort. Amer.	1991	A slow-growing plant with light green new, later dark-green foliage. Spreading to upright. **L.** Mitsch Nurs, Aurora, OR. **O.** and **I.** Arnesons Nurs, Canby, OR.		U.S.A.
- - **'Aurea'** Fortune ex Gordon	1862	Golden colour intermixed with the usual glossy-green foliage. **I.** Sent by R. Fortune from Japan to Standish & Noble Nurs, Bagshot, (c.1860). ('Argentea').	B,D,G,K,W	Hort. Japan
- - 'Aurea Conspicua'	1992	An illegit. name. **L.** Saville Gardens, Windsor Great Park, Berks.		
- - 'Aurea Crippsi' Hort.		See 'Crippsii'.		
- - 'Aurea Nana' Hort. Amer.		See 'Nana Aurea'.		
- - 'Aurea Youngii' Nash ex Bailey	1925	A clone of unrecorded, probably American origin. Foliage as 'Aurea' but branches pendulous and colour less bright. Probably NIC, but the name is sometimes misapplied to plants of 'Crippsii'.		U.S.A.
- - 'Aureaspicata' Hort. Europe		Now known as 'Goldspire'.		
- - 'Aurescens' Hort. Ireland	1981	Reported from National Botanic Gardens, Dublin.		
- - **'Aurora'** H.J. van de Laar	1984	In "Dendroflora **21**". Broadly conical; light green to yellow-green foliage. **O.** M. Koster & Zonen, Boskoop, (1940).	W3	Holland

- - 'Autumn Gold'   1989   In "The Plant Finder".(See 'Winter Gold').

- - 'Baldwin Variegated' Hort. Amer.

           1966   Variegated foliage with splotches of yellow. **O.** J.W.
                 Spingarn, then of Baldwin, L. I., N.Y. as a mutation of 'Nana
                 Gracilis' (1966).   U.S.A.

- - **'Bambi'** G. Haddow   1991   Dwarf globose plant wider than high, mid green, tight foliage.
                 O. C. Franklin, Reading. **I.** Kenwith Nurs, Bideford, Devon.   U.K.

- - **'Barkenny'** Hort. Amer.

           1983   In "Amer.Conif. Soc. Bull. **1**". Tight dark green foliage; squat
                 conical shape. **O.** Joséph Reis, L. I., N.Y.   W3   U.S.A.

- - 'Barronii' Rehder   1945   A superfluous name. See 'Tetragona'.

- - **'Bartley'** H.G. Hillier   1976   In "Something Old, Something New". A globose bush of
                 dense habit with congested sprays of blue-green foliage.   U.K.

This is the first of a number of extremely diminutive forms raised by Wm. Gardiner of Rogers Nursery, Chandlers
Ford, Hampshire around 1910, from seed set on an old plant of 'Nana Gracilis'. Of these, M. Hornibrook selected and
named 'Caespitosa', 'Juniperoides' and 'Tetragona Minima' (now known as 'Minima') in time for his book published in
1923. He later selected 'Flabelliformis', 'Juniperoides Compacta', 'Laxa', and 'Spiralis' in time for his second edition
issued in 1939. Numerous unselected seedlings were later sold on the Nursery to customers in the U.K. and America
under unpublished names of local villages such as 'Bartley', 'Bassett', 'Chilworth', 'Stoneham', etc., or of members of
the staff ('Verdonii'). Many such plants have been lost sight of, but those listed have one by one been brought into
cultivation.

- - **'Bassett'** Welch   1966   Similar to but more erect than 'Juniperoides'. **O.** Red Lodge
                 Nurs, Chandlers Ford, Hants.   K,W   U.S.A.

- - 'Beehive' T.J. Cole   1986   In "Woody Plant Source List", Can. Dept. Agric. NOM.   Canada

- - **'Bess'** Fincham   1983   In "Amer. Conif. Soc. Bull. **1**". Dense, dark green foliage;
                 narrow column. **O.** Joséph Reis, L. I., N.Y.   W3   U.S.A.

- - 'Blue Feather' Hort. Amer. Now to be 'Ivan's Column'.

- - var. *breviramea* (1) Maximowicz

           1883   Tall tree; thick glossy green foliage lacking stomata beneath.   B,D,K,W   Japan

- - 'Breviramea' (2) Hort. Amer.   An illegit. listed name for a similar selection found by Ray
                                       Williams.

- - 'Breviramea Aurea' Onuma ex Beissner

           1900   A clone of var. *breviramea* with yellow-tipped foliage.   B,K   Hort. Japan

- - **'Brigitt'** Sampson   1990   In "Nurs. Cat". A clone with clumps of fasciated foliage. **O.**
                 Cedar Lodge Nurs, New Plymouth.   N.Z.

- - 'Bronze Elegance'   1980   In "Nurs. Cat". A slow-growing form with foliage in fan-like
                 sprays, bronzing in winter. **I.** W.E. Th. Ingwersen Nurs,
                 Gravetye, East Grinstead, Surrey. **O.** Unrecorded.

- - 'Bronze Pygmy' Hort. Holland

           1989   H.J. van de Laar in "Naamlijst . . .". NOM. **O.** and **I.** K.W.
                 van Klaveren, Boskoop, Holland.

- - **'Buttonball'** Fincham

           1983   In "Amer. Conif. Soc. Bull.". Very dwarf, globose. **O.** Joséph
                 Reis, L. I., N.Y.   U.S.A.

- - **'Caespitosa'** Hornibrook

           1923   Small, dense bun wider than high, foliage very tight in cup-
                 like sprays. **O.** W.H. Rogers, Red Lodge Nurs, Chandlers
                 Ford, Hants.   B,D,G,H,K,W U.K.

- - 'Carmen' Hort. Amer.   1991   A listed name for an upright plant with congested, dark green
                 foliage.

- - 'Caudata' Hort. Holland   1992 An illegit. listed name.

- - 'Chabo-hiba' Hort.   Reported from Saville Gardens, Windsor Great Park, Berks. ('Chabo-miba'). But see 'Shamohiba'.

- - **'Chabo-yadori'** H.G. Hillier
                                  1971 In "Hillier's Manual". When young, foliage is mixed adult and juvenile, becoming later loose and untidy with foliage mainly adult. Sometimes wrongly distributed as 'Ericoides'.   G,W   Hort. Japan

- - **'Chilworth'** Welch   1966 Dwarf, round-topped; dull brownish tinge in winter. Foliage sprays recurved. **O.** W.H. Rogers, Red Lodge Nurs, Chandlers Ford, Hants, (c. 1930).   B,K,W   U.K.

- - **'Chimaani-hiba'** Hort. Canada
                                  1967 Slow-growing form of 'Pygmaea'. **L.** Michaud & Co., Alpenglow Gardens, Surrey, B.C. ('Chimo-hiba', 'Kamaani-hiba', etc.).   W3   Hort. Japan

- - 'Chirimen' D. Sampson   1991` Dwarf form with short dark green sprays of Filicoides type foliage. **I.** Oakdene Nurs, Heathfield, E. Sussex. **O.** Japan.

- - 'Clarke's Seedling'   1985 An illegit. listed name reported from Windsor Great Park, Berks.

- - 'Columnaris' Hort. Amer.   Now to be 'Green Diamond'.   W

- - 'Compacta' (1) Gordon   1875 Green conical, compact. NIC. A name now in use for several selections but never used in a botanical sense.   B,D,G,H,K,W   U.K.

- - 'Compacta' (2) Hort. Anglia   Now known as 'Compact Pyramid'.

- - 'Compacta' (3) Hort. Anglia   Now known as 'Compact Fernspray'.

- - 'Compacta Nana' Hort. Amer.   A mistake for 'Nana Compacta'.

- - **'Compact Fernspray'** R.S. Corley
                                  1964 Dwarf bush; leaves small, shiny green, bronze tips in winter. ('Compacta', 'Filicoid Dwarf', 'Filicoides Compacta' and 'Pygmy Filicoides' are misnomers).   K,W2   U.K.

- - **'Compact Pyramid'** Den Ouden/Boom
                                  1965 New name. A dense, conical seedling from 'Nana Gracilis' with spreading branches and crowded sprays. Clearly a cultivar, it was first distributed under the confused name *compacta* 'Den Ouden', corrected by it's author in 1965. **I.** Den Ouden Nurs, Boskoop.   B,H   Holland

- - 'Compressa' Hort. Amer.   1986 An illegit. listed name. L. E.A. Cope. "Native . . . Conifers". NOM.

- - **'Confucious'** Hort. N.Z.   1984 Faster growing and looser than 'Nana Aurea'. Small yellow-green foliage sprays. Conspicuous brown branchlets. **O.** and **I.** Duncan & Davies Nurs, New Plymouth.   W3

- - **'Contorta'** Den Ouden   1949 Dwarf, conical; deep green foliage, bronzing in winter, twisted. **O.** Raised from seed of 'Nana Gracilis' by H. Den Ouden Nurs, Boskoop. **I.** The same (1945).   B,G,K,W2   Holland

- - 'Contorta Minima' Hort. Holland
                                  An illegit. listed name.

- - **'Coralliformis'** Beissner   1909 Large open bush; with curled, twisted branches, thread-like foliage quite unlike the coarse, bloated foliage of 'Lycopodioides'.   B,D,G,H,K,W2   Germany

- - 'Coralliformis Nana' Hort. Amer.
> 1966 An illegit. listed name for a slow-growing selection of the previous item. **L.** J.W. Spingarn, Baldwin, L. I., N.Y. ('Coralliformis Dwarf').   U.S.A.

- - **'Crippsii'** Rehder
> 1901 Broadly conical tree; rich golden yellow, green within plant. **O.** and **I.** Thos. Cripps and Sons, Tunbridge Wells, Kent. ('Crippsii Aurea').   B,D,G,K,W   U.K.

- - **'Dainty Doll'** Welch
> 1979 Conical, round-topped plant. **O.** and **I.** J.W. Spingarn, Baldwin, L I., N.Y. (1966).   W3   U.S.A.

- - 'Den Ouden' H. Den Ouden
> 1926 In "Nurs. Cat". Now known as 'Compact Pyramid'.

- - **'Densa'** Hornibrook
> 1923 Dwarf bush; dark green congested foliage as 'Nana' but more open. **O.** W.H. Rogers, Red Lodge Nurs, Chandlers Ford, Hants.('Nana Densa').   H,K,W   U.K.

- - 'Dilatush' Hort. Amer.
> 1991 Slow-growing bushy plant with dark green fernspray foliage.   U.S.A.

- - 'Douglasii' Hort. Holland 1991 An illegit. name. Dwarf globose, yellow form. **L.** W. Linssen, Baexem, Holland.

- - **'Drath'** H.J. Grootendorst
> 1969 In "Dendroflora **15-16**". Conical, dark green fasciated foliage. **O.** H. Drath. (Pronounced "draht" - spelt "drath").   G,K,W3   Germany

- - 'Dwarf Fernspray' Hort. Anglia   Now known as 'Compact Fernspray'.

- - **'Elf'** Welch
> 1979 Dense little bush; dark green foliage with slightly glaucous underside. **O.** J.W. Spingarn, Baldwin, L. I., N.Y. (1966).   W   U.S.A.

- - **'Ellie B'** Hort. Amer.
> 1980 Dwarf, forming a tight, upright, round topped dense bush with mid-green foliage in small sprays. **O.** Raised from seed by J.W. Spingarn, Baldwin, L.I., N.Y.

- - 'Erecta' Waterer
> 1884 Slender column; foliage light green. **O.** Waterer's Nurs, Bagshot, Surrey, (1870). NIC. Probably used in the trade for other similar clones.   B,D,K   U.K.

- - 'Ericifolia' Hort. Amer.
> An illegit. listed name for a neat shrub with blue-green leaves.

- - 'Ericoides' (1) Beissner
> 1904 L. L. Bohmer Nurs. (1899) and other early writers. Now known as *THUJA (PLATYCLADUS) orientalis* 'Sanderi'.   B,G,H,K,W   Hort. Japan

- - 'Ericoides' (2) Hort.
> The name has been applied to other clones that retain juvenile foliage, but this abnormality is seldom, - if ever, permanent. See also 'Chabo-yadori'.

- - **'Erika'** Int. Con. Reg.
> 1983 Sage green juvenile foliage; twisted wiry look. leaves triangular and much larger than those of 'Chabo-yadori'. Reg'd. by D.W. Hatch, Chantry Nurs, Honiton, Devon. **I.** The same. (1975).   W3   U.K.

- - **'Fern Gold'** Hort. Australia
> 1990 Low bush with feathery, golden foliage. **L.** Yamina Rare Plants, Monbulk.

- - **'Fernspray Gold'** C.R. Harrison
> 1975 Spreading tree; yellow foliage in flattened sprays; very similar to Filicoides. Gold at the extremities to pale yellow inside. **I.** Duncan & Davies Nurs, New Plymouth.   W   N.Z.

- - **'Filicoid Dwarf'** Den Ouden/Boom
> 1965 Superfluous name for 'Compact Fernspray'   B

- - **'Filicoides'** R. Smith   1867 Large bush with arching branches; deep green leaves, glaucous beneath. **I.** Von Siebold, to Leiden, (c. 1860).   B,D,G,H,K,W   Hort. Japan

- - 'Filicoides Aurea' Kent in Veitch
  1900 Now known as 'Fernspray Gold' in the trade.   W2

- - 'Filicoides Compacta' H.G. Hillier
  1969 Now known as 'Compact Fernspray'.

- - 'Filicoides Graciosa' Hort. Amer.
  1986 An illegit. listed name. **L.** E.A. Cope. "Native . . . Conifers". NOM.

- - 'Filifera' Gordon   1881 A low tree of irregular outline with filiform branches and thread-like pencil branchlets. NIC.   U.K.

- - 'Filiformis' Beissner   1900 Conical; long, pendulous terminals. **I.** Imported (c. 1902), and introduced by H.A.Hesse Nurs, Weener-on-Ems. NIC.   B,G,K,W   Hort. Japan

- - 'Filiformis Aurea' Onuma ex Beissner
  1900 As previous entry, but yellow-variegated. NIC.   B,K   Hort. Japan

- - **'Flabelliformis'** Hornibrook
  1939 Very dwarf; habit and foliage as 'Nana', but slightly glaucous. Foliage in noticeably flattened tiers. **I.** W.H. Rogers Nurs, Chandlers Ford, Hants.   B,G,H,K,W2   U.K.

- - **'Fontana'** H.J. van de Laar
  1971 In "Dendroflora **8**". Sport of 'Nana Gracilis' but looser and bright-green. **L.** Van den C. Verboom. Nurs, Boskoop.   G,K,W3   Holland

- - var. ***formosana*** (Hayata) Rehder in Bailey
  1914 Formosan Hinoki Cypress.   30-40m   Taiwan

- - 'Gerda von Gimborn Dietz' Hort. Holland
  1972 Now known as 'Gimborn Beauty'.

- - **'Gimborn Beauty'** J.van Hoey-Smith
  1982 Glaucous juvenile foliage with broad sprays of adult foliage; strong grower. Formerly known as 'Gerda von Gimborn Dietz'. **O.** Found in Gimborn Arboretum.   G,W   Holland

- - **'Gnome'** Welch   1979 Green foliage; diminutive, bun forming. **O.** and **I.** J.W. Spingarn, Baldwin, L. I., N.Y. (1966).   W   U.S.A.

- - 'Gold Drop' Hort. Amer.   1982 Yellowish-green; globose to flat-topped when young. **L.** J.W. Spingarn, Baldwin, L.I., N.Y.   W   U.S.A.

- - **'Golden Ceramic'** T.J. Cole
  1986 In "Woody Plant Source List". Canada Dept. Agric. NOM.   Canada

- - 'Golden Christmas Tree' Hort. Amer.
  A superfluous name for 'Golden Ceramic'.

- - **'Golden Fairy'** Welch   1979 Bright golden-yellow spray; dense, conical plant. **O.** and **I.** J.W. Spingarn, Baldwin, L. I., N.Y. (1966).   W   U.S.A.

- - **'Golden Fern'**   1989 In "Conif. Soc. Australia Newsletter **5**". Compact and with a predominance of juvenile foliage. **O.** A mutation from 'Fernspray Gold' found by John Emery. (1980).

- - **'Golden Filament'** Welch
  1979 Mixture of green and gold tree-like spray, loose-growing bush. **O.** and **I.** J.W. Spingarn, Baldwin, L. I., N.Y. (1966).   W   U.S.A.

- - **'Golden Nymph'** Welch   1979 Squat, conical form; gold foliage, green cast; **O.** and **I.** J.W. Spingarn, Baldwin, N.Y. (1966).   W   U.S.A.

- - 'Golden Sensation' Hort. Amer.
  1991 A listed name for a broadly upright plant with up-cupped,
  golden foliage.

- - 'Golden Sprite' Welch   1979 A golden "tennis ball". Older plants spreading to globose. **O.**
  and **I.** J.W. Spingarn, Baldwin, L.I., N.Y. (1966).   W   U.S.A.

- - 'Goldilocks' H.J. Grootendorst
  1979 In "Dendroflora **15-16**". Same colour as "Crippsii" but
  smaller. A Sport from 'Nana Lutea'. **O.** F.J. Grootendorst &
  Sons Nurs, Boskoop.   K,W3   Holland

- - 'Goldspire' Den Ouden/Boom
  1965 Lemon-yellow tips; narrow conical and dense. **I.** J. Konijn &
  Co. Nurs, Reeuwijk, (1963). **O.** Found in Blijdenstein
  Pinetum, Hilversum, ('Aureaspicata').   B,G,K,W3   Holland

- - 'Gracillima' Fitschen   1930 A synonym of 'Gracilis Nana'. NIC.

- - 'Gracilis' Siebold   1868 In "Nurs. Cat". (Under *RETINOSPORA*.) Compact, conical;
  dark green foliage. **I.** From Japan by Von Siebold (c. 1862).   B,D,G,K,W   Hort. Japan

- - 'Gracilis Aurea' Veitch ex Gordon
  1875 Broadly conical, tops nodding; golden-yellow. **O.** James
  Veitch & Sons, Coombewood Nurs, Surrey. NIC. being
  largely replaced by 'Crippsii' in the trade.   B,D,K,W   U.K.

- - 'Gracilis Compacta' Hort. Amer.
  1982 An illegit. name. **L.** Weston Nurs. Hopkinton, MA.   U.S.A.

- - 'Gracilis Nana' Hort.   A mistake for 'Nana Gracilis'.

- - 'Graciosa' Den Ouden/Boom
  1965 A "gracious" sport of 'Nana Gracilis'; brighter green; looser
  habit. **I.** Konijn & Co. Nurs, Reeuwijk. The former name
  'Loenik' is no longer used in the trade.   B,G,K,W   Holland

- - 'Grayswood Bronze' D.W. Hatch
  As 'Crippsii' but deeper yellow, bronzing in winter. **I.** D.W.
  Hatch, Chantry Nurs, Honiton, Devon.   U.K.

- - 'Green Cushion' Hort. Amer.
  1981 Very dwarf; bun-forming. **L.** Gordon Bentham. **O.** Verkade's
  Nurs, Wayne, N.J.

- - 'Green Diamond' Hort. Holland
  1977 In "Dendroflora **13-14**". Dark green upright growing bush,
  spreading branches, pendulous tips. Received by Konijn & Co
  Nurs, from U.S.A. under illegit. name of 'Columnaris'. **L.**
  Konijn & Co. Nurs, Reeuwijk.   K,W3   Holland

- - 'Green Mound' Hort. Amer.
  1985 Mounded; dark green foliage. **L.** L.C. Hatch, in "Reference
  Guide".

- - 'Hage' Den Ouden   1949 As 'Nana' but brighter green. **O.** Wm Hage & Co. Nurs,
  Boskoop, (1928). (Several mis-spellings are found).   B,D,G,K,W   Holland

- - 'Hartekamp' H.J. van de Laar
  1989 In "Naamlijst . . .".   Holland

- - 'Hillock' D. and N. Sampson
  1991 In "Nurs. Cat". A diminutive plant with noticeably irregular
  growth. **O.** Cedar Lodge Nurs, New Plymouth, N.Z.   N.Z.

- - 'Hinoki Junior' Hort. Amer.   Now to be 'Junior'.

- - 'Hoersholm' Hort. Germany
  1992 **L.** Horstmann Nurs, Schneverdingen, Germany. NOM.

- - 'Hohman's Upright' Hort. Amer.
1985 Dark green foliage; columnar. L. L.C. Hatch. In "Reference Guide".

- - 'Hornibrook Nana' Hort. Amer.
1970 An illegit. name. L. H.J. Hohman, Kingsville Nurs, Kingsville, MD. NOM. NIC.

- - 'Hoseri' Hort. Amer. 1986 L. E.A. Cope, "Native . . . Conifers". NOM.

- - 'Hypnoides Nana' Hort. Anglia A dwarf plant in Royal Edinburgh Botanic Garden. Very dark green foliage in flattened sprays but also some filiform. I. Kenwith Nurs, Bideford, Devon. O. Unrecorded. (Possibly a mutation from one of the Roger's dwarf forms.)

- - **'Intermedia'** Den Ouden
1937 Miniature bush. O. and I. W.H. Rogers Nurs, Chandlers Ford, Hants, (c. 1930). ('Nana Intermedia').   B,K,W   U.K.

- - **'Ivans Column'** Hort. Amer.
1990 O. Found as a sport by Ivan Arneson, Canby, Oregon, (1979). ('Blue Feather'). Slow growing narrowly upright plant which retains juvenile foliage all it's life. I. Kasch's Nurs, Gresham, Oregon.

- - **'Jean Iseli'** Oliver 1988 In "Amer. Conif. Soc. Bull. 6". A dwarf with growth in clumps.

- - **'Joan-o'** Fincham 1983 In "Amer. Conif. Soc. Bull 1". Dwarf, conical. O. Joséph Reis, L. I., N.Y.   U.S.A.

- - **'Joel Spingarn'** Hort. Amer.
1991 A listed name for a dense, fastigiate dwarf; foliage dark green.

- - 'J.R.' Hort. Amer. Now known as 'Junior'.

- - **'Junior'** Fincham 1983 In "Nurs. Cat". Coenosium Gardens, Aurora, OR. Dense, dark green bun with foliage intermediate between 'Nana' and the tiny "tennis ball" clones. O. Joséph Reis, L. I., N.Y.   W3   U.S.A.

- - **'Juniperoides'** Rogers ex Hornibrook
1923 Dense, mid green globose form. Foliage leaves appressed to the branchlets except at the growing tips where they stand off at an angle of 30o. I. W.H. Rogers Nurs, Chandlers Ford, Hants.   B,D,G,H,K,W   U.K.

- - **'Juniperoides Compacta'** Den Ouden
1937 Similar to previous but growth more compact; foliage yellow-green. O. and I. W.H. Rogers Nurs, Chandlers Ford, Hants.   B,H,K,W   U.K.

- - 'Kamakurahiba' Onuma ex Beissner
1900 A monstrous form in the 'Lycopodioides' group. I. Into Germany A. Ungar. NIC.   B,K   Hort. Japan

- - 'Kamarachiba' Hort. 1990 Low growing gracefully spreading branches. Colour yellow to dark orange at the tips. Reported from Dortmund Botanic Gardens. O. Imported from Japan.   Hort. Japan

- - 'Kanaamihiba' Onuma ex Beissner
1900 Dwarf form with elongated thick branches, contorted at the tips, with cockscomb-like clusters. ('Kimaanihiba').   B,H,K   Hort. Japan

- - 'Kerdalo' H.J. van de Laar
1990 In "Dendroflora 27". Globose to spreading plant; growth dense; colour and habit like 'Crippsii'. Pendulous final growth.   France

- - 'Keteleerii' R. Smith   1867 Some leaves yellow, some green. **O.** Keteleer Nurs, (c. 1860). NIC.   B,D,K   Belgium

- - 'Kimanihiba' Hort. Holland
    1990 A listed name.

- - **'Kojolcohiba'** Welch   1979 Similar to 'Tetragona Aurea', but more vigorous. Less prone to wind burn and sun scorch.   K,W   N.Z.

- - **'Kosteri'** Hornibrook   1939 Glossy green foliage; intermediate between 'Nana Gracilis' and 'Pygmaea'. **I.** M. Koster & Sons, Boskoop, (c. 1915).   B,G,H,K,W   Holland

- - 'Kosteri Nana' Hort. Anglia
    1934 Reported from the Royal Botanical Gardens, Kew.   U.K.

- - **'Laxa'** Hornibrook   1939 Dwarf; open growth. **O.** W.H. Rogers, Red Lodge Nurs, Chandlers Ford, Hants, (c. 1966).   B,H,K,W   U.K.

- - **'Leprechaun'** Welch   1979 Squat, conical bush; foliage has a 'tufted' appearance. **O.** and **I.** J. W. Spingarn, Baldwin, L. I., N.Y. (1966).   W   U.S.A.

- - **'Little Ann'** Hort. Amer.   Dwarf, narrowly conical; fine, dark green foliage.**L** Iseli Nurs, Boring, OR. (1982) **O.** Joséph Reis, L. I., N.Y., U.S.A.   W3

- - **'Little Markey'**   1983 In "Dwarf Conifer Notes". Dwarf pillar shaped bush with yellow foliage. **O.** Raised from seed by J.W. Spingarn, Baldwin, L.I., N.Y. **I.** Kenwith Nurs, Bideford, Devon. (1988).   W3   U.S.A.

- - 'Little Spire' Hort. Holland
    1992 A listed name.

- - 'Loenik' Hort. Holland   Now known as 'Graciosa'. ('Lunik').   W3

- - 'Lorent' Hort. Amer.   1985 L. L.C. Hatch in "Reference Guide". NOM.

- - 'Loughead' Hort. Amer.   1986 A listed name. NOM. ('Loucheed').

- - 'Lowry' Hort. Amer.   1992 A listed name. In "Nurs. Cat". Foxborough Nurs, Maryland, U.S.A. without description.

- - **'Lutea Nova'** Beissner   1904 Upright spreading; foliage yellow; more tender than 'Crippsii'.   B,D,G,K,W   Germany

- - **'Lycopodioides'** Standish ex Gordon
    1862 Gaunt tree; foliage dark green, thick, monstrous. **I.** Received at the Royal Nurs, Bagshot, Surrey. (1861). (?='Rashahiba')   B,D,H,K,W   Hort. Japan

- - **'Lycopodioides Aurea'** Beissner
    1906 Similar to last but foliage butter-yellow. **I.** Sent by Yokohama Nurs, to Germany. (c. 1890).   B,G,H,K,W   Hort. Japan

- - 'Lycopodioides Gelbunt' Hort. Germany
    An illegit. listed name.

- - **'Lynn's Golden'** Hort. Amer.
    1986 Foliage turns orange in winter. See "Amer. Conif. Soc".   W3

- - 'Magnifica' Hort. ex R Smith
    1867 A vigorous clone; dark green.   B,D,K   U.K.

- - 'Magnifica Aurea' Hort. ex Beissner
    1891 As last; foliage yellowish. NIC.   B,K   Germany

- - 'Marian' Hort. Holland   1992 A listed name.

- - **'Maries' Gold'** Hort. Amer.
    1985 A listed name for a mutation from the following item with a yellow variegation. L. L.C. Hatch in "Reference Guide".   W3

- - **'Mariesii'** Kent in Veitch

    1900 Dwarf bush; foliage milky-white to yellow-green in winter. It seems to be variable; probably more than one clone is in cultivation.   B,D,G,H,K,W   U.K.

- - 'Marvin's Variegated' Hort. Amer.

    1985 A listed name. L. L.C. Hatch in "Reference Guide". NOM.

- - **'Mastin'** Hort. Amer.

    A listed name. L. Iseli Nurs, Boring, OR. (1982) **I.** G. Bentham.   Canada

- - 'Menzies' Sport' Hort. Amer.

    A listed name. Andréw Menzies listed Mitsch Nurs, Cat. 1988.

- - **Meroke'** Fincham   1983 In "Amer. Conif. Soc. Bull. **1**". Erect, slow-growing with golden lacy foliage. **O.** Joséph Reis, L. I., N.Y.   W3   U.S.A.

- - 'Meroke Twin' Hort. Amer.   A superfluous name for 'Little Markey'.

- - **'Minima'** Hornibrook   1939 Dense hemispherical cushion; foliage light green and consisting of only four sided branchlets, ends bronzing in winter. (As 'Tetragona Minima' in ed. **1**). **O.** and **I.** W.H. Rogers, Red Lodge Nurs, Chanders Ford, Hants, (several other names are wrongly in use).   B,H,K   U.K.

- - **'Nana'** (1) Hort. ex Carrière

    1867 Listed at first under (*RETINOSPORA*). Small bush; very slow-growing, foliage very dense, black-green. (Seldom supplied true to name).   B,D,G,H,W   Hort. Japan

- - 'Nana' (2) Hort.   This word is not now used in the trade with 'Bassett', 'Caespitosa', 'Contorta', 'Densa', 'Flabelliformis', 'Hage', 'Intermedia', 'Juniperoides', 'Juniperoides Compacta', 'Kosteri', 'Minima', 'Prostrata', 'Repens', 'Rigida', 'Spiralis', 'Stoneham', 'Tonia' and others which have no connection with 'Nana' (1) above.

- - 'Nana Albo-variegata' Hort. ex Beissner

    1891 A superfluous name for 'Mariesii', or a similar variegated clone.   Germany

- - 'Nana Argentea' Hornibrook

    1939 Doubtfully distinguishable from 'Mariesii' and could well have been 'Mariesii' as a grafted plant when the colour is brighter.   B,H,K,W   U.K.

- - **'Nana Aurea'** Carrière   1867 More vigorous than 'Nana' and with gold coloured foliage.   B,D,G,H,K,W   France

- - **'Nana Compacta'** Barron in Gordon

    1875 Dense round plant; bright green, glaucous beneath.   B,K,W   U.K.

- - **'Nana Gracilis'** R. Smith

    1867 Dense conical bush; rich lustrous green foliage. Widely grown.   B,D,G,H,K,W   U.K.

- - **'Nana Lutea'** Welch   1966 Compact small bush; pale golden-yellow foliage.   G,K,W   Holland

- - 'Nana Prostrata'   H

- - **'Nana Pyramidalis'** Hornibrook

    1939 Dwarf, conical; dark green. **O.** Den Ouden Nurs, Boskoop (1934), **I.** The same (1905).   B,H,K   Holland

- - 'Nyewood' Hort.   1970 L. Watnong Nurs, Morris Plains, N.J. **O.** Same as 'Chilworth'.   U.K.

- - **'Opaal'** Krüssmann   1960 Light green foliage with patches of creamy-yellow. **O.** Konijn Nurs, Reeuwijk.   G,K,W   Holland

- - **'Oregon Crested'** Hort. Amer.
  1989   A listed name for a sport from 'Kosteri' with open, upright growth. Terminal growth coxcomb-like, mid green bronzing in winter.   W3

- - 'Patsunamihiba' Onuma ex Beissner
  1900   A clone of var. *breviramea*? NIC.   B   Hort. Japan?

- - **'Paul's Select'** Hort. Amer.
  1990   A listed name for a dwarf, conical form with tightly congested dark green foliage. L. Iseli. Nurs, Boring, OR.   U.S.A.

- - **'Pendula'** Hort. ex Beissner
  1891   A strong-growing form with long, pendulous branches and branchlets. O. Raised on the Count Lobkowitz Nurs, Eisenberg, NIC.   B,K   Czechosl.

- - 'Pixie' Welch
  1979   Looks at a glance like 'Minima' but foliage is dense and in flat sprays which are not tetragonal. The name being already "occupied" in *CHAMAECYPARIS lawsoniana* is not permissable. A new name should be found. O. J. W. Spingarn, Baldwin, L.I., N.Y.   R,W3   U.S.A.

- - 'Plumosa' Carrière
  1867   A mistake for *CHAMAECYPARIS pisifera* f. *plumosa*.

- - 'Prostrata' Hornibrook
  1923   A prostrate form no longer identifiable. NIC. ('Nana Prostrata').   B,K

- - **'Pygmaea'** Gordon
  1862   A low, spreading bush; green foliage. Sent by Robert Fortune to the Royal Nurs, Bagshot, Surrey. (1861).   B,D,G,H,K,W   Hort.Japan

- - 'Pygmaea Aureovariegata' Hort. ex Beissner
  1891   Habit as previous item but leaves golden-variegated. NIC.   B,H,W

- - **'Pygmaea Aurescens'** Hornibrook
  1939   Brownish-green, rich copper colour in Autumn. O. K. Wezelenburg Nurs, Hazerwoude, Boskoop.   B,H,K,W   Holland

- - 'Pygmaea Densa' Hort. Anglia
     An illegit. name. Low growing spreading dwarf plant with slightly thickened foliage. We can see no difference between Hillier 'Pygmaea Densa' and 'Chimo-hiba'.

- - 'Pygmaea Haage' Hort. Anglia
     A mistake for 'Hage'.

- - 'Pygmaea Variegated' Hort. Australia
  1992   An illegit. name. See 'Pygmy White Fleck'.

- - 'Pygmy Fernspray' Hort. Anglia
     Now known as 'Compact Fernspray'.

- - 'Pygmy White Fleck' New Name
  1993   A mutation of 'Pygmaea' with spotted variegation.

- - 'Pyramidalis Nana' Hort. Amer.
     L. Watnong Nurs, Morris Plains. N.J. (1970). An illegit name. See 'Nana Pyramidalis'.

- - 'Rainbow' Hort. Amer.
     A listed name. L. Iseli Nurs, Boring, OR. O. Sturm ?   U.S.A.

- - 'Raraflora' J. le Conte
     An upright bush with attractive dark green foliage. I. J. le Conte. L. Fred Bergman, and probably originated at "Raraflora", Feasterville, PA.   U.S.A.

- - 'Rashahiba' Onuma ex Beissner
  1909   Monstrous clone with thick branches and abnormal foliage. It is probably the clone known in European cultivation as 'Lycopodioides'.   H   Hort. Japan

- - **'Reis' Dwarf'** Welch
  1979   A curious form with congested growth in tufts. O. Joseph Reis, L. I., N.Y. ('Reisii', 'Reese Dwarf', etc).   W   U.S.A.

- - **'Repens'** Den Ouden   1949   Habit similar to 'Pygmaea' but of much stronger growth and foliage always green. **O.** Wm Hage & Co, Boskoop.   B,G,K,W   Holland

- - 'Rezek Dwarf' Hort. Amer.   Conical dwarf bush with dark green foliage. **L.** H.G. Hillier in "Conif. Check-list" (1970). NOM. **O.** E. Rezek.

- - 'Rigida' Hort.   Now known as 'Rigid Dwarf'.

- - **'Rigid Dwarf'** Den Ouden/Boom
1965   Stiff-looking erect bush; foliage dark green. ('Nana Rigida' is illegit.)   B,G,K,W   U.K.

- - 'Sanderi' *Of early authers*   Now known as *THUJA (PLATYCLADUS) orientalis* 'Sanderi'.

- - **'Sarah Verkade'** T.J. Cole,
1986   In "Woody Plant Source List". (1987). Canada Dept. Agric. NOM.   Canada

- - 'Schnider' G. Bentham   1981   In "Nurs. Cat". Without description.   Canada

- - 'Shamohiba' Onuma ex Beissner
1900   Monstrous form in the 'Lycopodioides" group. NIC.   B,H   Hort. Japan

- - **'Snowflake'** John Emery
1989   In "Conif.. Soc. Australia Newsletter 5". Dwarf conical form with flecks of white in the foliage. **O.** Mutation on 'Chabo-yadori' found on the Drue Wholesale Nurs, Berry, Australia. Not stable in the juvenile foliage.

- - **'Snowkist'** Hort. Canada
.1981   In "Dw. Conif. Notes 2". A sport from 'Tonia'. Slower-growing, but with clearer variegation. **O.** Wm. Goddard, Floravista, Vancouver Is, B.C.   W3   Canada

- - **'Spiralis'** Hornibrook   1939   (As 'Nana Spiralis'). Upright form; foliage green in twisted whorls.   B,H,K,W   U.K.

- - 'Split Rock' Hort. Amer.   1983   Very blue, mostly juvenile foliage. **O.** Split Rock Nurs, N.J.   W3

- - 'Stephen' Hort. Amer.   1991   A listed name for a fastigiate dwarf form with tight, dark green foliage.

- - **'Stoneham'** Den Ouden/Boom
1965   A dwarf globular bush, foliage in very tight flattened sprays. **O.** W.H. Rogers Nurs, Chandlers Ford, Hants.   B,K,W   U.K.

- - 'Strangman' Hort. Anglia   1985   Dwarf globose eventually conical tightly furnished with foliage. Reported from Saville Gardens, Windsor Great Park, Berks. **O.** Strangman, Kent.

- - 'Suirova-hiba.' Hort.   Similar to 'Coralliformis'. **I.** Received by R.S. Corley from Dr. Rokujo. ('Suiryhiba' and other spellings are found).   K,W   Hort. Japan

- - **'Sunburst'** Hort. Amer.   1986   A listed name for a dwarf upright plant. New foliage golden fading to greenish later.   U.S.A.

- - 'Sunspray' Hort. N.Z.   1992   Very attractive upright informal pyramidal habit, with bright creamy golden swirled sprays. **O.** Duncan & Davies, New Plymouth.

- - 'Tabuliformis' H.G. Hillier
1970   In "Conifer Conference" list. NOM.

- - 'Tatsumi' Hort.   A mistake for 'Tsatsumi'.

- - 'Teddy Bear' Hort.   Probably a mistake for *CHAMAECYPARIS pisifera* 'Teddy Bear'. Otherwise an unacceptable name. (Art. 50 of I.C.N.C.P.)

- - **'Tempelhof'** Den Ouden/Boom
  1965 Green foliage, brownish tint in winter; twigs noticeably red.
  Compact upright form without a leader.   B,F,G,K,W   Holland

- - 'Tetragona' Hornibrook   1923 No green form of the cultivar 'Tetragona Aurea' is known to
  exist, or ever to have existed.   B,D,H,K,W3

- - **'Tetragona Aurea'** Barron in Gordon
  1875 Foliage in full sun is bronze-gold, in shade can be yellow-
  green to dark blue-green. I. By Wm. Barron Nurs.
  Borrowash, Derby, U.K. (1870). Wind tender.   B,D,G,H,K,W   Hort. Japan

- - 'Tetragona Intermedia' Hort.
  1962 A mistake for 'Intermedia'.

- - 'Tetragona Minima' Hornibrook
  1973 Now generally known as 'Minima'.

- - 'Tigida' Hort. Amer.   1970 A mistake for 'Rigida'.

- - 'Timothy' Hort. Anglia   1987 Dwarf to slow-growing pillar shaped golden plant. O. and I.
  Douglas Loundes, MacPennys Nurs, Branscore, Hampshire.

- - **'Tiny Tot'** Fincham   1983 In "Amer. Conif. Soc. Bull. 1". Dwarf, rounded bush. O.
  Joséph Reis. L.I., N.Y.   U.S.A.

- - **'Tonia'** Den Ouden   1949 A variegated sport from 'Nana Gracilis'. O. Wm. Hage
  Boskoop, (1928). Variegation in grafted plants is much better
  and more uniform.   B,G,K,W   Holland

- - **'Torulosa'** Hort. Amer.   ·1962 Reported from the Gotelli collection, South Orange N.J.,
  U.S.A. (1962). Upright tangled shrub, growth contorted,
  fasciated branch tips.   G,W

- - 'Torulosa Nana'   1962 An illegit. name. Reported from the Gotelli collection, South
  Orange, N.J., U.S.A. Probably young plants of 'Torulosa'.

- - 'Troubetzkoyana' Rovelli ex Masters in "Gar. Chron".
  1890 Bright green montrous foliage; dwarf compact. I. Rovelli
  Bros. Nurs, Pallanza, (1891). NIC.   B,D,H,K   Italy

- - **'Tsatsumi'** Slavin   1932 A dwarf, compact form with dark green twisted and tufted
  foliage. L. Elm City Nurs, as 'Tsatsunami', (1919).   B,H,K,W3   Hort. Japan

- - 'Tsatsumi Gold' H.J. van de Laar
  1990 In "Dendroflora 27". As previous item but slower growing
  and foliage golden-yellow, greenish inside plant. Probably a
  sport. (The name 'Tsatsumi Aurea' is illegit).   Hort. Japan

- - 'Two Twins' L. Walker   1989 In "Nurs. Cat". Dwarf form. Colour and foliage appear
  identical to 'Juniperoides Compacta'. Walker Nurs, Blaxton,
  Nr. Doncaster.   U.K.

- - **'Van Nes'** J. Konijn   1968 In "Sortimentslijst". Compact, conical loose with light green
  foliage. I. Konijn Nurs, Reeuwijk.   Holland

- - **'Variegata'** Nicholson   1884 Branches tinged yellow. NIC   B   U.K.

- - 'Verbanensis' Hort. Germany
  1978 An illegit. listed name.

- - **'Verdon'** Welch   1966 Compact, upright habit; yellow foliage, bronze in winter. O.
  W.H. Rogers Nurs, Chandlers Ford, Hants. (Not now known
  as 'Verdonii').   G,W   U.K.

- - 'Verdun' Hort. Holland   A mistake for 'Verdon'.   Not as G

- - 'Verkade's Golden Winter' Hort. Amer.
  1981 L. Gordon Bentham, B.C., Canada. O. Verkade's Nurs, N.J.

- - 'Verkade's Green Cushion' Hort. Amer.
       See 'Green Cushion.'

- - 'Watchi' Hort. Australia
       1989 Compact golden form with short graceful foliage sprays; **O.** A mutation on 'Nana Aurea found on Cotts Nurs, Sydney, Australia, where the new plant was labelled 'Watch 1' which became corrupted to 'Watchi'.

- - **'Well's Special'** Hort. Amer.
       1977 Green foliage, strong grower, similar in form to 'Nana Gracilis'. **L.** Mitsch Nurs, Aurora, OR.   W3   U.S.A.

- - **'White Imp'** Hort. Amer.
       1983 A listed name. **L.** Iseli Nurs, Boring, OR. **O.** E. Rezek.   U.S.A.

- - **'White Tip'** Hort. Amer. 1981 A listed name.**L.** Mitsch Nurs, Aurora, OR.

- - 'Winter Gold' Hort. Anglia
       One of the lesser known Red Lodge seedlings raised by Mr. Gardiner. It forms a globose bush foliaged yellow-green in summer turning to rich old-gold in the autum and this colour remains until new growth commences the following spring. **O.** and **I.** Rogers Nurs, Chandlers Ford, Hants. (possibly 'Autumn Gold' is the same plant).

- - 'Wissel' Hort. Germany 1990 Bun-forming dwarf with grey-green juvenile foliage which is coarse to the touch. **O.** and **I.** Jeddeloh Nurs. (1991).

- - 'Wyckoff' Hort. Amer. 1985 Compact, squatly conical bush with dark green foliage. **L.** Coenosium Gardens, Lehighton. PA.

- - **'Yellowtip'** Den Ouden/Boom
       1965 A mutation from 'Nana Gracilis'. Conical bush, dark green foliage: shoot tips yellow. **O.** and **I.** C.A. van den Akker, Boskoop.   B,K   Holland

- - 'Youngii' (1) Rehder in Bailey
       1923 In "Cult. Evergreens". A pendulous form with dull yellow foliage, probably now unidentifiable.   B,G,K   U.S.A.

- - 'Youngii' (2) Den Ouden/Boom
       1965 A mistake for *CHAMAECYPARIS lawsoniana* 'Youngii'.   U.K.

CHAMAECYPARIS pisifera (Siebold and Zuccarini) Endlicher
       1847 Sawara Cypress. First listed (along with many of its cultivars) as *RETINOSPORA* S. and Z. (1844).   20 m, Z4   Japan

All seedlings in this species, on their way to maturity, pass through several stages that are outwardly distinguished by differences in the foliage:- from the initial juvenile (technically "squarrose") leaf-form through a semi-juvenile (technically "plumose") stage to the final adult leaf. Rarely, a particular seedling will suspend its 'growing up' at some point and develop into an interesting and unusual little plant, and several cases where such a 'hang-up' has turned out to be a 'fixation' have been brought into cultivation, and in the past (no longer permitted) the explanatory words 'Squarrosa' and 'Plumosa' have been used in the cultivar names. This raises problems for the nomenclaturist. Such irregularities in development tend themselves to be irregular, so suspended development may re-start years later. The stages are not abrupt and may co-exist within a plant or regress following damage. Care must therefore be taken to ensure that only plants true-to-type in the recommended 'named forms' are propagated and that new selections are never introduced to the trade until they have been under test for many years.

- - **'Abel'** H.J. van de Laar 1989 In "Dendroflora 20". A sportfrom 'Boulevard' forming a conical bush with light-green, adult foliage. **O.** A. Kammings, Augustinusga.   Holland

- - 'Albo-picta' Hort. Anglia   Probably a mistake for 'Argentea'.

- - 'Albovariegata' Hort. Anglia   Now known as 'Argenteovariegata'.   C,W3

- - 'Allen' Hort. Amer. 1985 A listed name.

- - 'Argentea' (1) Fortune ex Gordon
          1862 Listed under *RETINOSPORA*. Now generally known as
                'Argenteovariegata'.   U.K.

- - 'Argentea' (2) Carrière   1867 Mistakenly citing Fortune ex Gordon. A dwarf bushy form.
                                    See 'Plumosa Argentea' (1).

- - 'Argentea Pygmaea' Helene Bergman
          1965 In "Plants and Gardens". Unstable version of 'Squarrosa
                Pygmaea'.   U.S.A.

- - **'Argenteovariegata'** Nicholson
          1884 Some of the branchlets silvery-white, regularly intermixed all
                over the plant. **I.** Sent by R. Fortune to the Royal Nurs,
                Bagshot, Surrey U.K. (1861). ('Argentea').   B,G,K   U.K.

- - **'Aurea'** (Gordon) Rehder
          1949 Golden-yellow, green within the plant. **I.** Introduced by R.
                Fortune (1861).   B,D,K,R,W   Hort. Japan

- - 'Aurea Compacta Nana' Hort. Amer.
          1982 An illegit. name for a dwarf mound; with gold-tipped foliage.
                L. Weston Nurs, Hopkinton, MA.

- - 'Aurea Nana' Hort. ex Beissner
          1891 Long supposed to be lost to cultivation. Probably now in
                cultivation as 'Strathmore'. See Welch 186 (1979). ('Aurea
                Compacta', 'Aurea Nana Fretsii').   B,H,K,W   Germany

- - **'Aureovariegata'** (Ottolander) Beissner
          1891 Leaves golden variegated; very slow grower.   B,K,W   Holland

- - **'Avenue'** Hort. Anglia   1979 A sport from 'Boulevard'. **I.** Wansdyke Nurs, Devizes,

- - **'Baby Blue'** New Name   1993 A mutation on 'Boulevard' smaller in all it's parts **O.** Andréws
                                     Nurs, Sydney. (See 'Boulevard Dwarf').   Australia

- - 'Blue Dwarf' Hort. Amer.   A mistake for 'Dwarf Blue'.

- - 'Blue Globe'   1988 A plant in Windsor Great Park, Berks., appearing identical to
                               'Tamu-Himuro' ('Tama Himiro').

- - 'Blue Tower' Hort. Anglia
                          1992 Reported from Windsor Great Park, Berks.

- - **'Boulevard'** Den Ouden/Boom
                          1965 Silvery blue-grey foliage. **I.** A sport on 'Squarrosa' on the
                               Boulevard Nurs, Newport, (1934). The name 'Cyano-viridis'
                               is no longer used in the trade.   B,G,K,R,W   U.S.A.

- - 'Boulevard Dward' J. Emery
                          1989 In "Conif. Soc. Australia Newsletter 5". Name changed to
                               'Baby Blue' by J. Emery (1993).   Australia

- - 'Boulevard Variegata' Hort. N.Z.
                          1986 An illegit. name raised for a mutation that proved to be
                               unstable.

- - 'Bowland' Hort Anglia   1987 Sport from 'Boulevard', low mound, soft foliage, purple tinted
                               and pink in winter. **O.** and **I.** Holden Clough Nurs, Lancs.
                               ('Squarrosa Bowland').

- - 'Brabaham' Hort. Anglia   Donated by R.S. Corley to Windsor Great Park, Berks.

- - 'Brackenwood' Hort. Anglia   Donated by R.S. Corley to Windsor Great Park, Berks.

- - 'Bright Gold' Hort. Amer.   An unacceptable listed name.

- - 'Cleary's Variegated' Hort. Amer.
        1983 A listed name. **L.** Iseli Nurs, Boring, OR. (1983).

- - **'Clouded Sky'** Den Ouden/Boom
        1965 A sport of 'Squarrosa'. Conical, loosely branched; foliage blue. **O.** Konijn & Son, Reeuwijk.   B,G,K,W3   Holland

- - 'Columnaris' Beissner   1907 A densely fastigiate form with short branches. **O.** Ansorge Nurs, Klein Flottbeck, near Hamburg, NIC.   B   Germany

- - **'Compacta'** Hartweg & Ruemplar
        1875 Compact bun-shape; adult foliage, variable in vigour. See Note following 'Nana', below.   B,K,R,W   Germany

- - 'Compacta Nana' Hort. Amer.   An illegit. name. Presumably for a selection intermediate between 'Compacta' and 'Nana'.

- - **'Compacta Variegata'** Hornibrook
        1939 Bold variegation in yellow splashes; looser habit than the all green form. ('Nana Aureovariegata').   B,H,K,W   U.K.

- - 'Compacta' Hort. Holland
        1993 An illegit. name.

- - 'Compressa Aurea Nana' Hort. Anglia
        See 'Plumosa Compressa Aurea'.

- - 'Concolor' Beissner   1909 A clone lacking the normal white stomata. NIC.   B   Germany

- - 'Cornish Blue' Hort. Anglia   A superfluous and ridiculous 'florists' name for 'Boulevard'. Not used in the horticultural trade.

- - **'Cream Ball'** L.C. Hatch
        1985 In "Reference Guide". Dwarf (in 'Plumosa' group); leaves divergent, foliage whitish. **O.** Wm Goddard, Floravista, Vancouver Is., B.C.   W3   Canada

- - 'Cresta' Hort. Ireland   1985 Reported from J.F. Kennedy Park, Co. Cork Ireland.

- - 'Curly Tops' Hort. Australia
        1989 In "Nurs. Cat". Yamina Nurs, Monbulk, Australia. A sport of 'Boulevard'. Foliage deep, bright blue, held in short curly branches, reminiscent of *CRYPTOMERIA japonica* 'Spiralis'.

- - 'Cyano-viridis' Hort.   Now known in the trade as 'Boulevard'.

- - 'Devon Cream' Hort. Anglia
        1983 A colour mutation from 'Boulevard' with creamy-white foliage in the growing season, much less pronounced in winter. **I.** D.W. Hatch, Chantry Nurs, Honiton, Devon.   U.K.

- - 'Dumosa' Hort. France   Probably a mistake for 'Squarrosa Dumosa'.

- - 'Dwarf Blue' Hort. Germany
        1938 A selection from f. *leptoclada* indistinguishable from 'Squarrosa Intermedia'. **O.** H. A. Hesse Nurs, Weener-on-Ems, (1938).   W   Germany

- - 'Erecta' Hort. ex R Smith
        1867 A conical tree no longer identifiable.   B   U.K.

- - **'Ericoides'** Regel   1883 Named for a plant with juvenile foliage that eventually 'grew up' and disappeared from view. *CHAMAECYPARIS thyoides* 'Ericoides' is now usually supplied in its place. (But see 'Gekko').   B,H,K,W   Russia

- - f. *filifera* (Endlicher) Rehder
1949 A botanical designation covering all the thread-leaf variants, nowadays usually listed as cultivars. Note. The word 'Filifera' may not now form part of a new cultivar name.

- - 'Filifera' Hort. ex R. Smith
1867 Conical, small tree branches spreading, branchlets pendulous; foliage threadlike, green above, glaucous beneath. I. Sent from Japan by R. Faber to the Royal Nurs, Bagshot, Surrey, (1861).   B,D,G,H,K,W   U.K.

- - 'Filifera Argenteovariegata' Hort. ex Beissner
1891 Dwarf, conical or globose bush with creamy-white flecked foliage.   B,K,W   Germany

- - 'Filifera Aurea' Veitch   1889 In "Roy. Hort. Soc. Journal". A golden thread-leaf form that becomes a small, bushy tree in time.   B,D,G,H,K,W   U.K.

- - 'Filifera Aurea Nana' Hort.   An unsatisfactory name sometimes used for slow-growing propagands of 'Filifera Aurea' that eventually will develop normal vigour. But see also 'Golden Mop'.

- - 'Filifera Aureomarginata' Hort. Anglia
Probably merely a superfluous name for 'Filifera Aureovariegata'.   W

- - 'Filifera Aureovariegata' Hort. ex Beissner
1891 Large bush with creamy-yellow variegation in bold splashes.   B,G,K,R,W   Germany

- - 'Filifera Compacta' Hort. France
An illegit. name. (Probably a mistake for 'Filifera Nana').

- - 'Filifera Crispa' Beissner   1897 Conical; foliage dense, bluish, curled. NIC.   B,K   Germany

- - 'Filifera Elegans' Hort. Ireland   Reported from the National Botanic Garden, Dublin.

- - 'Filifera Flava' Schelle   1909 Sulphur-yellow sport of 'Filifera'. O. E. Schelle at University Botanic Garden, Tubingen. NIC. This name has been sometimes misapplied in the trade to 'Green Mound'.   B,H,W2   Germany

- - 'Filifera Glauca' De Vos   1887 NIC. Probably a misidentification of a *CHAMAECYPARIS lawsoniana* form.

- - 'Filifera Gold Spangle' Hort.   See 'Gold Spangle'.

- - 'Filifera Golden Mop' Hort.   See 'Golden Mop'.

- - 'Filifera Golden Sunset' Hort. Germany
1985 In "Nurs. Cat". G. Horstmann, Schneverdingen, Germany and Nurs, List 1992 without desription. (See also 'Golden Sunset').

- - 'Filifera Gracilis' (1) Gordon
1891 Differing from 'Filifera' in having slender, drooping branches, branchlets few, mostly in whorls; leaves light green.   B,K,R,W   U.K.

- - 'Filifera Gracilis' (2) Welch
1966/79 This name was mistakenly applied to a hitherto unnamed clone. See 'Green Mound'.

- - 'Filifera Kócos' Hort. Hungary   See 'Kócos'.

- - 'Filifera Nana' Beissner   1897 A slow growing mutation on 'Filifera'. O. Forestry Nurs, at Tharandt, (and similar mutations have arisen elsewhere).   B,D,H,K,W   Germany

- - 'Filifera Pendula' Hort Amer.
1962 Reported from the Gotelli collection, South Orange, N.J.   U.S.A.

- - 'Filifera Sherwood Reversion' Hort. Amer.
  1985 Plant with long stems and clusters of foliage. More bizarre than beautiful. L. M. Kristick, Wellsville PA.

- - 'Filifera Sungold' Hort. Germany
  An illegit. name. Now to be 'Sungold'.   K

- - 'Filifera Variegata' Hort.   See 'Filifera Aureovariegata'.

- - 'Filiformis' Hort. ex R. Smith
  1867 Long, slender sprays; silvery hue. NIC.   U.K.

- - 'Flavescens' Carrière   1867 Foliage normal but pale yellow in colour. NIC.   B   Germany

- - 'Flavescens Nana' Hort. Anglia
  1984 Reported from the Royal Botanic Gardens, Kew.

- - 'Floral Arts' Hort. Amer.   Insufficiently distinct from 'Plumosa Albopicta' to retain.

- - 'Fuiri-tsukumo' Hort. Holland
  1993 A listed name. See 'Tsukumo'.

- - 'Gekira-Hiba' Hort. Germany
  1992 In "Nurs. Cat". without description. G. Horstmann, Schneverdingen, Germany.

- - 'Gekko' L.C. Hatch   1985 In "Reference Guide". A vigorous selection, upright habit, white growth tips.

- - 'Glauca Compacta Nana' Hort. Amer.
  1986 An illegit. name. L. Weston Nurs, Hopkinton, MA. (1982). NOM.

- - 'Globosa' Hort. Amer.   1986 An illegit. name. L. E.A. Cope. "Native . . . Conifers". NOM.

- - 'Gold Cushion' G. Haddow
  1987 A globose plant. The juvenile leaves are dark yellow. Trade plants tend to be conical. **O.** A mutation on 'Plumosa Aurea' at Kenwith Castle Nurs, Bideford, Devon, (1987).   U.K.

- - **'Gold Dust'** Hort. Canada A sport from 'Minima Aurea'; yellow variegated foliage, **O.** Wm Goddard, Flora-vista, Victoria, B.C., Canada.   W3

- - **'Gold Spangle'** Den Ouden
  1937 A sport of 'Filifera Aurea'. Partly thread-like foliage. **I.** Mesman Nurs, Boskoop. **O.** Koster Bros. Nurs, Boskoop, (c. 1900). ('Golden Spangle').   B,G,K,R,W   Holland

- - 'Gold Thread' Hort. Amer.   A listed name without description.

- - **'Golden Chimes'** Hort. N.Z.
  1984 L. Duncan & Davies Nurs, New Plymouth.

- - 'Golden Dwarf' Hort. Anglia
  1985 An unacceptable listed name. Probably = 'Strathmore'.

- - **'Golden Mop'** Welch   1966 A low growing, dense form of 'Filifera Aurea' with brighter colour, that appears to be reliably stable.   G,K,W   U.K.

- - **'Golden Pincushion'** Hort. Amer.
  1982 L. Iseli Nurs, Boring, OR, (1982), **I.** Wm Goddard,

- - 'Golf Ball' R. Critz   1985 In "Amer. Conif. Soc. Bull. **3**". A listed name for a bun-shaped miniature.

- - 'Gospangles' Hort. Amer.
  1985 L. Iseli Nurs, Boring, OR.

- - 'Gracilis' Hort. ex Gordon
  1875 Branches slender; foliage bright green. Still listed in U.S.A.   B,K   U.K.

- - 'Green Mound' Welch   1992 New name here proposed for a clone found by Welch on the
  Everton Nurs, near Lymington, Hants and misidentified by
  him in 1966 as 'Filifera Gracilis'. It's foliage is slightly more
  slender and regular than in most of these threadlike forms and
  it forms a neat dense, mounded bush of a yellowish grass-
  green, not at all a sulphur-yellow.

- - 'Green Velvet' Welch   1979 A clone of 'Squarrosa' insufficiently distinctive to justify
  retaining the name. See Note following 'Squarrosa'.   W

- - 'Greg' Hort. Amer.   Now known as 'Greg's Green Upright'.

- - **'Greg's Green Upright'** L.C. Hatch
  1988 In "Conifer Database". A recent slow-growing conical
  selection from 'Squarrosa'. O. G. Williams, Kate Brook Farm,
  Wolcott, VT.   U.S.A.

- - 'Hime-himuro' Hort. Japan
  1986 Slow-growing, conical bush with bluish-green juvenile
  foliage. Trompenburg Arboretum, Holland.   G

- - "Hime-sawara" Hort. U.S.A.   Dwarf slow-growing globose bush with tight, adult foliage.
  Seems similar to but slower growing and tighter than
  'Tsukumo' or 'Pygmy'. Sawara is the Japanese vernacular
  name for *CHAMAECYPARIS pisifera*.   Japan

- - **'Iceberg'** D and N Sampson
  1991 In "Nurs. Cat". Cedar Lodge Nurs, New Plymouth. A strong-
  growing mutation from 'Snow', with brighter young growth in
  Spring and Summer.   N.Z.

- - 'Ivánc' Barabits   1965 In "Magyar Fenyóújdonságok". Striking blue, loose foliage;
  conical, dwarf. O. Found as a seedling at Ivánc. (1955). I.
  Botanic Gardens, Sopron.   Hungary

- - 'Juniperoides Aurea' Hort. Amer.
  1965 See 'Plumosa Juniperoides'.

- - 'Kingin-hiba' Hort. Anglia   Reported from Windsor Great Park, Berks. No record of
  origin.

- - 'Kócos' Barabits   1966 In "Magyar Fenyóújdonságok". ('Kokos').   Hungary

- - 'Laetivirens' Carrière   1873 Named for a plant at Jardin des Plantes, Paris. NIC.   B   France

- - **'Lemon Thread'** L.C. Hatch
  1988 In "Conifer Database". A mutation of 'Lutescens' with foliage
  partly filiform. O. Mitsch Nurs, Aurora, OR.   W3   U.S.A.

- - f. *leptoclada* (Endlicher) Rehder
  1949 Refer to Welch 179 (1979).   W2

- - 'Leptoclada' Hort.   Now refers only to the clone 'Squarrosa Intermedia'.   W

- - 'Lombarts' Hort.   See 'Squarrosa Lombarts'. ('Lombards').

- - 'Lutea' Beissner   1909 A conical or globose shrub with yellowish foliage. NIC.
  (='Aurea Nana'='Strathmore'?).   B

- - 'Lutescens' Hort. Amer.   1986 An illegit. name for a conical tree with juvenile foliage; white
  to golden-yellow.

- - 'Mace' Hort. Australia   1989 In "Nurs. Cat". Yamina Nurs, Monbulk, Australia. Without
  description.

- - 'Mikko' Hort.   A superfluous name for 'Snow'. ('Miko').   W3

- - **'Milton Park'** Hort. Australia

    1989 A mutation on 'Nana aureovariegata'. The foliage has a golden sheen, but is also speckled with white. **I.** Drue Wholesale Nurs, Berry, Australia.

- - 'Minima' Dallimore & Jackson

    1948 See 'Squarrosa Minima'.   W3

- - 'Minima Aurea' Hort. Amer.   A mutation of 'Minima' showing a golden sheen on its foliage.   W3

- - 'Minima Gold Dust' Hort. Amer.

    A superfluous name for 'Gold Dust'.

- - 'Minima Silver Lode' Hort. Amer.

    An illegit and superfluous name for 'Silver Lode'.

- - 'Minima Variegata' Welch

    1979 An illegit name. A diminutive selection with a clear creamy-yellow variegation.   W3   U.K.

- - 'Monstrosa' Hort. Amer.   1962 Reported from the Gotelli collection, South Orange, N.J.

- - 'Monstrosa Nana' Hort. Holland

    1992 An illegit listed name.

- - 'Mops' Hort.   A mistake for 'Golden Mop'.

- - f. nana Beissner

    1891 A botanical designation for a group of very distinctive, bun-like plants carrying adult foliage.

- - **'Nana'** Hort. ex Beissner

    1891 Dark-green foliage, glaucous beneath with a golden sheen in the growing season.   B,D,G,H,K   Germany

There is a group of useful garden forms which make low, spreading bushes with adult foliage that can be distinguished by size (hence 'Compacta', 'Nana' and 'Minima') and colour ('Albovariegata', 'Aureovariegata', 'Variegata'). But they have probably all arisen by mutation from a common source, since the different forms are only relatively stable. The names used are those widely recognised in the trade, but the distinctions are somewhat arbitrary and must be maintained by careful selection of propagating material. It is not unusual to find several distinct 'cultivars' on a single old plant.

- - **'Nana Albovariegata'** Welch

    1966 A form of 'Nana' with a small, white, not very effective variegation. Name probably illegit. ('Nana Argenteovariegata').   K,W   U.K.

- - 'Nana Aurea' Hort.   A mistake for 'Aurea Nana'.

- - **'Nana Aureovariegata'** Hornibrook

    1939 A dense, bun-shaped plant with some golden variegation, and an overall golden sheen on foliage.   B,H,K,W   U.K.

- - 'Nana Combination' Hort. Australia

    1989 Name changed to 'Milton Park'.

- - 'Nana Compacta' Hort.   A superfluous and illegit.listed name of no clear application.

- - 'Nana Gold Globe' Hort. N.Z.

    1992 An illegit. name for an intense colour variant of 'Nana Aureovariegata'.

- - **'Nana Variegata'** Carrière

    1867 Similar to 'Compacta Variegata' but smaller in every way.   B,D,W

- - **'Obelisk'** Barabits   1966 In "Magyar Fenyóújdonságok".   Hungary

- - **'Parslori'** H.G.Hillier   1971   A flattened bun-shape plant; dense light-green foliage in short crowded sprays. ('Nana Parslori') **I.** Received by Wansdyke Nurs, Devizes, Wilts, from D.M. Thompson of Mount View Gardens, Summertown, South Australia, (1968).   W2

- - 'Pendula'   1986   An illegit. name. **L.** E.A. Cope. "Native . . . Conifers". NOM.   U.S.A.

- - **'Pici'** Barabits   1965   In "Magyar Fenyóújdonságok". Similar to 'Squarrosa Dumosa' in summer but slower growing, bronze in winter. **O.** Named for a plant in the Botanic Garden, Sopron.   W   Hungary

- - 'Pincushion' Hort. Amer.   A listed name.**O.** Wm Goddard, Floravista. Vancouver Is, B.C.   Canada

- - f. *plumosa* (Carrière) Beissner
   1887   A botanical designation covering all the variants with fixed semi-juvenile foliage. Note: The word 'Plumosa' may not now form part of a new cultivar name.   Japan

- - **'Plumosa'** Carrière   1867   (Under *CHAMAECYPARIS obtusa* in error). Conical tree or large, compact bush; plumose sprays of bright green semi-juvenile foliage soft to the touch. **I.** Imported by J.G. Veitch into U.K. (1861).   B,D,H,K,W   Japan

The numerous instances of 'Plumosa' - used in conjunction with other adjectives - in the names of undocumented cultivars in this variable group has produced a confusion impossible to disentangle. We suggest to the trade that propagation be restricted to clones characteristic of the cultivars here recommended, most or all of the other names being discarded.

- - 'Plumosa Alba' Hort. ex Beissner
   1891   A form with white shining foliage. NIC.   Germany

- - **'Plumosa Albopicta'** (Veitch) Nicholson
   1884   An upright bush; dark green with white speckled appearance. ('Plumosa Albospicata').   B,D,G,K,R,W   Hort. Japan

- - *"plumosa argentea"* (Beissner) Rehder
   1927   A 'garden form' name suggested by Rehder. It confuses the following two cultivars.

- - 'Plumosa Argentea' (1) Sénéclauze.
   1868   A dwarf plant with an erect trunk but few branches. Foliage has a snow-white variegation. Slightly tender. **O.** Sénéclauze Nurs, Bourg Argental, Loires. NIC.   France

- - **'Plumosa Argentea'** (2) Kent
   1900   Young growth creamy white, turning green the second year. **O.** Sent from Japan by R. Fortune to the Royal Nurs, Bagshot, Surrey, (1861).   B,D,K,W3   Japan

- - 'Plumosa Argentea Nana' Hort. Anglia
   1964   Reported from the Royal Botanic Gardens, Kew.

- - **'Plumosa Aurea'** Sénéclauze
   1868   Similar to 'Plumosa Argentea' in habit but foliage is golden yellow. **O.** As 'Plumosa Argentea', but several clones are now in cultivation that have presumably arisen as fresh mutations.   B,D,G,K,W   Hort. Japan

- - 'Plumosa Aurea Compacta' Hort. ex Beissner
   1909   A superfluous name for 'Plumosa Aurea Nana'.   B,G,H,K,W

- - **'Plumosa Aurea Nana'** Hort. ex Beissner
   1891   Dwarf, dense, conical bush; foliage soft, yellow.   B,K,W   Germany

- - 'Plumosa Aurea Pumila' R. Smith
   1867   Shoots yellow during Spring and Summer. NIC.   U.K.

- - 'Plumosa Aurea Pygmaea' Hort. Amer.
      1962 An illegit. name. Reported from the Gotelli collection, South Orange. N.J.

- - 'Plumosa Aurea Rogersii' Hort. Anglia
      1930 L. W. H. Rogers, Red Lodge Nurs, Chandlers Ford, Hants. Now known as 'Plumosa Rogersii'.   B,K   U.K.

- - 'Plumosa Aurea Variegata' Hort. Anglia
      1964 L. Ingwersen Nurs, E. Grinstead, Surrey.

- - 'Plumosa Aurescens' Hort. ex Beissner
      1909 Conical bush; foliage tipped light-yellow in summer, bluish-green in autumn. NIC.   B   Germany

- - 'Plumosa Compacta' Den Ouden
      1949 Slow-growing seedling from 'Plumosa'; foliage bluish-green. O. Raised on a nursery at Ede. NIC.   B,K,W   Holland

- - 'Plumosa Compacta Argentea'
      1964 A listed name. L. Ingwersen Nurs, E. Grinstead, Surrey.   U.K.

- - **'Plumosa Compressa'** Hornibrook
      1939 This low-growing plant, with very variable foliage, often close to f *squarrosa*, has given rise to numerous undocumented combinations. Latin adjectives such as *aurea, compacta, flavescens, glauca* and *nana,* for more or less unstable mutations. The following is the only variation worthy of recognition. O. Koster Bros Nurs, Boskoop.   B,G,H,K,W   Holland

- - **'Plumosa Compressa Aurea'** H.G. Hillier
      1971 A mutation of the last with golden foliage during the summer. Colour reasonably stable.   U.K.

- - 'Plumosa Cream Ball' Hort. Amer.
      An illegit. name. See 'Cream Ball'.

- - **'Plumosa Cristata'** Onuma ex Beissner
      1900 Possibly the most distinctive of the group, it maintains tight growth. I. H.A. Hesse Nurs, Weener-on-Ems,   B,H,K,W   Hort. Japan

- - 'Plumosa Decussata' Den Ouden/Boom
      1965 I. F.C. Hetz & Sons, Fairview Nurs, Fairview, PA. (1952).   B   U.S.A.

- - **'Plumosa Flavescens'** De Vos
      1874 Conical or globose; sulphur-yellow at first, turning green by autumn. I. Imported by von Siebold to Leyden in Holland, (c. 1866).   B,D,G,K,W   Japan

- - **'Plumosa Juniperoides'** Bergman
      1965 An illegit. name. In "Plants and Gardens". A medium size shrub with incurved juvenile foliage. Golden-yellow in summer, turning green later. (= 'Plumosa Juniperoides Aurea ' Hort. Amer.).   G,K,W   U.S.A.

- - 'Plumosa Lovettii' Hort. Amer.
      1985 An illegit. name. L. L.C. Hatch in "Reference Guide". NOM.

- - 'Plumosa Lutescens' Hort.Amer.
      See 'Lutescens'.

- - 'Plumosa Lutescens Compacta' Hort. Germany
      1984 An illegit. name. L. Hachmann Nurs, Barmstedt-in-Holstein.   Germany

- - 'Plumosa Minima' Hort. Amer.
      1962 Reported from the Gotelli collection, South Orange, N.J.   U.S.A.

- - 'Plumosa Minima Variegata' Hort. Amer.
      1986 L. E.A. Cope. "Native . . . Conifers". NOM.   U.S.A.

- - 'Plumosa Nana' Herre   1931 Sub-globose form. **O.** Raised from seed of 'Plumosa'. M. Herre, Worlitz, NIC.   B,K,W3   Germany

- - **'Plumosa Nana Aurea'** Hornibrook
1923 Low, compact bun-shaped bush; light golden-yellow foliage, liable to sun-scorch.   B,H,K   U.K.

- - 'Plumosa Pygmaea' Hort. Ireland
1959 Reported from the Glasnevin National Botanic Garden, Dublin. The green equivalent to 'Plumosa Rogersii'.   K,R,W3   Ireland

- - 'Plumosa Pygmaea Aurea'
1959 Doubtfully distinguishable from the last. **O.** The same.   W   Ireland

- - 'Plumosa Riverlea' Hort N.Z.
1992 See 'Riverlea'.

- - **'Plumosa Rogersii'** Hornibrook
1939 Dwarf, conical; branchlets upright, persistent golden-yellow foliage with Squarrosa-like leaves. **O.** W. H. Rogers, Red Lodge Nurs, Chandlers Ford, Hants. (c. 1930).('Plumosa Aurea Rogersii', 'Rogersii').   B,H,K,R.W   U.K.

- - **'Plumosa Variegata'**   Typical 'plumosa' foliage; white variegation. Reported from the Roy. Hort. Soc. Gardens, Wisley.   U.K.

- - **'Plumosa Vera'** Beissner
1904 A clone of f. *plumosa* with peculiar foliage.   B,G,K   Germany

- - 'Plumosa Zan Zetsu' Hort. Amer.
An illegit. name. See 'Zan Zetsu'.

- - 'Purple Dome' Hort. Anglia
1990 Listed Wansdyke Nurs, Devizes, Wilts.

- - **'Pygmaea'** H.G.Hillier   1971 A superfluous name for 'Plumosa Pygmaea' (Not=the following entry).

- - **'Pygmy'** R.S. Corley   1970 In "Bull. Alpine Gar. Soc.". A very dwarf bun with adult foliage. (Probably = 'Tsukumo').   G,W   Hort. Japan

- - 'Repens' Hort. Holland   1992 An unacceptable name. See Art. 50 of I.C.N.C.P.

- - 'Riverlea' Hort. N.Z.   1992 A listed name for a dwarf form with foliage an attractive open, lace-like frond. **O.** Riverlea Nurs, Wanganui, N.Z.

- - **'Ruck's Globe'** Welch   1979 Globose; a selection from 'Squarrosa Pygmaea'. **O.** W. Ruck, Merrick, L. I., N.Y. **I.** J.W. Spingarn, Baldwin, L. I., N.Y.   W   U.S.A.

- - 'Sanderi' Hort. Amer.   1992 A mistake for *THUJA orientalis* 'Sanderi'.

- - 'Silver and Gold' Hort. Anglia
1987 A mutation from 'Plumosa Aurea' with silver white variegations on the yellow foliage. For best effect plant in some shade. **O.** Unrecorded. **I.** Wansdyke Nurs, Devizes, Wilts. (1984).

- - **'Silver Lode'** L.C. Hatch
1985 In "Reference Guide". White variegated foliage. Mutation from 'Minima Aurea'. **O.** Wm. Goddard, Flora-vista, Vancouver Is., B.C. ('Minima Silver Lode', 'Min. Silberlade').   W3   Canada

- - **'Snow'** H.G. Hillier   1971 In "Hillier's Manual". Dwarf, bun shaped bush; mossy blue-grey foliage, tipped creamy-white. (Squarrosa Snow', 'Miko').   G,K,R,W   Hort. Japan.

- - 'Solar Flare' Hort. Amer.   1985 A sport of 'Plumosa Aurea' that retains its bright golden yellow colour. Under test at N. Carolina State Univ.   U.S.A.

- - **'Sopron'** Welch 1979 A low-growing form with light green foliage. O. E. Barabits of Sopron. In "Deutsche Baumschule 5". (As 'Repens', an illegitimate name). Hungary

- - f. *squarrosa* [Zuccatini] Beissner & Hochstetter ex Beissner
1887 A botanical designation covering all the variants with persistent juvenile foliage. Note: The Latin word 'Squarrosa' was usually but not invariably used in the cultivar name in this group, but this is no longer permitted..

- - **'Squarrosa'** Siebold & Zuccarini
1844 (Listed under *RETINISPORA)*. Tree or large bush; glaucous juvenile foliage, soft to touch. I. Imported by Von Siebold into Belgium in 1861. The word must not now be used as part of a cultivar name. B,G,R,W Hort. Japan

- - **'Squarrosa Albospica'** Hornibrook
1923 Foliage as 'Squarrosa' but young foliage white-tipped. No longer identifiable. B,H U.K.

- - 'Squarrosa Argentea' Endlicher
1847 Foliage as 'Squarrosa' but has mottled twigs and whitish-green leaves. No longer distinguishable. B,R,W2 Hort. Japan

- - 'Squarrosa Argentea Compacta' Hort.
1966 A name of no clear application. It has been used for slow-growing young propagands of 'Squarrosa' and also of 'Squarrosa Intermedia'. It should not be re-used.

- - 'Squarrosa Argentea Pygmaea' Hort. Anglia
The remarks under the last entry apply here also.

- - **'Squarrosa Aurea'** Nelson
1866 A vigorous form with golden-yellow foliage. O. Unrecorded. B,K,R,W U.K.

- - 'Squarrosa Aurea Nana' 1971 Dwarf, dense, compact, yellow foliage, paling in winter. L. "Hillier's Manual". See 'Squarrosa Lutea'. U.K.

- - 'Squarrosa Aurea Pygmaea' Hort. Amer.
1972 Reported from Longwood Gardens, Kennett Square, PA. See 'Squarrosa Lutea'. U.S.A.

- - 'Squarrosa Baby Blue' Hort. Holland
1990 See 'Baby Blue'.

- - 'Squarrosa Blue Globe' Hort. Anglia
1988 See 'Blue Globe'.

- - 'Squarrosa Bowland' Hort. Anglia
1987 See 'Bowland'.

- - 'Squarrosa Cristata' A mistake for 'Plumosa Cristata'.

- - **'Squarrosa Dumosa'** Beissner
1891 A compact, rounded shrub; grey-green foliage with a metallic bronze sheen. O. Found in Botanic Gardens, Berlin. B,H,K,R,W Germany

- - 'Squarrosa Elegans' Hornibrook
1939 Light yellow foliage, more compact than 'Squarrosa Sulphurea'. NIC. B,H,W Germany

- - **'Squarrosa Greg's Sport'** Hort. Amer.
A mistake for 'Greg's Green Upright'.

- - **'Squarrosa Intermedia'** Hornibrook
1923 The "type" of f. *leptoclada*. Coarse adult foliage will in time take over from the juvenile foliage unless checked in time. The latter can produce attractive garden forms. See 'Squarrosa Pygmaea'. B,H,K,R.W Hort.U.K.

- - **'Squarrosa Lombarts'** Welch
  1979 Deep blue foliage turning copper-bronze in winter; similar to but more vigorous than 'Dumosa'. L. L. Konijn in "Sortimentslijst 1968".   R,W3   France

- - **'Squarrosa Lutea'** Den Ouden
  1949 A slow-growing sport from 'Squarrosa' with yellow-white foliage. O. Koster Bros. Nurs, Boskoop.   B,K,R,W   Holland

- - 'Squarrosa Mici' Hort. Germany
  An illegit. name. Possibly a mistake for 'Pici'.   Germany

- - **'Squarrosa Minima'** Hornibrook
  1923 Name changed to 'Squarrosa Pygmaea' by Hornibrook in 1932.   B,H,K,W   U.K.

- - 'Squarrosa Nana' Hort. Anglia
  1984 Reported from the Royal Botanic Gardens, Kew.

- - 'Squarrosa Nana Aurea' Hort. Amer.
  1972 Reported from Longwood Gar. Kennett Square, PA.

- - 'Squarrosa Nana Mikko'   A superfluous name for 'Snow'.

- - 'Squarrosa Pici' Barabits   1965 An illegit. name. Now known as 'Pici'.

- - 'Squarrosa Pygmaea' (1) Hornibrook
  1923 A mistake for 'Squarrosa Intermedia'.   H

- - 'Squarrosa Pygmaea' (2) Hornibrook
  1932 A correction by Hornibrook to the name 'Squarrosa Minima' (1923).   H   U.S.A.

Careful selection of material over several cutting generations can produce very dense little plants, some of which have been named, but this dense growth soon disappears unless maintained by regular pruning back. Unchecked plants will, sooner or later, revert to 'Squarrosa Intermedia'. (or worse!).

- - 'Squarrosa Sieboldii' Bailey
  1933 Juvenile globose form, not now distinguishable. NIC.   B   U.S.A.

- - 'Squarrosa Snow' Hort.   A superfluous name for 'Snow'.

- - **'Squarrosa Sulphurea'** Nicholson
  1900 A dense, conical plant with sulphur-yellow juvenile foliage turning green in winter. O. Koster & Co Nurs, Boskoop. There appears to be more than one clone in cultivation.   B,G,K,R,W   Holland

- - 'Squarrosa Veitchii' Hort.   A superfluous name for 'Squarrosa'.

- - 'Standishii' Hort. ex Beissner
  1891 Dark green foliage, broad, strong-growing. NIC.   B   Germany

- - 'Starker's Very Dwarf' Hort. Amer.
  1991 In "Nurs. Cat". Foxborough Nurs, Maryland, U.S.A.

- - **'Strathmore'** C.R. Harrison
  1975 A spreading bush with yellow adult foliage. Probably = 'Aurea Nana'. See Welch 186 (1979), but this name is now in general use in the trade.   W2   Europe

- - 'Stricta' Hort. ex Beissner
  1891 Tips yellowish in spring; slender, ascending. NIC.   B   Germany

- - 'Stricta Lutescens' Hort. ex Beissner
  1891 Similar to last but more conspicuously yellow-green in summer, grey-green in winter. NIC.   B   Germany

- - **'Sulphurea'** Kent in Veitch
  1900 Sulphur-yellow adult foliage; strong grower. **O.** H.A. Hesse
  Nurs, Weener-on-Ems.   B   Germany

- - 'Summer Snow' Hort. Europe   A superfluous name for 'Snow'.

- - **'Sungold'** H.J. Grootendorst
  1969 In "Dendroflora 6". Seedling from 'Filifera Aurea' resistant to
  sun scorch. **O.** Wm. Goddard, Floravista, Vancouver Is. B.C.
  I. into Europe. F.J. Grootendorst & Sons Nurs, Boskoop.   G,R,W3   Canada.

- - 'Sunproof' Hort. Amer.   1988 A conical, golden clone, also claimed to be resistant to sun
  scorch. **L.** L.C. Hatch in "Conifer Database".

- - **'Süveg'** Barabits
  1965 In "Magyar Fenyóújdonságok". Blue-green foliage retaining a
  semi-juvenile form; compact, conical.   Hungary

- - 'Tama Himiro' H.J. van de Laar
  1990 In "Dendroflora 27". Diminutive globular plant with dark
  blue-green juvenile foliage. (Other spellings are found).   G   Hort. Japan

- - 'Tamarawardiana' Hort. Amer.
  1979 An illegit. name? Reported from Arnold Arboretum, Jamaica
  Plain, Mass. U.S.A.
- - 'Teddy Bear' Hort. Anglia   Reported from Windsor Great Park, Berks.

- - **'Törpe'** Barabits
  1965 In "Magyar Fenyóújdonságok". ('Thorpe') ('Toerpe').   Hungary

- - **'Tsukumo'** Hort. Amer.   1967 Small bun-shaped plant with dark green foliage. **L.** J.W.
  Spingarn, Baldwin, L. I., N.Y. (Probably identical with
  'Pygmy'). (Spelling varies).   W3   U.S.A.

- - 'Veitchii' Hort.   A mistake for 'Squarrosa'.

- - 'Villa Taranto' Hort. Italy
  1991 **L.** G. Horstmann, Schneverdingen, Germany. NOM.

- - 'Viridis' Beissner   1909 Similar to 'Standishii', but foliage vivid green. NIC.   B   Germany

- - 'Wahokuhiba' Onuma ex Beissner
  1900 Tips of branchlets broad, monstrous, fan-shaped. NIC.   B   Hort. Japan

- - 'Westermannii' Hort.   1986 A mistake for *CHAMAECYPARIS lawsoniana*
  'Westermannii'.

- - 'White Beauty' Hort. Holland
  1990 A cream and green globose bush originating as a sport of
  'Snow'. Stronger growing and with long terminal shoots. **O.**
  and **I.** Libo Nurs, Baexam, Holland.

- - **'White Pygmy'** R.S. Corley
  1970 In "Alpine Gar. Soc. Bull". Light green foliage with
  pronounced white young growth.   Hort. Japan

- - **'Winter Gold'** Zeigenfuss   Similar to 'Compacta Variegata' but with mottled yellow
  foliage. **L.** Hillside Nurs, Lehighton, PA. (1970).   U.S.A.

- - 'Zan Zetsu' Hort. Amer.   1980 In "Nurs. Cat". Raraflora Nurs, Feasterville, PA. NOM.

CHAMAECYPARIS sphaeroidea Spach
  1842 Now known as *CHAMAECYPARIS thyoides*.
  (*sphaeroidalia*).

CHAMAECYPARIS thyoides (L.) Britten, Sterns & Poggenburg
  1888 White Cedar. Formerly known as *CHAMAECYPARIS*
  sphaeroidea (thyodes).   15m, Z3   U.S.A.

- - **'Andelyensis'** Carrière   1867   Slow-growing pointed column; bluish-green foliage coning freely. **O.** Cauchois Nurs, Les Andelys, (1850). (Other spellings are incorrect).   B,G,H,K,W   France

- - 'Andelyensis Aurea' Meyer
     1963   In "Plant Explorations 1963". Now known as 'Andelys Yellow'.

- - 'Andelyensis Conica' Hort.
     1968   A superfluous name for 'Conica'.

- - **'Andelyensis Nana'** Hornibrook
     1939   Identical with 'Andelyensis' except in habit; it is a dwarf shrub broader than it is high bearing mostly adult foliage. **O.** Detriche Nurs, Angers.   B,G,H,K,W   France

- - **'Andelys Yellow'** Den Ouden/Boom
     1965   Similar to 'Andelyensis' but foliage yellowish.   B,K,W3   Holland

- - **'Atrovirens'** Lawson   1852   Darkish-green foliage. NIC.   B,K   U.K.

- - **'Aurea'** Ottolander   1874   A regular, conical form; yellow foliage in summer fading to brownish in winter. **O.** N. Gaujard Nurs, Ghent, (1872).   B,G,K,W3   Belgium

- - 'Blue Broom' Hort. Amer.
     1991   A listed name for an upright, loose clone with lace-like blue foliage.

- - 'Blue Sport' Hort. Amer.   1991   An unacceptable name.

- - **'Compacta'** Van Geert   1862   A compact form of moderate vigour.   B,G   Holland

- - **'Conica'** Den Ouden   1949   A slow-growing, conical sport from 'Andelyensis' with dense all-juvenile foliage. Bluish-green in summer, bluish-brown in winter. **O.** Konijn Nurs, Reeuwijk, Boskoop. (1940).   B,K,   Holland.

- - **'Ericoides'** Carrière   1855   A compact, pyramidal bush; dark grey-green in summer to violet-brown in winter. Often confused with *CHAMAECYPARIS pisifera* 'Ericoides'. **O.** Bergeot Nurs, Le Mans, (1840).   B,G,H,K,R,W   France

- - 'Ericoides Glauca' Beissner
     1900   Similar to previous entry but blue-green colour. NIC.   B,K,W2   Germany

- - 'Ericoides Kámon' Barabits
     1965   Name now to be 'Kámon'.

- - **'Fastigiata'** Nelson   1866   A fastigiate, upright tree. NIC.   B   U.K.

- - 'Fastigiata Glauca' Senclauze
     1868   Columnar; steel-blue foliage. **O.** Sénéclauze Nurs, Bourg Agental, Loires. NIC.   B   France

- - **'Glauca'** Endlicher   1847   Seedlings with glaucous blue foliage turn up from time to time. One such (known as 'Kewensis'), is indistinguishable.   G,R,W3

- - 'Glauca Pendula' Hort. Amer.
     1990   An illegit. (although presumably descriptive) name.

- - **'Golden Twig'** L.C. Hatch
     1988   In "Conifer Database". Blue-green with young growth yellow. L. Gordon Bentham, Canada, (1980).

.- - **'Heatherbun'** Welch   1979   A small round-topped shrub; dense juvenile foliage, plum-purple in winter, greyish-green in summer.   W

- - var. *henryae* (Li) Little   1966   A minor variant, not now distinguished from the species (per Rushforth, 1987).

- - 'Hopkinton' L.C. Hatch   1988 In "Conifer Database". Fastigiate open, vigorous. Blue-grey foliage. Cones freely. **O.** Weston Nurs, Hopkinton, MA, (1982).   U.S.A.

- - 'Hoveyi' Veitch   1881 Slender habit with dense terminal tufts, often contorted.   B,K   U.K.

- - 'Kewensis' Knight & Perry
   1850 In "Coniferous Plants . . .". NOM. Name raised for a clone of 'Glauca' that is indistinguishable from other glaucous seedlings. It should not be re-used.   U.K.

- - 'Little Jamey' Hort. Amer.
   1989 In "Nurs. Cat". Mitsch Nurs, Oregon, U.S.A. Dense dwarf, narrowly columnar; leaves tiny; bluish-green with good autumn colour.   U.S.A.

- - 'Meth Dwarf' L.C. Hatch   1988 Said to be an improvement on 'Andelyensis'. "Conifer Database".   U.S.A.

- - 'Nana' Loudon   1842 A dwarf, almost spherical. NIC.   B,H,K,W2   U.K.

- - 'Pendula' Nelson   1866 A form lacking in vigour, with branches pendulous. NIC.   U.K.

- - 'Purple Heather' Hillier & Son
   1981 In "Nurs. Cat". Possibly identical to 'Heatherbun'.   U.K.

- - 'Pygmaea' Carrière   1867 A cushion-shaped spreading shrub; bluish-green adult leaves. **O.** Sénéclauze Nurs, Bourg Argental, Loires. NIC.   France

- - 'Pyramidata' Carrière   1867 Columnar; small, densely set with short branches. NIC.   B,K   France

- - 'Raraflora' Hort. Amer.   1966 A listed name for an upright open shrub with twisted branches; graceful blue-green foliage.

- - 'Red Star' Hort. Holland and Hort. N.Z.
   1984 In "Dendroflora 23". A superfluous name for 'Rubicon'.   U.S.A

- - **'Rezek's Dwarf'**   1986 **O.** E. Rezek. In "Nurs. Cat". Foxborough Nurs, Maryland. NOM.

- - **'Rubicon'** J. Lewis   1972 Dense juvenile foliage turning plum-purple in winter; upright bush. **I.** Wansdyke Nurs, Devizes, Wilts. (1971) **O.** Found by H.J. Welch in Tennessee Valley Nurs, Tennessee.   W3   U.S.A.

- - 'Schumaker's Dwarf Blue' Hort. Amer.
   1978 A low growing, spreading dwarf blue plant, later stronger growing. **O.** and **I.** Schumaker's Nurs.

- - 'Top Point' Hort.   1992 **L.** Libo Nurs, Baexem, Holland. NOM.   Holland

- - **'Variegata'** Carrière   1855 Partly yellow variegated. ('Aureovariegata').   B,G,K,R,W   Ireland

- - 'Viridis' Sénéclauze   1868 Dark green foliage. NIC.   France

CHAMAECYPARIS taiwanensis Masamune & Suzuki.
   1933 Now treated as *CHAMAECYPARIS obtusa* var. *formosana*.

CRYPTOMERIA D. Don (1841)

Taxodiaceae

A monotypic genus of forest-size trees, long cultivated in Japan, whence have emanated many garden cultivars, including some quite diminutive plants. The nomenclature of the garden forms is complicated by the duplication of European and Japanese names. In Japanese horticulture names are often used more as descriptions than as cultivar names in the western sense and often with local variations in usage. The synonyms given must therefore be treated with caution since they may not be exact equivalents. Where they do relate to the same cultivar they may be accepted as "Commercial synonyms" in the two areas. The word "sugi", being the name of the species in Japan, should properly not be used as part of any cultivar name introduced since 1st Jan 1959, but is here retained where it was validly in use before that date.

CRYPTOMERIA fortunei Hooibrenk ex Otto & Dietrich
　　　　　　　　1853　Chinese Cryptomeria. Here listed as *CRYPTOMERIA japonica* var. *sinensis*.　　　　　　　　　　　　　　30m,Z7　　　China

CRYPTOMERIA japonica (L. fil.) D. Don
　　　　　　　　1841　Cryptomeria, Japanese Cryptomeria.　　　　　　30m,Z5　　　Japan

- - 'Alba Variegata' Young in Gordon
　　　　　　　　1874　Not now distinguished from 'Argenteovariegata' ('Albo-variegata').　　　　　　　　　　　　　　　　　H,W3　　　U.K.

- - 'Albospica' De Vos　　　1887　Branch tips at first white. O. Hellemän, Moorende near Bremen. ('Albospicata'), NIC.　　　　　　　B,K,W3　　　Germany

- - 'Albovariegata' Hort. ex Beissner
　　　　　　　　1891　A superfluous name for 'Variegata'.

- - 'Alpina' Hort. Germany　1992　An illegit. name. L. Horstmann, Schneverdingen, Germany. Without description.

- - **'Antique Gold'** Hort. N.Z.
　　　　　　　　1988　L. Cedar Lodge Nurs, New Plymouth, N.Z. A clone of 'Elegans' with distinctive winter colour, burnished gold.　　　　　　　　　　　　　　　　　　　　　N.Z.

- - f. *araucarioides* (Henkel & Hochstetter) Beissner
　　　　　　　　1887　A botanical designation covering all the thread-leaf forms.　　　　　　　　　　　　　　　　　　　　Sporadic

- - 'Araucarioides' (1) Siebold & Zuccarini
　　　　　　　　1844　A tall, conical tree, usually furnished to the ground, branches long, distant, horizontal or drooping, lacking short branches in whorls; leaves short, stout, incurved; a persistent bright or dark green. Sent by von Siebold to Leiden in 1859 but doubtless other clones are now in cultivation.　　B,D,G,K,R,W　Japan

This variation turns up in the seedbeds from time to time and has attracted many coiners of names. Any disentanglement of these names now is impossible because of inadequate descriptions and there being no record in many cases of what plant the writer was describing. The earliest descriptions, from actual plants, of *araucarioides* Carrière, (1867) and Sénéclauze the following year, (from the same trees), *dacrydioides* Carrière, (1867), and *lycopodioides* Carrière, (1875), are of clearly distinguishable plants. So, as the practicable way out of so much turmoil, we suggest that these three names be retained as collective or group names and that 'Athrotaxoides', 'Kewensis'. 'Mucronata', 'Selaginoides', 'Viminalis', 'Virgata' and similar names be treated as "Lost to cultivation". Distinctive clones of any real value in this rather unattractive group should receive new clonal names.

- - 'Araucarioides' (2) Hort.　　A collective or 'group' name for all tree-like clones with persistently green foliage, lacking tufts.　　　　　　W3

- - **'Archer's Greenbush'** Welch (1991)
　　　　　　　　A new name to replace 'Nana' SENSU Welch (1966) and 1979, and Krüssmann Plate 48 (1983). We apologise for this mistake, and especially to Herr Krüssmann who took the photo in the nursery.　　　　　　　　　　　　　　　U.K.

- - **'Archer's Redbush'** Welch (1991)
　　　　　　　　A new name to replace 'Pygmaea' SENSU Welch (1966) and 1979 and Krüssmann Plate 48.　　　　　　　　　　U.K.

- - 'Argenteospicata' Beissner
1909 Not now distinguishable from 'Albospica'.   B

- - **'Argenteovariegata'** Sénéclauze
1868 Tips of young foliage cream or silvery white.Somewhat variable, or possibly more than one clone is involved. ('Alba Variegata', 'Argentea Spicata', etc.).   D,W3

- - 'Aritaki' Hort. Japan   1985 A globose bush, rather loose, long branches with fine leaves pale green. In "Nurs. Cat". Wansdyke Nurs, Devizes, Wilts.

- - 'Ashio-sugi' Krüssmann   1972 Probably a selection within var. *radicans* for purposes of forestry. ('Ashigo-sugi').   K

- - 'Athrotaxoides' Sénéclauze
1868 A clone of f. *araucarioides*. **O.** Sénéclauze Nurs, Bourg Argental, Loires. NIC.   B,W   France

- - **'Aurea'** Hort. ex Beissner
1891 A golden clone, from seed. See 'Ogon-sugi'.   B,K,W   Hort. Japan

- - 'Aureovariegata' Sénéclauze
1868 A variegated seedling. **O.** Sénéclauze Nurs, Bourg Argental, Loires. NIC.   B,K   France

- - 'Aurescens' Den Ouden   1949 A conical tree, yellowish-green leaves. **O.** Blijdenstein Pinetum, Hilversum, (1937).   B,K,W   Holland

- - 'Aya-sugi' Hort. Japan   1892 **L.** Yokohama Gardeners' Association. Not in European cultivation ?

- - **'Bandai-sugi'** Hornibrook
1939 A popular dwarf form with congested foliage. Not always supplied true to name.   B,D,G,K,W   Hort. Japan

- - 'Bandai-Tongi' Hort. Anglia
1992 A plant in Windsor Great Park, Berks, different to 'Bandai-sugi'. Without description.

- - 'Barabits Gold' Hort. Hunary
1990 Indistinguishable from 'Sekkan'. **L. W.** Linssen, Baexem, Holland. Plant also in Windsor Great Park, Berks. (also called Hungarian Gold). **O.** Raised from seed at Sopron University, Hungary.

- - 'Beaumont's Dwarf' Hort. N.Z.
1984 Introduced into U.K. by Wansdyke Nurs, Devizes, Wilts, **O.** R. Blackman, Te Kaiti, (1972).   N.Z.

- - f. *beni-sugi* (Mayr) Beissner
1930 A minor variant. Not now distinguished within the species.

- - 'Benjamin Franklin' L.C. Hatch
1985 In "Reference Guide". Vigorous; foliage persistently green.   U.S.A.

- - 'Bennie's Best' Hort. Amer.   See 'Benjamin Franklin'

- - 'Birodo-sugi' (1) Hort. Japan
1909 A commercial synonym of 'Nana' (1). (per Beissner).

- - 'Birodo-sugi' (2) Hort. Japan
1987 A commercial synonym of 'Compressa' (per "Dendroflora **24**") but of conical habit (per Prof. H. Kruse, 1985).

- - **'Black Dragon'** Iseli   1985 In "Nurs. Cat". Upright conical; young growth light green ageing to dark green.   U.S.A.

- - **'Broom'** J.P. Kortmann   1987   In "Dendroflora **24**". Dwarf conical bush; bronzing in winter. **I.** Benckhuysen & Sons Nurs, Boskoop, Holland. **O.** Imported by Minier Nurs, Angers, (1968).   W3   Hort. Japan

- - **'Buckiscope'** J.P. Kortmann
       1987   In "Dendroflora **24**". A vigorous sport from 'Jindai-sugi'. **I.** K.A. Koemans Nurs, Boskoop.   Holland

- - **'Caespitosa'** Sugimoto   1978   A compact form, with foliage in tufts. See 'Mure-sugi'.   Hort. Japan

- - **'Chabo-sugi'** Sugimoto   1978   Not 'Nana' (1). Possibly = 'Archer's Greenbush'. ('Chabo-sugi').   Hort. Japan

- - **'Clark's Mossy'** Hort. Anglia
       1968   A superfluous name for 'Fasciata'.   W

- - f. *clathrata* Krüssmann   1972   ='Globosa Nana' (per Krüssmann, 1979).   Japan

- - **'Compacta'** (1) Carrière   1878   Dense form with blue-green foliage. **O.** Thibault & Keteleer, Sceaux, near Paris, (1877). The name 'Lobbii Compact' is superfluous. Similar seedlings arise.   B,G,H,K,W   France

- - **'Compacta'** (2) A.C. Mitchell
       1972   Name used for a round-topped tree with bright yellow-green foliage. Reported from Wakehurst Place, Sussex.   W   U.K.

- - **'Compacta albaspica'** Hort.   A mistake for 'Nana Albospica'.

- - **'Compacta Nana'** Hort. ex Beissner
       1891   A dense bush; leaves short, glossy green. NIC.   B,K   Germany

- - **'Compacta Nana Glauca'** Rovelli
       1913   In "Nurs. Cat". Rovelli's Nurs, Pallanza. Name only. NIC.   Itlay

- - **'Compactoglobosa'** Cheng et Fu
       1978   In "Florae Reipublica Popularis Sinicae". Text in Chinese.   China

- - **'Compressa'** Den Ouden
       1949   A globose dwarf. **I.** J. Blaauw and Co. Nurs, Boskoop (1942). (Not='Vilmoriniana', possibly = 'Birodo-sugi' (2)).   B,D,K,R,W   Hort. Japan

- - **'Crassifolia'** Sénéclauze   1868   A selection with horizontal branches, pendent at tips. NIC.   B   France

- - **'Cristata'** Beissner   1901   A monstrous but attractive upright form sent from Yokohama by L. Unger to Beissner as 'Sekka-sugi'. Forms large cock's combs.   B,D,G,H,K,W   Hort. Japan

- - **'Cristata Falcata'** Hort.   Probably a mistake for 'Spiraliter Falcata'.

- - **'Cupressa'** Hort. Amer.   Probably a mistake for 'Compressa'.

- - **'Dacrydioides'** (1) Carrière
       1867   A shrubby or pendulous tree with winter colour brown as in some *DACRYDIUM* species ('Dacryoides')   B,D,K,W   Japan

- - **'Dacrydioides'** (2) Hort.   A collective or group name to cover all snakelike clones of pendulous habit, characterised by bronzing winter foliage.

- - **'Dai-sugi'** Krüssmann   1972   Probably a selection within var. *radicans* distinguished for purposes of forestry.   K

- - **'Douglasii'** L.C. Hatch   1985   An illegit name. In "Reference Guide". Hardy arboreal clone not bronzing in winter.   U.S.A.

- - **'Dutch Discovery'** J.P. Kortmann
       1987   In "Dendroflora **24**". A mutation from 'Jindai-sugi'. **O.** C. G. Kuijf Nurs, Boskoop.   Holland

- - 'Eisan-sugi' Hort. Japan   Probably a local name for 'Uncinata'. (Eisan is a mountain near Kyoto).

- - **'Elegans'** Nelson   1866 A well known tree form with juvenile foliage and bright red winter colour. **O.** Sent by Th. Lobb to the Veitch Nurs, in 1854. (Several clones are in cultivation). B,D,G,H,K,W   Japan

- - **'Elegans Aurea'** R.E. Harrison
1959 A strong -growing bush with 'Elegans'-type foliage; yellow or yellowish-green, especially during the winter. G,K,R,W   N.Z.

- - 'Elegans Compacta' (1) Dallimore & Jackson
1948 A superfluous name for 'Elegans Nana'. See Welch (1979). K,W2

- - 'Elegans Compacta' (2) SENSU Welch
1966 A mistake for 'Elegans Nana'. W

- - 'Elegans Gracilis'   1937 Indistinguishable from 'Elegans Nana'. L. Kemp's Nurs, Adelaide, (1937). N.Z.

- - **'Elegans Nana'** (1) (Veitch) Nicholson
1881 A bushy form of 'Elegans' with similar juvenile foliage and winter colour. B,D,H,W   China

- - 'Elegans Nana' (2) SENSU Welch
1966 A mistake for 'Nana'. W3

- - **'Elegans Plumosa'** R.E. Harrison
1959 Unidentifiable from the description given. (Possibly = 'Plumosa' Hort. N.Z). N.Z.

- - **'Elegans Variegata'** De Vos
1887 A variegated form; rare but still in cultivation. B,K,W3   France

- - **'Elegans Viridis'** Hornibrook
1939 Similar to 'Elegans' in every way save that the foliage remains green during the winter. B,H,K,W   Holland

- - f. *elongata* Regel ex Gordon
1875 An unidentifiable plant. NIC.

- - 'Enko-sugi' Beissner   1909 A commercial synonym for 'Araucarioides'. (Yenko-sugi). W   Hort. Japan

- - 'Ericoides' Hort. France   An illegit. listed name.

- - **'Fasciata'** Dallimore & Jackson
1923 A stunted miniature with some leaves extremely small. A mere curiosity. ('Nyewood's Form', 'Clarke's Mossy'?). B,K,R,W   U.K.

- - 'Filifera' Magrini   1967 An illegit. and superfluous name for 'Araucarioides'. Named for a tree in E. Mosco Park, Biella, N. Italy. K   Italy

- - 'Fi-sugi' Hort. Japan   1930 A commercial synonym for 'Nana' (1), (per Fitschen in Beissner).

- - 'Fuiri-banda' Hort. Japan 1972 Probably indistinguishable from 'Argenteovariegata'. (per, Krüssmann).

- - f. *generalis* Krause   1906 An invalid name; probably representing the normal form. i.e.var. *japonica*.

- - 'Gigantea' Hort. ex Beissner
1891 A strong-growing form; leaves browning in winter. NIC B   Germany

- - 'Giokumo' Hort. Amer.   1968 A slow-growing shrub with coarse, green foliage. L. Alpenglow Gardens, Surrey, B.C., Canada. Various spellings are found including 'Giokomo', 'Giokuro', 'Gyokruya', 'Gyokruyu'. Canada

- - **'Globosa'** Den Ouden	1949	A globose form; leaves juvenile, rust-red in winter. **O.** Pierre Lombarts Nurs, Zundert, (1942).	B,K,W	Holland
- - 'Globosa Compacta Nana' Hort. Italy		A listed name.		
- - **'Globosa Nana'** Hornibrook	1923	A popular dwarf. No twisting of leaves.	B,D,G,K,W	Holland
- - 'Gold' Hort. Germany	1978	An unacceptable name. L. Horstmann "Nurs, Cat".		
- - **'Gold Tip'** T.J. Cole	1986	In "Woody Plant Source List", Canadian Dept. Agric.		Canada
- - 'Gracilis' (1) Siebold	1861	Now known as 'Elegans'. **I.** Sent by von Siebold to Leyden in 1859.		Japan
- - 'Gracilis' (2) Krüssmann	1972	A clone with loose but not snake-like habit.(='Tenuifolia' ?).	B,G,K	
- - "Granny's Ringlets" Hort.		Popular name for 'Spiralis'.		
- - 'Gyokuryu' Hort. Amer.	1967	L. J.W. Spingarn, then of Baldwin, L.I., N.Y. NOM. See 'Giokumo'.		
- - 'Haggo' Hort N.Z.	1991	A listed name for a dwarf clone, green in summer, bronze in winter; more colourful than 'Elegans'. It seems doubtfully distinctive from 'Elegans Nana' of Europe.		N.Z.
- - **'Ha-o-sugi'** Dallimore & Jackson	1923	A shrubby clone of f. *araucarioides*. Branches long, slender and curving. Leaves thick, pointed, incurved. ('Hoo-o-Sugi', 'Hor-sugi').	B,D,K,W	Hort. Japan
- -"Hime"		A word meaning "Princess" loosely used as a pet name in several cultivars and so is of no value. ('Hino', 'Hume').		
- - 'Hime-ikari-sugi' Hort. Japan		See 'Ikari-sugi' (1).		
- - 'Hime-sugi' Hort. Japan		A synonym of 'Elegans' (per Beissner, 1909).		
- -'Hino-sugi' Hort. Amer.	1991	An illegit. name. New name required. Globose when young, green turning bronze in winter. In "Nurs. Cat". Iseli Nurs, Boring, OR.		
- - f. *honsugi* Mayr ex Beissner	1909	Not now distinguished within the species.		
- - 'Hoo-o-sugi' Welch	1979	A mistake for 'Ha-o-sugi'.	W2	Hort. Japan
- - 'Howo-sugi' Hort. Japan	1892	L. Yokohama Gardeners' Assoc. (='Spiralis'), (per Beissner. 1909).		
- - f. *huberiana* Carrière	1867	Now known as 'Macrocephala'.		
- - **'Husari-sugi'** Dallimore & Jackson	1923	"Branches curiously bent". Possibly = 'Spiraliter Falcata'.	B,D	Hort. Japan
- - **'Ikari'** (1) J.P. Kortmann	1987	In "Dendroflora **24**". Dwarf form, branches erect, foliage fine. L. Wansdyke Nurs, Devizes, Wilts, U.K. (1974). ('Hime-ikari-sugi', 'Ikan-sugi').		Hort. Japan
- - 'Ikari-sugi' (2) Krüssmann	1972	Krüssmann lists this as a synonym of 'Lycopodioides', but it is not the 'Lycopodioides' of the trade in Europe.		
- - **'Ito-sugi'** Krüssmann	1972	A clone of f. *araucarioides* with peculiar leaf formation. ('Ito' = thread).	K,W	Hort. Japan

- - **'Jindai-sugi'** Hornibrook
1939 A widely grown conical bush-form with green foliage. B,G,H,K,W   Japan

- - 'Juvenile' Hort. Germany   An unsatisfactory listed name.

- - var. *kawaii* Fitschen in Beissner
1930 Not now distinguished within the species.

- - 'Kewensis' Hornibrook   1939 Named for a tree at the Royal Botanic Gardens, Kew. No
longer identifiable. NIC.   B,H,W2   U.K.

- - **'Kilmacurragh'** Welch   1966 A monstrous low growing form covered with small
fasciations, never coarse, as in 'Cristata'. O. Kilmacurragh,
Rathdrum, Co. Wicklow.   G,K,W1   Ireland

- - 'Kitayama-dai' J.P. Kortmann
1987 In "Dendroflora 24". I. Proefstation, Boskoop, Holland,
(1979).   Hort. Japan

- - **'Knaptonensis'** Lyttel   1934 A witch's broom on 'Argenteovariegata' with glistening white
variegated foliage. It is somewhat unstable and reversion can
occur.   B,D,G,H,K,W   Switzerl.

- - **'Kohui'** J.P. Kortmann   1987 A dwarf. I. Konijn and Co. Nurs, Ederveen, Holland.   Hort. Japan

- - **'Kokuryu'** J.P. Kortmann
1987 In "Dendroflora 24". Foliage similar to 'Monstrosa' but more
sparse. A dwarf form imported by the Wansdyke Nurs,
Devizes, Wilts, U.K. in (1974). ('Kokuryow', 'Kokuriyu', and
'Kokurua' are alternative spellings).   Hort. Japan

- - 'Koshiji' Hort. Japan   1973 A slow-growing form with incurved leaves and yellow brown
stems listed by the Nakamura Nurs, Nippa, Yokohama,
Japan. Now in Western cultivation.

- - 'Koshyi' Hort. Japan   A small globose plant with small bright green incurved
leaves. Dwarfer than the similarly named cultivar 'Koshiji'.

- - 'Kowby' Hort. Germany   1992 L. Horstmann Nurs, Schneverdingen, Germany. Without
description.

- - 'Koyo-sugi' Hort. Japan   1892 L. "Yokohama Gardeners' Association". (Possibly =
'Elegans').

- - f. *kuro-sugi* (Mayr) Beissner
1909 Not now distinguished within the species.

- - **'Kusari-sugi'** Dallimore & Jackson
1923 L. "Yokohama Gardeners' Assoc". (1892). (='Spiraliter
Falcata' ?). This name has been applied to several cultivars.   D   Hort. Japan

- - 'Kyoto-ito-sugi' Welch   1979 A particular selection of 'Ito-sugi', made by Prof. G. Isa of
Kyoto University. I. Wansdyke Nurs, Devizes, Wilts, U.K.
(1974).   W2   Hort. Japan

- - 'Little Diamond' H.J. van de Laar
1990 In "Dendroflora 27". A dense, more or less globose bush,
similar to 'Globosa Nana' but slower growing. O. Konijn
Nurs, Ederveen.   Holland

- - 'Little Globe' Hort Holland
1992 L. W. Linssen, Baexem, Holland. NOM.

- - 'Little Gnome' Hort. Anglia   A mistake for 'Littleworth Dwarf'?

- - **'Littleworth Dwarf'** Welch
1991 A congested dwarf with green foliage. **I.** Wansdyke Nurs, Devizes, Wilts,.**O.** Witch's broom found by J.W. Archer and H.J. Welch at Littleworth, near Farnham, Surrey, ('Littleworth Gnom' and ' Littleworth Gnome' are incorrect).   G,W3   U.K.

- - **'Lobbii'** Carrière 1855 A clone with foliage in large clumps. **I.** Sent by Th. Lobb to U.K. in 1853. No longer distinguished botanically. See Mitchell 89, (1972).   B,D,G,K,R,W   Java

- - 'Lobbii Compacta' (1) Hort. Anglia.
A mistake for 'Nana' (1).

- - 'Lobbii Compacta' (2) Hort. Holland
A mistake for 'Compacta'.   G

- - 'Lobbii Nana' (1) Dallimore & Jackson
1923 A mistake for 'Nana'. N.B. There is no plant entitled to this name, which should on no account be used.   B,K,W

- - 'Lobbii Nana' (2) Hort. Europe   A mistake for 'Compacta', 'Globosa Nana' and possibly other cultivars.

- - 'Lobbii Nana' (3) Hillier   1964 A mistake for 'Globosa Nana'.

- - 'Lycopodiiformis' Hort. ex Beissner
1891 Name changed to 'Lycopodioides' in ed. **2** (1909).

- - **'Lycopodioides'** (1) Carrière
1875 An irregular shrub, long branches & foliage in whorls or tufts. **O.** Imported by M. Mazel of Montsauve Nurs, Anduza, France.   B,K,R,W   Hort. Japan

- - 'Lycopodioides' (2) Hort.   A collective name covering all the snake-like clones characterised by tufts or whorls of foliage.

- - 'Lynn's Ringlets' J.P. Kortmann
1987 In "Dendroflora **24**". Mutation from 'Spiraliter Falcata'. **O.** G. Huizer Nurs, Boskoop.   Holland

- - 'Macrocarpa' Sénéclauze 1868 A variant with large, conical cones. NIC.   France

- - 'Macrocephala' Carrière 1867 Named for a tree at Hyeres, Alpes Maritimes. NIC.   B   France

- - 'Majiro' Hort. Amer.   (='Argenteovariegata', or near) L. Alpenglow Gardens, Surrey, B.C. Canada, (1967). ('Mejero', 'Mejiro').

- - 'Manhishi' Hort.   See 'Mankichi'.

- - **'Mankichi'** Hort. Japan   A commercial synonym of 'Monstrosa Nana' (per Krüssmann, 1979). **I.** Wansdyke Nurs, Devizes, Wilts. U.K. (1974).   K

- - 'Mankitiana' Hort. Japan   Same as last.

- - 'Marj' Hort. Amer.   1985 An upright or globose bush, leaves tipped white in Spring. **L.** L.C. Hatch. In "Reference Guide".   U.S.A.

- - 'Midare' H.G. Hillier   1971 In "Hilliers' Manual". A bush resembling 'Elegans' but with some congested clumps. The word means "confused" or "monstrous".   Hort. Japan

- - 'Midori' Hort. Japan.   Used for any form with green leaves (Midore = green).   Hort. Japan

- - 'Mitama-sugi' Hort. Japan   A commercial synonym for 'Globosa Nana' (per Krüssmann, 1979).

- - 'Miyazima'   1982 L. Raraflora Nurs, Feasterville, PA. Without description.   U.S.A.

- - **'Monstrosa'** Beissner   1909 A large bush or small tree. Leaves and branchlets congested and irregular in size.   B,G,K,W   Hort. Japan

- - 'Monstrosa Compacta' Hort. Holland
    1939 Superfluous name for 'Monstrosa Nana'.

- - **'Monstrosa Nana'** Hornibrook
    1939 Intermediate in all respects between 'Monstrosa' and 'Bandai-sugi'.   B,D,G,H,K,W   Hort. Japan

- - 'Mucronata' Henkel & Hochstetter
    1865 A clone possibly indistinguishable from 'Araucarioides'. NIC.   B   France

- - 'Mure-sugi' Hort. Japan   A commercial synonym of 'Caespitosa' (per Prof. Kruse, 1973).

- - **'Nana'** (1) Knight & Perry
    1850 A flat-topped bush; stiff, straight, juvenile leaves and congested growth. Clusters of male flowers in winter.   B,G,W   Japan

- - 'Nana' (2) Welch   1966 A mistake followed by Krüssmann, (1972). Now known as 'Archer's Greenbush'.   W3

- - **'Nana Albospica'** SENSU Den Ouden/Boom
    1965 A name now in general use in the trade. Slow-growing; old plants are indistinguishable from 'Argenteovariegata'.   B,K,W   France

- - 'Nana Albo-spicata' Beissner
    1901 A superfluous name for the last entry, described for a small plant.   H

- - 'Nankin-sugi' Hort. China   A clone introduced into Japan, according to Kaempfer. Possibly 'Elegans'.

- - 'Nejire-sugi' Fitschen in Beissner
    1930 A commercial equivalent of 'Spiralis'. ('Negire-sugi').   Hort. Japan

- - 'Nigricans' Carrière   1870 Discovered by Carrière in Jardin des Plants, Paris. NIC.   B   France

- - 'Nochide' H.J. van de Laar
    1987 In "Dendroflora **24**". Reported from the Botanical Garden at Hiroshima. Possibly the same as 'Mankitiana'.   Hort. Japan

- - 'Nyewoods Form' Hort. Anglia
    1966 A superfluous name for 'Fasciata'.   W1

- - 'Ogon' Hort. Japan   A commercial synonym of 'Aurea' (per Uehara).

- - 'Okina' Hort. Japan   A commercial equivalent of 'Nana Albospica' (per Krüssmann, 1972).

- - 'Osaka-tama' Hort. Japan   I. Wansdyke Nurs, Devizes, Wilts, U.K. (1974). (= 'Vilmoriniana'?).

- - 'Pendula' Leroy ex Dallimore & Jackson
    1923 An unidentifiable clone with slightly elongated branches and pendulous. NIC. (Not = 'Dacrydioides').   B,D

- - 'Pendulata' Bronsart   1914 Same as previous item. NIC.   B,D   Germany

- - 'Phoenix' Hort. Japan   1896 A translation of 'Hoo-o-sugi'. L. Tokyo Nurs, Tokyo, Japan.

- - 'Pickard's Gold' Hort. Ireland
    1985 Reported from Mount Congreave, Co. Waterford, Ireland.

- - 'Pipo' Hort. Holland   1990 O. and I. L. Konijn & Co., Ederveen.

- - 'Plumosa' Hort. N.Z.   I. Duncan & Davies Nurs, New Plymouth, (1953). (Possibly ='Elegans Plumosa').   B   N.Z.

- - **'Pungens'** Carrière   1867   Foliage similar to *ARAUCARIA cunninghamia* 'Glauca'. **I.** Sent to U.K. by R. Fortune in 1861. NIC.   B,D,K   Hort. Japan.

- - 'Pungens Rubiginosa' Carrière
   1873   As last, but foliage reddish in winter. NIC.   B   France

- - 'Pygmaea' (1) Knight & Perry (in synonymy)
   1850   The name 'Nana' is recommended as best preserving long standing usage, following Hornibrook 1923, not 1939.   D,W3

- - 'Pygmaea' (2) Hornibrook
   1939   A name used in error for a plant of 'Nana' at the Royal Botanical Gardens, Kew.   H

- - 'Pygmaea' (3) SENSU Welch
   1966   A mistake. Now to be known as 'Archer's Redbush'.   K,W3

- - 'Pyramidalis' Hort. Holland
   1987   **L.** Esveld Nurs, Boskoop. NOM. (='Pyramidata'?).   Holland

- - **'Pyramidata'** Carrière   1891   A conical form. **O.** L. Paillet Nurs, Chataney-les-Sceaux.   B,K   France

- - var. *radicans* Nakai   1941   A tree with columnar habit, widely used in forestry in Japan.   K,W   Japan

- - 'Rasen' H.J. Grootendorst
   1977   In "Dendroflora **13 - 14**". A commercial equivalent of 'Spiraliter Falcata'.   G ,W3   Hort. Japan

- - **'Rein's Dense Jade'** Hort. Amer.
   1977   Dense form ex witch's broom on 'Lobbii'. Foliage dark-green. **L.** Vermeulen & Son Nurs, Neshanic Station, N.J.

- - 'Rubiginosa' Nicholson   1900   NOM. NIC.   U.K.

- - 'Ryoku' Hort. Amer.   1988   **L.** Mitsch Nurs, Aurora, OR. Without description.

- - 'Sandersii' Nicholson   1900   A variety of dense habit. NIC.   U.K.

- - 'Satsamanka' Hort. Amer.
   1970   **L.** Watnong Nurs, Morris Plains, N.J., U.S.A.

- - 'Sekka-sugi' Fitschen in Beissner
   1930   Commercial synonym of 'Cristata' (per Fitschen in Beissner 1930). Other spellings are 'Sekkwa'sugi' and 'Sekkvia'sugi', but not 'Sekkan-sugi').   Hort. Japan

- - 'Sekkan Dwarf' Hort. Amer.
   1985   Similar to 'Sekkan-sugi' but dwarf. **L.** L.C. Hatch. In "Reference Guide".   U.S.A.

- - **'Sekkan'** Hort.   1970   Shrub, eventually a tree with foliage creamy-white. (Lit. "snow-crowned"). **L.** Hillside Nurs, Lehighton, PA. Not to be confused with following entry; ('Sekkan-sugi').   G,W3   Hort. Japan

- - 'Sekkwia-sugi' Dallimore & Jackson
   1923   A synonym of 'Cristata'. ('Seka-sugi').   Hort. Japan

- - 'Selaginoides' Dallimore & Jackson
   1923   **L.** Rovelli Nurs, Pallanza, (1913). No longer distinguishable from 'Lycopodioides'. (per Fitschen in Beissner, 1930).   H,W   Italy

- - 'Sennin-sugi' Beissner   1909   NOM. Listed by Beissner as the Japanese equivalent of 'Dacrydioides'. NIC.   Hort. Japan

- - 'Shishi-gashira' Hort. Japan
   1972   Near to or identical with 'Monstrosa Nana' (per Krüssmann 1972).**L.** Wansdyke Nurs, Devizes, Wilts. (1974).   K

- - var. *sinensis* Siebold ex Siebold & Zuccarini
1844 The form indigenous to China. By some authorities it is
treated as a separate species, *CRYPTOMERIA fortunei*.   B,K,R,W3   China

- - **'Spiralis'** Siebold ex Siebold & Zuccarini
1844 Shoots stout; leaves spirally curled around shoot.This and
'Spiraliter Falcata' are frequently confused.   B,D,G,H,K,W   Hort. Japan

- - 'Spiralis Elongata' Hort.   A mistake for 'Spiraliter Falcata'.

- - **'Spiraliter Falcata'** Siebold
1844 Shoot thin; leaves twisted as last item. (='Kusari-sugi, Rasen-
sugi', 'Yore-sugi').   B,G,H,K,W   Hort. Japan

- - 'Taisho-tama' Hort. Japan
1974 Broad-conical; foliage dark green. **L.** Wansdyke Nurs,
Devizes, Wilts, U.K. from Aritaki Arboretum, Japan,
Koshigaya, Saitama-Ken, Japan('Taisho-sugi').

- - **'Tansu'** Hort. Amer.   1982 A diminutive form with tiny leaves. **L.** Iseli Nurs, Boring,
OR. U.S.A. (1982), (At first it was described as 'Yatsubusa').   W3

- - 'Tansu Sport' Hort Amer.
1988 An unacceptable name. New name required. **L.** Mitsch Nurs,
Aurora, OR.

- - 'Tara' Sugimoto   1978 A listed name, possibly = 'Kitayama'.

- - 'Tashi' J.P. Kortmann   1987 In "Dendroflora **24**". Possibly the same as 'Taisho-tama'.   Hort. Japan

- - 'Tateyama' Hort. Germany
1990 A listed name. **I.** Botanic Garden at Goteborg, Sweden.

- - 'Tenuifolia' Carrière   1867 A spreading tree with leaves appressed to branches. NIC.   B   France

- - **'Tenzan'** Hort. Amer.   1981 A diminutive form with short light-green leaves bronzing in
winter. **L.** Iseli Nurs, Boring, OR. U.S.A.   W3

- - 'Tilford Cream'   1992 A plant in Windsor Great Park, Berks. Without description
(probably the same as 'Tilford Gold').

- - 'Tilford Gold' Hort. Anglia
1990 Globose golden form. **O.** and **I.** Kelvin Lawrence Nurs,
Farnham, Surrey.

- - **'Torta'** Krüssmann   1972 ='Spiraliter Falcata' or a similar clone.   K   Hort. Japan

- - 'To-sugi' Hort. Japan   A synonym of 'Elegans' (per Krüssmann, 1909).

- - 'Typica' Dallimore & Jackson
1923 Obsolete name for the typical form of the species, i.e. var.
japonica.   U.K.

- - f. *uncinata* Siebold & Zuccarini
1842 Not now distinguished within the species, but see 'Eisan-sugi'.   Japan

- - 'Uncinata' Sugimoto   1978 See 'Eisan-sugi'.   Japan

- - 'Unryu' Hort. Japan   A listed name for a weak, twisted form. ('Unrya') (Lit. ='Loud
Dragon').

- - **'Variegata'** Van Geert   1862 In "Nurs. Cat". Leaves pale green, white variegated. **O.** Van
Geert Nurs, Kalmthout. NIC.   B,D,G,K   Belgium

- - var. *vera*.   As 'Typica'.

- - 'Vilmorin Gold' G.Haddow
  1986 Globose plant as 'Vilmoriniana'. Foliage turns yellow gold from early summer onwards. **O.** and **I.** Kenwith Castle Nurs, Bideford, Devon.   U.K.

- - 'Vilmorin Variegated'   1992 **I.** P.W. Plants, Norfolk.

- - **'Vilmoriniana'** (Hornibrook)
  1924 Popular dwarf globose form. **O.** Imported (c. 1904) by Philippe de Vilmorin (as *JUNIPERUS japonica*).   B,D,G,H,K,W   Hort. Japan

- - 'Viminalis' Hort. Fitschen in Beissner
  1930 Indistinguishable from 'Lycopodioides' and 'Selaginoides'. NIC.   H,K,W   Hort. Japan.

- - 'Virgata' Mayr   1906 Indistinguishable from 'Araucarioides'. NIC.   B   Germany

- - 'Viridis' Nelson   1866 "The very green leaf form". NIC.   B   U.K.

- - 'Vitellina' Hort. Anglia   1984 Reported from the Royal Botanical Gardens, Kew. NOM.   U.K.

- - **'Winter Bronze'** J.P. Kortmann
  1987 In "Dendroflora 24". A dwarf shrub, descriptively named. **I.** W. Huizer Nurs, Boskoop. **O.** Unrecorded.   Holland

- - 'Wogon-sugi' Hort. Japan   See 'Ogon-sugi'.

- - 'Wood's Dwarf' Hort. Amer.   A listed name.

- - 'Yaku' Hort. Amer.   1972 Reported from the Gotelli collection, South Orange, N.J. (as 'Yaku-sugi').   U.S.A.

- - 'Yamamoto' Hort. Japan   **O.** Imported by Wansdyke Nurs, Devizes, Wilts. U.K. in 1974 from Aritaki Arboretum, Koshigaya, Saitama-Ken, Japan.

- - 'Yatsubusa' (1) Hort. Amer.   A word meaning "crowded" or "congested", loosely used for 'Tansu'. Not acceptable as a cultivar name.

- - 'Yatsubusa' (2) Hort. Europe
  1974 Now to be 'Yokohama'. Whether (1) and (2) relate to the same plant needs clarification.

- - 'Yawa-sugi' Beissner   1909 A synonym of 'Elegans'. ("Yawara" = soft).   China

- - **'Yenko-sugi'** Dallimore & Jackson
  1923 **L.** Tokyo Nurs, (1896). Now spelled in the trade 'Enko-sugi' (per Krüssmann, 1960).   D,K

- - **'Yokohama'** H.J. van de Laar
  1983 In "Dendroflora 20". Dwarf spreading bush, dark green juvenile foliage. **O.** Received from the Aritaki Arboretum,Koshigaya, Saitama-Ken, Japan by Wansdyke Nurs, Devizes, Wilts, in 1974 as 'Yatsubusa'.   Hort. Japan

- - **'Yore-sugi'** (1) Krüssmann
  1972 = 'Spiraliter Falcata' (per Krüssmann, 1972).   K   Hort. Japan

- - 'Yore-sugi' (2) Hort. Japan= 'Spiralis'. See also last entry.

- - **'Yoshino'** Yoshino   1928 An upright columnar form. Bright green, browning slightly in winter. In "Nurs. Cat". Yokohama Nurs, **L.** Raraflora Nurs, Feasterville, PA, (1966).   G,W3   Hort. Japan

- - 'Yuantouliusha' Cheng & L.K. Fu
  1978 In "Flora Reipublicae Popularis Sinicae". Text in Chinese. Probably 'Cristata'.   China

- - 'Zindai' Sugimoto   1978 In "New Keys to Woody Plants of Japan".   Hort. Japan

- - 'Zwerg Form' Hort. Germany
>1992 An illegit. name. **L.** Horstmann Nurs, Schneverdingen, Germany. Without description.

CRYPTOMERIA kawaii. Hayata
>1917 Not now distinguished within the species.

CUNNINGHAMIA R. Brown ex Richard (1826)

Taxodiaceae

A genus of two (or possibly three) species of large and ornamental trees, all closely alike. The adult foliage differs only slightly from the juvenile foliage which persists on the tree for some years.

CUNNINGHAMIA cupressoides Zuccarini
        Now known as *ATHROTAXUS cupressoides.*

CUNNINGHAMIA kawakamii Hayata
        1915 Not now distinguished from *CUNNINGHAMIA konishii* by some authorities. (per Krüssmann, 1983).

CUNNINGHAMIA konishii Hayata			
1908 Formosan Cunninghamia.		20m,Z8	Taiwan
CUNNINGHAMIA lanceolata (Lambert) Hooker			
1827 Chinese Fir. Introduced by Wm. Kerr in 1804.		20m,Z7	China
- - **'Bánó'** Evi B. Loeb	1988 In "Royal Hort. Soc. Journ". New name to replace 'Compacta' for a dwarf form, seldom larger than a bush. O. I. Bánó, Kámoni For. Exp. Sta.		Hungary
- - 'Compacta' Barabits	1966 In "Deutsches Baumschule 5". An illegit. name. Now to be 'Bánó'.	G,K,R,W	Hungary
- - **'Glauca'** Knight & Perry	1850 Young foliage glaucous. A hardy form.	B,D,G,K,W	U.K.
- - 'Glauca Pendula' Dallimore & Jackson	1931 A graceful weeping form with silvery foliage. NIC.	B	U.K.
- - var. *konishii* Hayata	1932 See *CUNNINGHAMIA konishii.*		
- - **'Möllifolia'** Cheng & Fu	1978 In "Flora Reipublicae Popularis Sinicae 7".Description in Chinese.		China
- - 'Nana' Hort. Anglia	An illegit. name.. Dwarf; bright green foliage. Probably = 'Bánó'.	R	
- - **'Raraflora'** Hort. Amer.	1966 A listed name.		
- - 'Starling's Dwarf' G. Haddow	1992 A dwarf cushion shape to globular bush with short leaves to 2 cms. long. Green in summer, red to violet in winter. The original plant at seven years of age was no more than 10 cms. high. O. B.N. Starling, grown from seed collected in China. I. Kenwith Nurs, Bideford, Devon.		U.K.
CUNNINGHAMIA sinensis R. Brown ex Richard			
1826 Now known as *CUNNINGHAMIA lanceolata.*			
CUNNINGHAMIA unicanicuta Wang & Liu			
1982 A newly described species; close to *CUNNINGHAMIA lanceolata.*			S. China

CUPRESSOCYPARIS Dallimore (1977)

Cupressaceae

Tall-growing bi-generic hybrids between *CHAMAECYPARIS* and *CUPRESSUS*, in all of which *CHAMAECYPARIS nootkatensis* is one parent.

x *CUPRESSOCYPARIS arilosa* Hort. N.Z.
Listed but unpublished name for a supposed hybrid, *CUPRESSUS arizonica* (or *CUPRESSUS glabra*) with *CHAMAECYPARIS nootkatensis* under investigation at Crop Res. Div. DSIR, Lincoln N.Z. **O.** F.R.I. clone No 850/329.

x *CUPRESSOCYPARIS leylandii* Dallimore & Jackson
1938 Leyland Cypress. *CUPRESSUS macrocarpa* x *CHAMAECYPARIS nootkatensis*.   35m,Z7   U.K.

- - 'Arilosa' Hort. N.Z.   See x *CUPRESSUS notabilis* 'Arilosa'

- - 'Barden's Gold' Hort. Anglia
1986 A superfluous synonym for 'Castlewellan'.

- - 'Belvoir Castle' Hort. Anglia   A superfluous synonym for 'Robinson's Gold'.

- - **'Castlewellan'** L.S. Slinger
1973 In "Good Garden Plants". The first and most widely planted colour form, but not the most golden. At first named *CUPRESSUS macrocarpa* 'Keown', it spread through the trade and when its hybrid origin became recognised was distributed as 'Barden's Gold', 'Castlewellan Gold', 'Galway Gold' and possibly other names. **O.** Raised from seed by John Keown at Castlewellan, Co. Down (1962). **I.** Slieve Donard Nurs, Newcastle, Co. Down.   G,K,R,W   Ireland

- - **'Clun'** A.F. Mitchell   1985 In "Int. Dendr. Soc. Yearbook". Named for a large tree in the garden of the vicarage in the village of Clun in Shropshire. The name 'Clun Rectory' was based on a misunderstanding.   W   U.K.

- - 'Contorta' Hort. Amer.   1965 An illegit. name. (See Notes under 'Picturesque').   W3   U.S.A.

- - **'Ferndown'** J. Jobling   1984 In "Nurseryman and Garden Centre 172". **O.** Barthelemy Nurs, Stapehill, Wimborne, Dorset. Parentage uncertain.   W3   U.K.

- - 'Galway Gold' Hort. Anglia   A superfluous name for 'Castlewellan'.

- - **'Golconda'** Int. Con. Reg.
1977 A lemon-gold sport on 'Haggerston Grey' which retains its colour well. Reg'd. by D. F. Wyant, Wyboston, Bedfordshire.   R,W3   U.K.

- - 'Gold Cup' Hort. Amer.   1985 L. L.C. Hatch in "Reference Guide". Foliage yellow. **O.** N.Z.?   W3

- - **'Golden Sun'** A.F. Mitchell
1985 A slow-growing selection with bright yellow foliage colour. **O.** A sport on 'Haggerston Grey'. Barnham Nurs, Bognor Regis, Sussex, (1966).   W   U.K.

- - **'Goldness'** Int. Con. Reg.
1976 Patches of yellow-variegated foliage. Reg'd. by S. G. McMinn. **I.** Ness Nurs, Londonderry.   Ireland

- - **'Gold Rider'** H.J. van de Laar
1985 In "Dendroflora 22". A golden mutation of unrecorded origin. ('Golden Rider' is incorrect).   Holland

- - 'Green Spire' Ovens, Blight & Mitchell
1964 In "Quart. Journ. Forestry". (Clone 1). This clone has been but little propagated.   B,K,R,W   U.K.

- - **'Haggerston Grey'** Ovens, Blight & Mitchell
1964 As above. (Clone 2). The most popular Haggerston clone.   B,K,R,W   U.K.

- - **'Harlequin'** A.F. Mitchell
1985 As above. A white-variegated sport of 'Haggerston Grey'. **O.**
Lord Bradford, Weston Park, Shifner, Shropshire, (1975).   R,W   U.K.

- - 'Herculea' Hort. Holland   1993 A listed name.

- - **'Hillspire'** Hort. Amer.   1985 L. L.C. Hatch in "Reference Guide". NOM.   W3

- - **'Hyde Hall'** Int. Con. Reg.
1976 Slow-growing conical bush. Reg'd. by and **O.** R.H M.
Robinson. Raised from a witch's broom at Hyde Hall.   G,W3   U.K.

- - 'Jubilee' Hort. Anglia   A slightly variegated form not worth retention. **O.** A mutation
at Wansdyke Nurs, Devizes, Wilts, but no longer propagated
there.   W3   U.K.

- - **'Kyloe'** Hort. Anglia   1984 Reported from the Royal Botanic Gardens, Kew. NOM.

- - **'Leighton Green'** Ovens, Blight & Mitchell
1964 In "Quart. Journ. Forestry". **O.** (Clone 11). Leighton Hall,
Welshpool, (1911). The most widely propagated clone.   B,K,R,W3   U.K.

- - 'Manor Farm'   A listed name. No information.

- - 'Mellow Yellow' Hort. Anglia   A superfluous name for 'Robinson's Gold'.   W3

- - **'Minier'** Hort. France   A clone of normal growth but foliage pale green. **O.** S.A.
Minier.

- - **'Naylor's Blue'** Ovens, Blight & Mitchell
1964 Foliage blue-green. **O.** (Clone 10) Leighton Hall, Welshpool.   B,K,R,W   U.K.

- - **'Netherton Gold'** Hort. Anglia
1987 Formerly listed as 'Barden's Gold'.   U.K.

- - **'New Ornament'** H.J. van de Laar
1987 In "Dendroflora **24**". **I.** L. Konijn & Co, Ederveen, **O.** An
unrecorded source in U.K.   U.K.

- - 'Picturesque' Int. Con. Reg.
1988 Name possibly invalid if issued against expressed wish of
originator. (Art. 41). The names 'Contorta' and *CUPRESSUS
macrocarpa* 'Tortuosa' are unacceptable.   W3   U.S.A.

- - **'Robinson's Gold'** Int. Con. Reg.
1977 Foliage golden-yellow, fading to green. Reg'd. by Dept.
Agric., N.I. **O.** Natural seedling at Belvoir Castle, Co. Down
(1964). (*macrocarpa x nootkatensis*). Foliage is closer to
nootkatensis.   K,R,W3   N.Ireland

- - **'Rostrevor'** A.F. Mitchell
1985 In "Int. Dend. Soc. Yearbook **98**". Named for a large tree at
Rostrevor, Co. Down. Near to 'Leighton Green'. **O.** According
to J. Jobling of the Forestry Commission of U.K., this
probably arose as a seedling at Daisy Hill The date is not on
record, but by 1908 the plant was sufficiently large to yield
cuttings for propagation.   W3   N.Ireland

- - **'Rua'** Hort. N.Z.   1960 An F2 seedling from 'Leighton Green'. A very vigorous tree
with foliage resembling the Nootka cypress. **O.** Miss Pat
Bates, late of Ruakura. (M.A.F.).   W3   N.Z.

- - **'Silver Dust'** Int. Con. Reg.
1976 Foliage irregularly variegated in white, flushed creamy-white.
O. A branch sport on 'Leighton Green' found in U.S. National
Arboretum, Washington DC. (1960).   G,R,W3   U.S.A.

- - 'Sirebo' Hort. Holland   1992 A variegated sport on 'Castlewellan'. **O.** Stichting Siertedt Regio, Boskoop.

- - 'Smith's Gold' Hort.   Superfluous name for 'Spring Gold'.   W3

- - **'Sparkler'** Hort. Amer.   1985 **L.** L.C. Hatch in "Reference Guide". Sport of 'Haggerston Grey'. Foliage yellow-tipped.   W3   U.S.A.

- - **'Spring Gold'** A.F. Mitchell
    1985 As above. Golden-yellow sport. **O.** A branch sport on 'Harlequin', raised by Steven Smith, Pickering, Yorks. (1984).   W3   U.K.

- - **'Stapehill 20'** Ovens, Blight & Mitchell
    1984 In "Nurseryman and Garden Centre". As above. **O.** M. Barthelemy Nurs, Stapehill, Wimborne, Dorset. (1940). Parentage uncertain. Originally listed as 'Stapehill 20', per Ovens, Blight and Mitchell, (1964).   R,W3   U.K.

- - 'Stapehill 20' and 'Stapehill 21'
    1964 Now known as 'Stapehill' and 'Ferndown', respectively.   W3

- - 'Tortuosa' Hort.   1981 "Int. Dendr. Soc. Yearbook". See note under 'Picturesque'.

- - 'Variegata' Hort.   An illegit name. Probably a mistake for 'Harlequin'.

x *CUPRESSOCYPARIS notabilis* A.F. Mitchell
    1972 Alice Holt Cypress. A natural hybrid. *CHAMAECYPARIS nootkatensis* x *CUPRESSUS glabra*. **O.** Leighton Hall, Welshpool.   K   U.K.

- - 'Arilosa' Hort. N.Z.   1948 An unpublished name in use in the trade for a clone of this hybrid distinct only in its slower rate of growth. The cultivar name was mistakenly applied to a hybrid (*CUPRESSUS arizonica* x *CUPRESSUS torulosa)* raised by Lindsay Prior at Canberra (1948), but now apparently lost to cultivation.

- - 'Brookhill' Int. Con.. Reg.
    1990 A seedling with golden-yellow foliage. **O.** and **I.** B.J.Ireland, Brookhill, Upper Ballinderry, Lisburn, Co. Down, (1985).   Ireland

x *CUPRESSOCYPARIS ovensii* A.F. Mitchell
    1972 Oven's Cypress. A hybrid: *CUPRESSUS lusitanica* x *CHAMAECYPARIS nootkatensis*. **O.** Westonburt Arboretum, Tetbury, Glos.   K   U.K.

CUPRESSUS L. (1753)

Cupressaceae

The true Cypresses form a group of about a dozen species widely distributed, mostly in drier areas of either the Old or the New World. Isolated geographical groups show minor variations and there remains disagreement as to the most satisfactory classification. A good historical survey will be found in the International Conifer Register, Part Three (1992). Prior to its recognition as a separate species by Spach in 1842, *Chamaecyparis* was included in *Cupressus*, and that name continued in use by some authors for many years later.

CUPRESSUS abramsiana Wo
1948 Santa Cruz Cypress. Now listed under *CUPRESSUS goveniana* by some authorities (per Silba, 1984).

CUPRESSUS x arilosa Hort N.Z.
1988 See *CUPRESSOCYPARIS* x *notabilis* 'Arilosa'.

CUPRESSUS arizonica Greene
1882 Rough-barked Arizona Cypress. Note that many garden varieties are here listed under *CUPRESSUS glabra*, this being the usual practice in the trade.   20m,Z7   U.S.A.

- - var. *bonita* Lemmon   1895 A name of no clear application. ('bonito').

- - 'Clemson Greenspire'   See under *CUPRESSUS glabra*.

- - var. *glabra* (Sudworth) Little
1966 The smooth-barked Arizona Cypress. Now often treated as a distinct species, *CUPRESSUS glabra*, along with its numerous cv. (per Rushforth, 1987).   R   U.S.A.

- - 'Janice'   See under *CUPRESSUS glabra*.

- - var. *montana* (Wiggins) Little
1966 San Pedro Cypress. By some authorities listed as a separate species (per Silba, 1984).   K,W3   U.S.A.

- - var. *nevadensis* (Abrams) Little
1966 Piute Cypress. By some authorities listed as a separate species, (per Silba, 1984).   K,W3   U.S.A.

- - var. *revealiana* Silba   1981 Now merged in *CUPRESSUS glabra*. (per Silba, 1984).   W   U.S.A.

- - var. *stevensonii* (Wolf) Little
1966 Cayamaca Cypress. By some authorities regarded as a separate species. (per Silba, 1984).   K,W   U.S.A.

CUPRESSUS atlantica Gaussen
1950 See *CUPRESSUS sempervirens* var. *atlantica*. (per Silba, 1984).

CUPRESSUS attenuata Gordon
1858 Now known as *CHAMAECYPARIS lawsoniana*..

CUPRESSUS bakeri Jepson
1909 Baker Cypress.   10-15mZ6   California

- - 'Arnold' Hort. Holland   1986 L. H.J. van de Laar in "Naamlijst . . .". NOM.

- - ssp. *matthewsii* C.B. Wolf
1948 Modoc Cypress.No longer distinguished within the species. (per Silba, 1984).   B,K

CUPRESSUS benthamii Endlicher
1847 Now known as *CUPRESSUS lusitanica* var *benthamii*.

CUPRESSUS cashmeriana Royle ex Carrière
1867 Kashmir Cypress. It is not known "in the wild" and is listed as *CUPRESSUS torulosa* var. *cashmeriana* by some authorities, (per Silba, 1984).

- - 'Glauca' Hort. N.Z.   An illegit. name. L. Duncan & Davies Nurs, New Plymouth.

CUPRESSUS chengiana Hu
1964 Cheng Cypress. A little-known species.   30m,Z6   W. China

CUPRESSUS corneyana (Knight & Perry) Carrière
1855 Bhutan Cypress, Mr. Corney's Cypress. (per Rushforth, 1987).
See also under *CUPRESSUS torulosa* 'Corneyana'.   40m,Z8   Bhutan

CUPRESSUS duclouxiana Hickel ex Camus
1914 Ducloux Cypress, Yunnan Cypress.   20m,Z8   China

CUPRESSUS dupreziana Camus
1926 Sahara Cypress. A geographical form listed as *CUPRESSUS sempervirens* var. *dupreziana* by some authorities. (per Silba, 1984).   Algeria

CUPRESSUS faberi Jepson   1923 A mistake for *CUPRESSUS forbesii*.   B   California

CUPRESSUS fallax Franco   1969 Not now distinguished from *CUPRESSUS chengiana*, (per Silba, 1984).

CUPRESSUS forbesii Jepson
1922 Tecate Cypress. Listed as *CUPRESSUS guadaloupensis* var. *forbesii* by some authorities. (per Silba, 1984).

CUPRESSUS funebris Endlicher
1847 Now known as *CHAMAECYPARIS funebris*. (per Silba, 1984).

CUPRESSUS gigantea Cheng & L.K. Fu
1975 Tsangpo River Cypress.   30m,Z7   Tibet

CUPRESSUS glabra Sudworth
1910 Smooth-bark Arizona Cypress. By some authorities listed as *CUPRESSUS arizonica* var. *glabra*.(per Silba, 1984). See Note under *CUPRESSUS arizonica*.   15m,Z7   U.S.A.

- - **'Angaston'** P.C. Nitschke
1989 In "Con. Soc. Australia Newsletter No. 5". An upright blue tree with strongly pendulous branches. O. Found as a seedling in a garden in the Barossa Valley, (1980).   S. Australia

- - **'Arctic'** Hort. N.Z.   1984 Open tree; green, bluish leaf-tips. L. Duncan & Davies Nurs, New Plymouth. (The spelling 'Artic' is incorrect).   W3   N.Z.

- - 'Arthur Greene' Hort. Australia   Reported from the Adelaide Botanic Garden.

- - **'Aurea'** Kemp   1957 In "Adelaide Botanic Gar. Journ". Broadly conical densely branched tree; young foliage mustard-yellow, fading to green by winter. O. Seedling raised by J. Canny in Woods & Forestry Dept. Belair Park, (1956). I. Kemp's Nurs, Aldgate, (1957).   S. Australia

- - 'Blue Beauty' Hort. N.Z.   1992 A listed name.

- - **'Blue Ice'** Hort. N.Z.   1984 Upright symmetrical habit. Foliage frosty grey-blue. L. Duncan & Davies Nurs, New Plymouth.   W3   N.Z.

- - **'Blue Pyramid'** Hort. N.Z.   Vigorous tree; foliage silvery-grey. I. Duncan & Davies Nurs, New Plymouth, O. Ken Burns, Timaru, (1972).   W3   N.Z.

- - **'Blue Spire'** Hort. Australia
1979 Pendulous; good blue colour. I. P.C. Nitschke, Hahndorf. O. The same, named for a tree found in a garden at Tanunda, (1979).   W3   S. Australia

- - 'Blue Streak' (1) Harrison
  1975 In "Nurs. Cat". An old clone, largely replaced by newer
       selections in N.Z. nurseries.   W3   N.Z.

- - 'Blue Streak' (2) J. Emery
  1989 A narrowly columnar form with bright blue foliage. Unless it
       is the same as previous entry, it is an unacceptable re-use of
       the name. L. Leveys Nurs, Beaudesert, Australia.

- - 'Canny' T.R.N. Lothian 1967 In "Adelaide Bot. Gar. Journ". Foliage at first golden-yellow.
       O. Same as 'Aurea'. I. Woods and Forestry Dept., Adelaide,
       S. Australia. (1967). Named for J. Canny. ('Canny's Gold' is
       incorrect).   W3   Australia

- - 'Caroline Sapphire' Int. Con. Reg.
  1987 A loose-growing clone with rather dark, steel-blue foliage.
       Reg'd. by Dept. Forestry, Clemson University, S. Carolina.   W3   U.S.A.

- - 'Catt's Dwarf' J. Emery 1989 In "Con. Soc. Australia Newsletter No. 5". A dense globose to
       conical dwarf with greyish foliage. O. and I. Graeme Catt,
       Catt's Nurs, Carlingford, Sydney.   Australia

- - 'Chaparral' J. Emery 1989 In "Con. Soc. Australia Newsletter No. 5". A narrowly
       columnar form, foliage creamy-white, persisting throughout
       the year. O. John Emery. I. Drue Nurs, Berry, (1988),.   Australia

- - 'Clemson Greenspire' Int. Con. Reg.
  1980 A fast-growing clone with foliage bright green. Reg'd. by
       Dept. Forestry, Clemson University, S. Carolina (As
       CUPRESSUS arizonica).   W3   U.S.A.

- - 'Compacta' Schneider in Silva Tarouca
  1913 Slow-growing dwarf bush with congested grey foliage. O.
       Unrecorded. ('Nana').   B,D,G,K,W   Germany

- - 'Compacta Glauca' Hort. France
  1952 An illegit. name. L. Detriche, Angers, France.

- - 'Conica' Den Ouden 1937 In "Naamlijst van Coniferen". A slow-growing conical clone
       with ascending branches and numerous twigs; leaves grey-
       blue striking blue. Origin unknown. See also 'Conica Glauca'
       and 'Pyramidalis'.   B,K,W   France?

- - 'Conica Albovariegata' Hort. France
  An illegit. name and probably a superfluous name for
  'Variegata'.

- - 'Crowborough' Welch 1979 A semi-dwarf. I. Wansdyke Nurs, Devizes, Wilts. O. H.E.
       Bawden, Crowborough, Kent.   G,W   U.K.

- - 'Donard Glauca' 1985 An illegit. name. Reported from the Castlewellan National
       Arboretum, Co. Down.   G,W   Ireland

- - 'Drue Blue' J. Emery 1989 In "Con. Soc. Australia Newsletter No. 5". Conical form with
       branches numerous and ascending, foliage silver-blue, semi-
       juvenile. I. Drue Nurs, Berry.   Australia

- - 'Fastigiata' Gino Bartolini ex Krüssmann
  1972 An illegit. name. Narrowly upright, compact, blue-grey. L.
       Minier Nurs, Angers, (1962).   K,W3   France

- - 'Fastigiata Aurea' Krüssmann
  1972 An illegit. name. Foliage lemon-yellow.   G,K,W3   France

- - 'Gareei' Monrovia 1973 In "Nurs. Cat". A popular blue selection. L. Monrovia Nurs,
       Azusa, Cal. O. M. Garee, Nobles Nurs, Noble. Okla. (1958).   W3   U.S.A.

- - 'Glauca' (1) Woodall 1916 The original clone, with juvenile foliage. No longer
       identifiable.   B,D,G,K,W

- - 'Glauca' (2) Hort. Australia
  1950 A clone raised from seed in Canberra in 1950 for which
       another name should be found.

- - 'Golden Pyramid' Hort. N.Z.
  1972 L. Duncan & Davies Nurs, New Plymouth. O. R. Levy of
       Brisbane. ('Gold Pyramid').   W3   N.Z.

- - 'Greenwood' Hort. Amer.   O. Selected for its good colour by M. Garee of U.S. Dept.,
                                   Agric. Field Sta. Woodward, Okla.   W3

- - 'Greyangold' J. Emery   1989 In "Con. Soc. Australia Newsletter No. 5". Foliage juvenile,
                                  evenly variegated, grey and creamy-yellow. L. F.D. Catt
                                  Wholesale Nurs, Sydney.   Australia

- - 'Hodginsii' E.E. Lord   1948 A strong-growing tree with silvery-grey foliage resin
                                  speckled. O. Hodgins' Nurs, Essendon, Melbourne.
                                  ('Hodgins').   W3   Australia

- - 'Janice' Int. Con. Reg. 1984 A fastigiate tree. Regd. by J.D. Thomas, Porth, Mid-
                                  Glamorgan. (Reg'd. as CUPRESSUS arizonica 'Janice').   W3   U.K.

- - 'Lakeview' Hort. Canada   Dwarf; foliage grey. O. E.H. Lohbrunner of Vancouver Is., B.C.   W3   Canada

- - 'Nana' Hort.   A superfluous name for 'Compacta'.

- - 'Patens' Schaefer   1922 Clone with conspicuously horizontal branches. NIC.   B,K   Germany

- - 'Pendula Aurea' Hillier 1928 In "Nurs. Cat". A clone presumably descriptively named. NIC   U.K.

- - 'Pyramidalis' Hillier   1928 In "Nurs. Cat". A dense symmetrical, narrowly conical tree,
                                  blue grey. I. Hillier & Sons Nurs, Winchester, U.K. (Not
                                  since 1970, distinguished by them from 'Conica'). Specimens
                                  of 'Pyramidalis' are faster growing then 'Conica' but of similar
                                  general appearance.   B,K,R,W   U.K.

- - 'Raywood Weeping' J. Emery
  1989 In "Con. Soc. Australia Newsletter No. 5". An irregularly
       conical form with branches weeping steeply; foliage greyish.
       I. Raywood Nurs, Delamere. O. Quentin Woolaston.   Australia

- - 'Shawnee' Hort. Amer.   1972 Reported from Longwood Gars, Kennett Square. PA.   U.S.A.

- - 'Silver Smoke' Hort. N.Z.
  1984 Compact, silvery-grey. L. Duncan & Davies Nurs, New
       Plymouth.   W3   N.Z.

- - 'Staura' Hort. France   1972 L. Renault Frères Nurs, Gorron.   France

- - 'Sulfurea' Hort. France   An illegit. name. An erect small tree with sulphur-yellow
                                  foliage. L. Renault Frères Nurs, Gorron.   G,K,W3   France

- - 'Summertown' J. Emery
  1989 In "Con. Soc. Australia Newsletter No. 5". Conical with
       foliage evenly variegated grey and yellow-gold. Slow-
       growing. O. Thomsons Nurs, Summertown.   Australia

- - 'Variegata' Krüssmann   1983 Slow growing, with good cream-white variegation. L. Minier
                                  Nurs, Angers, France. ('Albovariegata').   G,K,W3   France

- - 'Watersii' Monrovia   1973 In "Nurs. Cat". Dense, upright habit; foliage grey L.
                                  Monrovia Nurs, Azusa, Cal.   U.S.A.

CUPRESSUS goveniana Gordon ex Lindley
  1849 Gowen Cypress.   15m,Z8   California

- - var. abramsiana (Wolf) Little
  1970 Santa Cruz Cypress. Now accepted as a species (per
       Rushforth, 1987).   R,W3   U.S.A.

- - 'Bregeonii' R. Smith   1865   Bush with slender, glaucous branches. NIC.   B,K   U.K.

- - 'Californica' S.G. Harrison
         1966   Now listed as 'Pendula'.

- - **'Compacta'** André   1896   Broadly conical compact tree. O. Charles Detriche Nurs.   B,K   France

- - 'Cornuta' Carrière   1867   Named for a curious tree at Hyres, Alpes Maritimes. NIC.   B,K   France

- - 'Glauca' Carrière   1867   A robust tree with glaucous foliage. O. Sahut Nurs,
         Montpellier. NIC.   B   France

- - 'Gloria' Hort. Canada   1981   L. Gordon Bentham, Vancouver, BC. Without description.

- - 'Gracilis' Carrière   1867   Graceful, pendulous habit. NIC.   B   France

- - **'Pendula'** Henry   1910   Graceful, pendulous habit. NIC.   B,K,W   U.K.

- - var. *pygmaea* Lemmon   1895   Not now distinguished within the species. It is an ecological
         dwarf, or at most a minor variant. (*parva*).   W3   U.S.A.

- - 'Pyramidalis' Hort.   1986   An illegit. name. Reported from the Arboretum Blijdenstein,
         Hilversum.   Holland

- - 'Pyramidalis Lutea'   As last, but differing in colour of foliage.   Holland

- - 'Viridis' Carrière   1867   Foliage bright green. NIC.   B   France

CUPRESSUS guadalupensis S Watson
         1879   Guadalupe Cypress. A very rare species.   20m,Z9   Mexico

- - var. *forbesii* (Jepson) Little
         1970   Forbes Cypress. Now accepted as a distinct species. (per
         Rushforth, 1987).   Mexico

- - 'Glauca' Bailey   1933   A clone with leaves glaucous blue.   B   U.S.A.

CUPRESSUS horizontalis Miller
         1768   Now known as *CUPRESSUS sempervirens* var *horizontalis*.

CUPRESSUS jiangensis Zhao
         1980   Not now distinguished from *CUPRESSUS chengiana*. (per
         Silba, 1984).

CUPRESSUS lambertiana Gordon
         1838   In "The Pinetum". This unpublished name was dropped when
         the identity with *CUPRESSUS macrocarpa* was realised, but
         not before it had become widely used in Australia. See
         Gordon "The Pinetum 1858" and Veitch "Manual 1900".

CUPRESSUS lawsoniana Hort.   Now known as *CHAMAECYPARIS lawsoniana*.

CUPRESSUS lindleyi (1) Klotsch ex Endlicher
         1847   Not now distinguished within var. *benthamii*.

CUPRESSUS lindleyi (2) Hort. Mexico
         A mistake for *CUPRESSUS lusitanica*.(per Rushforth, 1987).

CUPRESSUS lusitanica Miller
         1768   Mexican Cypress, Cedar of Goa.   20m,Z8   Mexico

- - **'Adelaide Gold'** T.R.N. Lothian
         1978   In "Adelaide Bot. Gar. Journ". A strong-growing golden-
         yellow form.   W3   Australia

- - 'Argentea' Hillier   1928   In "Nurs. Cat". L. Hillier & Sons Nurs, Winchester, (1928).
         Indistinguishable from 'Coerulea'   U.K.

CUPRESSUS LUSITANICA

- - var. **benthamii** (Endlicher) Carrière
  1867 Bentham Cypress. A regional variant that has been given several names in the past.   B,D,K,W   Mexico

- - **'Blue Swirl'** John Emery
  1989 In "Con. Soc. Australia Newsletter No. 5". A seedling from 'Mossvale', with compact, green, fern-like foliage. **O.** P.C. Nitschke, Hahndorf, S. Australia.   Australia

- - 'Chamaecyparissoides' Hillier
  1925 In "Nurs. Cat". Branches whip-like. **I.** Hillier & Sons Nurs, Winchester. **O.** Cripps & Sons Nurs, Tunbridge Wells. NIC.   B   U.K.

- - 'Coerulea' Carrière   1867 Foliage and cones glaucous blue. NIC.   B,K   France

- - 'Corneyana' Hort. Anglia   Mr Corney's Cypress. It was not used as a cultivar name by Knight and Perry. See *CUPRESSUS corneyana.*

- - 'Fastigiata' Mitchell   1972 Named for a tree at Westonbirt Arboretum, Glos.   U.K.

- - 'Flagellifera' Jackson   1927 (? = 'Chamaecyparissoides'). NIC.   B,D,R,K   U.K.

- - **'Glauca'** Henry   1910 A clone with glaucous-blue leaves found at Montserrat. Other such seedlings turn up of varying colour intensity.   B,D,K,R,W   Sporadic

- - **'Glauca Pendula'** Hillier
  1925 **O.** Hillier & Sons Nurs, Winchester.   B,D,K,W   U.K.

- - 'Knightiana' Knight & Perry
  1850 A minor sporadic variant with mauve or glaucous young shoots. The clone named for Mr Knight is no longer identifiable.   B,D,K   U.K.

- - 'Majestica' Dallimore & Jackson
  1948 A vigorous clone seldom seen today.   B,D   U.K.

- - 'Mangamahoe' Hort. N.Z.
  1992 A weeping clone of var *benthamii* selected by Brian Rapley.

- - **'Mossvale'** P.C. Nitschke
  1987 In "Con. Soc. Australia Newsletter No. 1". A dwarf conical dark green bush forming an inverted cone. **O.** A witch's broom found by Nitschke at Mossvale, N.S.W. (1982).   Australia.

- - 'Nana' Hort. Anglia   1981 An illegit. listed name for a dwarf with dense, blue-green foliage.   W   U.K.

- - 'Pendula' Lawson   1851 A pendulous clone no longer identifiable. Similar variants occur.   U.K.

- - 'Pygmy' Hort. Holland   1982 A dwarf globose bush with foliage in tight congested sprays. **O.** Unknown. **L.** Bressingham Nurs, Diss, Norfolk.

- - var. *skinneri* Henry   1910 Not now distinguished from var. *benthamii.*

- - 'Tristis' (Endlicher) Carrière
  1855 Branches and shoots narrowly pendulous. NIC.(='Pendula' Gordon (1958)?   B   France

- - 'Variegata' Lawson   1851 A clone with some scattered white variegation. (Listed as *foliis variegatis*).   B,K   U.K.

CUPRESSUS macnabiana Murray
1855 Macnab Cypress.   25m,Z8   U.S.A.

- - **'Fastigata'** Welch   1979 **O.** A plant at Westonbirt Arboretum, Glos., since dead. **I.** Wansdyke Nurs, Devizes, Wilts.   W3   U.K.

- - **'Lilah'** Int. Con. Reg.   1984   Persistent white variegation. Reg'd. by A. Stewart, Highgate Wood, London, N10.   W3   U.K.

- - **'Sulphurea'** Berckmans ex Bailey
    1923   Form with yellow tips.   B,K,W3   U.S.A.

- - 'Winter Grey' Hort. Amer.
    1985   Dense, conical; foliage bright silvery-grey. **L.** L.C. Hatch in "Reference Guide".

CUPRESSUS macrocarpa Hartweg ex Gordon
    1847   Monterey Cypress.   30m,Z7   California

- - **'Adelaide Gold'** Hort. Australia
    See *CUPRESSUS lusitanica* 'Adelaide Gold'.

- - **'Antarctic'** Hort. N.Z.   1984   Young variegated foliage has frosted appearance. **O.** Edwin B. Perrett, Tanilba Nurs, Pukeatua.   W3

- - **'Arctic'** Hort. N.Z.   1984   Similar, but colour less pronounced. **O.** The same as previous item.   W3   N.Z.

- - 'Argentea' Hort. Ireland   1989   Reported from the National Botanic Garden, Dublin.

- - 'Aurea' (1) Boom   1965   A mistake for 'Horizontalis Aurea'.   B,W3   Australia

- - 'Aurea' (2) Hort. Australia
    1972   In "Nurs. Cat". Woods and Forestry Dept., Adelaide, S. Australia (as 'Berri Strain'). Now known as 'Berrigold'.

- - 'Aurea Saligna' E.E. Lord
    1948   A commercial equivalent of name 'Coneybearii Aurea', but widely in use in its place.   W3   Australia

- - 'Barnham Gold' Hort. Anglia   A listed name.

- - **'Beaufront'** P.C. Nitschke
    1989   In "Con. Soc. Australia Newsletter No. **5**". An almost prostrate plant with very dark green compact foliage. **O.** A witch's broom found in Tasmania, Midlands by P.C. Nitschke and Ron Radford, (1983).

- - **'Berrigold'** Hort. Australia
    1972   In "South Australian Nurs., Assoc. Bulletin". Medium size conical tree. branches horizontal drooping at tips; foliage golden-yellow persistent. **O.** Raised from seed at Dept. of Agric. Stat. Nurs. at Berri, S. Australia (1930's).   W3   Australia

- - 'Bower Bank' Hort. Australia   A strongly pendulous form with deep green leaves. **O.** Found by Quentin Wollaston of Raywood Nurs. Delamere, South Australia.

- - 'Brighton' Hort. Australia
    1989   A listed name for a witch's broom found by P.C. Nitschke that is no longer in production.

- - 'Brunniana' E.E. Lord   1948   A mistake for 'Brunniana Aurea'.   Australia

- - **'Brunniana Aurea'** R.E. Harrison
    1959   (In "Nurs. Cat". (or earlier?). An early seedling with ascending branches and fine, golden foliage. **O.** and **I.** Geo. Brunnings and Sons Nurs. Ripponlea, Victoria, (1915).   W3   Australia

- - 'Brunnings Variegated' Hort. Australia
    1989   Named for a similar plant of unrecorded origin but with a white variegation. Probably not in production.

- - **'Cascade'** D. and N. Sampson
1988 Resembling *CHAMAECYPARIS lawsoniana* 'Imbricata Pendula', but broader in habit. **O.** and **I.** Cedar Lodge Nurs. New Plymouth.   W3   N.Z.

- - **'Chandleri'** P.C. Nitschke
1989 In "Con. Soc. Australia Newsletter No. 5". An old selection forming an irregularly shaped small tree with very dark green compact foliage. **O.** Chandlers Nurs, Hobart. (Date unrecorded).   Tasmania

- - **'Charles Detriche'** Krüssmann
1979 A very old, narrowly conical, golden form. Formerly known as 'Souvenir de Charles Detriche'.   K,W3   France

- - 'Chilcott'
1991 Listed by Wansdyke Nurs, Devizes. Wilts. Without description.

- - 'Collyer's Gold' Hort.Anglia
1970 Named for a slow-growing golden tree at Everton Nurs, near Lymington, Hants.   U.K.

- - 'Compacta' Hornibrook
1923 Later renamed 'Globosa' by Hillier. but the name 'Globe' is now in general use.   B,H   U.K.

- - **'Coneybearii Aurea'** Hazlewood
1933 In "Nurs. Cat". Pendulous; golden thread leaf foliage. It needs stem-training. **I.** Hazlewood Bros. Nurs, Epping, N.S.W., as *CUPRESSUS coneybeariiaurea*. **O.** Seedling at Woolich Nurs, Olinda, Victoria, the mother plant was purchased by a Dr. Conybear in the mid 1920's.   K,W   Australia

- - 'Contorta' Hort. Anglia
An illegit. name for a contorted clone of x *CUPRESSOCYPARIS leylandii*.

- - **'Crippsii'** R. Smith
1867 Young growth creamy white. **O.** Thos. Cripps Nurs. Tunbridge Wells, Kent.   B,K,W3   U.K.

- - 'Depressa' Carrière
1867 Named for a curious tree at Thuret. Antibes. NIC.   B   France

- - **'Donard Gold'** Donard
1940 In "Gold Medal Shrubs". Conical tree; golden-yellow foliage. **O.** Slieve Donard Nurs, Newcastle, Co. Down.   B,K,R,W3   Ireland

- - **'Erecta Aurea'** R.E. Harrison
1959 An illegit. name for a tree of erect habit with yellow foliage. **O.** Hazlewood Nurs, Sydney (c 1950).   W3   Australia

- - 'Evandale' P.C. Nitschke   1983 A listed name. No further information.

- - 'Everton Gold' Hort. Anglia
Reported from Windsor Great Park, Berks. A slow-growing, upright, yellow tree. **O.** Everton Nurs, Hants. (Probably = 'Collyer's Gold').

- - 'Farallonensis' Masters
1896 A curious form. **O.** Uncertain; probably in the Calif. University Botanic Garden. NIC.   B   U.S.A.

- - 'Fastigiata' Carrière
1855 The original clone is no longer identifiable, but others have no doubt taken its place.   B,G,K,W3   France

- - 'Filiformis' Beissner
1903 Named for a tree in the Botanic Garden in Bonn.   B   Germany

- - 'Filipendula' J. Emery
1989 In "Con. Soc. Australia Newsletter No. 5". An illegit. name for a plant best described as the green equivalent of 'Coneybearii Aurea'.

- - **'Fine Gold'** Hort. N.Z.
1972 A fast-growing golden selection. **L.** Duncan & Davies Nurs. New Plymouth.   B,W3

CUPRESSUS MACROCARPA

- - 'Flagelliformis' Cripps ex Gordon
  1875 Branches thin, whipcord. **O.** Cripps and Son, Tunbridge
  Wells, Kent. NIC.   U.K.

- - **'Globe'** Den Ouden/Boom
  1965 A dwarf, globose plant. **O.** Hillier & Sons Nurs, Winchester.
  The name 'Compacta' is now seldom used.   B,G,K,W   U.K.

- - **'Goldcrest'** Treseder   1948 In "Nurs. Cat". Golden-yellow, with persistent juvenile
  foliage. **O.** Treseder Nurs, Truro, Cornwall.   G,K,R,W3   U.K.

- - **'Golden Cone'** Krüssmann
  1979 **O.** Barthelemy Nurs, Wimborne, Dorset. ('Gold Cone').   K,R,W3   U.K.

- - 'Golden Flame' Hort. Holland   Reported from Blijdenstein Pinetum, Hilversum.

- - 'Golden Halo' Hort. N.Z.   1984 Sport from 'Gold Spread'. **I.** D.J. Liddle, Waikanae, N.Z.   W3

- - **'Golden Pillar'** Welch   1979 Narrowly erect, if on its own roots. **I.** Geo. Jackman Nurs,
  Woking, Surrey. **O.** Unrecorded.   K,R,W   U.K.

- - 'Gold Rocket' Hort. N.Z.   A listed name. No further information.

- - **'Gold Spire'** D.W. Hatch
  1974 In "Nurs. Cat". Then of Heath End Nurs, Farnham, Surrey.
  An upright-growing clone of good colour. **I.** J.W. Archer,
  Farnham, Surrey. (1968). **O.** A seedling by W. Hart at
  Warnham Court, Surrey. ('Golden Spire', 'Warnham Gold').   W3   U.K.

- - **'Gold Spread'** R. Barry   1973 In "Nurs. Cat". South Taranaki Nurs, Hawera, N.Z. A
  spreading plant similar to cultivariants of 'Horizontalis Aurea'
  but much slower and more prostrate and with denser foliage.
  O. An unrecorded source in Australia; probably 'Berrigold'
  but as it seems indefinitely stable when so grown, it is
  becoming popular also in Europe under this name.   W   N.Z.

- - **'Greenstead Emerald'** J. Emery
  1989 In "Con. Soc. Australia Newsletter No. 5". A light green
  equivalent of the following entry. **I.** Drue Wholesale Nurs,
  Berry.   Australia

- - 'Greenstead Magnifica' Hort. Australia
  An illegit. name. Now known as 'Greenstead Magnificent'.

- - **'Greenstead Magnificent'** Welch
  1979 Mutation on a tree of 'Horizontalis', 25' from the ground that
  forms a dense, almost prostrate plant with blue-grey foliage.
  I. Newman and Son's Nurs, Tea Tree Gully, S. Australia. **O.**
  Mr R. Hall. Not by any means a dwarf.   G,W   S. Australia

- - **'Greenstead Magnificent Variegated'** John Emery
  1989 In "Con. Soc. Australia Newsletter No. 5". A mutation of
  'Greenstead Magnificent' but with yellow and white
  variegation. **O.** Drue Wholesale Nurs, Berry.   Australia

- - 'Hagley' Hort. Australia   1983 A listed name for a witch's broom that has not proved
  satisfactory in cultivation.

- - 'Hatch's Sport of Sulphur Tip'   See 'Sulphur Cushion'.

- - **'Hodginsii'** E.E. Lord   1948 Horizontally branched, variegated foliage. **O.** From seed on
  Hodgins Nurs, Essendon, Melbourne. (c 1940).   W3   Australia

- - **'Horizontalis'** Brunning 1898 Large upright tree with long horizontal branches. **I.**
  Brunning's Nurs, St. Kilda, Melbourne (as *CUPRESSUS*
  lambertiana horizontalis). (1898). **O.** (c 1873).   W3   Australia

- - **'Horizontalis Aurea'** (1) Brunning
  1898 **O.** and **I.** Same as last entry, but with golden foliage.   W3   Australia

- - **'Horizontalis Aurea'** (2) Hort. If prevented from forming a leader. young plants will develop into a strong growing widespread bush with a rigid branch structure in which strong branches rise at 20-25 degrees. G Australia

- - 'Horizontalis Hodginsii' R.E. Harrison
1959 A superfluous name for 'Hodginsii'. Australia

- - 'Indoor Beauty' Hort. Holland
1986 **L.** H.J. van de Laar in "Naamlijst . . .". (1986) NOM. **I.** W.M. van Nierop, Boskoop. (1980).

- - 'John Keown' See next entry.

- - **'Keown'** E.C. Nelson
1984 In "An Irish Flower Garden". **I.** "Good Garden Plants" (as 'Keownii'), 1972. **O.** John Keown, Head Forester, Castlewellan, Co. Down. G Ireland

- - 'Lambertiana' Lord
1948 A mistake for 'Horizontalis'. Australia

- - 'Lambertiana Aurea' Hort. Australia
A mistake for 'Horizontalis Aurea'. Australia

- - 'Lebretoni' Hillier
1925 See 'Variegata' ('Lebrotoni'). U.K.

- - 'Lemon Drop' Hort. Amer.
1986 Listed name for a compact, upright plant with lemon colour foliage.

- - 'Lemon Pillar' Hort. Anglia Reported from Windsor Great Park, Berks. NOM.

- - 'Limelight' Hort. Anglia Reported from Windsor Great Park, Berks. NOM.

- - **'Lohbrunner'** Hort. Amer.
1976 A dense dwarrf globose to conical plant. **O.** E.H. Lohbrunner. **I.** (To U.K.) by Wansdyke Nurs, Devizes, Wilts. W3 Canada

- - **'Lutea'** Webster
1896 Tall, broadly columnar tree: foliage soft yellow, turning green. **O.** Dicksons Nurs, Chester, (c 1893). An early selection still widely planted. Very resistant to salt spray. B.G,K,R,W3 U.K.

- - 'Lutea Horizontalis' A listed name.

- - 'Mangalore' Hort. Australia
1986 Listed name for a flat, green, prostrate plant. No further information.

- - **'MacLaren Vale'** P.C. Nitschke
1987 In "Con. Soc. Australia Newsletter No **1**". Dwarf, golden. **O.** A witch's broom found by P.C. Nitschke at MacLaren Vale. S. Australia (1982). Australia

- - **'Merriott Gold'** Hort. Anglia Upright tree; light golden-yellow. **I.** Scotts Nurs. Merriott, Somerset. U.K.

- - **'Minima'** Corley
1962 A dwarf form tending to have coarse foliage and reversions as an older plant. **O.** R. Menzies, Golden Gate Park, San Francisco, Cal. (before 1959). The change to 'Minimax' is probably unnecessary. ('Nisbet's Gem' is incorrect). B,K,W U.K.

- - **'Monstrosa'** A listed name.

- - 'Mortlake' Hort. Australia
1986 A listed name for a slow-growing, upright selection. **O.** P.C. Nitschke. Probably NIC.

- - 'Nana Aurea' Hort. Anglia A listed name. No further information.

- - 'Otto Quast' Hort. Canada
1981 L. G. Bentham, Vancouver, BC.

- - 'Pendula' (1) Hillier   1952 In "Nurs. Cat". Named for a tree at Glencormac. Co. Down.   B,K,R,W3   Ireland

- - **'Pendula'** (2) Hort. Anglia   I. Wansdyke Nurs, Devizes, Wilts. O. A truly pendulous tree found by H.J. Welch at Devizes, Wilts.

- - 'Pendula Aurea' Hort. Australia   A listed name.

- - **'Pygmaea'** A.B. Jackson   1938 An extreme dwarf globose bush with mixed juvenile and adult dark green foliage. O. Marsham, Carshalton Nurs, Carshalton, Surrey, (1929).   B,H,K,W2   U.K.

- - 'Ragamuffin' Hort. Australia
    1993 A dwarf form with dark green juvenile foliage. O. and I. John Emery, Drue Wholesale Nurs. (1983).

- - **'Ross'** P.C. Nitschke   1989 In "Con. Soc. Australia Newsletter No. 5". Forms a prostrate plant with dense, yellowish foliage. O. A witch's broom found by P. Nitschke and R. Radford at Ross, Tasmania, (1985).

- - 'Saligna Aurea'   A mistake for 'Coneybearii Aurea'.   W

- - 'Snowstorm' Hort. N.Z.   A listed name.

- - **'South Road'** P.C. Nitschke
    1989 In "Con. Soc. Australia Newsletter No.5". An irregular, small tree with golden foliage. O. A witch's broom found by Peter Nitschke in Adelaide, (1982). Probably NIC.   Australia

- - 'Souvenir de Charles Detriche'   Now known as 'Charles Detriche'.

- - 'Stewartii' Hornibrook   1929 Named for a dwarf seedling that was never propagated.   B,H   U.K.

- - 'Sulphur Cushion' G. Haddow
    1984 Dwarf bush cushion-shaped to globose. very slow-growing with outer foliage creamy yellow. found as a mutation on 'Sulphur Tip'. O. D.W. Hatch, Honiton. I. Kenwith Nurs, Bideford, Devon. (formerly listed as 'Hatch's Sport of Sulphur Tip').   U.K.

- - **'Sulphur Tip'** Welch   1979 A slow-growing dwarf bush with pale yellow tips to the foliage. I. D.W. Hatch, Chantry Nurs, Honiton, Devon. ('Albospica' is illegit').   W   U.K.

- - 'Sulphurea' Hort. Anglia   A superfluous name for 'Sulphur Tip'.

- - **'Sunshine'** R.E. Harrison
    1972 In "Nurs. Cat". Golden foliage, semi-weeping. L. Harrison Nurs, Palmerston.   N.Z.

- - 'Tortuosa' Hort. Amer.   An illegit. name. See "Int. Dend. Soc. Yearbook, 1981". A form often with grossly contorted growth.

- - 'Variegata' Nelson   1866 Variegation white, irregular. NIC.   B,K,W3   U.K.

- - 'Violacea' Carrière   1867 Loose growing. NIC.   B,K   France

- - **'White Lightning'** J. Emery
    1989 In "Con. Soc. Australia Newsletter No. 5". A small conical tree with grey foliage, white in spring. fading to greenish-white.   Australia

- - **'Wilma'** H.J. van de Laar
    1991 In "Dendroflora 27". Narrow, conical with branches almost upright. O. Mutation from 'Goldcrest' found by P. Overkleeft, 's-Gravenzande (1987).   Holland

- - 'Woking' Corley   1962 A dwarf form; upright conical bush with light juvenile foliage. O. Geo. Jackmans Nurs, Woking, Surrey.   B,K,W3   U.K.

CUPRESSUS montana (Wiggins) Little
    1906 San Pedro Cypress. Now merged in *CUPRESSUS arizonica*
          var. *glabra* by some authorities. (per Silba, 1984).   Z8   U.S.A.

CUPRESSUS nevadensis Abrams
    1919 Piute Cypress. Now merged in *CUPRESSUS arizonica* by
          some authorities. (per Silba, 1984).   Z8   U.S.A.

CUPRESSUS nootkatensis   Now known as *CHAMAECYPARIS nootkatensis.*

CUPRESSUS obtusa   Now known as *CHAMAECYPARIS obtusa.*

CUPRESSUS pendula Lambert
    1803 Now known as *CHAMAECYPARIS funebris.*

CUPRESSUS pisifera   Now known as *CHAMAECYPARIS pisifera.*

CUPRESSUS pygmaea Lemmon
    1895 Not now distinguished within *CUPRESSUS goveniana.*

CUPRESSUS sargentii Jepson
    1909 Sargent Cypress.   20m,Z9   U.S.A.

CUPRESSUS sempervirens Linnaeus
    1753 Italian Cypress. (A wide selection of other names have been
          used in the past for this species).   20m,Z7   Mediterr.

- - 'Anja' H.J. van de Laar   1986 In "Naamlijst . . .". (1986). NOM. I. P. Zwijnenburg Jr.,
          Boskoop. A selection named for his wife.   Holland

- - var. *atlantica* (Gaussen) Silba
    1981 A minor local variant. Treated as a separate species by some
          authorities (per Rushforth, 1987).   Atlas Mts.

- - **'Aurea'** Hort. Australia   Reported from the Adelaide Botanic Garden.

- - 'Borik Jugo'   Reported from Algeria ?

- - 'Cereiformis' Carrière   1859 Closely columnar. O. Ferrand Nurs, Cognac, (1858). NIC.   France

- - 'Contorta' Carrière   1867 Contorted growth. NIC.   B   France

- - var. *dupreziana* (Camus) Silba
    1981 Now recognised as a distinct species. (per Rushforth, 1987).   Algeria

- - 'Flagelliformis' Todaro ex Masters
    1896 Clone with peculiar cones. NIC.   B   France

- - 'Fortuselli' Carrière   1867 Dwarf; branches erect. NIC.   B   France

- - 'Glauca' Monrovia   1989 In "Nurs. Cat".

- - 'Globosa' Hort. Ireland   Reported from the National Botanic Garden, Dublin.   Ireland

- - 'Globulifera' Parlatore   1860 Cones globose. NIC.   B   France

- - 'Gold Rocket' Hort. N.Z.   1983 L. Cedar Lodge Nurs, New Plymouth. Without description.

- - 'Gracilis' Hort. N.Z.   A listed name. No further information.

- - **'Green Pencil'** Hillier   An extremely slender clone with bright green foliage. O.
          Hillier & Sons Nurs, Winchester. (Originally and still
          distributed as 'Greenspire').   U.K.

- - var. *horizontalis* Miller ex Gordon
    1858 If regarded as being the typical form, the varietal name must
          be *sempervirens*, not *'horizontalis'*.   B

- - var. *indica* Royle ex Gordon
1858 A regional variant of uncertain identity. NIC.   B   India

- - **'Karoonda'** John Emery   1989 In "Conif. Soc. Australia Newsletter 5". A very compact, narrowly columnar selection with dark green foliage. O. Quentin Woolaston. I. P.C. Nitschke.   Australia

- - 'Kees Sipkes' Hort. Holland
1993 A listed name.

- - 'Monstrosa' (Carrière) Gordon
1858 Named for a tree with fasciated, montrous growth. NIC.   B,H   France

- - var. *numidica* Trabut & Barr
1913 A local form with distinctive branch structure. NIC.   Tunisia

- - 'Pendula' Lawson   1851 A spreading tree with pendent branches. NIC.   B   U.K.

- - 'Protuberans' Carrière   1867 A spreading tree bearing peculiar cones. NIC.   B   France

- - var. *sempervirens*   The typical, spreading form found in the wild. (per Silba, 1984).   Mediterr.

- - var *sphaerocarpa* Parlatore
1860 A minor variant bearing peculiar cones.   B   Italy

- - var. *stricta* Aiton   1789 Botanical designation embracing all the upright-habit trees, including most trees in cultivation.

- - 'Stricta' Hort.   The horticultural loose equivalent of last. Such names should not be used for any particular clone. ('Fastigiata').

- - 'Stricta Aurea' R.E. Harrison
1959 Slow-growing, yellowish-green.   N.Z.

- - **'Swane's Golden'** R.E. Harrison
1959 A narrowly columnar tree with bright golden-yellow foliage. O. Swane Bros Nurs, Erarington, Sydney, (1944). I. The same, (1956). (Spelling varies. 'Swanes Gold' is now in general use).   G,KR,W   Australia

- - 'Swane's Variegata' Hort. N.Z.
1992 An illegit. name for a variegated sport (dark green and gold) from the last item.

- - 'Thujaefolia' Carrière   1855 Foliage peculiarity NIC.   B   France

- - 'Tito' Hort. Anglia   1980 Dwarf pencil form with dark green foliage. O. Unknown. I. Wansdyke Nurs, Devizes, Wilts.

- - **'Totem'** Hort. N.Z.   1984 A dark green, columnar plant selected in the seed bed by Trevor Davies and Cyril Watson of Eastwood Hill. ('Totem Pole').

- - f. *umbilicata* Parlatore   1860 Not now distinguished within the species.   B   Italy

- - 'Variegata' Knight & Perry
1850 NIC.   B   U.K.

- -'Warnham' Hort. Anglia   A listed name.

- - 'Worthiana'   A listed name.

CUPRESSUS stephensonii Wolf
1948 Cayamaca Cypress. Merged with *CUPRESSUS glabra* by some authorities. (per Silba, 1984).   Z8   U.S.A.

CUPRESSUS thyoides   Now known as *CHAMAECYPARIS thyoides*.

CUPRESSUS torulosa D. Don ex Lambert
1824 West Himalayan Cypress.   20m,Z7

- - **'Arctic Green'** Levey   1972 In "Australia Homes & Gardens". Narrowly conical tree:
foliage light-green, compact. **O.** Vic Levey's Nurs.
Beaudesert, Australia. (1965). **I.** The same, (1972).   Australia

- - 'Aurea' (1) Hort. N.Z.   A clone that at best is lime-green, not golden. **O.** Bruce Hago
of Dawn Nurs, Te Atatu, Auckland. (It is possibly the same
as 'Gold Spangle').

- - 'Aurea' (2) Duncan & Davies   A good golden form. **O.** Mr. Lumsden, Northfield Gardens,
Dolma Street, -Methven.   N.Z.

- - 'Aurea' (3) Hort. N.Z.   There is a third clone in cultivation which is much dwarfer. In
all cases, the name is illegitimate.

- - 'Battley's' Sampson   1992 In "Nurs. Cat". A light green, narrowly upright clone with
pale lemon-yellow growth tips. **O.** Raised from imported seed
by a Mr. Battley who came to N.Z. (c 1900). The Mother-tree
is in a cemetery between Napier and Tempo ('Aurea, Battley's
Form').   N.Z.

- - var. *cashmeriana* (Carrière) Kent in Veitch
1900 A strikingly attractive tree with long, hanging branches and
blue-grey foliage. Various names are found. Now usually
listed as a cultivar.   Unknown

- - 'Corneyana' Knight ex Carrière
1867 Corney's Cypress. It was not and is not a cultivar name.(Art.
42). See *CUPRESSUS corneyana*.   W3

- - 'Elegans' Lawson   1851 Clone with unusual branch arrangement and attractive
foliage. NIC.   B   U.K.

- - 'Erecta Glauca' Sénéclauze
1868 A beautiful tree, with erect branching, glaucous. NIC.   B   France

- - 'Ericoides' Hornibrook   1932 An unstable juvenile form, lost to cultivation.   B,K   U.K.

- - 'Fernside'   L. Cedar Lodge Nurs, New Plymouth, N.Z.

- - 'Flagelliformis' Sénéclauze
1868 NIC.

- - 'Glauca' Hort. N.Z.   An illegit. listed name, possibly a mistake for 'Cashmeriana'.

- - 'Gold Spangle' Welch   1979 A tree to 3m, golden in summer, fading to greenish-yellow.
O. R. Barry, South Taranaki Nurs, Hawera.   R,W2   N.Z.

- - 'Hill's Golden' Hort. Australia   A tree with golden foliage persistent throughout the year. **O.**
Found in a private garden by John Emery.

- - 'Juniperoides' Carrière   1867 An unstable juvenile form. NIC   B   France

- - **'Majestica'** Knight ex Carrière
1855 A vigorous clone, in cultivation but rare.   B,K,W3   France

- - 'Microcarpa' Carrière   1855 A widespreading pendulous tree with unusually small clones.
NIC.   B   France

- - 'Nana' Gordon   1858 Dwarf, foliage congested.   B,R   U.K.

- - 'Pendula Glauca' R.E. Harrison
1959 In "In Trees . . . Southern Hemisphere". A dwarf with
glaucous green foliage, sulphur-tipped.

- - **'Silversplash'** J. Emery   1989   In "Con. Soc. Australia Newsletter No.5". **O.** A mutation from 'Nana' with a 50% white variegation. ('Nana Silversplash' is illegit.).

- - 'Stricta Aurea'   An illegit. listed name.

- - **'Tinty's Pencil'** Hort. Australia

                              A listed name. Further information required.

- - 'Variegata' Nelson	1866	Leaves variegated. NIC.	B	U.K.
- - 'Viridis' (1) Lawson	1851	Leaves bright green. NIC.	B	U.K.
- - 'Viridis' (2)		**O.** U.S. Dept. Agric. Field Sta, Woodward Okla. NIC.		U.S.A.

DACRYCARPUS (Endlicher) De Laubenfels (1969)

Podocarpaceae

A genus of nine species recently carved out of *PODOCARPUS* on rather technical grounds. Details can be found in an article by De Laubenfels in *Journ. Arnold Arb.* **50**: 274-369 (1969). All the species come from warm-temperate or sub-tropical areas in the Southern hemisphere, so will not be hardy in cool temperate regions.

DACRYCARPUS dacrydioides (Richard) De Laubenfels
                1969   Formerly known as *PODOCARPUS dacrydioides*.
- - **'Dark Delight'** Int. Con. Reg.
                1990   Differs only in foliage colour, which is a dark purple-brown. **O.** Raised from seed by County Park Nurseries, Hornchurch, Essex. ('Bronze Form').   U.K.

The following species also are recognised, all having been formerly listed under *PODOCARPUS*.

DACRYCARPUS cinctus (Pilger) De Laubenfels (1969); *D. cumingii* (Parlatore) De Laubenfels (1969); *D. expansus* De Laubenfels (1969); *D. imbricatus* (Blume) De Laubenfels (1969) and vars. *curvulus* (Miquel) De Laubenfels (1969), var. *patulus* De Laubenfels (1969) and var. *robustus* De Laubenfels (1969); *D. kinabaluensis* (Wasscher) De Laubenfels (1969); *D. steupii* (Wasscher) De Laubenfels (1969); *D. viellardii* (Parlatore) De Laubenfels. There are no recorded cultivars.

DACRYDIUM Solander ex Forster (1786)

Podocarpaceae

This is a large genus from the warm temperate and sub-tropical areas of the Southern hemisphere that has not yet been fully studied. It formerly included the genus now recognised as *HALOCARPUS*, but proposals to re-allocate some species to a one-time recognised genus *LAGAROSTROBUS* or a new genus *LEPIDOTHAMNUS* proposed by Quinn in 1982 are not accepted by all botanists.

DACRYDIUM bidwillii (Hooker f. ex T. Kirk) Quinn
　　　　　　　1878　Now known as *HALOCARPUS bidwillii*.

- - 'Copper Glow'　　　　1991　See under *HALOCARPUS bidwillii*.

DACRYDIUM biforme (Hooker) Pilger ex Engelmann
　　　　　　　1903　Now known as *HALOCARPUS biformis*.

DACRYDIUM Colensoi (Hooker) Quinn
　　　　　　　1982　Now known as *LAGAROSTROBUS colensoi*. (But see Silba, 1984).

DACRYDIUM cupressinum Solander ex Forster
　　　　　　　1786　Rimu. An important timber tree in New Zealand.　　　　　　　　　　N.Z

DACRYDIUM fonkii (Phillipi) Bentham & Hooker
　　　　　　　1860　Now known as *LEPIDOTHAMNUS fonkii*. (But see Silba, 1984).

DACRYDIUM franklinii Hooker f.
　　　　　　　1845　Huon Pine. Now known as *LAGAROSTROBUS franklinii*.
　　　　　　　　　　(But see Silba, 1984).　　　　　　　　　　　　　　　　　　　　Tasmania

- - 'Pendulum' Krüssmann　1972　Named for a pendulous tree at Garnish.　　　G　Ireland

- - 'Roosevelt' Hort. Australia
　　　　　　　1990　Habit like a weeping willow. Shoots threadlike.　　　　　　　Tasmania

DACRYDIUM intermedius T. Kirk
　　　　　　　1878　Now known as *LEPIDOTHAMNUS*. (But see Silba, 1984).

- - 'Gracilis' Hort. N.Z.　　　A listed name　　　　　　　　　　　　　　　　　　N.Z.

DACRYDIUM laxifolium Hooker f. ex Hooker
　　　　　　　1845　A proposal to transfer this species to *LEPIDOTHAMNUS* is
　　　　　　　　　　not accepted here. (per Silba, 1984).　　　　　　　　　　　　　N.Z.

- - 'Blue' Hort. N.Z.　　　　An illegit. name. See 'Blue Gem'.

- - 'Blue Form' Hort. N.Z.　1989　An illegit. name. See 'Blue Gem'.

- - **'Blue Gem'** Welch　　1979　A colour form selected by Otari Native Plant Museum.
　　　　　　　　　　Wellington.　　　　　　　　　　　　　　　　　　　W　　N.Z.

- - **'Blue Pygmy'** Hort. N.Z.　See 'Blue Gem'.

- - 'Green Cascade' Hort. N.Z.
　　　　　　　1991　A widespreading bush. **O.** Found by Mr. Ray Mole of the
　　　　　　　　　　Otari Native Plant Museum, Wellington. It is probably a
　　　　　　　　　　hybrid with *DACRYDIUM intermedius*.

- - 'Homers Tunnel' Hort. Anglia
　　　　　　　1976　Now known as 'Blue Gem'.

DECUSSOCARPUS De Laubenfels (1969)

Podocarpaceae

Another genus recently separated from *PODOCARPUS* (See *DACRYCARPUS*). It embraces 12 species from that Genus with pine-cone-like male flowers. All are from sub-tropic and rainfall areas and so are never found in cool temperate zones. No cultivars are recorded.

DISELMA Hooker f. (1857)

Cupressaceae

A monotypic genus found only in Australia and west Tasmania.

DISELMA archeri F. Hooker

 1857 In "Flora of Tasmania". 40m,Z9 Tasmania

EPHEDRA Linnaeus (1753)

Ephedraceae

A large genus of primitive, reed-like shrubs, including the familiar "Horse-tail". Although, strictly speaking, gymnosperms they have no claim to be conifers for the purposes of this Manual, and they have little or no place in garden cultivation.

FALCATIFOLIUM De Laubenfels (1969)

Podocarpaceae

A species containing 5 species separated from *DACRYDIUM* on account of differences in the flowering parts. All are from semi-tropical areas. No cultivars are recorded.

FITZROYA Hooker f. (1851)

Cupressaceae

A monotypic species from South America, hardy in U.K.

*FITZROYA **cupressoides*** (Molina) Johnston
1924 Dark green Cupressus-like leaves in whorls of three.   15-50m,Z8   S. Amer.

FITZROYA patagonica F. Hooker ex Lindley
1851 Now known as *FITZROYA cupressoides.*

FOKIENIA Henry & Thomas (1911)

Cupressaceae

A monotypic genus with foliage somewhat similar to *THUJOPSIS.*

*FOKIENIA **hodginsii*** Henry & Thomas
1911   5-15m,Z7   China

FOKIENIA kawayii Hayata (1917) and *FOKIENIA maclurei* Merrill are not now regarded as
being distinct species.

GINKGO Linnaeus (1771)

Ginkgoaceae

A mono-typical species that is a survival from prehistoric times. It is unique among conifers in almost every
imaginable way. At one time it was known as *SALISBURIA.*

GINKGO adiantifolia Sprecher
1907 As *SALISBURIA adiantifolia.*

*GINKGO **biloba*** Linnaeus   1771 The Ginkgoor, Maidenhair tree. Formerly known as
SALISBURIA adiantifolia Smith, (1797).   40m,Z3   China

- - 'Argentea' Nelson   1866 "The Silvery form". A clone no longer identifiable. NIC.   W3   U.K.

- - 'Aurea' Nelson   1866 "The golden-variegated form". NIC.   K,R   U.K.

- - 'Aureo-variegata' Sénéclauze
1868 A fine form with large, almost entire leaves, with many large
golden-yellow stripes. NIC.

- - **'Autumn Glory'** P.L.M. van der Bom
1982 In "Dendroflora 19". Upright oval. I. Saratoga Horticultural
Foundation, Saratoga. Cal. O. Nelson Nurs. San Leandro,
Cal. In "Nurs. Cat". 1959. NOM.   W3   U.S.A.

- - **'Autumn Gold'** M. van Rensselar
1956 In "Journ. Cal. Hort. Soc". A male clone with an oval, upright
crown. O. Named for a tree in San José, Cal. Selected in
1957.   K,W   U.S.A.

- - 'Bell' Hort. Amer.   Named for a tree at the home of James Bell, Atherton, Cal.
Propagated at the Saratoga Horticultural Foundation until
renamed 'Canopy', (1959).

- - 'Canopy' Hort. Amer.   1959 A listed name. No information.

- - 'Cleveland' Hort. Amer.   Unpublished name for a fastigiate tree found at Cleveland,
Ohio. Propagated by the Saratoga Horticultural Foundation,
not introduced to the trade.

- - 'Cutleaf' Hort. Amer.   1942 In "Standardised Plant Names". See 'Laciniata'.

- - **'Damaling'** W.C. Cheng & L.K. Fu
1978 In "Flora Reipublicae Popularis Sinicae". ("Flora of China")
Vol. 7. Description in Chinese.   Hort. China

- - **'Dameihai'** W.C. Cheng & L.K. Fu
1978 In "Flora Reipublicae Popularis Sinicae", ("Flora of China")
Vol. 7. Description in Chinese.   Hort. China

- - 'Dissecta' Hochstetter   1882 Now known as 'Laciniata' (per Rehder, 1949).

- - **'Dongtinghuan'** W.C. Cheng & L.K. Fu
1978 In "Flora Reipublicae Popularis Sinicae", ("Flora of China")
Vol. 7. Description in Chinese.   Hort. China

- - 'El Abra' Hort Amer.   Unpublished name for a tree found on Sierra Street, San José,
Cal., and propagated by the Saratoga Horticultural
Foundation but not introduced to the trade.

- - f. *epiphylla* Shirai   1891 In "Tokyo Bot. Mag.". A curiosity. bearing abnormal fruits.   K,W   Hort. Japan

- - **'Fairmount'** Krüssmann   1972 A vigorous, narrowly upright clone, raised from a tree in
Fairmont Park, Philadelphia, PA, planted in 1876. I. Saratoga
Horticultural Foundation.   K,W   U.S.A.

- - 'Fastigiata' Masters   1896 In "Kew Hand-list". A clone no longer identifiable. New
fastigiate selections should be given new cultivar names. (The
tree propagated at the Saratoga Horticultural Foundation
under the name 'Kew' but not introduced to the trade would
have been the same).   D,K,W   U.K.

- - **'Fozhi'** W.C. Cheng & L.K. Fu
1978 In "Flora Reipublicae Popularis Sinicae". ("Flora of China").
Vol. 7. Description in Chinese.   Hort. China

- - **'Galanfoshou'** W.C. Cheng & L.K. Fu
1978 In "Flora Reipublicae Poplularis Sinicae". ("Flora of China").
Vol. 7. Description in Chinese.   Hort. China

- - 'Globus' Hort. Holland   1993 A listed name.

- - **'Horizontalis'** Hort. Holland   Named for a spreading tree in the Botanic Gardens at Leiden.   W   Holland

- - 'King of Dongting' Hort. Holland
1985 A form with big fruits. O. Imported from China by W. Bömer
of Zundert, Holland.

- - **'Laciniata'** Carrière   1854 In "Revue Horticole". O. M. Reynier at Avignon. This name
is now used for any tree with deeply dentate leaves.
('Longifolia' and 'Macrophylla Incisa').   D,K,W   France

- - **'Lakeview'** P.L.M. van de Bom
  1982 In "Dendroflora 19". Narrowly conical male tree. **O.** and **I.**
  E.H. Scanlon, Cleveland, Ohio, (1962). W U.S.A.

- - 'Largeleaf' Hort. Amer. 1942 In "Standardised Plant Names". See 'Macrophylla'.

- - **'Luanguofoshou'** W.C. Cheng & L.K. Fu
  1978 In "Flora Reipublicae Popularis Sinicae". ("Flora of China").
  Vol. 7. Description in Chinese. Hort. China

- - 'Macrophylla' Carrière 1855 **O.** Sénéclauze Nurs, Bourg Argental, Loires, (1854). A clone
  no longer identifiable. ('Longifolia'). France

- - 'Macrophylla Laciniata' Masters
  1896 In "Kew Hand-list". NOM. NIC. Similar forms are not
  uncommon. U.K.

- - **'Mayfield'** E.H. Scanlon 1961 In "Plant Propagator Soc. Proc. **1**". A narrow, strictly
  fastigiate clone. **O.** E.H. Scanlon, Cleveland, Ohio, (1948). K,W U.S.A.

- - **'Mianhuaguo'** W.C. Cheng & L.K. Fu
  1978 In "Flora Reipublicae Popularis Sinicae". ("Flora of China").
  Vol. 7. Description in Chinese. Hort. China

- - 'Microphylla' Nelson 1866 The smaller-leafed form. NIC. U.K.

- - 'Moraine' Hort. Amer. A tree obtained from the Siebenthaler Co., Dayton, Ohio and
  propagated by the Saratoga Horticultural Foundation but not
  introduced to the trade.

- - 'Ohatsuki' J. Ohwi 1965 In "Flora of Japan". Probably the equivalent of f. *epiphylla*.
  ('Ohazuki'). W3

- - 'Overlook' Hort. Amer. Named for a tree selected by E.H. Scanlon on Mount
  Overlook Avenue, Cleveland, Ohio and propagated by the
  Saratoga Horticultural Foundation but not introduced to the
  trade.

- - **'Palo Alto'** P.L.M. van de Bom
  1982 In "Dendroflora **21**". Selected as representing a good form,
  with a broad, spreading crown. **O.** E.H. Scanlon, Cleveland,
  Ohio, (1962). W3 U.S.A.

- - **'Pendula'** (1) Carrière 1967 Irregular, slow- growing tree with pendent branches. **L.** C.
  van Geert Nurs. (1862). D,W Belgium

- - 'Pendula' (2) A truly pendulous clone reported from the Botanic Garden at
  Nancy. K France

- - 'Pragensis' J.P. Krouman 1969 In "Gard. Chron". An illegit name for a low, spreading,
  parasol-shaped clone. Czechosl.

- - 'Princeton Gold' Hort. Amer.
  1966 A clone selected and patented by the Princeton Nurs,
  Princeton, N.J. but discontinued by them because of
  propagating difficulties.

- - **'Princeton Sentry'** P.L.M. van der Bom
  1982 In "Dendroflora **19**". Narrowly conical tree. **I.** Princeton
  Nurs. N.J. (1967). W3 U.S.A.

- - 'Prostrata' Hort. Anglia 1992 An illegit. listed name.

- - 'Pyramidalis' Hort. Amer.
  1963 An invalid name for a male clone. **L.** Vermeulen Nurs,
  Neshanic Station, N.J.

- - 'Robin'   Named for a male tree of good shape obtained from the Cole
                                   Nurs, Circleville, Ohio and propagated by the Saratoga
                                   Horticultural Foundation but not introduced to the trade.

- - 'Roosevelt'   Named for a tree on Roosevelt Boulevard, Philadelphia, PA,
                                   propagated by the Saratoga Horticultural Foundation but not
                                   introduced to the trade.

- - **'Saint Cloud'** F.G. Meyer
                          1959   In "Plant Explorations". An open, upright tree. **O.** Named for
                                   a tree in Jardin Kahn, St. Cloud-sur-Seine, Bois de Boulogue,
                                   Paris.   K,W   France

- - 'San José Gold' Hort. Amer.
                          1969   L. J. Clarke Nurs, San José, Cal. NOM.

- - 'Santa Cruz' E.H. Scanlon
                          1959   An umbrella-shaped tree, low and spreading
                                   ('Umbraculifera'). It turns up under several names.

- - **'Saratoga'** Saratoga   1976   Densely leafed small tree. A male clone. **O.** and **I.** Saratoga
                                   Horticultural Foundation. Saratoga, Cal.   W   U.S.A.

- - 'Sentry' Hort. Amer.   A confused name for more than one clone.

- - 'Sinclair' Princeton   1977   Another selection to which the remarks under 'Princeton Gold'
                                   apply.

- - 'Slim Jim' Hort. Amer.   1968   Named for a fastigiate male tree selected by M.W. Staples in
                                   Kent, Ohio, propagated by the Cole Nurs, Circleville, Ohio.

- - **'Tit'** H.J. Grootendorst   1978   In "Dendroflora 15-16". Congested dwarf form of irregular
                                   growth.   K,W3   Hort. Japan

- - **'Tonziguo'** W.C. Cheng & L.K. Fu
                          1978   In "Flora Reipublicae Popularis Sinicae", ("Flora of China").
                                   Vol. 7. Description in Chinese.   Hort. China

- - **'Tremonia'** Krüssmann   1972   Narrowly fastigiate. **I.** Dortmund Botanic Garden, (1970). **O.**
                                   The same, (1930).   K,R,W   Germany

- - f. *triloba* Masters   1896   In "Kew Hand-list". No longer recognisable in such a variable
                                   species. NIC.   U.K.

- - 'Tubiformis' Hort. Amer. 1990   **L.** Coenosium Gardens, Supplement. NOM.

- - 'Umbraculifera' Hort. Amer.
                          1965   A superfluous name for 'Santa Cruz'.

- - 'Umbrella' Hort. Hungary
                          1975   An unsatisfactory name. Presumably descriptive.

- - **'Variegata'** Carrière   1854   In "Revue Horticole". A variegated and delicate form. **O. M.**
                                   André Leroy Nurs, Angers. Said to be a female clone. ('Fuiri-
                                   Icho').   D,K,R,W   France

- - **'Wuxingyinxing'** W.C. Cheng & L.K. Fu
                          1978   In "Flora Reipublicae Popularis Sinicae". ("Flora of China").
                                   Vol. 7. Description in Chinese.   Hort. China

- - **'Xiafoshu'** W.C. Cheng & L.K. Fu
                          1978   In "Flora Reipublicae Popularis Sinicae". ("Flora of China").
                                   Vol. 7. Description in Chinese.   Hort. China

- - **'Yaweiyinxing'** W.C. Cheng & L.K. Fu
                          1978   In "Flora Reipublicae Popularis Sinicae". ("Flora of China").
                                   Vol. 7. Description in Chinese.   Hort. China

- - 'Yuandifoshuo' W.C. Cheng & L.K. Fu
   1978 In "Flora Reipublicae Popularis Sinicae, ("Flora of China").
   Vol. 7. Description in Chinese.

Hort. China

Much of the above information has been drawn from a very valuable Article "Checklist of Cultivated Conifers" by Frank Santamour, Jr., Shan-an He and Alice Jalot McArdle in *Journal of Arboriculture*. March 1963. That Article contains a good Bibliography of literature cited in the Article and adds the following list of the 'varieties' in cultivation in China as a fruit crop. Although these are 'culinary varieties' rather than 'cultivars' some might turn up in garden cultivation, so they are listed here.

- - var *biloba* (= *meihe-yinxing*).   The plum-stone shaped stone group.

- - 'Dameihe'   Large plum stone.

- - 'Mianhuaguo'   Cotton-fruit like; often with twin fruit.

- - 'Nanhuiwuxin'   Nanhui inembryonate; (fruit without embryos).

- - 'Suanpanguo'   Abacus-bead like.

- - 'Tongziguo'   Tung-tree fruit like.

- - 'Ximeihe'   Small plum stone.

- - 'Yuanzhu'   Round beads. There is some question whether this is a
                           collective name for several cultivars with round fruit. It is
                           being considered as a valid group name with the described
                           variations probably derived from this cultivar; 'Dayuanzhu' -
                           large round beads, 'Xiaoyuanzhu' - small round beads.
                           'Yapigu-Yuanzhu' - duck's buttocks.

- - var *huahar* (= *fushon-yinxing*)   The finger citron shaped group.

- - 'Changbing-fushon'   Long petiole finger citron.

- - 'Dafushon'   Large finger citron.

- - 'Dongtinghuang'   King of Dongtinshan Mountain, fruit largest, 500-year old
                           tree is 16 meters tall.

- - 'Fuzi'   Buddha's finger.

- - 'Ganlan-fushon'   Chinese olive-like finger citron.

- - 'Jiafushon'   Domestic finger citron = Dafuzi. large Buddha's finger.

- - 'Jianchu'   Sharp pestle; poor quality.

- - 'Jiangho-fushon'   Sharp-top finger citron.

- - 'Jinguo-fushon'   Golden-fruited finger citron.

- - 'Luanguo-fushon'   Ovate-fruited finger citron.

- - 'Xiao-fushon'   Small finger citron.

- - 'Yuandi-fushon'   Round-bottom finger citron; superior type.

- - 'Zaozi-fushon'   Chinese date-like finger citron; name reported but without
                           description.

- - var *apiculata* (= *Maling Yinxing*). The intermediate group with a small apicular on the top of
                           the fruit.

- - 'Damaling'   Large horse's bell.

- - 'Huangpigui'   Yellow peel fruit.

- - 'Longyan'   Dragon's eye.

- - 'Oingpiguo'	Green peel fruit.
- - 'Ximaling'	Small horse's bell;.
- - 'Zhongmaling'	Medium horse's bell.

GLYPTOSTROBUS Endlicher (1847)

T a x o d i a c e a e

A genus (probably monotypic) sharing many of the characteristics of *TAXODIUM*.

GLYPTOSTROBUS lineatus (Poiret) Druce.
        1917 Not now accepted as a valid species. Probably a case of
        mistaken identification..

GLYPTOSTROBUS pensilis (Staunton) K. Koch
        1873 Chinese Swamp Cypress.   8-20m,Z8   China

HALOCARPUS Quinn. (1982)

P o d o c a r p a c e a e

A small genus recently separated from *DACRYDIUM* on technical grounds.

HALOCARPUS bidwillii (Hooker f. ex Kirk) Quinn
        1982 Tarwood. Formerly known as *DACRYDIUM bidwillii*.   Z8   N.Z.

- - 'Copper Glow' Hort. N.Z.
        1985 Carries, juvenile growth, copper coloured in winter.

- - 'Erecta' Hort. N.Z.   Reported by J. W. Goodwin, Director of Parks, New
                                Plymouth.

- - 'Reclinata' Hort. N.Z.   As previous entry.

HALOCARPUS biformis (Hooker) Quinn
        1982 Formerly known as *DACRYDIUM biforme*.   13m,Z8   N.Z.

HALOCARPUS kirkii (F. Mueller ex Parlatore) Quinn
        1982 Formerly known as *DACRYDIUM kirkii*.

JUNIPERUS Linnaeus (1753)

Cupressaceae

The Junipers are a taxonomically difficult group: mainly shrubs or small trees although several species reach 20m. In the foliage they are similar to *CUPRESSUS* and other genera of *Cupressaceae* but they are quite different in the fruit. Although this is a true cone the scales do not become hard and woody but remain fleshy, forming a berry. Some authorities (see Flora of China) still retain a section of the genus recognised by Muller (1754) as a different genus. i.e., *SABINA* Miller (1754), and the best classification of several other species is still in some dispute.

JUNIPERUS africana Hort. N.Z.   A mistake for *JUNIPERUS chinensis* 'Stricta', (per J.W. Goodwin, 1973).

JUNIPERUS albanica Penzes
1970 Now merged in *JUNIPERUS communis* var. *oblonga*. (per Silba, 1984).

JUNIPERUS ashei Buchholz
1930 Ashe Juniper, Mountain Cedar.   5m,Z8   Mexico, U.S.A.

- - var. **saltillensis** (Hall) Silba
1984 Saltillo Juniper. By some authorities listed as *JUNIPERUS saltillensis*.   Mexico

JUNIPERUS bacciformis Carrière
1855 Now known as *JUNIPERUS phoenicia*.

JUNIPERUS barbadensis Linnaeus
1753 West Indies Juniper. Now includes *JUNIPERUS ekmanii* and *JUNIPERUS lucayana* and possibly others. (per Silba, 1984).   15m,Z9   West Indies

- - var. *urbaniana*   No longer distinguished within the species. (per Silba, 1984).

JUNIPERUS bermudiana Linnaeus
1753 Bermuda Juniper. Very rare in the wild.   15m,Z9   Bermuda

JUNIPERUS blancoi Martinez
1946 Blanco Juniper. A species near to *JUNIPERUS virginiana*.   15m,Z8   Mexico

JUNIPERUS brevifolia Antoine
1857 Azores Juniper. A species related to *JUNIPERUS oxycedrus*.   3m,Z9   Azores

JUNIPERUS californica Carrière
1854 California Juniper. I. to U.K. by W. Lobb (1853).   15m,Z9   Californ.etc.

- - var. *utahensis* Engelmann
1887 Now known as *JUNIPERUS osteosperma*. (per Silba, 1984).

JUNIPERUS canadensis Loddiges
1920 In "Nurs. Cat". Now known as *JUNIPERUS communis* var *depressa*.

JUNIPERUS canariensis Gujot
1942 Now merged in *JUNIPERUS phoenicia*. (per Silba, 1984).

JUNIPERUS cedrus Webb & Berthelot
1836 Canary Islands Juniper. Almost extinct.   20m,Z9   Canary Is.

JUNIPERUS centrasiatica Komarov
1924 Kuen-luen Juniper.   12m,Z5   China

JUNIPERUS cernua Roxburgh
1832 Not now distinguished with in *JUNIPERUS chinensis*.

JUNIPERUS chinensis Linnaeus
1767 In "Mant. Pl.". Chinese Juniper.   25m,Z3   China

The nomenclature of this species (or group of associated species) has a long record of confusion that, hopefully, at lease in the horticultural world seems to have been resolved acceptably. The history, beginning with the work of P.J.van Melle in 1946, is traced in Welch (1964), (1979) and (1992). See also under *JUNIPERUS x media*.

- - 'Alba' (1) Standish 1875 Now known as 'Variegata'.

- - 'Alba' (2) Rehder 1925 In "Journ. Arnold Arboretum 6". See 'Expansa Variegata'.

- - 'Albospica' Hort. Amer. 1986 A listed name for a form with mixed white and yellow variegations.

- - 'Albovariegata' Veitch 1881 Superfluous synonym of 'Variegata'. H

- - **'Ames'** D. Wyman 1963 In "Amer. Nurs". A vigorous bush or small tree with blue-green foliage. O. Seed by Prof. T.J. Maney at Iowa State College, (1935). B,K,W U.S.A.

- - 'Angelica Blue' Hort. Amer.
1991 See under JUNIPERUS virginiana.

- - **'Aquarius'** Hort. Amer. 1986 A listed name. Growth compact; foliage blue-green.

- - 'Arbuscula' Van Melle 1946 Now listed under JUNIPERUS x media. B,K,W

- - 'Arctic' Hort.Amer. Now listed under JUNIPERUS x media. W3

- - 'Arenaria' Wilson ex Hornibrook
1928 In "Journal Arnold Arb. 9". A dwarf spreading clone with predominately juvenile leaves. H

- - 'Argenteovariegata' R. Smith
1867 A superfluous name for 'Variegata'. ('Argentea'). U.K.

- - 'Armstrong Gold' Hort. Amer. Now known as JUNIPERUS x media 'Gold Coast'. W3

- - 'Armstrongii' Hort. Amer. Now listed under JUNIPERUS x media. B,D,R,W3

- - **'Aurea'** R. Smith 1865 O. Young's Nurs, Milford, Godalming, Surrey (c.1855). Normal habit, golden-yellow foliage (a male clone). B,D,G,H,W U.K.

- - 'Aurea Globosa' Rehder 1923 Superfluous name for the plant now widely grown as 'Plumosa Aurea'.

- - 'Aurea Pendula' Beissner 1891 The name is descriptive. NIC. B Germany

- - 'Bakaurea' Hort. Amer. 1990 L. Mitsch Nurs, Aurora, Or. Without description.

- - 'Belvedere' Hort. Anglia 1992 A listed name for a selection similar to 'Echiniformis' but more vigorous. I. Wansdyke Nurs, Devizes, (1973). Austria

- - 'Berry Hill' Krüssmann 1983 Now listed under JUNIPERUS x media. K,W3

- - **'Blaauw'** H.J. Grootendorst
1940 Rich blue-grey foliage, main branches upright giving rugged outline. ('Blaauw's Varietet'). I. J. Blaauw & Co, Boskoop, (c.1924). B,K,R,W3 Hort. Japan

- - **'Blue Alps'** Int. Con. Reg.
1983 A large bush with ascending main branches, overhanging tips, overall silver-blue. Reg'd. by van Klaveren, Wansdyke Nurs, Devizes, Wilts. O. Found by H.J. Welch in the Alpengarten Frohnleiten. It was at first distributed as 'Willow Pattern'. G,K,R,W3 Austria

- - 'Blue and Gold' Hort. Now listed under JUNIPERUS x media. W3.

- - 'Blue Cloud' Hort. Now listed under JUNIPERUS virginiana. B,W3.

- - 'Blue Mountain' Hort. Now listed under JUNIPERUS virginiana.

- - **'Blue Point'** Monrovia 1973 In "Nurs. Cat". This forms a symmetrical cone with dense blue-grey foliage. L. Monrovia Nurs. Azusa. Cal. G,K,W U.S.A.

- - 'Blue Vase' M.A. Dirr   1983   In "Manual of Woody Plants". A spreading plant with steel-blue foliage, here listed under *JUNIPERUS* x *media*.   W3   U.S.A.

- - 'Carrière' Carrière   1855   An old name of no clear application. NIC.   B,H,W2   France

- - 'Chugai' Hort. Amer.   Now listed as 'Olympia'.

- - **'Columnaris'** Fairchild   1920   A narrowly columnar form with blue foliage. **O.** and **I.** U.S. Dept. Agric. raised from seed collected in Hopeh Provence. Probably more than a single clone is now in cultivation under this name.   B,D,K,R,W   China

- - **'Columnaris Glauca'** Den Ouden   1937   Silvery-grey, columnar. **O.** and **I.** Same as previous entry.   B,K,W   U.S.A.

- - 'Columnaris Hetzii' Hort.   Now known as 'Fairview'.

- - 'Columnaris Viridis' Hort. Amer.   Superfluous name for 'Columnaris' (or perhaps an indistinguishable selection).

- - 'Compacta' Hort. Amer.   Now known as *JUNIPERUS* x *media* 'Armstrong'.

- - 'Coolwater' Hort. Amer.   1980   **L.** Raraflora Nurs, Feasterville, PA. Without description.

- - 'Daub's Frosted'.Hort.Amer.   1987   Now listed under *JUNIPERUS* x *media*.   W3

- - 'Decumbens' Hort.   1923   See *JUNIPERUS chinensis* 'Parsonsii'.

- - 'Den Boer' Reg'd. A.A.N.   1951   Name registered by G.H. Heard, Des Moines, Iowa. (1930) **O.** A.F. den Boer, Des Moines, Iowa. Now listed under *JUNIPERUS* x *media*.   B,W3   U.S.A.

- - 'Densa' Cornman   1949   Similar to 'Pyramidalis', but looser. **O.** K. Sawada, Overlook Nurs, Crichton, Alabama. Probably NIC.   B   U.S.A.

- - 'Densa Erecta' Hort. Amer.   Now known as 'Spartan'.   W3

- - **'Densa Glauca'** Hort. Canada   1986   **L.** T.J. Cole in "Woody Plant Source List". NOM.

- - 'Densata' Hort. ex R. Smith   1867   Dense, conical shrub, Female clone.Leaves large. Branch tips pendulous. NIC.   U.K.

- - **'Dropmore'** Krüssmann   1972   An extremely slow-growing, dense, bun-shaped dwarf with greyish-green adult foliage. **O.** Found by Frank L.Skinner at Dropmore, Manitoba. **I.** The Arnold Arboretum.   K,W   Canada

- - **'Echiniformis'** Welch   1979   Very slow-growing; flattened or globose bush with dark green juvenile foliage. Grows best in well drained soil. For many years wrongly listed as *JUNIPERUS communis* 'Echiniformis' and also under *JUNIPERUS oxycedrus*. **O.** Unknown. **I.** S.J.Rinz Nurs, Frankfurt-am-main, Germany.   G,K,W   Germany

- - 'El Blue' Hort. Amer.   A listed name. **L.** Interstat Nurs, Hamburg, Iowa.

- - 'Eureka' Hort. Amer.   1940   Reported from Univ. of Washington Botanic Garden. No information.   U.S.A.

- - 'Excelsior' Wyman   1943   In "Amer. Nurs. **117**". A female columnar tree. **O.** The Morris Arboretum, Philadelphia, PA. NIC.   B,K   U.S.A

- - 'Expansa' H.J. Grootendorst   1940   Now known as *JUNIPERUS chinensis* 'Parsonsii'.   W3   U.S.A.

- - **'Expansa Aureospicata'** H.J. Grootendorst

    1940 Medium green foliage, splashed with yellow; spreading habit. Mistakenly transferred to *JUNIPERUS davurica* by P.J. van Melle.   W3   U.S.A.

- - **'Expansa Variegata'** Hornibrook

    1939 Mistakenly transferred to *JUNIPERUS davurica* by P.J. van Melle.   H,W3   U.S.A.

- - **'Fairview'** H.J. hGrootendorst

    1958 In "Nurs. Cat". (Not distinguished from 'Hetz Columnaris') Columnar; bright green. **O.** Fairview Evergreen Nurs, Fairview, PA., U.S.A.   B,G,K,W Holland

- - *femoena*   Linnaeus used this word and *mascula* to distinguish between male and female specimens. Neither is a cultivar name. But see 'Mas'.   B,D,K,W3 Sporadic

- - 'Fiore' Hort. Amer.   Now listed under *JUNIPERUS virginiana*.

- - 'Flagelliformis' Carrière   1855 An unidentifiable female clone.   France

- - 'Fortunei' Rehder in Bailey

    1933 A columnar form with bright-green mainly awl-shaped leaves. Named for Robert Fortune, for no recorded reason.   U.S.A.

- - 'Fruitland' Hort. Amer.   Now listed under *JUNIPERUS* x *media*.   W3

- - 'Gelber Samling' Hort. Germany

    1983 **O.** and **I.** Horstmann Nurs, Schneverdingen. An acceptable name required.

- - 'Glauca' Nicholson   1885 In "Dict. Gardening". A form with glaucous-blue foliage.   B   U.K.

- - 'Glauca Hetz' Hort. Amer.   See *JUNIPERUS virginiana* 'Hetz'.

- - **'Globosa'** Hornibrook   1923 More symmetrical, lighter green than 'Plumosa'; branches stand at wide angles.   B,D,H,R,W Hort. Japan

The history of this and the 'Plumosa' group of shrubby clones is traced by Welch (1979) under *JUNIPERUS* x *media* (following van Melle), whose transference of these groups from *JUNIPERUS chinensis* is now regarded as having been a mistake. (See Welch, 1992).

- - 'Globosa Aurea' Hornibrook

    1923 Not distinguishable from 'Plumosa Aurea', as now known in the trade.   H,W3

- - **'Globosa Cinerea'** Hornibrook

    1923 Grey-green foliage. Similar to 'Blaauw' but broader and less rugged in outline. It was probably the same as the now popular 'Shimpaku'.   B,W   U.K.

- - 'Globosa Hillbush' Hort. Amer.   Reported from Denver Botanic Garden, U.S.A.

- - 'Gold Coast' Hort.   Now listed under *JUNIPERUS* x *media*.   W

- - 'Gold Lace' Hort. Amer.   Now listed under *JUNIPERUS* x *media*.

- - 'Gold Star' Hort.   1972 Now listed under *JUNIPERUS* x *media*. Reg'd., Arnold Arboretum by J.C. Bakker & Sons Nurs, St. Catherines, Ontario.   Canada

- - 'Golden Saucer' Hort.   Now listed under *JUNIPERUS* x *media*.

- - 'Goldkissen' Hort.   Now listed under *JUNIPERUS* x *media*.

- - 'Green Jungle' Hort.   Now listed under *JUNIPERUS* x *media*.

- - 'Greysport' Hort. Australia
1989 A non-variegated sport of *JUNIPERUS chinesis* 'Variegata'.
Ross Conifers, Terana, Australia.

- - 'Helle' Hort. Amer.   A superfluous name for 'Spartan'.   K,W

- - 'Hetz Columnaris' Wyman
1963 Now known as 'Fairview'.   W   U.S.A.

- - 'Hetzii' F.C. Hetz   1937 In "Nurs. Cat". A vigorous spreading shrub; branches thin,
leaves glaucous. O. F.C. Hetz, Fairview Evergreen Nurs,
Fairview, PA, (1920). ('Hetz Blue', 'Hetzii Glauca').   U.S.A.

- - 'Hetzii Glauca' Hort.   See 'Hetzii'.

- - 'Hill's Blue' Hort.   Now listed under *JUNIPERUS* x *media*.

- - 'Holbert' Hort. Amer.   Now listed under *JUNIPERUS* x *media*.

- - 'Idylwyld' Hort.Amer.   1986 A listed name for a dense quick-growing, conical tree.

- - 'Ikast' Hort. Amer.   1972 A listed variety. L. Vermeulen Nurs, Neshanic Station, N.J.   Denmark

- - **'Iowa'** Haber & Lantz   1948 Similar to 'Ames' but more spreading; free fruiting. I. Iowa
State College (1930).   B,K,W   U.S.A.

- - **'Jacobiana'** De Vos   1887 As *JUNIPERUS jacobiana*, a very old name for a narrowly
and densely conical variety with mainly blue green juvenile
leaves. No longer identifiable. ('Jacobiniana').   B,K   Holland.

- - **'Japonica'** Carrière   1855 Spreading bush. Eventually becomes a small upright tree;
rich green leaves. Young plants have all-juvenile, prickly
foliage. Older plants have a proportion of adult foliage.   B,D,G,K,W   France

- - 'Japonica Aureovariegata' (1) Veitch
1881 Now known as *JUNIPERUS chinensis* 'Plumosa
Aureovariegata'.   W2

- - (*procumens*) 'Aureovariegata' (2) Beissner
1891 Now known as 'Expansa Aureospicata'.

- - **'Japonica Variegata'** Carrière
1867 A variegated form of the last item. (Not the same as
'Variegated Kaizuka').   W   France

- - **'Kaizuka'** Hornibrook   1939 Dark, rich green, upright bush with blue berries.   B,G,H,K,R,W   Hort.Japan

- - 'Kaizuka Blue' Hort. N.Z.   A listed name. Possibly 'Robusta Green'.

- - 'Kaizuka Variegata' Hort.Amer.   See 'Variegated Kaizuka'.

- - 'Kallay's Compact' Hort.Amer.   Now listed under *JUNIPERUS* x *media*.

- - 'Kék' Hort. Anglia   1992 An illegit. name. Reported from Windsor Great Park. Berks.
NOM.

- - **'Keteleeri'** Beissner   1910 Glaucous, bloomy dark blue foliage; narrow upright
form.O.Keteleer Nurs. Brussels. (Sometimes listed wrongly
under *JUNIPERUS virginiana*).   B,D,G,K.W3   Belgium

- - **'Kohankie's Compact'** Wyman
1963 A dense, globose plant with foliage bluish-green. Probably no
longer in cultivation. O. Kohankie Nurs, Painsville, Ohio.   B,W3   U.S.A.

- - 'Kosteri' Hort.   See following entry.

- - 'Kosteriana' Hort.   Now listed under *JUNIPERUS virginiana*.

- - **'Kuriwao Gold'** H.J. van de Laar
  1984 In "Dendroflora 21". Golden-green foliage; distinct upright, branching habit. O. Ross Stuart, Clinton, South Otago.   W3   N.Z.

- - **'Kuriwao Mist'** Hort. N.Z.   Seasonal colour changes from misty to blue to bluey-green. O. Ross Stuart, Clinton, South Otago.   W3   N.Z.

- - **'Kuriwao Sunbeam'** Hort. N.Z.
  O. Ross Stuart, Clinton, South Otago. ('Kuriwao Sunburst' and 'Kuriwao Sunshine' are incorrect).   W3

- - **'Langoldiana'** Beissner   1900 Slender, mostly adult foliage. NIC.   B   Germany

- - **'Leeana'** R. Smith   1865 As *JUNIPERUS leeana.* A dense upright clone with nodding branch-tips. O. Raised by Lee at the Hammersmith Nurs. NIC.   B,K

- - **'Lemon Hill'** Hort. Amer.   Now listed under *JUNIPERUS* x *media.*   W

- - **'Lombarts'** Hort. Anglia   A listed name. Reported from Windsor Great Park, Berks. NOM.

- - **'Luptonii'** Van Melle   1946 A male clone no longer identifiable. NIC.   B

- - **'Mac's Golden'** Hort Amer.
  1989 Sport found in Michigan. Upright spreader, bright yellow-gold with bluish-green interior. O. F.M. 'Mac' Alexander, Michigan. I. Iseli Nurs, Boring, OR. ('Max').

- - **'Maney'** Haber & Lantz   1948 A large bush with ascending branch system. Origination same as 'Ames'.   B,G,K,W   U.S.A.

- - **'Mas'** Gordon   1858 An upright, loose, clone. Numerous yellow male flowers in Spring.   B,D,K,W   U.K.

- - **'Mascula'** Carrière   1867 See 'Mas'.

- - **'Mathot'** Hort. Amer.   Now listed under *JUNIPERUS* x *media.*   B

- - **'Meyeri'** Hort. Amer.   See under *JUNIPERUS squamata.*

- - **'Milky Way'** Hort. Europe   Now listed under *JUNIPERUS* x *media.*

- - **'Mint Julep'** Hort. Amer.   Now listed under *JUNIPERUS* x *media.*   B

- - **'Mission Spire'** Hort. Amer.   Glossy bluish-green foliage; upright. L. Mission Gardens.   K,W3

- - **'Monarch'** H.J. Grootendorst
  1965 In "Dendroflora 2". Upright, conical. O. F.J. Grootendorst & Sons Nurs, Boskoop, from Japanese seed.   G,K,W   Holland

- - **'Moraine'** Hort.   Now listed under *JUNIPERUS* x *media.*

- - **'Mordigan'** A.A.N. Proc.   1951 Now listed under *JUNIPERUS* x *media.*

- - **'Mordigan Aurea'** Hort. Amer.   Now listed under *JUNIPERUS* x *media.* ('Mordigan Gold').

- - **'Mountbatten'** Ashworth
  1948 In "Amer. Nurseryman". Grey-green, dense, narrowly conical. Named by consent of Lord Mounbatten during his visit to Toronto to open the Canadian National Museum. ('Mounbatten' is incorrect) I. Sheridan Nurs, Georgetown, Ontario.   B,K,W   Canada

- - **'Neaboriensis'** Veitch   1881 A male clone similar to 'Mas'. (*=JUNIPERUS sphaerica* var. *neaboriensis* of Van Melle). NIC.   B,K,G

- - **'Nick's Compact'** Hort. Amer.
  Now listed as *JUNIPERUS* x *media.* ('Pfitzeriana Compacta').

- - **'Obelisk'** H.J. Grootendorst
  1946 In "Nurs. Cat". Narrowly conical. Dense, prickly foliage: greyish-green. O. F.J. Grootendorst & Sons Nurs, Boskoop, raised from seed imported about (1930) from the Chugai Nurs, Co. Yamamota, near Kobe. B,G,K,R,W Japan

- - **'Oblonga'** Slavin
  1932 A clone with mixed juvenile and dark green adult foliage, similar to 'Japonica' but lower and more widely spreading. O. Bobbink and Atkins Nurs, Rutherford, N.J. B,H,W U.S.A.

- - 'Old Gold' Hort.
  Now listed under *JUNIPERUS* x *media*. B

- - **'Olympia'** H.J. Grootendorst
  1956 In "Nurs. Cat". A slender columnar form with glaucous juvenile foliage. O. As 'Obelisk'. L. F.J. Grootendorst & Sons Nurs, Boskoop. ('Chugai'). B,G,K,W Holland

- - 'Ontario Green' Hort. Amer.
  1980 In "Amer. Nurs". A listed name for a slender columnar form; some juvenile leaves. U.S.A.

- - 'Owen' Hort. Amer.
  1979 A listed name for a low, compact dense bush; some juvenile foliage.

- - **'Parsonsii'** Hornibrook
  1939 Light green glaucous foliage, stout, horizontally-spreading primary branches. (Not spelt 'Parsonii') (= *JUNIPERUS chinensis* 'Expansa' and *JUNIPERUS davurica* var *parsonsii* SENSU Van Melle). H,W

- - **'Paul's Gold'** Int. Con. Reg.
  1990 See *JUNIPERUS* x *media* 'Paul's Gold'.

- - **'Pendula'** (1) Franchet
  1884 (=*JUNIPERUS spherica* var. *pendula* of Van Melle). B

- - 'Pendula' (2) Späth
  1896 Now known as *JUNIPERUS* x *media* 'Pfitzeriana'. (Note: The mother-plant was a stem-strained conical specimen with pendulous branch-tips on the Späth Nurs, Stuttgart, hence the misleading epithet). B,D,W3

- - "Pfitzer Juniper" Hort.
  Colloquial name used for any clone deriving from *JUNIPERUS* x *media* 'Pfitzeriana'.

- - 'Pfitzeriana' Hort.
  (And numerous names based on it) See under *JUNIPERUS* x *media*'. (The spelling 'Pfitzerana' is now regarded as being incorrect). B Germany

- - **'Plumosa'** Hornibrook
  1923 The Plume Chinese Juniper. A low spreading male bush; leaves dark green, adult. (See notes under 'Globosa'). B,D,H,W3 Germany

- - **'Plumosa Albovariegata'** (Otto) Hornibrook
  1939 Similar to previous entry but foliage speckled white. (See notes under 'Globosa'). B,H,W3 U.K.

- - **'Plumosa Aurea'** Hornibrook
  1923 Similar to 'Plumosa' but with yellow-green foliage turning to golden-bronze by winter. (See notes under 'Globosa'). B,D,H,W U.K.

- - **'Plumosa Aureovariegata'** (Otto) Hornibrook
  1939 Similar to 'Plumosa' but with bright golden variegation. ('Plumosa Argenteovariegata'). B,W3 U.K.

- - 'Plumosa Tremonia'
  See 'Tremonia'.

- - 'Procumbens' (1) Siebold
  1844 Now known as *JUNIPERUS procumbens*

- - 'Procumbens' (2) Endlicher
  1947 A mistake for *JUNIPERUS chinensis* 'Parsonsii' (and its variegated forms).

- - 'Pyramidalis' (1) Carrière 1867 I. Into Belgium by D. von Siebold (1843).   B,D,K,W   France

- - 'Pyramidalis' (2) Kumlien
1936 Superfluous name for *JUNIPERUS chinensis* 'Columnaris
Glauca'.   U.S.A.

- - 'Pyramidalis Viridis' Kumlien
1946 In "The Friendly Evergreens". Superfluous name for
JUNIPERUS chinensis 'Columnaris'.   U.S.A.

- - 'Ramlosa'   Now listed under *JUNIPERUS* x *media*. (Not to be confused
with *JUNIPERUS ramulosa*).

- - 'Reevesiana' Hort. Carrière
1855 (Listed as a species.) Now regarded as a clone of
JUNIPERUS chinensis 'Femina'. NIC.   China

- - 'Richeson' Hort. Amer.   Now listed under *JUNIPERUS* x *media*.   B

- - **'Robusta Green'** H.J. van de Laar
1975 In "Dendroflora 11-12". A slow-growing, irregularly upright
tree: blue-green. I. Monrovia Nurs, Azusa, Cal. (1973).   G,W3

- - 'Rockery Gem' Hort.   See under *JUNIPERUS sabina*.   K,W

- - **'San José'** W.B. Clarke 1938 In "Nurs. Cat". A dwarf wide-spreading, low shrub with
mostly juvenile foliage as a young plant. O. Sport at Clarke's
Nurs, San José.   B,K,W   U.S.A.

- - var. *sargentii* (Henry) Takeda
1913 Now listed, (with its forms 'Compacta', 'Glauca', and
'Viridis'), under *JUNIPERUS sargentii*.   B,D,H,W3   Japan

- - 'Saybrook Gold' Hort. Amer.
1991 Low spreader with brilliant gold colour. I. Iseli Nurs, Boring,
OR.

- - 'Scrolle' Hort. Ireland 1985 Reported from Mount Congreve. Co. Waterford.   Ireland

- - 'Sea Green' Hort. Amer.   Now listed under *JUNIPERUS* x *media*.

- - 'Sea Spray'   Now listed under *JUNIPERUS* x *media*.

- - 'Sheppardii' Veitch 1881 Listed as a species. NIC.   B,D,G,H,K,W   U.K.

- - **'Shimpaku'** Welch 1966 Dull, dark-green foliage, slow-growing plant popular for
bonsai. Tends to produce short branches with bunches of
foliage. Sometimes wrongly listed under *JUNIPERUS* x
media.   W   Hort. Japan

- - 'Shimpaku Gold' Hort. N.Z.   A listed name. L. Duncan & Davies Nurs. New Plymouth.

- - 'Shimpaku Nana' Hort. Amer.   An illegit. listed name.

- - **'Shoosmith'** Shoosmith 1930 In "Nurs. Cat". A loose, bushy form with juvenile foliage. O.
Southside Nurs, PA. I. Fred Shoosmith.   B,K,W   U.S.A.

- - 'Shugai' Hort. 1964 Reported from the Belmonte Arboretum, Wageningen. O. The
Shugai Nurs, Yamamota, near Kobe.   Hort. Japan

- - 'Smithii' (1) Loudon 1838 A vigorous tree. I. Smith of Ayr Nurs. O. Seed imported from
Nepal. NIC.   B

- - 'Smithii' (2) Hort. ex Slavin
1932 Broadly conical form. Bright green adult foliage, free
fruiting.

- - **'Spartan'** Monrovia 1961 In "Nurs. Cat". Dense pyramid, rich, green foliage. L.
Monrovia Nurs, Azusa, Cal. (Originally listed as 'Helle').   B,K,W   U.S.A.

- - 'Spearmint' Hort. Amer.   1986 A listed name for a selection with upright growth and bright green foliage.

- - **'Story'** D. Wyman   1963 In "Amer. Nurs". Dark green adult foliage, branches horizontal. **O.** Same as 'Ames', above.   B,W   U.S.A.

- - **'Stricta'** Den Ouden   1949 A dwarf form with blue juvenile foliage. Often wrongly listed under *JUNIPERUS excelsa*, and also as *JUNIPERUS squamata* 'Campbellii'. It is a plant that does not age well.   B,G,K,W   Europe

- - 'Stricta Variegata' Hort. Holland
    1986 A mistake for 'Variegata'. (Not G).

- - 'Sunbeam' Hort.   See 'Kuriwao Sunbeam'.

- - **'Templar'** J. Konijn   1983 In "Dendroflora **20**". A small upright plant with very sharp, grey to blue-green leaves. **O.** An unnamed seedling received from America (1968). **I.** Konijn Nurs, Reeuwijk.   G   Holland

- - **'Titlis'** Draijer   1972 An irregular, very compact fastigiate form. Silvery-blue foliage, sharp to the touch. **L.** Draijer Nurs, Heemstede.   K,W   Holland

- - var. *"torulosa"* Bailey   1933 Now usually listed as a cultivar. See 'Kaizuka.'   D   U.S.A.

- - var.*"torulosa variegated"* Hort. Amer.
    See 'Kaizuka Variegated'.

- - **'Tremonia'** Welch   1979 Rich golden-yellow foliage; upright habit, similar to 'Blaauw'.   W3   Germany

- - **'Variegata'** R. Smith   1865 Slow growing, but eventually a large bush, creamy-white variegation. 'Argentea', 'Argenteo-variegata' and 'Albovariegata' are superfluous synonyms.   B,W   U.K.

- - **'Variegated Kaizuka'** Den Ouden/Boom
    1965 Creamy-yellow variegation. **O.** Mutation on the Monrovia Nurs, Azusa, Cal.   B,G,W   U.S.A.

- - 'Veitchii' Hornibrook   1939 No longer identifiable.   B,H

- - 'Veroides' Hort. Amer.   1986 A listed name. No information.

- - 'Willow Pattern' Hort. Amer.   Name changed to 'Blue Alps'.   W

- - 'Wilson's Weeper' Clarke
    1934 Possibly a cultivariant? See Van Melle.   B,K,W   U.S.A.

- - **'Wintergreen'** Monrovia   Conical; dense; with deep green leaves. **L.** Monrovia Nurs, Azusa, Cal.   U.S.A.

- - 'Winter Surprise' Hort. Amer.   Now listed under *JUNIPERUS* x *media*.

JUNIPERUS comitana Martinez
    1944 Chiapas Juniper, Comitan Juniper.   10-15m,Z8   Mexico

JUNIPERUS communis Linnaeus
    1753 The Common Juniper. Shrub or small tree.   5m,Z2   N. Hemisphere

This circumpolar species is very variable and difficult to classify because the variations do not follow any clear geographical pattern. Here the treatment follows Welch (1979) in recognising four "varieties". *communis, depressa, montana* and *sphaerica*.. If these taxa are regarded as sub-species, they retain their name except that var. *montana* Aiton becomes sub, sp *nana* Syme. Several minor groups have been retained as "forms", but many early 'named forms' were clearly selections and are here listed as cultivars.

- - var. *alpina* Endlicher   1847 Now merged in var. *montana*.

- - 'Anna Maria' Hort. Germany
    1992 A listed name without description. Horstmann Nurs, Schneverdingen.

- - var. *arborea* Kuphaldt   1937 In "Gartenflora 6". No longer distinguished within the
species.   B

- - f. *arborea pyramidalis* Kuphaldt
  1937 In "Gartenflora 6". No longer distinguished within the
species.   B

- - 'Argyrophylla' Sudworth   1897 Foliage somewhat more silvery. NIC.   B

- - **'Arnold'** H.J. Grootendorst
  1965 In "Dendroflora 2". Near to 'Hibernica' but slower growing. **I.**
Gebr. Boer Nurs, Boskoop, Holland, (1964).   K,W   Germany

- - **'Ashfordii'** Kammerers   1932 Named for a Spire-like tree in Morton Arboretum.   B,W3   U.S.A.

- - 'Atholl' R. Brien   1980 Columnar form similar to 'Hibernica' but insides of the leaves
have more stomata giving the plant a more silvery
appearance. **O.** and **I.** Found by Bob Brien growing wild on
the estate of the Duke of Atholl, Perthshire.   U.K.

- - **'Aurea'** Nicholson   1900 An elegant drooping form golden tinted. NIC.   B,D,K,W   U.K.

- - 'Aureospica' Rehder   1923 A superfluous name for 'Depressa Aurea'. (1).   W

- - **'Aureovariegata'** Beissner
  1891 Habit normal; tips of all new growth and some leaves a
beautiful yellow. ('Variegata Aureo').   W   Germany

- - 'Bakony' Barabits   1965 In "Magyar Fenyóújdonságok". A hardy, strong-growing
fastigiate clone.   W   Hungary

- - 'Baldwin' Hort. Amer.   A listed name. **O.** J.W. Spingarn, then of Baldwin, N.Y.

- - **'Barmstedt'** Hackmann   1983 A very vigorous and narrowly columnar form. **O.** and **I.**
Hackmann Nurs, Barmstedt-in-Holstein.   Germany

- - 'Barton' Hort. Anglia   1985 Slow-growing, semi-prostrate, low grey-green foliage,
speckled white in early summer. **L.** Holden Clough Nurs,
Lancs.

- - **'Berkshire'** Welch   1979 Dark green foliage with silvery sheen; violet-tinted in winter;
slow growing, cushion forming shrub. **I.** Arnold Arboretum,
Jamaica Plain, Mass. (1974).   K,R,W   U.S.A.

- - 'Blondii' Hort. Germany   1992 A listed name. **L.** Horstmann Nurs, Schneverdingen, without
description.

- - f. *brevifolia* Sanio   1883 In "Deutsche Bot. Monats 1". A horizontal form with very
short leaves, found by E. Sanio in East Prussia.   B   Germany

- - 'Brien' Hort. Scotland   1985 A dwarf very prostrate form with leaves held in many cases
tightly round the branchlets. **O.** and **I.** Found in the wild in
Perthshire. Scotland by J. Brien Nursery, Perthshire.

- - **'Bruns'** Den Ouden/Boom
  1965 A bluish-green strictly erect, vigorous, disease resistant clone.
I. Timm Nurs, Elmshorn, Germany. (1953).   B,K,W   Sweden

- - var *canadensis*   1867 Louden 1838. Now known as var *depressa*.

- - 'Canadensis Aurea' Beissner
  1891 Now known as 'Depressa Aurea'.   W   U.S.A.

- - 'Candelabrica' Luescher   1909 In "Allg. Bot. Zeitsche". Small conical tree with up-turned
branches. Probably never propagated.   B,K   Switzerl.

- - **'Candelabriformis'** Kuphaldt
1937 In "Gartenflora **86**". A small tree with a compact crown and pendent branches found in Littonia. Like *JUNIPERUS rigida* in habit. **I.** H.A. Hesse Nurs, Weener-on-Ems. (1938).   B,K   Germany

- - 'Carpet' H.J. van de Laar 1986 In "Naamlijst . . .". (Same as 'Green Carpet').   U.K.

- - var. *caucasica* Endlicher 1847 Now known as var. *oblonga*. (per Silba, 1984).   Mediterr.

- - 'Clywyd' Hort. Anglia   A listed name for a prostrate plant with blue foliage.

- - **'Columnaris'** Hornibrook
1929 In "Gar. Chron". Indistinguishable from 'Compressa'.   B,H,R,W   U.K.

- - var. *communis*   See Welch, "Man. Dwarf Conif". 211 (1979).

- - 'Compacta' Hort. Amer. 1986   An illegit. listed name.

- - **'Compressa'** Carrière 1855 Columnar, compact, extremely dwarf form, somewhat tender in winter. Often replaced in the trade with similar, but stronger-growing clones. See 'Columnaris'.   B,D,G,H,K,W

- - 'Conspicua' Den Ouden 1937 An upright, spreading bush with decurving tips. **I.** Den Ouden Nurs, Boskoop, (1934) under the name 'Den Ouden'. NIC.   B,K   Holland

- - 'Constance Franklin' Int. Con. Reg.
1982 Creamy-white variegated foliage. Variegated sport of 'Hibernica'. Variegation tends to run out on older plants. Reg'd. by E.C. Franklin, Earley, Berks.   W   U.K.

- - f. *contorta* Kuphaldt 1937 In "Gartenflora **86**". Named for a plant with a twisted stem. NIC.   B

- - 'Controversa' Den Ouden
1949 A columnar selection with decurving branch-tips. **O.** Found in the Gimborn Arboretum, Doorn. **I.** Den Ouden Nurs, Boskoop. NIC.   B,K   Holland

- - **'Corielagen'** D.W. Hatch
1980 A dense, mat-forming selection found in the Scottish Highlands by Dr. Coombe. **I.** Holden Clough Nurs, Lancs.   W3   Scotland

- - f. *coronata* Sanio 1883 In "Deutsche Bot. Monat". A local variant found by Dr. C. Sanio but no longer distinguished. NIC.   B   Russia

- - **'Cracovia'** (Loddiges) Knight
1850 The Polish Juniper. A vigorous upright-spreading bush. **O.** Found near Krakow. **L.** Loddiges Nurs, Hackney near London, (1826) (as *JUNIPERUS cracovia*).   B,D,G,H,K,W   Poland

- - f. *cupressoides* Kuphaldt
1937 In "Gartenflora **86**". NIC. Named for a cypresslike plant found by G. Kuphaldt in Littonia, (1936). NIC.   B

- - 'Dayii' Hort. Amer. 1918 An unpublished name for a form found by S. Bowditch in Connecticut and named in honour of David Fisher Day (1829-1909). NIC.

- - var. *depressa* Pursh 1814 The low-growing forms found in Eastern North America. By some authorities listed as sub-species. But see Welch (1979) (= *JUNIPERUS canadensis* of some early authors).   B,D,H,K,W   East N.Amer.

- - **'Depressa Aurea'** (1) Hornibrook
1939 A wide-spreading golden form of the previous item.   B   N. Amer.

- - 'Depressa Aurea' (2) Hort. Europe
A mistake for 'Nana Aurea'.   B,K,W   Europe

- - 'Depressa Vase-Shaped' Hort. Amer.
Now known as 'Vase'. ('Depressa Vase').

- - **'Depressed Star'** Den Ouden/Boom
1965 Fresh green feathery foliage becoming bronze in winter. A prostrate clone of *JUNIPERUS communis* var. *montana* widely distributed from the plant in the Experimental Station at Boskoop.   B,K,W   Holland

- - 'Derrynane' Hort. Anglia
1975 Originated as a berry-bearing plant similar to 'Repanda' found in Eire. See "Royal Hort. Soc. Journal".   Eire

- - **'Dumosa'** Den Ouden
1934 In "Nurs. Cat". A broad, dwarf shrub. **O.** Found on the Gimborn Estate at Doorn. **I.** Den Ouden Nurs, Boskoop (1934). A clone of *JUNIPERUS communis* var. *depressa*.   B,K   Holland

- - 'Echiniformis' Knight
1850 This plant has probably never existed and early plants labelled with this name were *JUNIPERUS chinensis* or alternatively they may have been *JUNIPERUS oxycedrus* 'Echiniformis' which at the moment appears lost to cultivation. (See *JUNIPERUS oxycedrus* 'Echiniformis'.

- - 'Edgbaston' Welch
1979 Insufficiently distinctive from 'Hornibrookii' to retain.   W2

- - **'Effusa'** Den Ouden
1949 Another shrubby selection of *JUNIPERUS communis* var. *depressa*. **O.** and **I.** As 'Dumosa'.   B,D,G,K,W   Holland

- - **'Ellis'** A. Jensen
1950 In "Nurs. Cat". Rather similar to 'Depressed Star'. **O.** and **I.** Asger M. Jensen, Holmstrup.   B   Denmark

- - f. *elongata* Sanio
1883 In "Deutsche Bot. Monat 1". A minor variant found in the forest of Baran, near Lyck, East Russia.   B   E. Russia

- - 'Erecta' Den Ouden/Boom
1965 A clone narrower than 'Hibernica'. L. Hesse Nurs, Weener-on-Ems, (1896), but no longer catalogued by them.   B,K   Germany

- - 'Fastigiata' Dallimore & Jackson
1914 Not now distinguished from 'Hibernica' in the trade.   U.K.

- - **'Fontan'** H.J. van de Laar
1986 In "Naamlijst . . .". NOM.   Sweden

- - **'Gew Graze'** Welch
1979 Female clone, similar to 'Repanda'. Found in Cornwall by Dr. D.E. Coombe, Christ's College, Cambridge.   W   U.K.

- - **'Gimborn'** Den Ouden
1949 A dense, prostrate form: a clone of *JUNIPERUS communis* var. *depressa*. **O.** and **I.** Same as 'Dumosa'.   B,K,W3   Holland

- - 'Gnome' Hort. Holland
1992 L. W. Linssen, Baexam. Without description.

- - **'Gold Beach'** Wyman
1968 In "Arnoldia **19**". Bright yellow new growth, turning green; prostrate form; dense, wide-spreading growth.   K,W   U.S.A.

- - 'Gold Coin' Hort. Germany
1992 A listed name without description. Horstmann Nurs, Schneverdingen.

- - **'Gold Cone'** Hort. Germany
1980 Bright golden-yellow foliage with a leader; similar in habit to 'Hibernica'. L. Kordes Nurs, Bilsen. Not to be confused with 'Suecica Aurea'.   G,W3

- - 'Golden Schnapps' Hort. Amer.   A listed name.

- - 'Golden Showers' Hort. Anglia   See 'Schneverdingen Goldmachandel', but the descriptive name will almost certainly replace it in the trade.

- - **'Graciosa'** H.J. Grootendorst
      1969 In "Dendroflora 6". Light green foliage; broad, shrubby habit.
      O. Raised from seed and **I.** L. Konijn, Reeuwijk.   K,W   Holland

- - 'Grayi' Den Ouden   1949 An exceptionally narrow, columnar form, foliage silvery.   B

- - **'Green Carpet'** A. Bloom.
      1984 In "Nurs. Cat". Dwarf form. Foliage dark green in winter,
      light in summer, ground hugging. **I:** Bressingham Nurs, Diss,
      Norfolk, U.K. **O.** Found in a coastal location in Norway.   W3   Norway

- - **'Greenmantle'** Int. Con. Reg.
      1987 Dense, dark green foliage; prostrate or ground-hugging habit.
      Reg'd. by T. Forbes, Plaxtol Nurs, Sevenoaks, Kent.   U.K.

- - 'Grinden' Hort. Holland   Incorrect name for 'Kantarell'.

-,- **'Haverbeck'** Krüssmann   1983 Dwarf globular, dense habit, grey-green foliage. **O.** G.
      Horstmann.   K,W3   Germany

- - **'Heidegeest'** Krüssmann
      1983 Silvery-grey-blue foliage; open columnar habit. **O.** G.
      Horstmann.   K,W3   Germany

- - var. *hemispherica* (Presl) Parlatore
      1867 The low-growing bushy form found in the mountainous
      regions of Europe, N. Africa, and Asia. By some authorities
      listed as sub-species, but see Welch, (1979).   B,W2   Europe

- - **'Hemispherica'** (Presl) Parlatore
      1868 Name for a clone of the above in cultivation, but not
      common.   B,H,W

- - 'Hemsen' Hort. Germany   1986 A listed name without description. Horstmann Nurs,
      Schneverdingen.

- - **'Hibernica'** Gordon   1858 Irish Juniper; Foliage bluish-white above, bluish green below;
      Columnar, narrow, dense habit. L. Loddiges Nurs, Hackney
      near London, (1836), as *JUNIPERUS hibernica*.   B,K,W   U.K.

    Apart from several clones that have been named, the descriptive epithets *fastigiata, hispanica, pyramidalis* and
stricta have been used for now unidentifiable erect-growing selections, but the use of 'Hibernica' is now general.

- - 'Hibernica Gelbunt' Hort. Germany
      1983 An illegit. listed name.

- - 'Hibernica Variegata' Nelson
      1866 NIC. But see 'Constance Franklin'.

- - **'Hils Freiburg'** F.G. Meyer
      1963 Low and slow growing habit; tips ascending. **I.** Hesse Nurs,
      Weener-on-Ems, (1952).   B,W   Germany

- - *hondoensis* Satake   A local spreading mountain form. (? x *nipponica*).   K   Japan

- - var *hornibrookii* Grootendorst ex Hornibrook
      1939 The low-growing bushy, prostrate or mat-forming forms with
      small, straight, long-pointed leaves.   W   Europe

- - **'Hornibrookii'** Hornibrook
      1939 Greyish appearance, small, prickly leaves, very prostrate
      habit.   B,D,G,H,K,W   Ireland

- - **'Hornibrook's Gold'** H.J. van de Laar
      1979 In "Dendroflora 13-14". A mutation that is bronze-yellow in
      winter, greenish-yellow in summer. **O.** M. van Klaveren &
      Zoon Nurs. Boskoop, (1970).   K,R,W   Holland

JUNIPERUS COMMUNIS

- - **'Horstmann'** H.J. van de Laar
  1983 In "Dendroflora 20". A grotesque, pendulous form. O. G. Horstmann, (1978). — G,K,R — Germany

- - 'Horstmann's Pendula' — 1978 An illegit name. L. Jeddeloh Nurs, Oldenburg. — Germany

- - 'Horstmann's Special' — 1986 In "Nurs. Cat". A mini-dwarf form. Horstmann Nurs, Schneverdingen.

- - **'Hulkjaerhus'** Thomsen — 1962 In "Nurs. Cat". A columnar form, greener and less prickly than 'Suecica'. I. Thomsen Nurs, Skalborg. — B,K,W3 — Denmark

- - 'Hungaria' Hort. — 1992 Reported from Windsor Great Park, Berks, for a fastigiate plant.

- - f. *intermedia* Sanio — 1850 In "Deutsche Bot. Monat". NIC. Intermediate in character between vars *communis* and *montana*. — B — Germany

- - 'Inverleith' Welch — 1979 A bushy clone of var *hornibrookiana* found in Edinburgh Botanic Garden. — W2 — Scotland

- - f. *jackii* Rehder — 1907 In "Mitt. d.d.d. Ges"..Local variant with whip-like main branches. — B,H,K,W — U.S.A.

- - 'Jensen' A. Jensen — 1944 In "Nurs. Cat". A pendulous; strong growing form. O. Asger M. Jensen Nurs, Holmstrup. — B,K,W — Denmark

- - **'Jura'** Draijer — 1980 In "Nurs. Cat". A slow-growing bush with tufted growth. O. Draijer Nurs, Heemstede. — Holland

- - **'Kantarell'** H.J. van de Laar
  1986 In "Naamlijst . . .". NOM. L. Horstmann Nurs, Schneverdingen, (1992), without description. ('Cantarell'). — Sweden

- - **'Kelleriis'** Den Ouden/Boom
  1965 A clone of var.*montana* with yellow foliage. NIC. — B — Denmark

- - **'Kenwith'** Jeddeloh — 1991 In "Nurs. Cat". Slow, low-growing plant. Foliage turns purple in winter. O. Kenwith Nurs, Bideford, Devon. I. Jeddeloh Nurs, Oldenburg, Germany.

- - **'Kiyonoi'** Kiyonoi — 1930 In "Nurs. Cat". Cottage Hill Nurs, Mobile, Ala. Similar in growth to 'Hibernia' but resistant to summer heat. — B,W — U.S.A.

- - 'Kizorio' Hort. Amer. — 1964 Tall, slender, grey form. L. Watnong Nurs, Morris Plains, N.J.

- - f. *latifolia* Sanio — 1883 "Deutsche Bot. Monat". No longer indentifiable. — B — Germany

- - **'Laxa'** F.G. Meyer — 1963 In "Plant Explorations". Upright, columnar form; yellow-green foliage. O. G.D. Bohlje Nurs, Westerstede, (1930). — B,K — Germany

- - 'Lela' Int. Con. Ref. — 1991 Broadly spherical or spreading bush. O. Found on the Papuk Mts. — Yugoslavia

- - **'Loensgrab'** Krüssmann — 1983 Light green needles; very dense, pendulous. O. G. Horstmann. — K,W3 — Germany

- - 'Mayer' Hort. — See 'Meyer'

- - **'Meyer'** Den Ouden/Boom
  1965 A selection with a broadly conical habit. I. Timm Nurs, Elmshorn (1958) O. Erich Meyer, Barmstedt (1945). — B,K,W3 — Germany

- - 'Miniatur' Hort. Germany
  1992 A slow-growing sport from 'Suecica Erecta'. L. Hachmann Nurs, Barmstedt-in-Holstein, Germany.

- - **'Minima'** H.J. Grootendorst
  1940 In "Mitt. d.d.d. Ges". Slow-growing prostrate form building up in centre. Leaves light green with silvery white inner surface. (syn. 'Windsor Gem'?).　　B,K,R,W　　Holland

- - var. ***montana*** Aiton
  1789 Low-growing forms found in Europe, Asia and Western N. America with often bluntly pointed boat shaped grey-green foliage with white dense habit. By some authorities listed as sub-species Nana, but see Welch, (1979).

- - sub-sp. *nana* Syme in Sowerby
  1868 Here listed as var. *montana*. See Welch, (1979).

- - **'Nana Aurea'** Beissner　　1884 A low-growing prostrate plant. Leaves golden-yellow. Not vigorous, needs planting in a dryish situation.　　B,G,H,W

- - 'Nana Prostrata' Hornibrook
  1939 Dwarf prostrate form rising in the centre. Leaves dark green, inner sides bluish.　　H　　U.K.

- - **'Niemannii'** E. Wolf　　1922 In "Mitt. d. d. d. Ges". A sporadic bushy variant. NIC.　　B　　Russia

- - var. *nipponica* (Maximowicz) Wilson
  1916 Now known as *JUNIPERUS rigida* sub-sp. *nipponica*.　　Japan

- - **'Norwegen'** Horstmann　　1978 In Nurs. Cat". More open, hardier and faster growing than 'Compressa'. L. Horstmann Nurs, Schneverdingen (1978).　　W3　　Germany

- - **'Nutans'** Hornibrook　　1939 A bushy selection with many short leaves. I. H. den Ouden Nurs, Boskoop. O. Selected in the wild from the Veluwe district.　　B,H　　Holland

- - 'Obergaertner Bruns' Hort.　　See 'Bruns'.　　W

- - f. *oblonga* (Bieberstein) Loudon
  1844 A local variant. Long leaves and small, oblong fruits.　　B,D,K　　Transcaucasia

- - **'Oblonga Pendula'** Loudon
  1838 "The broad weeping common Juniper". The name has been incorrectly applied to *JUNIPERUS rigida*.　　B,D,G,K,W　　U.K.

- - 'O' Donnell' Don Smith　　In "Arnoldia". L. Watnong Nurs, Morris Plains, N.J.　　U.S.A.

- - **'Paddos'** Hort. Germany
  1978 A listed name. O. G. Horstmann, Schneverdingen.　　Germany

- - 'Pencil Point' Hort. Amer.　　Now known as 'Sentinel'.

- - 'Pendens' Den Ouden　　1949 A weeping form introduced by H.A. Hesse of Weener-on-Ems, (1937), but no longer in production by 1965.　　B　　Germany

- - 'Pendula' Carrière　　1855 A pendulous clone no longer identifiable. NIC.　　B,K　　France

- - 'Pendula Aurea' Sénéclauze
  1868 NIC.　　B

- - **'Pendulina'** C. Kuphaldt
  1937 In "Gartenflora". Tree like but pendulous habit, resembling *PICEA breweriana*. I. Hesse Nurs, Weener-on-Ems. O. Found by C. Kuphaldt in Littonia (1936).　　B,K,R　　Germany

- - 'Ploem' Den Ouden　　1949 Columnar form with ascending branches. O. V.G. Ploem Kirkrade, Limburg, Holland. (c.1932).　　B　　Holland

- - **'Prostrata'** (1) Hornibrook
  1923 Of similar prostrate habit, but stronger growth than in 'Hornibrookii'.　　B,D,H,K,W　　Germany

- - 'Prostrata' (2) Beissner   1896 The Prostrate Common Juniper. Named for a collection made by Rettig in the chalky hills near Jena. Often mis-named var. *depressa*. See var. *montana*.   Germany

- - 'Pyramidalis' Den Ouden/Boom
   1965 Broad pyramidal habit; not so blue as 'Hibernica'. L. Hesse Nurs, Weener-on-Ems, (1910).   B,K   Germany

- - 'Reflexa Pendula' Carrière
   1867 Probably identical with *JUNIPERUS communis* 'Oblonga Pendula'.

- - 'Repanda' H.J. Grootendorst
   1940 Almost creeping, brownish green, leaves not prickly. More than one clone in cultivation.   B,G,K,R,W   Holland

- - 'Rom' Hort. Germany   1992 A dwarf form. L. Horstmann Nurs, Schneverdingen.

- - 'Ronaldsay' Hort. Anglia   1992 Collected in the wild of the Outer Hebrides. Reported from Windsor Great Park, Berks.

- - 'Ruud' Int. Con. Reg.   1977 A semi-erect habit with long pendulous branches; foliage silvery-green. Reg'd by Einar Ruud, Vest Agder Hort. School, Sogne. I. The same. O. The same, found in Northern Telemark, (1971).   W3   Norway

- - 'Salen' Hort. Anglia   1986 Very dwarf globose plant, foliage quite bluish in summer and silver violet blue in winter. Found growing wild at Salen, near Loch Shiel by J. Strachan M.R.C.V.S. L. Almondell Nurs, Methven, Perthshire.

- - var. *saxatilis* Pallas   1788 A name of no clear standing or application. (See Taxon 17(5): 545 (1968)). Plants so labelled are usually a clone of var. *montana*.   B

- - 'Schneverdinger Goldmachandel' Krüssmann
   1983 O. and I. G. Horstmann (1978). Upright golden form with gracefully spreading branch tips. This is being sold under the trade name 'Golden Showers' (See Art. 31A (c) in the Cultivar Code).   K,R   Germany

- - 'Sentinel' H.J. Grootendorst
   1961 In "Dendroflora 2". Narrow, columnar, almost pointed form.   B,G,K   Canada

- - var. *sibirica* Burgsdorf   1787 Now merged in var. *montana*.   W

- - 'Sieben Steinhauser'   1983 Slow-growing upright form with inner leaves noticeably blue. O. G.Horstmann.   W   Germany

- - 'Silver Lining' Welch   1966 A little slow as a young plant, but eventually to one metre or more across. Prostrate, insides of leaves, very silver. O. H. Bawden, East Sussex. I. Wansdyke Nurs, Devizes, Wilts.   U.K.

- - 'Siskyou Mountains' Hort. Germany
   A superfluous name for f. *jackii*.

- - 'Soapstone' Welch   1979 The male form of 'Gew Graze'.   W   U.K.

- - 'Spotty Spreader' Hort. Holland
   1990 A white-speckled, spreading plant. O. Raised by M. Droogh, Boskoop. I. L. Konijn, Ederveen, Holland.

- - 'Steingrund' Hort. Germany
   1983 A listed name. O. G. Horstmann.   Germany

- - 'Stricta' Carrière   1855 A superfluous name for 'Hibernica'.   D

- - 'Suecica' Miller   1789 The Swedish Juniper. Pillar shaped, round topped, shoot tips nodding out in summer.   B,D,K,R,W

- - 'Suecica Aurea' Hort. Sweden
  1970 Slow-growing, fine gold foliage. The plant has a natural
  round top. O. and I. Tage Lundell. Helsingborg.   Sweden

- - 'Suecica Major' Hort. Germany   Mistake for 'Meyer'.

- - **'Suecica Nana'** Bailey   1933 Dwarf, columnar form. Round topped, inside of leaves
  noticeably grey.   B,H,K,R,W   U.S.A.

- - 'Suecica Variegata' Nelson
  1866 A mutation from 'Suecica' having some of it's leaves spray
  variegated. NIC.

- - **'Tage Lundell'** Krüssmann
  1983 Slow-growing, upright form. Foliage on branch ends yellow.
  O. Tage Lundell, Helsingborg, Sweden. I. Horstmann Nurs,
  Schneverdingen.   K,R,W   Germany

- - 'Taurifolia' Hort. Amer.   1977 An illegit. name. L. Mitsch Nurs, Aurora, OR.   W3

- - 'Tempelhof' H.J. van de Laar
  1984 In "Dendroflora 21". A low round-topped bush; bronze
  foliage in winter. L. Konijn Nurs, Reeuwijk.   W3   Holland

- - f. *thyocarpos*   1912 Name no longer recognised.   B

- - **'Tigerstedtii'** Schwerin   1926 In "Mitt. d.d.d. Ges. 36". Pyramidal tree; branches spreading,
  branchlets pendulous.   B   Finland

- - 'Trollii' Hort. Germany   1986 In "Nurs. Cat". Dwarf form. Horstmann Nurs,
  Schneverdingen.

- - 'Tunheim' Hort. Holland   1992 Reported from Arboretum Trompenburg, Rotterdam. NOM.

- - 'Variegated Aurea' Carrière
  1867 See 'Aureovariegata'.   H

- - **'Vase'** Kumlien   1936 A dwarf "vase-shaped" bushy clone of *JUNIPERUS
  communis* var. *depressa*. ('Vase-shaped').   B,K,R   U.S.A.

- - **'Velebit'** H.J. van de Laar
  1984 In "Dendroflora 21". Bronze green foliage; low open bush.   G,W3   Yugoslavia

- - 'Vlierskov' Hort. Canada   1980 A listed name. L. Gordon Bentham, Victoria, B.C.

- - **'Volcano'** H.J. van de Laar
  1986 In "Naamlijst . . .". Vase-shaped bush; silvery-grey foliage.
  NOM.   W3   Holland

- - **'Wallis'** Draijer   1980 Densely clothed bush; upright habit. branches arching. L.
  Draijer Nurs, Heemstede.   W3   Holland

- - 'Weckii' Ascherson & Graebner
  1897 An upright form with peculiar foliage and cones. NIC.   B,K   Sporadic

- - 'Wilsede' Hort. Germany   1978 See 'Wilsede Berg'. O. G. Horstmann.

- - **'Wilsede Berg'** Krüssmann
  1983 Narrowly columnar, bright green foliage. O. G. Horstmann.   K,R   Germany

- - 'Windsor Gem' Welch   1979 See 'Minima'.   W   U.K.

- - 'Youngii' Hort. Amer.   A mistake for 'Aurea'?

- - **'Zeal'** Welch   1979 A low-growing spreading bush-form. Dark blue-green
  appearance. O. Found in a garden in Devon by H.J. Welch. I.
  Wansdyke Nurs, Devizes. Wilts.   W   U.K.

JUNIPERUS conferta Parlatore

	1863 Shore Juniper. A prostrate shrub. Formerly known as *JUNIPERUS litoralis*.	Z6	Japan
- - **'Akebono'** "Arnoldia"	1983 New growth is creamy-white, becoming green later in season.	W3	Hort. Japan
- - **'Blue Pacific'** Monrovia	1972 In "Nurs. Cat". Blue-green foliage; low, trailing habit.	G,K,R,W	U.S.A.
- - 'Blue Tosho' Hort. Amer.	1989 A listed name for a rigid, silver-green selection. L. Iseli Nurs. Could be clone of *JUNIPERUS taxifolia* as leaves are arranged as in that species and very soft to the touch.		
- - **'Boulevard'** Welch	1979 Very prostrate; branches, horizontal, foliage glaucous green.	W	U.S.A.
- - 'Brookside Variegated' Hort. Amer.	1988 A listed name. Mitsch Nurs, without description.		
- - 'Emerald Green' Hort. Amer.	1985 An unacceptable name; possibly a mistake for 'Emerald Sea'.		
- - 'Emerald Ruffles' Hort N.Z.	1991 A Duncan & Davies selection. Bright green foliage. Spreading ground cover. L. Cedar Lodge Nurs, New Plymouth.		
- - **'Emerald Sea'** D.M. Whitt	1972 In "U.S. Dept. Agric. Release Notice". Emerald green foliage, turning yellow-green during Winter; widely spreading branches.	K,R,W	U.S.A.
- - 'Horridus' Hort. N.Z.	1991 A prickly form no longer in production.		
- - var. *maritima* Wilson ex Nakai	1922 Now known as *JUNIPERUS taxifolia* var. *luchuensis*.		
- - 'Murasaki-tosho' Hort. Holland	1986 In "Naamlijst . . .". NOM. A variety reported from Japan.		Hort. Japan
- - 'Rosedora' Hort. Amer.	1988 L. Mitsch Nurs, Aurora, OR.		
- - **'Silver Mist'** Reg'd. Arn. Arb.	1983 Similar in habit to 'Blue Pacific'; short, dense, grey leaves. I. Brookside Nurs, Wheaton, MD.	W3	Hort. Japan
- - 'Takane' H.J. van de Laar	1986 In "Naamlijst . . ". NOM.		

JUNIPERUS convallium Rehder & Wilson

	1914 Mekong Juniper. Formerly listed as *JUNIPERUS mekongensis* and also as *JUNIPERUS ramulosa*.		China
- - var. *microsperma* (Cheng & Fu) Silba	1984 A geographical form with smaller cones.	W3	Tibet

JUNIPERUS coxii A.B. Jackson

	1932 The Coffin Juniper. In "New Flora and Silva". This is now considered to be within the range of variation of *JUNIPERUS recurva* by some authorities. (See Rushforth, 1987).	10m,Z7	Upper Burma

JUNIPERUS davurica Pallas

	1788 Dahurian Juniper. A species widely distributed in Asia but little, if at all, known in western cultivation.		Siberia

The following cultivars were mistakenly transferred to this species by van Melle. But see Welch, (1991).

- - 'Expansa' Hort.   Now listed under *JUNIPERUS chinensis*.

- - 'Expansa Albovariegata' Hort.   Now listed under *JUNIPERUS chinensis*.

- - 'Expansa Aureospica' Hort.   Now listed under *JUNIPERUS chinensis*.

- - 'Parsonsii' Hort.   Now listed under *JUNIPERUS chinensis*.

JUNIPERUS deppeana Steudel
    1840 Broadly conical; Bluish-green foliage. cones globose.   10m,Z8   Mexico

- - 'Conspicua' Barbier   1909 In "Nurs. Cat". NIC.   B   France

- - 'Elegantissima' Barbier   1909 In "Nurs. Cat". A spreading form with blue, juvenile foliage.
    O. Barbier & Co., Orleans. NIC.   B

- - 'Ericoides' Barbier   1909 In "Nurs. Cat". A columnar form with blue, juvenile foliage.
    O. Barbier & Co., Orleans, NIC.   B,K

- - 'McPhetter' Hort. Amer.   1988 A listed name for a clone with strikingly blue foliage. O.
unknown.

- - 'Mount Santos' Hort. Amer.
    1990 A listed name. L. Coenosium Gardens "Nurs. Cat". 1990
Supplement.

- - var. **pachyphlaea** (Torrey) Martinez
    1946 Alligator Juniper. Deeply cracked bark.   W20m,Z8   Mexico

- - var. *patoniana* (Martinez) Zanoni
    1946 A sporadic variant, not recognised by some authorities.

- - var. *robusta* Martinez   1956 Not now distinguished within the species (per Silba, 1984).   D

- - 'Silver Spire' Hort. Anglia
    1983 A listed name for a clone with silvery leaves. Possibly NIC.   W3

- - f. *sperryi* (Correll) Adams
    1966 No longer distinguished within the species (per Silba, 1984).

- - var. *zacatecensis* Martinez
    1946 No longer distinguished within the species (per Silba, 1984).   D

JUNIPERUS distans Florin   1927 Now merged in *JUNIPERUS tibetica* (per Silba, 1984).

JUNIPERUS drobovii Sumner
    1948 Now merged in *JUNIPERUS semiglobosa*. (per Silba, 1984).

JUNIPERUS drupacea Labillardiere
    1791 Syrian Juniper.   15m,Z8   Syria

JUNIPERUS durangensis Martinez
    1946 Durango Juniper. A shrub or small tree.   5m,Z8   Mexico

JUNIPERUS ekmanii Florin
    1928 Now merged in *JUNIPERUS barbadensis*. (per Silba, 1984).

JUNIPERUS erythrocarpa Cory
    1936 Cory Juniper. By some authorities treated as a variety of
JUNIPERUS pinchotii, (per Silba, 1984).   6m,Z8   Mexico

- - var *coahuilensis* Martinez
    1946 Same as previous item.   D

JUNIPERUS excelsa Bieberstein
    1800 Greek Juniper. Conical with rounded crown.   20m,Z7   Asia Minor

- - **'Glauca'** (1) Sénéclauze   1868 A narrowly conical clone of a light glaucous green colour.   B,D   France

- - 'Glauca' (2) Hort.   A mistake for *JUNIPERUS chinensis* 'Stricta'.

- - f. *microcarpa* Carrière   1867 A minor variant with much smaller cones.   B

- - 'Nana' Endlicher	1847	A shrubby form, with branches nodding. NIC.		
- - 'Pendula' Sénéclauze	1868	A vigorous tree with pendent branch system and pendulous sprays. NIC.	B	
- - var. *polycarpus* (C. Koch) Silba	1984	A low bush with stout brs. Variously once known as *JUNIPERUS isophyllos. JUNIPERUS macropoda, JUNIPERUS polycarpus* and *JUNIPERUS turkomanica.*	W3	
- - 'Pygmaea' Sénéclauze	1868	A dwarf shrub with crowded branchlets. O. Sénéclauze Nurs, Bourg Argental, Loires. NIC.	B	
- - 'Pyramidalis' Carrière	1867	A selection with ascending branches, forming a compact, pointed cone. NIC.		
- - 'Stricta Variegata" Hort.		A mistake for *JUNIPERUS chinensis* 'Variegata'.		
- - 'Variegata' Carrière	1855	Named for a yellowish-variegated sport on a tree in the Botanic Gardens at Orleans. NIC.	B	France
- - 'Viridis Stricta' Sénéclauze	1868	A conical tree with foliage a glaucous blue-green. O. Raised on the Sénéclauze Nurs, from seed collected in the Crimea.		
JUNIPERUS fargesii Komarov	1926	Usually treated as a variety of *JUNIPERUS squamata.*		
JUNIPERUS flaccida Schlechtendal	1838	Mexican Weeping Juniper. Plants in cultivation under this name are frequently *JUNIPERUS monophylla.*	12m,Z8	Mexico
- - var. *poblana* Martinez	1946	A geographical variant, differing in leaves and cones.	D,K,W3	Mexico
JUNIPERUS foetidissima Willdenow	1886	Stinking Juniper.	15m,Z9	E Eur, SW Asia
- - f. *pindicola* Forman	1895	No longer distinguished within the species, (per Silba, 1984).	B,K	
- - f. *squarrosa* Medwedew	1902	A minor variant with spreading leaves.	B	
JUNIPERUS formosana Hayata	1908	Taiwan Juniper.	12m,Z9	China, etc.
JUNIPERUS gamboana Martinez	1944	Gamboa Juniper.	5m,Z9	Mexico
JUNIPERUS gaussenii Cheng	1940	Gaussen Juniper. Now merged with *JUNIPERUS chinensis* (per Silba, 1984).		
JUNIPERUS glaucescens Florin	1927	Now merged with *JUNIPERUS komarovii.* (per Silba, 1984).		
JUNIPERUS gracilior Pilger	1913	Now known as *JUNIPERUS barbadensis.* (per Silba, 1984).		
JUNIPERUS gymnocarpa	1936	(Lemmon) Cory. Now merged in *JUNIPERUS monosperma.* (per Silba, 1984).		
JUNIPERUS horizontalis Moench	1794	Creeping Juniper		East N.Amer.
- - 'Admirabilis' Plumfield	1936	In "Nurs. Cat". Similar to 'Emerson' but a male clone: foliage yellow-green with a grey bloom. I. Plumfield Nurs, Fremont, NEB.	B,K,W	U.S.A.

- - **'Adpressa'** Plumfield   1936   In "Nurs. Cat". (Incorrectly as 'Adpressus'). Dense, mat-forming habit; foliage green, whitish on young growth. **I.** Plumfield Nurs, Fremont, NEB.   K,W   U.S.A.

- - 'A. J.' Hort. Amer.   See 'Aunt Jemima'. These initials may record the similarity in shape to the flat Aunt Jemima pancakes, or (more probably) was in honour of Arthur Jensen, a senior employee at D,. Hill Nurs, for many years.

- - 'Alberta' Hort. Amer.   A listed name. No further information.

- - f. *alpina* (Loudon) Rehder
   1925   One year shoots are upright, but later become procumbent.   B,D,G,K,W   U.S.A.

- - "Andorra" Hort. Amer.   The Andorra Juniper. See 'Plumosa'.   K

- - **'Andorra Compact'** Krüssmann
   1972   (Formerly distributed 'Plumosa Compacta' coming an illegit. name). A compact form of 'Plumosa'; dense, spreading but seemingly full in centre, foliage bronze-purple in winter.   G,K,W3   U.S.A.

- - **'Argentea'** Plumfield   1941   In "Nurs. Cat". (incorrectly as 'Argenteus'). Smooth, silver-grey foliage. 6-8" high.   K,W3

- - 'Armstrongii' Hort. Amer.   A mistake for *JUNIPERUS* x *media* 'Armstrong'.

- - **'Aunt Jemima'** Wyman   1963   A compact form of 'Plumosa' selected by the D. Hill Nurs, Dundee, Ill. in 1957.   W   U.S.A.

- - var .*aurea* Bailey   1941   In "Hortus II". A name of doubtful botanical standing.   U.S.A.

- - **'Banff'** H.J. van de Laar   1984   In "Dendroflora **21**". Forms a broad bush with branchlets arising from the main branches. Foliage grey blue. **O.** Found in the National Park, Banff, Calgary.   Canada

- - **'Bar Harbor'** Hornibrook
   1939   A low-growing, wide-spreading form, leaves predominantly adult, bluish-green, turning purplish in winter. 'Bar Harbour' is wrong. **O.** Found on Mt. Desert Island, Maine. ('Hollywood Variety').   B,D,G,H,K,W   U.S.A.

- - 'Black Hills Creeper'   1965   Den Ouden/Boom. An obsolete name for 'Emerson'.

- - **'Blue Acres'** Sheridan   1973   In "Nurs. Cat". Low, spreading form. Young growth blue, turning to blue green. **O.** Raised by Prof. C.E. McNinch and Joerg Leiss from seed collected in Alberta (1973). **I.** Sheridan Nurs, Georgetown, Ontario, Canada.   G,W   Canada

- - 'Blue Arp' Hort. Germany
   1990   A compact, mat-forming plant with ascending branchlets. Foliage heathlike. **L.** Jeddeloh Nurs, Oldenburg, Germany.   Germany

- - **'Blue Chip'** D. Hill   An excellent selection maintaining a good blue colour throughout the year. **O.** Raised from seed by Asger M. Jensen, Orting, Denmark, selected by Thomsens Planteskole, Skalborg, Sweden. Sent by him to D. Hill Nurs, Dundee, Ill. (as No. l) and there named 'Blue Chip'. Thomsen withdrew his own suggested name 'Blue Moon', to save confusion with *JUNIPERUS scopulorum* 'Blue Moon'.   G,K,W   U.S.A.

- - 'Blue Forest' Hort. Amer.   A listed name for a plant with upright branches.   G

- - **'Blue Horizon'** Welch   1979   A name of uncertain application for a low-growing clone now seldom planted.   W   U.S.A.

- - **'Blue Mat'** W.A. Dino   1983   A dense, slow-growing blue-green prostate selection.   W3   U.S.A.

- - 'Blue Mist' D.M. van Gelderen
    1984 In "Dendroflora **21**". A mat-forming plant with upstanding
        branch tips. Foliage is greenish-blue. **O.** Am. Dept. Agric.,
        Ottowa, (1964).   Canada

- - 'Blue Moon' Thomsen 1970 Name raised by Thomsens Planteskole but later dropped in
        favour of the name 'Blue Chip'. q.v.   Denmark

- - **'Blue Pearl'** Thomsen 1970 A compact clone, blue-grey colour. **O.** and **I.** Same as 'Blue
        Chip'.   W3   Denmark

- - 'Blue Pygmy' Jeddeloh 1990 In "Nurs. Cat". Very dwarf and dense; blue-grey juvenile
        foliage. **O.** Seedling found by Mr. Neumänn, head propagator
        at the Jeddeloh Nurs. **I.** Jeddeloh Nurs, Oldenburg, Germany. W   Germany

- - 'Blue Rug' Hort. Amer.   An incorrect but often used name. ('Wiltonii').

- - 'Brandts' Hort. Amer. 1962 Reported from Michigan State Univ. No information.

- - **'Cabot Trail'** Hort. Amer. A very compact form. **O.** Found by Prof. R.B. Livingstone of
        Univ. of Massachusetts on Cabot Trail, Highlands National
        Park.   W3   Nova Scotia

- - 'Caespitosus' Hort. Amer.
        1968 Reported by U.S. Dept. Agric. No information.

- - 'Cascade Valley' Hort. Amer.
        1965 Reported from Univ. Washington Arb. No information.

- - 'Clearwater Blue' Reg'd. C.O.P.F.
        1979 Quick-growing spreader. Foliage silver-blue, turning to
        purple. **O.** and **I.** T.H. Machin.   W3   Canada

- - 'Coast of Maine' H.G. Hillier
        1971 In "Hilliers' Manual". Low-growing form forming flat
        mounds. Leaves juvenile, grey-green, purple tinted in winter.
        O. Unrecorded, indistinguishable from 'Grey Carpet' or 'Bar
        Harbor'.   W3   U.S.A.

- - 'Compacta' Hort. Amer.   Now known as 'Andorra Compact'.

- - 'Compacta Turesi' Hort. Amer.
        1980 An illegit. name. See 'Ture's Compact'.

- - f. *douglasii* Rehder 1915 A botanical category covering all the several clones in
        cultivation of the "Waukegan Juniper".   U.S.A.

- - **'Douglasii'** Douglas 1878 In "Nurs. Cat". A fast-growing trailing female form;steel blue
        foliage turning greyish-purple during the winter. **O.** Douglas
        Nurs, Waukegan, Ill. (1855).Name strictly valid only for the
        clone originally selected. "The Waugan Juniper". B,G,R,W U.S.A.

- - **'Dunvegan Blue'** Beaverlodge
        1964 A creeping form with silvery blue juvenile foliage turning
        purple in autumn. **O.** Found by J.A. Wallace on the bank of
        the Peace River, near Dunvegan (1959) **I.** Beaverlodge
        Research Station.   W   Canada

- - 'Dunvegan Green' Hort. Canada
        Probably a mistake for 'Wapiti'.

- - 'Emerald Green' Walter S. Lee
        1967 In "Amer. Nurs. **126**". A very low, dense. carpetting clone,
        emerald green. An unacceptable name. changed to 'Emerald
        Spreader'.

- - **'Emerald Isle'** Hort. Amer.
        1974 Slow-growing. compact. low-growing form; foliage rich
        green, branches fernlike. **L.** Greenleaf Nurs.   U.S.A.

- - **'Emerald Spreader'** Monrovia
          1973 In "Nurs. Cat". (formerly known as 'Emerald Green'). q.v.   G,K,W   U.S.A.

- - **'Emerson'** (Marshall) Wyman
          1963 In "Amer. Nurs. **91**". A very low growing female clone with adult foliage. The blue colour maintained throughout the winter. **O.** Found in Black Hills, S. Dakota by Geo. A. Marshall of Arlington Neb. and professor Emerson of the University of Nebraska. Intro 1929 as 'Marshall' and re-named by introducer. Other incorrect names are 'Black Hill Creeper',and 'Emerson's Creeper'.   B,K,W   U.S.A.

- - **'Eximia'** Plumfield   1936 In "Nurs. Cat". (Incorrectly as 'Eximius'). Slightly more upright in growth than 'Emerson' and a lighter, greyish-green.   W   U.S.A.

- - **'Filicina'** Robert E. More
          1956 In "The Green Thumb". (Incorrectly as 'Filicinus'). Low, creeping, female clone with upright branchlets. Foliage blue, purplish in winter in delicate sprays.   B,K,W

- - 'Filicinus Minimus' Plumfield
          1936 In "Nurs. Cat". The shorter name 'Filicina' is now usual.   B   U.S.A.

- - **'Fountain'** Welch   1979 Similar to 'Aunt Jemima' but soon making a higher but flat-topped plant. **I.** D. Hill Nurs, Co. Dundee, Ill.   W   U.S.A.

- - **'Girard'** Girard   1969 In "Nurs. Cat". **I.** Girard Nurs, Geneva, Ohio.   U.S.A.

- - 'Glacier' Hort. Amer.   1980 Prostrate dwarf, slow-growing with light-blue foliage in the growing season. Found in the U.S. Rocky Mts., in Montana, U.S.A. In "Nurs. Cat". Horstmann Nurs, Schneverdingen.

- - 'Glauca' Hornibrook   1939 The validity of this name and the ultimate origin of Hornibrook's plant is unrecorded. The name is loosely applied to any glaucous plant so should not be used in any clonal sense. See also 'Wiltonii' and 'Douglasii'.   U.S.A.

- - 'Glauca Hetz' Hort.   See *JUNIPERUS* x *media* 'Hetz'.

- - **'Glauca Major'** H.J. Grootendorst
          1940 In "Mitt. d.d.d. Ges. **53**". A low growing, thickly branched form. Very fine needles, steely blue even in winter. **O.** Cole Nurs, Painsville, Ohio.   U.S.A.

- - 'Glauca Nana' Hort.Amer.   An illegit. mistake for 'Wiltonii'.

- - **'Glenmore'** Robert E. More
          1956 In "The Green Thumb". Probably the lowest and slowest selection. It forms a berry bearing dark green plant, browning during the winter. **O.** Found by Robert E. More, Denver, Colorado in Wyoming (1926). **I.** Marshall Nurs, Denver, Colorado.   B,K,W   U.S.A.

- - f. *glomerata* Rehder   1925 In "Journal Arnold Arb. **6**".   B,D,K,W   U.S.A.

- - **'Glomerata'** Hort.   A clone in cultivation of the previous entry; very dwarf and with congested growth, grass-green, adult foliage in dense clusters.   U.S.A.

- - 'Golden Carpet' H.J. van de Laar
          1992 In "Dendroflora **29**". A sport on 'Wiltonii' with yellowish foliage. **O.** H. Kruse of Bad Zwischenahn, Germany. **I.** Van Vliet Bros, Boskoop.

- - **'Gracilis'** Wyman   1963 In "Amer. Nurs. **70**". Not very distinctive and seldom planted nowadays.   K,W   U.S.A.

- - 'Green' Hort. Amer.   An unacceptable name. See Art. **31**A (g) of the "Cultivar Code".

- - **'Green Acres'** Sheridan 1973 In "Nurs. Cat". Similar to 'Blue Acres' excepting that the colour is dark green. **O.** Prof. C.E. McNinch and J. Leiss. **I.** Sheridan Nurs, Oakville, Ontario.   W   Canada

- - **'Green Bowers'** Hort. Amer.
1979 A listed name. **L.** McClintock & Lester Nurs.

- - 'Green Jungle' H.J. van de Laar
1986 In "Naamlijst . . .". **O.** L. Konijn Nurs, Lunteren, (Ederveen).   Holland

- - 'Gregory Ferry' Hort. Amer.
1977 In "West Canada Hort. Soc. Ann. Proc. **33**". A very prostrate blue clone collected by G.A. Smith, Brookes, Alberta, Canada.

- - **'Grey Carpet'** Kammerer
1931 In "Morton Arb. Bull **6**". A trailing form with ascending branchlets, differing from 'Bar Harbor' by its rather more green foliage. See also 'Coast of Maine'.   B,W   U.S.A.

- - **'Grey Pearl'** Thomsen 1970 In "Nurs. Cat". A compact form, grey in colour. **O.** and **I.** Thomsen Planteskole, Skalborg.   G,W   Denmark

- - **'Hermit'** Reg. Arn. Arb. 1972 Compact spreader, foliage juvenile, deep green turning silver in winter. **O.** Collected near Hermit Island, Maine, by R.B. Livingston, Univ. Massachusetts. **I.** University of Vermont Agric. Exp. Sta. Not a hybrid.(Formerly 'Livingston No.1').   W   U.S.A.

- - 'Hetz' Hort.   Now listed as *JUNIPERUS* x *media* 'Hetz.'('Hetzii', 'Hetz Glauca').

- - 'Hicksii' Hort.   A mistake for *JUNIPERUS sabina* 'Hicksii'.

- - 'Hopkins' Hort. Canada 1987 A listed name. No further information.

- - **'Hughes'** (1) W.A. Dirr 1975 A low-growing mat-forming selection with radial branch-system; foliage silvery blue slightly tinged purple in winter. **O.** Cedar Rapids Nurs, Iowa, (1970).   G,K,W   U.S.A.

- - 'Hughes' (2) Welch 1979 Described as having an ascending branch system : it would appear to be a misuse of the name for a different plant.   W2   U.S.A.

- - 'Hugheson' Hort. Holland   Possibly = 'Hughes' (2). NIC.

- - 'Humilis' Hornibrook. 1939 No longer identifiable from the available descriptions.   B,H,K,W   U.S.A.

- - **'Huntington Blue'** Monrovia
1983 In "Nurs. Cat". Widely spreading mat-forming dense branch habit; covered by very intense blue-grey foliage.   W3   U.S.A.

- - **'Jade River'** H.J. van de Laar
1984 In "Dendroflora **21**". A low, mat-forming selection with blue-grey foliage. **O.** Reimer Nurs, Yarrow, (1980). **I.** to Holland, C. Klijn Nurs, Boskoop, (1984).   G,W3   Canada

- - **'Jade Spreader'** Monrovia
1969 In "Nurs. Cat". A similar plant to previous entry, but described as having dense jade-green foliage.   K,W3   U.S.A.

- - **'Limeglow'** L.C. Hatch 1988 In "Conifer Database". A mutation from 'Youngstown' with the young foliage a chartreuse-yellow colour.   W3   U.S.A.

- - **'Livida'** Plumfield 1941 In "Nurs. Cat". (Incorrectly as 'Lividus'). Foliage silver-blue on slender branches, making a solid, fast-growing ground cover but better forms are now available. **O.** Selected by Plumfield Nurs, Fremont, NEB. (1936).   K,W   U.S.A.

- - **'Livingston'** Reg'd Arn. Arb.

  1972 Reg'd. N.E. Pellett. (Formerly Livingston No 7). A widespreading procumbent shrub; leaves mainly scale-like, minute, steel-blue in summer, turning bluish-green in autumn. A female clone. **O.** Found on Hermit Island, Maine by Professor R.B. Livingston of University of Massachusetts. W U.S.A.

- - 'Low Green' Hort. Amer. 1974 An unsatisfactory name. L. Washington Evergreen Nurs. No longer in production? Canada

- - **'Magic Carpet'** Int. Con. Reg.

  1983 A sport from 'Wiltonii' with a general cream-coloured variegation. **O.** and **I.** F.A. Menser, Cedar Pond Nurs, Rock Hill, S. Carolina 29730. W3 U.S.A.

- - **'Marcella'** Plumfield 1940 In "Nurs. Cat". (Incorrectly as 'Marcellus'). A ground-hugging selection, good dense habit, pale green foliage. G,K,W2 U.S.A.

- - 'Marshall' Hort. An obsolete name for 'Emerson'. (= 'Marshall Creeper'). W3

- - **'Montana'** Hort. Amer. 1971 A listed name for a widespreading clone with long, slender, filiform branches and short, ascending branchlets and densely packed, scale-like leaves of an intense glaucous blue. U.K.

- - 'Morton' Hort. Amer. A listed name: possibly = 'New Morton'.

- - 'Mother Lode' Hort. Amer.

  1982 A listed name for a golden sport of 'Wiltonii', of much slower growth.

- - 'Neumänn' H.J. van de Laar

  1990 In "Dendroflora 27". An extremely slow-growing selection. **O.** J. zu Jeddeloh Nurs, Oldenberg, (1980). Germany

- - 'New Morton' Hort. Amer.

  1970 L. Hillside Nurs, Lehighton, PA. NOM.

- - **'Petraea'** Plumfield 1940 In "Nurs. Cat". An early selection, similar to but inferior to 'Marcella' as a ground cover plant. K,W U.S.A.

- - **'Planifolia'** Plumfield 1936 In "Wholesale Trade List". (Incorrectly as 'Planifolius'). A rapid grower with long, palmy, silver-blue branches. K,W U.S.A.

- - f. *plumosa* Rehder 1925 A botanical category covering all the clones in cultivation of or derived from the "Andorra Juniper". U.S.A.

- - **'Plumosa'** Andorra 1919 In "Nurs. Cat". A wide-spreading, dense clone; branches rise at ±45% foliage grey-green. **O.** and **I.** Andorra Nurs, Philadelphia, PA (1907). The name is strictly only valid for the clone originally selected by Andorra but is in general use as a collective name. U.S.A.

- - 'Plumosa Compacta' Hort. Amer.

  Now known as 'Andorra Compact'. W U.S.A.

- - **'Prince of Wales'** Reg. Arn. Arb.

  1968 A procumbent, mat-forming clone, bright green, turning to purplish to purplish-brown in winter. **O.** Found by Wellesley White at Pelisko Creek, High River, Alberta (1931) and given to the Canada Dept. Agric. Research Station, Morden, Manitoba. **I.** Potmore Nurs, Brandon, Manitoba (1967). G,W Canada

- - 'Procumbens' Slavin 1932 (And other authors). Probably a misidentification of *JUNIPERUS procumbens* 'Nana'. Not as K. B,H,W U.S.A.

- - 'Prostrata' H.J. Grootendorst

  1940 In "Mitt. d.d.d. Ges. 53". A dense, mat-forming selection widely offered in U.K. Formerly distributed as *JUNIPERUS sabina prostrata* by European Nurseries. B,G,K,W Holland

- - **'Pulchella'** Robert E. More
1959 In "The Green Thumb". A very slow-growing, dense, compact type, forming a symmetrical plant 1 m across by only 40-50 cm high: Greenish-grey owl-like leaves. I. Plumfield Nurs.   B,K,W   U.S.A.

- - **'Repens'** H.J. Grootendorst
1940 In "Mitt. d.d.d. Ges. **53**". A grey-green plant, usually spreading in one direction only. Probably no longer in production. It may have been a form of *JUNIPERUS sabina*.   B,K,W   U.S.A.

- - var. *saxatilis* Hort.   An illegit. listed name. Probably a mistaken identity.

- - **'Sea Spray'** F.F. Serpa   In "Nurs. Cat". Hines Wholesale Nurs., Santa Ana, Cal. NOM.   K   U.S.A.

- - **'Schmidt'** Hort. Amer.   1968 L. Watnong Nurs, Morris Plains, N.J. O. Found by J.H. Schmidt, Milburn, N.J.

- - **'Schoodic Point'** Hort. Amer.   Flat, flexible, creeping habit. O Found by Prof R.B. Livingston, near Schoodic Point, Maine.   W3   U.S.A.

- - **'Silver Sheen'** L.C. Hatch & P.R. Fontz
1986 A clone of the "Wankegan Juniper" becoming widely distributed in U.S.A. See Article in Hort. Science **21** (3): 534-5 (1986).   U.S.A.

- - **'Sunspot'** Hort. Amer.   1970 A clone of the "Wankegan Juniper" but with foliage variegated and spotted yellow throughout the branches. I. Girard Nurs, Geneva, Ohio.   W3   U.S.A.

- - **'Tures Compact'** Hort. Canada
1972 L. Evergreen Nurs.   Canada

- - **'Turquoise Spreader'** Monrovia
1973 In "Nurs. Cat". A low-growing widespreading form, densely clothed with soft, juvenile turquoise-green foliage. I. Monrovia Nurs, Azusa, Cal.   K,W   U.S.A.

- - **'Two Medicine'** Iseli   1990 In "Nurs. Cat". A grey-blue ground cover plant: full and dense. L. Iseli Nurs, Boring, OR.

- - **'Variegata'** Slavin   1932 A vigorous prostrate form with creamy-white variegation. Several variegated clones are in cultivation.   B,D,H,K,W   U.S.A.

- - **'Venusta'** Hort. Amer.   1964 A ground hugging, dense form similar to 'Wiltonii' but foliage a darker, bluish-green. L. Raraflora Nurs, Feasterville, PA. (NOM).   W

- - **'Viridis'** H.J. Grootendorst
1940 Very deep green; prostrate, densely branched, broad form.   B,D,H,K,W   Holland

- - **'Walton's Blue'** Hort. Amer.
1972 Reported from Michigan State Univ. No information.

- - **'Wapiti'** Beaver Lodge   1965 A vigorous form with lustrous, dark green, foliage, dull purple in winter; thick, even ground cover. O. Found by J.A. Wallace near Wapiti River I. The Beaverlodge Research Station.   K,W   Canada

- - **'Watnong'** Reg'd. Arn. Arb.
1967 Female clone; berries well; rich colour. Reg'd. by Don Smith, Watnong Nurs, Morris Plains, N.J. O. Not on record so it might have a different valid name.   W3   U.S.A.

- - **'Webberi'** Sherwood   1971 A low mat-like spreading form, with glaucous blue sheen to foliage. I. Sherwood Nurs, Portland, OR. O. Not on record.   W

- - **'White's Silver King'** Hort. Amer.
No information. ('Silver King').

- - **'Wilms'** Reg'd. Arn. Arb.
1975 A slow-growing sport found on 'Andorra Compact', with adult grey-green foliage; Reg'd. by K.B. Frost, Gwenn Gary Nurs, Columbiana, Ohio. **I.** The Same. (1972). **O.** The same (1960). (The spelling 'Welms' is incorrect). W3 U.S.A.

- - 'Wilton Carpet' Hort. A superfluous name for 'Wiltonii'.

- - **'Wiltonii'** Vermeulen
1953 In "Nurs. Cat". The now generally accepted name for a low,trailing clone with intense silver-blue foliage. **I.** South Wilton Nurs, Wilton, Conn. (as var *glauca*). **O.** Found by Jacob C. van Heiningen on the island of Vinalhaven in Maine (1914). ('Glauca', 'Blue Rug', 'Blue Vase', 'Blue Wilson' and 'Wilton Carpet' should not be used). B,G,K,R,W U.S.A.

- - **'Winter Blue'** Welch
1979 Similar to 'Plumosa' but with a distinctive brighter blue winter colour. **I.** Heasley. G,W U.S.A.

- - **'Wisconsin'** L.C. Hatch
1988 In "Conifer Database". A selection of moderate vigour with juvenile foliage of rich blue. U.S.A.

- - **'Youngstown'** Plumfield
1973 Similar to 'Plumosa Compacta'; bright green foliage, low. prostrate habit. **O.** Plumfield Nurs. Fremont. NEB. ('Plumosa Youngstown'). K,W U.S.A.

- - **'Yukon Belle'** Plumfield 1970 Bright silvery-blue foliage; broadly spreading, ground-hugging habit. **I.** Plumfield Nurs, Fremont, NEB. K,W U.S.A.

JUNIPERUS hudsonica De Vos
1868 A form of *JUNIPERUS horizontalis* found in Missouri. Not now identifiable.

JUNIPERUS indica Bertoloni
1862 Black Juniper. A species with connections with *JUNIPERUS pseudosabina*. A low spreading bush. 0.5mZ4 Himalayas

JUNIPERUS isophyllos C.Koch
1849 Now known as *JUNIPERUS excelsa* var. *polycarpus* (per Silba, 1984).

JUNIPERUS jaliscana Martinez
1946 Jalisco Juniper. 5-10m,Z9 Mexico

JUNIPERUS japonica Carrière
1855 See *JUNIPERUS chinensis* 'Japonica'.

Juniperus japonica is no longer recognised as a species. The following citings are typical of the confusion resulting from the uncritical use of the epithet *japonica* by early writers.

- - 'Aurea' Carrière 1867 Probably *JUNIPERUS chinensis* 'Plumosa Aurea'.

- - 'Aureamarginata' R. Smith 1867 Probably *JUNIPERUS chinensis* 'Plumosa Aureovariegata'.

- - (*chinensis*) 'Procumbens Aureovariegata' Beissner
1891 Probably *JUNIPERUS chinensis* 'Expansa Aureovariegata'.

- - 'Nana' D. Hill 1940 Probably *JUNIPERUS procumbens* 'Nana'.

JUNIPERUS jarkeudeusis Komarov
1925 Now merged in *JUNIPERUS semiglobosa* (per Silba, 1984).

JUNIPERUS x *kanitzii* Csató
1886 A presumed hybrid: *JUNIPERUS communis* x *JUNIPERUS sabina*.

JUNIPERUS kansuensis (Komarov) Dallimore & Jackson
1966 Now known as *JUNIPERUS squamata* var. *fargesii*.

JUNIPERUS komarovii Florin
    1927 Komarov Juniper.   10m,Z5   China

JUNIPERUS litoralis Maximowicz
    1868 Now known as *JUNIPERUS conferta.*

JUNIPERUS lucayana Britton
    1908 Now merged in *JUNIPERUS barbadensis.* (per Silba, 1984).

- - 'Bedfordiana' (Parlatore) Rehder
      Possibly a form of *JUNIPERUS virginiana.* NIC.   B

JUNIPERUS macrocarpa Sibthorp & Smith
    1813 Now known as *JUNIPERUS oxycedrus* sub-sp. *macrocarpa.*
       (per Silba, 1984).

JUNIPERUS macropoda Boissier
    1924 Now known as *JUNIPERUS excelsa* var. *polycarpos.* (per
       Silba, 1984).

JUNIPERUS martinezii Perez de la Rosa
      A newly discovered species near to *JUNIPERUS flaccida.*   Mexico

JUNIPERUS x *media* P.J.van Melle
    1946 In "Phytologia **2**". A hybrid species: *JUNIPERUS chinensis* x
       JUNIPERUS sabina. See note under *JUNIPERUS*
       *chinensis.*Not accepted by some authorities, who continue to
       list the following selections under *JUNIPERUS chinensis*, but
       now widely in use in the trade.   Hort.

- - 'Aorangi Gold' Hort. N.Z.
    1993 A listed name.

- - 'Arbuscula' P.J. van Melle
    1946 In "Phytologia **2**". See above note. Female clone, fruit on
       slender stalk; erect bush. Doubtful identity. W3   U.S.A.

- - **'Arctic'** D. Hill.   1972 Bluish green appearance; wide-spreading habit, rapid growth. W   U.S.A.

- - 'Armstrong Gold' Hort. Amer.   Now known as 'Gold Coast'. ('Golden Armstrong').

- - **'Armstrongii'** Armstrong
    1932 In "Nurs. Cat". Formerly known as 'Pfitzeriana Nana'. Small,
       light green lacy foliage, branches slightly arching. O.
       Armstrong Nurs, Ontario. ('Armstrongii'). K,W Canada

- - *'Armstrongii fastigiata mordigani'* Hort. Amer.
      See 'Green Lace'.

- - 'Armstrongii Nana' 1974 An illegit name for a dwarf mutation of 'Armstrongii'. L.
       Select Nurs. L.C. Hatch proposes the name 'Armstrong
       Dwarf'.   U.S.A.

- - **'Berry Hill'** D.M. van Gelderen
    1984 In "Dendroflora **21**". A low-growing, compact sport from
       'Pfitzeriana' with grey foliage. L. Minier Nurs, Angers,
       (1976).   K,W3 France

- - 'Blaauw' Hort.   Now listed under *JUNIPERUS chinensis.*

- - "Blound"   Not a cultivar name. See 'Gold Sovereign'.   U.K.

- - **'Blue and Gold'** D.M. van Gelderen
    1984 In "Dendroflora **21**". A strong-growing mutation from
       'Pfitzeriana Glauca'; with flecks of pale yellow. Origin
       unrecorded.   G,W3 Holland

- - 'Blue Cloud' Hort.   See *JUNIPERUS virginiana* 'Blue Cloud'

- - **'Blue Vase'** Monrovia   1957 In "Nurs. Cat". A dense form with blue foliage. Naturally
takes a vase shape. Monrovia Nurs, Azusa, Cal.   U.S.A.

- - **'Carbery Gold'** Hort. Anglia
1987 Circular, flat growing plant with pale golden foliage.
Younger plants have some juvenile foliage. Older plants have
higher arching branches in the Pfitzer style. Becoming very
popular. **O.** A seedling at Carbery Nurs, near Bournemouth.
I. Acquired by Douglas Loundes of MacPenny's Nurs,
Branscore, Dorset.

- - 'Compacta Nelsonii' Wyman
1963 In "Amer. Nurs".

- - **'Dandelight'** N.M. Sampson
1989 In "Commercial Horticulture (N.Z.)". A mutation with bright
lemon-yellow young foliage darkening to light golden yellow
by winter. **O.** and **I.** Cedar Lodge Nurs, New Plymouth.   N.Z.

- - **'Daub's Frosted'** Mitsch
1987 In "Nurs. Cat". Low spreading plant with pendulous branch-
tips. Golden frosted foliage that is blue and green along the
underside. Mitsch Nurs, Aurora, OR.

- - **'Den Boer'** Reg'd. A. A. N.
1951 (As a *JUNIPERUS chinensis* form). Compact, spreading
bush; foliage not changing colour in winter. **O.** A.F. den
Boer, Des Moines, Iowa, (1930). Reg'd. by G.H. Heard,
Heard's Landscape Nurs, Des Moines, Iowa.   K,W3   U.S.A.

- - **'Dierks'** R.G. de Bree   1992 In "Dendroflora **28**". A spreading shrub with stout branches,
yellow foliage. **O.** K. Kierks, Edern, Germany, (before 1983).   Germany

- - **'Evergold'** Hort. Australia
`1993 Sport from *JUNIPERUS* x *media* 'Reid's Goldrift'. Very
bright golden yellow throughout the year, similar to 'Plumosa
Aurea'. More vase-shaped and upright than most 'Pfitzers'. **O.**
and **I.** John Emery, Drue Wholesale Nurs.

- - **'Fruitland'** Monrovia   1977 In "Nurs. Cat".Dense bright green, juvenile foliage. Semi-
prostrate form. An improved 'Pfitzeriana Compacta'.   K,W   U.S.A.

- - 'Glauca Hetz' Hort.   Now listed under *JUNIPERUS chinensis.*

- - 'Globosa' Hort.   Now listed under *JUNIPERUS chinensis.* See Note under that
species.

- - 'Globosa Aurea' Hort.   Now listed under *JUNIPERUS chinensis.* ('Aurea-globosa').
See above Note.

- - 'Globosa Cinerea' Hort.   Now listed under *JUNIPERUS chinensis.* See above Note.

- - **'Gold Coast'** Monrovia   1965 In "Nurs. Cat". **I.** Monrovia Nurs, Azusa, Cal. **O.** Sakiyama
Nurs, Cal. A sport from 'Old Gold', more compact; deeper
chrome yellow. Foliage mainly adult. ('Armstrong Gold').   G,W   U.S.A.

- - 'Golden Feather' Hort. Anglia   See 'Goldfeder'. A translation is unacceptable.

- - **'Golden Saucer'** D.M. van Gelderen
1984 In "Dendroflora **21**". **I.** W.M. van Neirop, Boskoop. **O.** Nic.
Bosman Nurs, Boskoop, (1976). Very compact mutation from
'Pfitzeriana Aurea'.   G,K,W3   Holland

- - **'Golden Sun'** H.J. van de Laar
1987 In "Dendroflora **24**". A sport from 'Old Gold'. **O.** A.M. van
Eijk, Boskoop.   Holland

JUNIPERUS X MEDIA

- - 'Goldfeder' H.J. van de Laar
1992 In "Dendroflora 28".I. Into Holland by Le Feber & Co. Nurs, Boskoop. — Germany

- - **'Goldkissen'** D.M. van Gelderen
1983 In "Dendroflora 20". O. G. Oltsmans Nurs. Ekern. Oldenburg. Bright yellow adult foliage at tips; blue-green juvenile interior; compact form of 'Pfitzeriana Aurea'. W3 — Germany

- - **'Gold Lace'** Int. Con. Reg.
1989 A vigorous sport from 'Gold Star' but a more intense colour. O. and I. J.C. Bakker Nurs, St. Catherine's, Ontario. — Canada

- - **'Gold Sovereign'** Hort. Anglia
1985 A sport from 'Old Gold'. (="Blound"). Good gold colour all year. W3 — U.K.

- - 'Gold Splash' Hort. Amer.
1988 A listed name for a golden-variegated 'Pfitzer' Juniper.

- - **'Gold Star'** Reg'd C.O.P.F.
1976 All juvenile golden yellow foliage; compact mutation from 'Pfitzeriana Aurea'. O. by J.C. Bakker Nurs, Ontario. (1961). W3 — Canada

- - 'Green Jungle' Hort. Formerly listed under *JUNIPERUS chinensis*.

- - **'Green Lace'** Hort. Amer.
1974 A listed name for a fastigiate version of 'Armstrongii' with contorted branches. L. Select Nurs, ('Armstrongii Fastigiata Mordigani').

- - 'Green River'
1981 A listed name for a plant similar to 'Armstrongii' but foliage pale green. L. Amfac Select Nurs.

- - **'Hill's Blue'** D. Hill
1939 Close to 'Pfitzeriana Glauca' but making a flatter plant, with less juvenile foliage. I. D. Hill Nurs. Dundee, Ill. W — U.S.A.

- - 'Holbert' Hort. Amer.
1987 A listed name. L. Hines Wholesale Nurs, Santa Ana, Valaville, Cal. — U.S.A.

- - **'Kallay's Compact'** Kallay
Deep green, mostly juvenile foliage; a roughly spherical, flat topped form. O. Kallay Nurs, Painesville, Ohio. W — U.S.A.

- - 'Kelseyii' Hort. Anglia
1992 Reported from Windsor Great Park. Berks. Without description.

- - 'Kohankie's Compact' Wyman
1963 Now listed under *JUNIPERUS chinensis* . W

- - 'Kosteriana' Hort.
Now listed as *JUNIPERUS virginiana* 'Kosteri'. W

- - 'Kuriwao Gold' Hort.
See under *JUNIPERUS chinensis*.

- - **'Lemon Hill'** Monrovia
1975 In "Nurs. Cat". Grey-green; compact dwarf. L. Monrovia Nurs, Azusa, Cal. — U.S.A.

- - 'Lodense' Hort. Amer.
1969 "Lodense Blue Juniper". L. Kansas Nurs, Co., Salina, Kansas.

- - **'Mathot'** Den Ouden
1949 Generally glaucous appearance; similar to but denser growth than 'Kallay's Compact'.O. Gebr. Mathot Nurs, Boskoop, (1947). K,W — Holland

- - 'Matthew's Blue'
1988 A slow-growing form of the 'Pfitzer Juniper' with blue colour.

- - 'Mayhew' Hort. Amer.
1983 Reported from Morton Arboretum. Lisle, Ill.

- - **'Milky Way'** Konijn
1968 In "Sortimentslijst". Very green foliage with creamy-white variegation. NOM. O. Konijn Nurs. Heemstede. (1940). W — Holland

- - **'Mint Julep'** Monrovia   1960   In "Nurs. Cat". Female clone; rich mid-green colour; makes a flat, spreading bush. L. Monrovia Nurs. Azusa, Cal.   G,K,W   U.S.A.

- - **'Moraine'** Reg. A.A.N.   1951   Blue-green juvenile foliage; compact habit. Reg'd. by J.B. Siebenthaler, Dayton, Ohio.   K,W   U.S.A.

- - **'Mordigan'** Reg. A.A.N.
   1951   A compact but irregular shrub with foliage a silvery-blue. Some juvenile foliage. O. and I. F. Mordigan, San Fernando, Cal.   W   U.S.A.

- - 'Mordigan Aurea' Hort.   An illegit. name. See 'Mordigan Gold'.

- - **'Mordigan Gold'** Monrovia
   1975   In "Nurs. Cat".Juvenile, golden-yellow foliage predominantly juvenile; tips slightly nodding; low spreading, graceful habit.I. Monrovia Nurs, Azusa, Cal. O. Hillside Nurs, Lehighton. PA. (1970). ('Mordigan Aurea').   W3   U.S.A.

- - 'Nick's Compact' D. Wyman
   1963   In "Amer. Nurs". An excellent compact, low-growing mutation from 'Pfitzeriana' with nearly 100% juvenile leaves. O. Nick's Nurs, Anchorage, K.Y. (c 1930). Indistinguishable from 'Pfitzeriana Compacta'.   K,W3

- - **'Old Gold'** H.J. Grootendorst
   1958   In "Nurs. Cat". A slow-growing golden-yellow mutation from 'Pfitzeriana Aurea'. O. F.J. Grootendorst & Sons Nurs, Boskoop.   G,K,W   Holland

- - **'Ozark Compact'** Hort. Amer.
   1964   Similar to 'Nicks Compact' but blue colour and with less vigorous growth. I. Watnong Nurs, Morris Plains, N.J.   W   U.S.A.

- - 'Paul's Frosted' Hort. Germany
   1992   L. Horstmann Nurs, Schneverdingen, without description.

- - **'Paul's Gold'** Int. Con. Reg.
   1989   Similar to 'Pfitzeriana' but slow-growing and rather upright habit. Foliage bright yellow. O. and I. P. van der Kroft, Strathroy, Ontario.   Canada

- - **'Pfitzeriana'** (Beissner) Van Melle
   1946   General grey-green appearance, picturesque habit, strong main branches at 45 degrees. O. Späth Nurs. Stuttgart.   B,G,K,W   Germany

Here listed as a cultivar, this is the type-plant for the 'hybrid species' named by P.J. van Melle and now widely used in the trade. It was so named for a plant that had been stem-trained into a conical tree 10m high in the Späth Nurs, Berlin (1899): but similar specimens had been unknowingly circulated for some years in Europe as *JUNIPERUS chinensis* var. *pendula*. The spelling 'Pfitzerana' at one time favoured, is no longer regarded as correct. The name must not be used in a cultivar name. Where necessary, the connection can be made clear by the words in brackets (Pfitzer Group).

- - **'Pfitzeriana Aurea'** Hill   1936   In "Hill's Book of Evergreen's". Foliage yellow turning yellow-green in winter; flattish habit. O. A sport on 'Pfitzeriana'. D. Hill Nurs, Dundee, Ill. (1923).   B,G,K,W   U.S.A.

- - 'Pfitzeriana Blue Cloud' Hort. Amer.
   See *JUNIPERUS virginiana* 'Blue Cloud'.

- - **'Pfitzeriana Compacta'** Hort. Amer.
   1930   Grey-green appearance; prickly foliage; flat-topped and compact. L. Bobbink & Atkins Nurs, Rutherford, N.J. (1930?).   B,K,W   U.S.A.

- - **'Pfitzeriana Glauca'** Hort. Amer.
   1940   Foliage silvery-blue to dull grey-blue; prickly; wide spreading branches. L. Texas Nurs, Sherman, Texas.   B,G,K,W   U.S.A.

- - 'Pfitzeriana Glauca Prostrata' Hort.
     Information, please.

- - 'Pfitzeriana Nana' Hort. Amer. An illegit. name. See 'Armstrongii'.

- - 'Pfitzeriana Silver Blue' Hort. Amer.
    1957 Reported from the Denver Botanic Gardens.

- - 'Plumosa' Hort.   Now listed under *JUNIPERUS chinensis*. See note under
           JUNIPERUS chinensis.

- - 'Plumosa Albovariegata' Hort. Now listed under *JUNIPERUS chinensis*. See above note.

- - 'Plumosa Aurea' Hort.   Now listed under *JUNIPERUS chinensis*. See above note.

- - 'Plumosa Aureovariegata' Hort. Now listed under *JUNIPERUS chinensis*. See above note.

- - **'Ramlosa'** D.M. van Gelderen
    1984 In "Dendroflora **21**". A wide-spreading bush with almost
      horizontal habit of growth. O. H. Jensen, Helsingborg,
      (1975). (Not to be confused with *JUNIPERUS ramulosa*).   W3   Sweden

- - **'Reid's Goldrift'** Hort. Australia
    1989 In "Nurs. Cat". A very compact form of *JUNIPERUS* x *media*
      'Pfitzeriana Aurea' with a large proportion of juvenile foliage.
      No record of **O.** and **I.**

- - **'Richeson'** Armstrong   1946 In "Nurs. Cat". Armstrong Nurs, Co., Ontario, Cal. Bluish-
      green foliage; low, compact habit. A sport of 'Pfitzeriana'
      found by L.J. Richeson of Ontario, Cal. (1941).   W3   U.K.

- - **'Saybrook Gold'** Girard 1983 In "Nurs. Cat". Foliage fresh green in Spring, bronze-yellow
      in Winter; low habit. O. Girard Nurs, Geneva, Ohio, (1980). W3   U.S.A.

- - 'Schröder' Hort. Amer.   1972 A listed name. No further information.

- - 'Sea Green' Hort. Holland
    1976 Probably a superfluous name for 'Mint Julep'.   W3

- - **'Sea Spray'** Reg'd. Arn. Arb.
    1973 (as *JUNIPERUS chinensis*). Sea- green colour; a prostrate
      mutation from 'Pfitzeriana Glauca'.with tight, compact centre.
      Reg'd. by J.W. Hines Nurs. O. J. Serpa, Fremont, Cal.,
      (1963).   W   U.S.A.

- - 'Shimpaku' Hort.   Now listed under *JUNIPERUS chinensis*.

- - 'Shimpaku Gold' Hort.   Now listed under *JUNIPERUS chinensis*.

- - 'Silver Tip' Hort. Anglia   A strong-growing form of 'Pfitzeriana'. with bolder, more
      effective variegation than 'Plumosa Argenteovariegata'; strong
      grower. **O.** ?   W

- - 'Sulphur Spray' H.J. Grootendorst
    1969 In "Dendroflora **6**". A colour sport from 'Hetz'. Whitish-
      yellow appearance all year; semi-prostrate habit. O. J. Konijn
      Nurs. Here listed under *JUNIPERUS virginiana*.   W2   Holland

- - 'Sunsplash' L.C. Hatch 1990 A sport of 'Pfitzeriana Compacta' with blue-green juvenile
      foliage heavily mottled yellow.O. Found by L.C. Hatch in
      Raleigh, 1985.   U.S.A.

- - 'Tremonia' Hort. Holland   Now listed under *JUNIPERUS chinensis*.

- - **'Winter Surprise'** D.M. van Gelderen
    1984 In "Dendroflora **21**".Yellow tinted on soft green, low-growing
      sport from 'Pfitzeriana Aurea'.   W3   Holland

JUNIPERUS mekongensis Komarov
       1924 Now merged in *JUNIPERUS convallium.*(per Silba, 1984).

JUNIPERUS monosperma (Engelmann) Sargent
       1896 Cherrystone Juniper, One-stone Juniper.   15m,Z7   U.S.A.

- - var. **gracilis** Martinez   1946 A geographical variant differing only in foliage details.   Mexico

JUNIPERUS monticola Martinez
       1946 Mountain Juniper. Now known as *JUNIPERUS sabinoides*
             by some authorities, (per Rushforth, 1987).   Z6   Mexico

- - f. *compacta* Martinez   1946 Not now distinguished within the species.

- - f. *orizonensis* Martinez   1946 Not now distinguished within the species.

JUNIPERUS morrisonicola Hayata
       1908 (= *JUNIPERUS squamata* var. *morrisonicola* of some
             authorities).   5-10m,Z4   Taiwan

JUNIPERUS nana Willdenow
       1806 "Sp.Pl. 4". Now know as *JUNIPERUS communis* var
             montana, in part.

JUNIPERUS nipponica Maximowicz
       1868 Now known as *JUNIPERUS rigida* subsp. *nipponica.*

JUNIPERUS oblonga Bieberstein
       1808 Now known as *JUNIPERUS communis* 'Oblonga Pendula'.

JUNIPERUS occidentalis Hooker fil.
       1839 Western Juniper   15m,Z7   U.S.A.

- - var. *australis* (Vasek) Holmgren
       1972 San Bernandino Juniper. Not now distinguished within the
             species, (per Silba, 1984).

- - 'Drewsey Column' Hort. Amer.
       1992 A compact, narrowly upright, grey-green plant. Raised as a
             seedling. **O.** Warren Carnefix, Drewsey, OR. (1988).

- - 'Glenmore Blue Sierra' Hort. Amer.
       1970 **L.** Watnong Nurs, Morris Plains, N.J., NOM.

- - 'Hunter's Find' Hort. Amer.
       1991 Dwarf, spreading, grey-green plant, similar to a Mugo Pine.
             Originated as a seedling. **I.** Timothy C. Kasch, Gresham,
             Oregon. **O.** A seedling raised by John Day, Oregon, (1990).   U.S.A.

- - 'Pendula' J. Noble   1951 In "Journ. Calif. Hort. Soc. **12**". Named for a pendulous tree
             found by James Noble on the Sierra Nevada, a few miles west
             of Echo Summit.

- - **'Sierra Silver'** Monrovia
       1960 In "Nurs. Cat". Distinctive glaucous foliage. **I.** Monrovia
             Nurs, Azusa, CAL.   B,R   U.S.A.

- - 'Silver Falls' Hort. Amer. 1988 **L.** Mitsch Nurs, Aurora, OR.

JUNIPERUS oophora Kuntze
       1846 Now merged in *JUNIPERUS phoenicea.* (per Silba, 1984).

JUNIPERUS osteosperma (Torrey) Little
       1948 Utah Juniper. Now includes *JUNIPERUS utahensis.*   12m,Z6   U.S.A.

JUNIPERUS oxycedrus Linnaeus
       1753 Prickly Juniper.   15m,Z9   Europe

- - var *brachyphylla* Loret   A regional variant found at St. Beet, Haute Garoume.   D,K   France

- - 'Echiniformis' Knight   1850   Named for a globose dwarf plant found on the upper region of Mount Etna, with the typical foliage, giving an appearance suggestive of a hedgehog. A tender plant at present lost to cultivation. The cultivars 'Berkshire' and 'Haverbeck' of the present day are probably similar to this early plant.   H

- - var. *brevifolia* Hochstetter
   1844   Now known as *JUNIPERUS brevifolia*.

- - sub-sp. **macrocarpa** (Sibthorp & Smith) Ball
   1868   Large-berried Juniper. A sporadic form with large fruits. formerly known as *JUNIPERUS macrocarpa*.   Sporadic

- - var. *transtagana* (Franco) Silba.
   1984   By some authorities listed as a sub-species.   S.W. Portugal

JUNIPERUS pachyphlaea Torrey   Now known as *JUNIPERUS deppeana* var. *pachyphlaea*.

JUNIPERUS patoniana Martinez
   1946   Now merged in *JUNIPERUS deppeana*. (per Silba, 1984).

JUNIPERUS phoenicea Linnaeus
   1753   Phoenician Juniper.   8m,Z8   Mediterr.

- - f. *megalocarpa* Moire   A local form, with larger fruits.   D

- - 'Myosurus' Hort. France
   1868   L. Sénéclauze Nurs, Bourg Argental, Loire. NIC.   B,K   France

- - var. *turbinata* (Gussone) Parlatore
   1868   Not now distinguished within the species (per Silba, 1984).   B,D,K   Mediterr.

JUNIPERUS pinchotii Sudworth
   1905   Pinchot Juniper. A shrub or small tree.   6m,Z8   U.S.A.

- - var. **erythrocarpa** (Cory) Silba
   1984   Formerly known as *JUNIPERUS erythrocarpa*.

JUNIPERUS pingii Cheng   1939   A species formerly included within *JUNIPERUS squamata*.   30mZ7   China

- - 'Forrestii' Welch   1979   Upright habit, mainly green juvenile foliage.   K,W   U.K.

- - 'Glassell' Ashberry   1958   Low-growing shrub with an old gnarled appearance, even when small.   B,G,W   U.K.

- - 'Loderi' Hornibrook   1932   Dense, conical bush or small tree.   B,G,K,R,W   U.K.

- - 'Prostrata' Hornibrook   1923   Formerly included in *JUNIPERUS squamata*. The growing tips arch over, as is characteristic of f. *wilsonii*. Sometimes confused with *JUNIPERUS procumbens* 'Nana'.   B,K,W   U.K.

- - 'Pygmaea' Welch   1964   Smaller leaves and habit, eventually forming a rounded, spreading bush. I. Wansdyke Nurs. Devizes, Wilts. O. Found in National Pinetum, Bedgebury, Kent. Formerly included in *JUNIPERUS squamata*.   G,W   U.K.

- - 'Wilsonii' Rehder   1920   A rounded bush with short, boat-shaped leaves. Formerly included in *JUNIPERUS squamata*.   B,K,W2

- - var. **wilsonii** (Rehder) Silba.
   1984   A botanical term probably embracing all the foregoing cultivars.   R

JUNIPERUS polycarpos C.Koch
   1849   Now known as *JUNIPERUS excelsa* var. *polycarpos* (per Silba, 1984).

JUNIPERUS potaninii Komarov
   1924   Now merged in *JUNIPERUS tibetica*. (per Silba, 1984).

JUNIPERUS procera Hochstetter ex Endlicher

	1847 East African Juniper. Yellow-green foliage, glaucous fruit; tender.	40m,Z10	E Africa

- - var. *africana* Harrison 1975 (and of some authors). A mistake (?) for *JUNIPERUS chinensis* 'Stricta'. W

JUNIPERUS procumbens Siebold ex Miquel

	1870 Japanese Juniper, Creeping Juniper. A spreading shrub.	Z4	Japan

- - **'Bonin Isles'** Welch 1979 Dense, mat-forming habit but a stronger-grower than 'Nana'; foliage green. **I.** Ingwersen Nurs, E. Grinstead, Sussex. **O.** Collected in Japan and given to W.E. Th. Ingwersen by the finder. ('Bonin Island' is wrong). R,W Japan

- - 'Golden' Krüssmann 1979 An unacceptable name. (See Art. 31A, (g). of I.C.N.C.P.) **L.** Monrovia Nurs. Azusa, Cal. K,R U.S.A.

- - **'Green Mound'** Hort. Amer. A listed name. It is possibly a mistake for *JUNIPERUS procumbens nana*. U.S.A.

- - **'Kiyomi'** Mitsch 1990 In "Nurs. Cat". Probably a selection from 'Nana'. Hort. Japan

- - **'Nana'** Grootendorst ex Hornibrook

	1939 A slow-growing cushion-forming, ground hugging form. **O.** Brought back from Japan by Arther Hill of the D. Hill Nurs, Dundee, Ill. U.S.A. **I.** In "Nurs. Cat". as *JUNIPERUS japonica nana* (1904). ('Nana Glauca'). The similar but stronger growing clone 'Bonin Isles' is sometimes wrongly offered in the trade. It is also confused with a mysterious plant *JUNIPERUS squamata* var. *prostrata* (q.v.).	B,D,G,H,K,W	Japan

- - 'Nana Californica' Dirr 1983 An illegit. name Possibly the typical form of the species. (See Bailey, 1933).

- - 'Santa Rosa' Hort. Amer. 1972 A listed name for a very slow-growing form. K,R

- - 'Variegata' Hort.Amer. 1989 An illegit. name for a selection with bursts of creamy-white foliage. Possibly a mistake for *JUNIPERUS chinensis* 'Expansa Albovariegata'.

JUNIPERUS przewalskii Komarov

	1924 Przewalskii Juniper.	12m,Z7	China

JUNIPERUS pseudosabina Fischer & Meyer

	1842 Xinjiang Juniper.	3-4m,Z6	Asia

- - var. *turkestanica* (Komarov) Silba 1984 A rare, taller growing, geographical variant.

JUNIPERUS ramulosa Florin 1927 Now merged with *JUNIPERUS convallium*. (per Silba, 1984).

JUNIPERUS recurva Buchanan-Hamilton ex D. Don.

	1825 Himalayan weeping Juniper.	20m,Z7	Himalayas

- - **'Castlewellan'** Den Ouden/Boom 1965 A beautiful pendulous selection with filiform foliage. B,G,K,R,W Ireland

- - var. *coxii* (Jackson) Melville 1958 In "Kew Bulletin". Here listed as a species, but plants in cultivation may be merely a clone of *JUNIPERUS recurva*, which is variable in the wild. Often listed as a cultivar. B,D,K,W

- - **'Densa'** Carrière 1855 A low, spreading bush. Foliage green with greyish tone; when crushed smells strongly. K,W U.K.

- - **'Embley Park'** Welch   1961   A large, spreading bush with dense, deep green foliage. **I.**
Wansdyke Nurs, Devizes, (1965). Formerly listed as
JUNIPERUS recurva var. *viridis*.   B,G,K,R,W   U.K.

- - var. *viridis* H.G. Hillier   1964   In "Dwarf Conifers".Now known as 'Embley Park'.

JUNIPERUS rigida Siebold & Zuccarini
     1846   Temple Juniper.   10m,Z6   Japan etc.

- - 'Filiformis' Maximowicz ex Beissner
     1909   Presumably a threadleaf form. NIC.   B

- - subsp. *nipponica* (Maximowicz) Franco
     1962   Nippon Juniper. A prostrate shrub.   B,W   Japan

- - 'Shirya-tosho' Hort. Germany
     1978   A listed name of uncertain application.   Hort. Japan ?

- - 'Spiraliter Falcata' Mayr   1906   A listed name for a form with twisted leaves. NIC.   B   Hort. Japan

- - **'Wansdyke Spreader'**   1992   New Name. A completely prostrate, spreading plant; foliage
normal. **I.** Wansdyke Nurs, Devizes, Wilts, U.K. **O.** Received
from the Aritaki Arboretum. (1975).   Hort. Japan

JUNIPERUS rivularis Hort. Anglia
     1976   A listed name for an unidentified plant.   U.K.

JUNIPERUS sabina Linnaeus
     1753   Savin, Savin Juniper. Foliage, when bruised, smells of cats.   2m,Z4   Europe, Asia

- - 'Albovariegata' Hort. Amer.
     1986   Probably a mistake for 'Variegata'.

- - var. *alpina* Forbes   1839   In "Pinetum Wobernense".No longer distinguished within the
species.

- - **'Arcadia'** Den Ouden   1949   A shrub similar to 'Tamariscifolia', but lower. Foliage light
green. **O.** One of several seedlings raised on the D. Hill Nurs,
Dundee, Ill. U.S.A, from Russian seed **I.** by the F.J.
Grootendorst & Sons Nurs, Boskoop, Holland.   B,K,R,W   Russia

- - 'Aureovariegata' Hornibrook
     1939   Named for a plant with bright yellow variegation found at
Abbeyleigh House, Queen's County. NIC.   B,H,K,R   Ireland

- - **'Blaue Donau'** Blaauw   1956   A rather coarse, low, wide-spreading shrub, with light grey-
blue foliage. **O.** L. Vissers Nurs, Presbaum. Austria. **I.**
Blaauws Nurs, Boskoop.   B,K,R,W   Austria

- - **'Blue Danube'**   A translation of 'Blau Danau' that is now unjustifiably used in
the trade.

- - 'Blue Forest' Hort. Amer.
     1986   A listed name for a dwarf, spreading selection.

- - **'Broadmoor'** Robert E. More
     1956   In "The Green Thumb". Graceful bright-green foliage: wide-
branching habit; forms a dense mound. **O.** Same as 'Arcadia'.   B,K,R,W   Holland

- - **'Buffalo'** Robert E. More
     1956   In "The Green Thumb". Feathery bright-green foliage: widely
spreading branches.**O.** Same as 'Arcadia'.   G,K,W   Holland

- - **'Calgary Carpet'** Monrovia
     1978   In "Nurs, Cat". Soft green foliage; lower and more spreading
than 'Arcadia'.   G,W3   U.S.A.

- - f. *cupressifolia* Aiton   1789   The wild, female form. Sometimes listed as 'Humilis' or
'Prostrata'.   B,H,W   Europe

- - 'Cupressifolia Aureo-variegated' Hornibrook
          1939 See 'Aureovariegata'.   H,K

- - 'Cupressifolia Glauca' Hornibrook
          1939 See 'Glauca'.   H

- - 'Cupressifolia Holmbury Hill' . Hornibrook
          1939 See 'Holmbury Hill'.   H

- - 'Cupressifolia Knap Hill' Hornibrook
          1939 See 'Knap Hill'.   H

- - 'Depressa' Knight & Perry
          1850 Name only. NIC.   H

- - **'Erecta'** Beissner	1891 Superfluous name for the rather upright growing form typical of the species in the wild.	B		Europe
- - **'Fastigiata'** Beissner	1891 Columnar Savin Juniper. Dark green, glaucous bloomy foliage; columnar, slender, often with many-headed top.	B,W		Holland

- - 'Femina' Den Ouden/Boom
          1965 Name loosely used for any female clone.   B,K,W   Sporadic

- - *foliis-variegatis* Knight & Perry
          1850 Name only. See 'Variegata'.

- - **'Glauca'** Hornibrook   1939 Named for a very glaucous plant found at Leonardsleigh in Sussex, U.K. NIC.   B   U.K.

- - 'Golden Tam' Hort. Amer.
          1985 A listed name. No further information.

- - f. *gymnospermae* Schweiz.
          1903 In "Bot. Ges". No longer identifiable.   B

- - 'Heidi' Vermuelen   1975 In "Nurs. Cat". A low-growing form with dark-green foliage. I. Vermeulen Nurs, Neshanic Station, N.J.   U.S.A.

- - 'Helcon' Hort. Germany   1978 A listed name. No futher information.

- -'Hennemann' H.J. van de Laar
          1986 In "Naamlijst . . .". NOM. I. F.J. Grootendorst & Sons, (1985).   Sweden?

- - **'Hicksii'** H.J. Grootendorst
          1940 In "Mitt.d.d.d. Ges". Wide grey pyramid; upright branches. I. Hicks and Son Nurs. Westbury, N.Y.   B,W   U.S.A.

- - **'Holmbury Hill'** Hornibrook
          1939 No longer identifiable. O. Found by Mr Trotter on Holmbury Hill, Dorking. NIC.   B,W   U.K.

- - 'Hornibrookii' Gibbs ex Hornibrook
          1939 Named for a very low-growing plant with yellowish-green adult foliage found at Ballyfin. NIC.   B,H,W   Ireland

- - 'Hudsonica' Knight & Perry
          1850 NOM. NIC.   B,H   U.K.

- - var. *humilis* Endlicher   1847 No longer identifiable. (See 'Cupressifolia').   U.K.

- - 'Humilis Aureovariegata' Hornibrook
          1939 A mistake. Now to be 'Aureovariegata'.   U.K.

- - 'Humilis Glauca' Hornibrook
          1939 A mistake. Now to be 'Glauca'.   U.K.

- - **'Jade'** Krüssmann   1979 Fine, blue-green foliage. L. Evergreen Nurs, Fairview, Penn.   K,W   U.S.A.

- - 'Knap Hill' Hornibrook	1939	Indistinguishable from *JUNIPERUS* x *media* 'Pfitzeriana' **O.** Anthony Waterer Nurs, (c. 1914).	B,D,W	U.K.
- - var. *lusitanica* Miller	1768	No longer identifiable. NIC.	B,D	Europe
- - 'Mas' H.J. Grootendorst	1940	Name used to identify a male clone.	B,K,W	
- - 'Mint Julep' Hort. Amer.		A mistake for *JUNIPERUS* x *media* 'Mint Julep'.		
- - **'Musgrave'** Hort. Anglia	1961	Very narrow glaucous foliage; spreading habit. **O.** Found by Charles Musgrave, Hascombe Place, Godalming, (1930). **I.** Ingwersen Nurs, E. Grinstead, Sussex. ('Musgrave's Form').	B,K,W	U.K.
- - **'New Blue'** Monrovia	1976	In "Nurs. Cat". A disease-resistant selection. **I.** Monrovia Nurs, Azusa, Cal. ('Tamariscifolia New Blue'). See 'Tamariscifolia New Blue'.		
- - 'Pegu' H.J. van de Laar	1986	In "Naamlijst . . .". NOM. **O.** and **I.** Raised by P.E. Guldemoud (hence the name) many years ago. NIC.		Holland
- - 'Prostrata' Loudon	1838	No longer identifiable. Was probably a form of *JUNIPERUS horizontalis*.		
- - **'Rockery Gem'** H.J. Grootendorst	1967	In "Dendroflora **4**". Grey-green appearance; low, flat trailing habit. (At first distributed as a *JUNIPERUS chinensis* form in error).	G,W	Holland
- - **'Skandia'** D. Wyman	1953	In "Amer. Nurs". Soft, bright-green foliage; dense, spreading form. **I** . F.J. Grootendorst & Sons Nurs, Boskoop. ('Scandia').	B,K,W	Holland
- - 'Stricta' Knight & Perry	1850	NOM. NIC.		
- - var. *tamariscifolia* Aiton	1789	Botanical designation including all the clones in this group.	B,D,G,H,K,W	Europe
- - **'Tamariscifolia'** J. Forbes	1839	In "Pinetum Woburnense". Name loosely used for several clones: some now badly affected by die-back. Blue-green foliage; low spreading habit.		U.K.
- - 'Tamariscifolia Nana' Hort. Amer.	1984	An illegit. listed name. No further information.		
- - 'Tamariscifolia New Blue' Hort. Amer.		See 'New Blue'.	K	U.S.A.
- - 'Tam No Blight' D.M. van Gelderen	1984	In "Dendroflora **21**". This name appears to be a "commercial equivalent" of 'New Blue'.	W	Holland
- - **'Thomsen'** Hort.	1964	Foliage dark green; very low, creeping. **L** . Thomsen Nurs, Skalborg.	B,K,W	Denmark
- - **'Variegata'** Hayne	1822	A variegated sport will appear from time to time.	B,D,G,H,K,W	
- - **'Von Ehren'** Kumlein	1936	Grows to 3' tall, 8' across. Similar to *JUNIPERUS sabina* but more vigorous and a darker colour. **L**. D. Hill Nurs, Dundee, Illinois, U.S.A.	B,K,W	Germany

JUNIPERUS sabinoides (Humboldt, Bompland & Kunth) Nees
Here listed as *JUNIPERUS monticola* (per Silba, 1984).

JUNIPERUS saltillensis
Here listed as *JUNIPERUS ashei* var. *saltillensis*. (per Silba, 1984).

JUNIPERUS saltuaria Rehder & Wilson in Sargent
        1914 Sichuan Juniper, Blackseed Juniper.   15m,Z6   Asia

JUNIPERUS sargentii Takeda ex Koidz
        1919 A spreading or prostrate shrub. Foliage smells of camphor
             when bruised.   Z4   Japan

- - 'Compacta' J. Noble   1950 In "Journ. Cal. Hort. Soc". A very compact selection. NIC?   B,K,R,W   U.S.A.

- - **'Glauca'** H.J. Grootendorst
        1940 Rich blue-green dense foliage; rising branches.   B,G,K,R,W   U.S.A.

- - 'Manay' Hort. Amer.   1986 A listed name. Possibly a case of misidentification.

- - 'Variegata' Hort. Amer.   1986 A listed name. No information.

- - **'Viridis'** H.J. Grootendorst
        1940 Rich green foliage; widespreading.   R,W2

JUNIPERUS saxicola Britt & Wils
        1923 Now merged in *JUNIPERUS barbadensis* (Silba, 1984).

JUNIPERUS schuganica Komarov
        1932 Now merged in *JUNIPERUS semiglobosa.*

JUNIPERUS scopulorum Sargent
        1897 Rocky Mountain Juniper.   15m,Z3   N. America

There is much confusion in the naming of cultivars in this species. It is variable in habit and leaf colour and in the degree to which the stomata give blue or silvery-white tints. During the 1930s an absurd number of selections were listed in nurserymen's catalogues. Of the names used, those consisting solely of colour adjectives are unacceptable, others are palatable misspellings or mistakes. Piracy, re-christening and bad recording all played a part, but what caused the greatest confusion was the propensity of outstanding seedlings to lose their attractiveness and turn out to be non-descript with age. In result, many of the listed names have "sunk without trace".

The following selection of "recommended" names (i.e. those printed in Bold type) is sufficient to cover the range of variations in this species and to meet the practical needs of horticulture. Other names should be discarded unless distinctive and known to be currently in production on at least a regional scale. WCDP would welcome information on the current situation regarding these, or any cultivar.

- - **'Admiral'** Mount Arbor   1956 In "Nurs. Cat". Grey-green foliage; broad pyramidal shrub. **L.**
                                  Mount Arbor Nurs, Shenandoah, Iowa.   B,K,W   U.S.A.

- - 'Alba' Hort. Amer.   1958 L. Monrovia Nurs, Azusa, Cal. but no longer listed by them.   U.S.A.

- - 'Albino' Hort. Amer.   1947 A listed name for an upright, glaucous clone. No further
                                  information.

- - 'Argentea'(1) D. Hill   1923 In "The Cultivated Evergreens". See 'Hill's Silver'.   D

- - 'Argentea'(2) Hort. Amer.
        1974 L. Vermeulen Nurs, Cat. See 'Wichita Blue'.

- - 'Big Blue' Hort. Amer.   1952 Reported from Univ. Washington Arb. U.S.A.

- - **'Blue Arrow'** Int. Con. Ref.
        1987 Habit similar to 'Skyrocket' but growth more compact; deeper
              in colour. **O.** Pine Grove Nurs, Niagara-on-the-Lake, Ontario.   Canada

- - 'Blue Banff'   1976 Flat habit; striking grey-blue. "Canada Hort. Ill. Report". **O.**
              Found by R. Almey.   W3   U.S.A.

- - 'Blue Bush' Hort. Amer. 1958 L. Monrovia Nurs, Cat. Azusa, Cal. but no longer listed.   U.S.A.

- - 'Blue Colorado' Hort. Amer.
        1940 L. Plumfield Nurs, Fremont, NEB See 'Colorado Blue'.

- - 'Blue Column' Hort. Amer.   Reported from Will Rogers Park, Oklahoma. NOM.

- - 'Blue Creeper' Hort. Amer.
               1986 A typical, rounded form. L. Monrovia Nurs Cat. Azusa, Cal.

- - 'Blue Green' Hort. Amer.   1958 L. Monrovia Nurs, Azusa, Calif., but no longer listed by
                     them.   U.S.A.

- - 'Blue Haven' Hort. Amer.
               Same as 'Blue Heaven' and possibly its 'correct' name.   U.S.A.

- - **'Blue Heaven'** Wyman   1963 In "Amer. Nurs". Striking blue foliage; neat pyramidal habit.
                     O. Plumfield Nurs, Fremont, NEB..   B,K,R,W3   U.S.A.

- - 'Blue Moon' Wyman   1963 L. D. Hill Nurs, Co. Dundee, Illinois. (1947). An upright,
                     glaucous clone.   U.S.A.

- - 'Blue Pillar' Hort. Amer. 1954 L. Girard Nurs, Geneva, Ohio, U.S.A.

- - 'Blue Pyramid' Brander & Thomsen
               1973 Fine blue appearance.   Denmark

- - 'Blue Queen' Hort. Amer.
               1958 L. Monrovia Nurs, Azusa, Cal. but no longer listed.   U.S.A.

- - 'Blue Trail' Hort. Canada   A listed name. No further information.

- - **'Boothman'**   1971 L. Heath End "Nurs. Cat". as 'Boothman's Variety'.   H,W   U.K.

- - 'Burk's Green'   A listed name. No further information.   Canada

- - 'Chandleri' Hort. Amer.   1947 An upright glaucous clone. No further information.

- - 'Chandler's Blue'   See 'Chandler's Silver'.

- - **'Chandler's Silver'** Kumlein
               1936 Glaucous-green foliage; pyramidal, open, loose form. 'The
                     Chandler Silver Juniper'. O. Selected in the Black Hills of S.
                     Dakota.   B,K,R,W   U.S.A.

- - 'Cold Blue'   1972 An unacceptable listed name. Neilson Nurs.

- - **'Cologreen'** Robert E. More
               1956 Bright-green, closely knit foliage; upright; conical habit.
                     Found by Mr. Marshall at Arlington, NEB. (1935).   B,W3   U.S.A.

- - **'Colorado Blue'** Robert E. More
               1945 Bluish-Silver foliage; branches horizontal. ('Blue Colorado')
                     I. 1941 Plumfield Nurs, Fremont, NEB.   K,W   U.S.A.

- - 'Colorado Green' Hort. Amer.
               1965 Now known as 'Cologreen'.

- - 'Columnaris' Fassett   1945 In "Bull. Torrey. Bot. Club". A columnar form found in the
                     wild in N. Dakota (1941).   B,D,K   U.S.A.

- - 'Columnar Sneed' Den Ouden/Boom
               1965 Compact, grey-blue foliage; columnar. I. Monrovia Nurs,
                     Azusa, Cal., but no longer listed (1956).   B   U.S.A.

- - **'Commando'** Hort. Amer.
               1956 Dark green foliage; narrow, pyramidal form. L. Mount Arbor
                     Nurs, Shenandoah, Iowa..   B   U.S.A.

- - "Communis type" Robert E. More
               1951 Indistinguishable from 'Table Top'.

- - 'Compact Dewdrop' Robert E. More
               1960 In "The Green Thumb". NOM.   U.S.A.

- - 'Compact Pathfinder' Robert E More
           1960 In "The Green Thumb". NOM.   U.S.A.

- - 'Concecil' Hort. Amer.   1972 A listed form. L. Neilson Nursery.

- - 'Cone' Robert E. More   1960 In "The Green Thumb". NOM.   U.S.A.

- - 'Crawford' Robert E. More
           1960 In "The Green Thumb". NOM.   U.S.A.

- - 'Cupressifolia Erecta' Hort. Amer.
                Now known as 'Greenspire'.   W

- - **'Cupressifolia Glauca'**   1940 Silvery grey foliage; dense, pyramidal form. **L.** F.C. Hetz &
Sons, Fairview Evergreen Nurs, Fairview, PA. Known in
cultivation since 1932.   B,W3   U.S.A.

- - 'Decumbens Argentatus' Hort. Amer.
           1941 Shining, silver-green foliage; New branches grow downwards
at first and then upwards. In a mature tree branches grow
horizontal. **L.** Plumfield Nurs, Fremont, NEB. (Spelling
varies).   U.S.A.

- - 'Dewdrop' Monrovia   1958 Compact, upright, silvery form. In Monrovia Nurs, Azusa,
Cal. **O.** Mr Kenyon, Dover, Okla. Wrongly known as
'Kenyoni'.   W3   U.S.A.

- - 'Dover' Hort. Amer.   1972 A listed name. L. Neilson Nurs.

- - 'Emerald' Robert E. More
           1947 In "The Green Thumb". A handsome compact green clone. **O.**
The Marshall Nurs, Denver.   U.S.A.

- - 'Emerald Green' Hort. Amer.
           1960 **L.** Monrovia Nurs, Azusa, Cal. An unacceptable name, no
longer listed by them.   U.S.A.

- - 'Erecta Glauca' H.G. Hillier
           1971 Silvery-glaucous foliage, turning purple in winter; erect,
columnar habit. **L.** Monrovia Nurs, Azusa, Cal. (1958) but no
longer listed by them.   U.S.A.

- - 'Fain Variegated' Robert E. More
           1960 NOM.   U.S.A.

- - **'Fainii'** D.Wyman   1963 In "Amer. Nurs". Soft, feathery, silver-blue foliage; semi-
prostrate habit. **I.** Fain Nurs, Bethany, Okla.   U.S.A.

- - 'Fulgens' Hort. Amer.   1941 Blue-green foliage; upright pyramidal. **O.** Plumfield Nurs,
Fremont, NEB.   U.S.A

- - 'Funalis' Hort. Amer.   1941 Bluish-green foliage whip cord; pyramidal. **O.**Plumfield
Nurs, Fremont, NEB.   U.S.A.

- - **'Gareei'** H.J. Grootendorst
           1940 A low dwarf, shrub-like form with bluish-green foliage.
Selected by Mr. Garee, Noble, Okla. (1935). **I.** Willis Nurs,
Ottawa, Kansas (1939).   B,K,W   U.S.A.

- - 'Glauca Compacta' Monrovia
           1958 In "Nurs. Cat". No longer listed by them.   U.S.A.

- - 'Glauca Erecta' Robert E More
           1960 NOM.   U.S.A.

- - 'Glauca Pendula' H.G. Hillier
           1971 Greyish-green foliage; loose, open habit, branchlets drooping;
not robust.   G   U.K.

- - 'Glenmore Globe' Robert E. More
  1960 NOM.   U.S.A.

- - 'Glenmore Green' Robert E. More
  1960 NOM.   U.S.A.

- - 'Glenmore Queen' Robert E. More
  1947 In "The Green Thumb". A round-topped conical tree, berrying
       freely.   U.S.A.

- - 'Glenmore Weeping' Robert E. More
  1960 NOM.   U.S.A.

- - **'Globe'** Den Ouden/Boom
  1965 Globose habit. Silvery-grey, juvenile foliage. **L.** Monrovia
       Nurs. Azusa, Cal. Listed as 'Globosa' (1962).   B,K,W   U.S.A.

- - 'Gold Flash' Hort. N.Z.   **I.** Blackman.   N.Z.

- - 'Gracilis' Hort. Amer.   1950 **L.** Plumfield Nurs, Fremont, NEB.   U.S.A.

- -**'Gray Gleam'** Reg'd. Arn. Arb
  1950 Dense, silery-grey-blue foliage, at all seasons: columnar form.
       I. Scott Wilmore Nurs. (1949) ('Grey Gleam').   B,K,W3   U.S.A.

- - 'Green King' Robert E More
  1960 NOM.   U.S.A.

- - 'Green Mount' Hort. Amer.   Marshall Cat.?

- - **'Greenspire'** Hort. Amer.
  1970 Rich green foliage with silvery-blue undertones; tall
       pyramidal form. Bakker Nurs. ('Cupressifolia Erecta')   Canada

- - **'Grizzly Bear'** Hort. Amer.
  1949 Grey-green colour with lighter tips; upright, open habit.
       Patmore Nurs, Brandon, Manitoba.   Canada

- - 'Hall Special' Robert E. More
  1960 A listed name. NOM.

- - 'Hall's Sport' Robert E. More
  1958 In "Green Thumb". Juvenile foliage of good colour; compact
       pointed habit.   B   U.S.A.

- - 'Heasley' Monrovia
  1958 In "Nurs. Cat". as 'Heasley Globe', but no longer listed by
       them.   U.S.A.

- - **'Hilborn's Silver Globe'** H.G. Hillier
  1971 Silvery-blue foliage; small dense shrub; irregular rounded
       habit. Other spellings occur.   W   U.S.A.

- - **'Hill's Silver'** D. Hill   1922 Narrow conical form, silvery-white foliage. **O.** Selected by D.
       Hill in the mountains of S. Dakota.   B,K   U.S.A.

- - 'Holman Blue' Robert E. More
  1960 In "The Green Thumb". NOM.   U.S.A.

- - 'Holman Green' Robert E. More
  1960 In "The Green Thumb". NOM.   U.S.A.

- - 'Holme's Silver' Hort. Amer.   **O.** Holmes Nurs, Oklahoma. ('Hohlm's Silver').   U.S.A.

- - 'Horizontalis' D. Hill ex Bailey
  1923 An upright plant with horizontally spreading branches.
       bluish-white foliage. **O.** D. Hill Nurs, Dundee, Ill. B,K   U.S.A.

- - 'Hughes' Hort. Amer.   Probably a mistake for *JUNIPERUS horizontalis* 'Hughes'.

- - **'Kansas Silver'** Wyman 1963 Silvery-blue foliage; pyramidal form. **O.** The Kansas
Landscape and Nurs. Co. Salma, Kansas. B,W U.S.A.

- - 'Kenyoni' Wyman 1963 Superfluous name for 'Dew Drop'. B,K,W U.S.A.

- - 'Lakewood Globe' 1958 Blue-green foliage, compact, globose form. Monrovia Nurs,
Azusa, Cal. but no longer listed. K,W U.S.A.

- - 'Linwood' Hort. Amer. 1947 A listed name for an upright, glaucous clone.

- - 'MacFarland' Robert E. More
1960 A listed name.NOM. U.S.A.

- - 'Madorra' Hort. Amer. See 'Medora'.

- - 'Manhattan Blue' Hort. Amer.
1947 A listed name for an upright, glaucous clone.

- -'Marshall' Marshall 1940 In "Nurs. Cat". Conspicuous silvery-blue foliage; upright
loose pyramidal form. An early selection by G.A. Marshall of
the Marshall Nurs, Arlington, Nebraska. ('Marshall's Silver'). B U.S.A.

- - **'Medora'** Robert E. More
1947 Bluish-green foliage; columnar. Named for the town Medora
in N. Dakota. W U.S.A.

- - 'Minima' Hort. Amer. 1962 Reported from Gotelli Collection. South Orange, N.J.

- - 'Mission' Hort. Amer. 1947 A listed name for an upright, glaucous clone.

- - **'Moffetii'** Plumfield 1941 In "Nurs. Cat". Mixed green and silver-foliage; conical. **O.** A
selection by L.A. Moffet of the Plumfield Nurs, Fremont,
Nebraska. B,K U.S.A.

- - "montana" Hort. Amer. 1941 An unrecognised name used for seedlings distributed at one
time by Plumfield Nurs, some of which have later been given
names consisting of descriptive adjectives.

- - 'Montana' Monrovia 1958 In "Nurs. Cat". but no longer listed by them. K U.S.A.

- - 'Monument' Robert E. More
1960 A listed name. NOM.

- - 'Moonglow' Hort. Amer. 1970 Intense silver-blue foliage; broad, pyramidal form. L. Hillside
Gardens, Lehighton. PA. W3 U.S.A.

- - 'Moonlight' D. Hill 1936 Loose open pendulous form; light grey-blue foliage. NIC. B,G U.S.A.

- - **'Mountaineer'** Monrovia
1960 In "Nurs. Cat". Dark green foliage; upright, pyramidal form.
L. Monrovia Nurs, Azusa, Cal. No longer listed by them.
('Mounteneer' is incorrect). B U.S.A.

- - 'Mrs Marriage' J. Drake 1990 In "Nurs. Cat". as "Mrs Marriage's Form". U.K.

- - **'North Star'** Kumlein 1946 Bright green foliage and a neat, compact upright habit. **O.**
and **I.** The Westover Farm Landscaping Co., St. Louis, MO. B U.S.A.

- - 'Northern Beauty' Robert E. More
1960 A listed name. NOM.

- - **'O'Connor'** Krüssmann 1979 A distinctive broad form, almost weeping habit, silver-blue in
summer. **O.** Not known. **L.** H. Korden, Pilsen-Holstein.
(1976). G,K Germany

- - **'Palmeri'** H.J. Grootendorst
1940 A dwarf, prostrate form; distinctly blue, tips purplish. **O.**
Found by P.C. Palmer near Lake Windermere, Ontario. B Canada

- - 'Park' Robert E. More   1951   Indistinguishable from 'Table Top'.

- - *patens* Fassett   1945   In "Bull. Torrey Club 72". A designation suggested to include all selections with a prostrate habit. Note: The relation of this group to *JUNIPERUS horizontalis* is uncertain.

- - **'Pathfinder'** Kammerer   1939   In "Bull Morton Arb. **IA**". A blue clone. **O.** Lloyd Moffitt, Plumfield Nurs, Fremont, NEB, U.S.A.   B,K,W3

- - **'Pendula'** Kumlein   1946   Upright growth with pendulous branches. **O.** Said to have originated at the Boyce Thompson Arboretum in Arizona (c.1950).   B   U.S.A.

- - 'P.G. Green' Robert E. More
       1960   A listed name. NOM.   U.S.A.

- - 'Pillaris' Wyman   1963   Now known as 'Skyrocket' ('Pilaris').   U.S.A.

- - **'Platinum'** Wyman   1963   In "Amer. Nurs". Bright silvery-blue foliage; upright, dense pyramid. **O.** Selected by the Willis Nurs, Co., Ottawa, Kansas.   B,K   U.S.A.

- - 'Platt's River Blue' Hort.Amer.
       1947   Listed name for an upright, glaucous clone.

- - **'Plumfield'** Monrovia   1940   A broad, pyramidal form; blue-grey foliage. **O.** Plumfield Cat.? **L.** Monrovia Nurs.   U.S.A.

- - **'Priorsport'** Hort. Australia
       1989   A listed name for a slow-growing form similar to 'Repens'. ('Repens Priosport'). No record of **O.** or **I.**

- - 'Prostrata' Chadwick   1940   A listed name.

- - 'Pyramidal Green' Hort. Amer.   See 'Viridifolia'.

- - 'Repens' Hornibrook   1939   Bluish-green foliage; dwarf form, prostrate branches. **O.** Found by P.C. Palmer of the Experimental Station, Summerland, B.C.   B,H,K,W   Canada

- - 'Robin Hood' Wyman   1949   In "Amer. Nurs". A listed name.

- - 'Rocket' Hort.   A mistake for 'Skyrocket'.

- - 'Rocky Mountain' Hort. Amer.   A listed name.

- - 'Rollerensis' Bailey   1941   A listed name.   U.S.A.

- - 'Salina' Robert E. More   1960   A listed name. NOM.   U.S.A.

- - **'Salome Blue'** Robert E. More
       1960   U.S.A.

- - 'Select Blue' Robert E. More
       1960   An unacceptable name.   U.S.A.

- - 'Schottii' Hort.   A mistake for *JUNIPERUS virginiana* 'Schottii'.

- - 'Sierra Silver'   G

- - 'Silver Beauty' Kammerer
       1939   Greenish-silver foliage; upright, slender, full at base. **I.** Lloyd Moffet of Plumfield Nurs, Fremont, NEB.   B,K   U.S.A.

- - 'Silver Column' Reg'd. C.O.P.F.
       1968   Silvery foliage, symmetrical, narrow, compact form.   W3   Canada

- - 'Silver Cord' Robert E. More
       1960   A listed name. NOM.   K   U.S.A.

- - 'Silver Globe' Hort. Amer.
1972 **L.** Neilson Nurs.   U.S.A.

- - 'Silver Glow' Kumlein   1946 Intense silver-blue foliage; upright habit. NIC.   U.S.A.

- - 'Silver Grey' Hort. Amer.
1947 A listed name for an upright, glaucous clone.

- - **'Silver King'** C. White   1955 In "Nurs. Cat". Silvery-blue foliage; dwarf, spreading form. **O.** and **I.** White Nurs, Walla Walla, Washington. ('White's Silver King').   B,K,R,W   U.S.A.

- - 'Silver Montana' Hort. Amer.   See "montana".

- - 'Silver Moon' Hort. Amer.
1947 A listed name for an upright, glaucous clone.

- - **'Silver Queen'** Kumlein   1946 Very glaucous foliage; narrow, pyramidal form. **O.** D. Hill Nurs, Dundee, Ill.   B   U.S.A.

- - 'Silver Radiance' Wyman
1963 In "Amer. Nurs".   U.S.A.

- - 'Silver Slipper' Hort. Anglia
1992 Reported from Windsor Great Park, Berks. NOM.

- - **'Silver Star'** Bergman   1965 In "Plants and Gardens **21**". Vivid light-green young growth turning silvery; spreading habit.   K,R,W   U.S.A.

- - 'Skylon' Hort. Anglia   1992 Reported from Windsor Great Park, Berks. NOM.

- - **'Skyrocket'** H.J. Grootendorst
1957 Narrow-columnar; silver-blue foliage. ('Pilaris') Often listed under either *JUNIPERUS chinensis* or *JUNIPERUS virginiana*.   K,R,W   Holland

- - 'Slender' Hort. Amer.   1992 An unacceptable listed name.

- - 'Sneedii' Robert E. More   1960 See 'Columnar Sneed'.

- - 'Southerland' Hort. Amer.   See 'Sutherland'.

- - 'Sparkling Skyrocket' Vermeulen
1986 In "Nurs. Cat".   U.S.A.

- - **'Springbank'** H.J. Grootendorst
1969 In "Dendroflora **2**". Intense, silver-blue foliage; narrowly ascending branch system, graceful, open texture. At first listed as 'Springbank Park'.   G,K,R,W   Holland

- - 'Springtime' Hort. Amer.   1956 Dark green colour; pyramidal. **L.** Mount Arbor "Nurs. Cat".   B   U.S.A.

- - 'Staver' Monrovia   1958 In "Nurs. Cat". Rich green foliage; upright form. **L.** Monrovia Nurs, Azusa, Cal. No longer listed by them.   U.S.A.

- - 'Steel Blue' Hort. France   1977 An unacceptable name. A showy, deep steel-blue foliage; pyramidal habit. **L.** Minier Nurs, Angers.   K   France

- - 'Sterling Dwarf' Robert E. More
1960 A listed name. NOM.   U.S.A.

- - 'Sterling Silver' Hort.   A listed name.

- - 'Steven's Green' Hort. Amer.
1971 Reported from Will Rogers Park, Oklahoma.   U.S.A.

- - 'Stovepipe' Robert E. More
1947 A listed name for a slender, columnar tree. NIC.   U.S.A.

- - 'Stuhr's Silver' Hort. Amer.
1949 In "Amer. Nurs". Nebraska Cat?   U.S.A.

- - 'Sutherland' Robert E. More
1947 Dark green foliage; dense bush. An early selection by W.J.
Sutherland. Boulder, Colorado.   B,K   U.S.A.

- - **'Table Top'** Robert E. More
1956 Rich silvery-blue foliage; semi spreading, flat topped plant.
('Table Top Blue').   B,K,W   U.S.A.

- - 'Teepee' Robert E. More   1960 A listed name. NIC.   U.S.A.

- - **'Tolleson's Blue Weeping'** Hort. Amer.
1978 Silvery-grey, string-like foliage from arching branches. L.
Behnke Nurs. As 'Tolleson's Weeping'.   K,W   U.S.A.

- - **'Tolleson's Green Weeping'** Monrovia
1978 Soft green foliage; habit as above. O. Monrovia Nurs, Azusa,
Cal. Previously listed as 'Tolleson's Weeping Viridis'   W   U.S.A.

- - 'Victory' Robert E. More   1940 L. D. Hill Nurs, Dundee, Ill. An upright, glaucous clone.   U.S.A.

- - 'Viridifolia' D. Hill ex Rehder
1923 Pyramidal form, bright green foliage.   B,D,K   U.S.A.

- - 'Weirii' Plumfield   1941 True blue foliage; dense conical form. L. Plumfield Nurs, in
"Nurs. Cat". (Wieri').

- - **'Welchii'** Monrovia   1961 Silvery-green foliage; compact cone-shaped habit. O. The
Plumfield Nurs, Fremont, Nebraska.   B,K,W   U.S.A.

- - 'White's Silver King' Hort. Amer.
See 'Silver King'.

- - **'Wichita Blue'** Monrovia
1976 In "Nurs. Cat". Blue foliage; pyramidal. I. Monrovia Nurs,
Azusa, Cal.   G,K,W   U.S.A.

- - **'Winter Blue'** Reg.C.O.P.V.
1977 Dense silver-blue foliage; semi-prostrate, spreading. Reg'd. by
C.V. Berg.   B,W3   Canada

- - 'Woodward' Hort.   A superfluous name for 'MacFarland'.

- - 'Wyoming' Robert E. More
1960 A listed name. NOM.   U.S.A.

JUNIPERUS semiglobosa Regel
1879 Russian Juniper. Now includes *JUNIPERUS drobovii*,
JUNIPERUS jarkendeusis, *JUNIPERUS schuganica* and
JUNIPERUS standleyii. (per Silba, 1984).   12m,Z4   Russia, China

JUNIPERUS seravschanica Komarov
1932 Now merged in *JUNIPERUS excelsa* var. *polycarpus*. (per
Silba, 1984).

JUNIPERUS sheppardii (Veitch) Van Melle
1946 in "Phytologia 2". See *JUNIPERUS chinensis* 'Sheppardii'
and note following *JUNIPERUS chinensis*.

- - var. *pyramidalis* (Carrière) Van Melle.
1946 In "Phytologia 2". See above note.

- - var *torulosa* (Eastwood) Van Melle
1946 In "Phytologia 2". See above note.

- - var. *torulosa* f. *alba-notata* Van Melle
1947 In "Phytologia 2". See above note

- - var. *torulosa* f. *aureo-variegata* Van Melle
          1946 In "Phytologia 2". See above note.

JUNIPERUS sibirica Burgsdorf
          1787 Here merged in *JUNIPERUS communis* var. *montana*, (by some authorities *JUNIPERUS communis* sub-sp. *nana*).

JUNIPERUS silicicola (Small) Bailey
          1933 Now known as *JUNIPERUS virginiana* var. *silicicola*.

JUNIPERUS sphaerica Lindley
          1850 In "Paxton's Flower Garden 1". Merged with *JUNIPERUS chinensis* by Rehder (In "Bibliography" 1949). See Notes under *JUNIPERUS chinensis* re contrary proposals by P.J. van Melle, not accepted here.

- - f. columnaris (U.S. Dept. Agric.)
          1946 In "Phytologia 2". See above Note.

- - var. *dioica* Van Melle   1946 In "Phytologia 2". See above Note.

- - var. *keteleerii* Van Melle
          1946 In "Phytologia 2". See above Note.

- - var. *luptonii* Van Melle   1946 In "Phytologia 2". See above Note.

- - var. *neaboriensis* (Veitch) Van Melle
          1946 In "Phytologia 2". See above Note.

- - var. *pendula* (Franchet) Van Melle
          1946 In "Phytologia 2". See above Note.

- - var. *pseudo-mas* Van Melle
          1946 In "Phytologia 2". See above Note.

- - var. *pseudo-mas* f. *columnaris* (Meyer) Van Melle
          1946 In "Phytologia 2". See above Note.

- - var *pyramidalis* (Carrière) Van Melle.
          In "Phytologia 2". See above Note.

- - f. *variegata* (Carrière) Van Melle.
          1946 In "Phytologia 2". See above Note.

JUNIPERUS squamata Buchanan-Hamilton ex Lambert
          1824 Flaky Juniper. Shrub or small tree.   5m,Z4   China

- - 'Blue Alps' Hort. Europe   A mistake for *JUNIPERUS chinensis* 'Blue Alps'.

- - **'Blue Carpet'** H.J. van de Laar
          1972 In "Dendroflora 9". Intense grey-blue foliage; prostrate habit.   G,K,R,W   Holland

- - **'Blue Spider'** H.J. van de Laar
          1980 In "Dendroflora 17". As 'Blue Carpet' but young shoots are orange-brown and some stronger branchlets protrude above the rest giving the look of a spider.   G,W3   Holland

- - **'Blue Star'** H.J. Grootendorst
          1965 In "Dendroflora 2". Steel-blue foliage; dwarf form. spreading, mounding habit.   K,R,W   Holland

- - 'Blue Swede' Hort. Europe   A trade name for 'Hunnetorp'?

- - 'Campbellii' Krüssmann   1960 Probably a misidentification of *JUNIPERUS chinensis* 'Stricta'. Not as K.   G,K,W

- - **'Chinese Silver'** H.G. Hillier
  1971 In "Hillier's Manual". A large, loose shrub. Foliage silvery-green; tips of branches droop outwards; Formerly incorrectly listed as Sp. Yu 7881. **L.** Hillier's Nurs, Winchester.   G,K,R,W3   China

- - 'Embley Park' Hort.   Here listed under *JUNIPERUS recurva*.

- - var. *fargesii* Rehder & Wilson in Sargent
  1914 An erect small tree, branchlets drooping; apple-green foliage. Formerly known as *JUNIPERUS kansuensis*.   B,D,G,K,W   S.W. China

- - **'Filborna'** Welch
  1979 Foliage blue-green; more upright and vigorous than 'Holger'.**I.** Wansdyke Nurs, Devizes, Wilts. U.K. **O.** Raised from seed by Holger Jensen of the Ramlosa Plantskola, Helsingborg (1946). ('Filborne' is incorrect).   W3   Sweden

- - 'Forrestii' Welch   1979 Now listed under *JUNIPERUS pingii*.   K,W

- - 'Glassell' Ashberry   1958 Now listed under *JUNIPERUS pingii*.   B,G,K,W

- - **'Golden Flame'** Krüssmann
  1979 A sport on 'Meyeri' with a considerable amount of yellow foliage mixed with the blue. **L.** Konijn Co., Reeuwijk, Holland in "Sortimentslijst, 1968".   G,K,R,W3   Holland

- - **'Gold Flash'** Hort. N.Z.
  1986 Variegated form of 'Meyeri', upright, arching, spreading, vase-shaped bush. **L.** Cedar Lodge, Egmont Rd, New Plymouth, (Other variegated sports have occurred).   N.Z.

- - **'Holger'** Welch
  1979 A low, spreading bush; young foliage is butter-yellow, older foliage glaucous-blue, Name registered by Wansdyke Nurs, Devizes, Wilts. U.K. in 1983.   G,K,R,W   Sweden

- - **'Hunnetorp'** Hort.
  1976 Distinctly glaucous foliage; has the same history as 'Filborna'. ('Hohlentorp' is incorrect).   G,W   Sweden

- - 'Kék' Barabits   1965 In "Magyar Fenyóújdonságok".   Hungary

- - 'Loderi' Hornibrook   1932 Now listed under *JUNIPERUS pingii*.

- - **'Meyeri'** Rehder
  1922 In "Journ. Arnold Arb". A strong-growing bushy form with striking blue foliage. **O.** Found in cultivation in China by F.N. Meyer of U.S. Dept. Agriculture. Not know in the wild.   B,D,G,H,K,W

- - var. *morrisonicola* (Hayata) L. & Keng
  1908 A geographical form.   10m,Z7   Taiwan

- - 'Procumbens' Hornibrook
  1923 A case of mistaken identity.

- - 'Prostrata' (1) Hornibrook
  1923 Now listed under *JUNIPERUS pingii*.

- - 'Prostrata' (2) Van Melle (NON Hornibrook)
  1946 This plant if it ever existed; would almost certainly have been a clone of *JUNIPERUS procumbens* similar to but distinguishable from 'Nana', which in nurseries in Eastern U.S.A., was distinguished as 'Nana' (the D. Hill strain).

- - 'Pygmaea' Welch   1964 Now listed under *JUNIPERUS pingii*.

- - 'Spence's Silver' N.Z.   1992 A seedling found in S. Island that makes a vase-shaped plant, more compact than 'Meyeri'.

- - var. *wilsonii* Rehder   1920 In "Journ. Arnold Arb". Now known as *JUNIPERUS pingii* var. *wilsonii*.

- - 'Wilsonii' Hort.   Now listed under *JUNIPERUS pingii*.

- - 'Yellow Tip' Hort. Holland   Upright growing with tips of leaves yellow. Origin unknown.
Probably a superfluous name for 'Holger'.

JUNIPERUS standeyii Steyermark
          1943   Standley Juniper.   15m,Z8   Mexico

JUNIPERUS talassica Lispay
          1912   Now merged in *JUNIPERUS semiglobosa.*

JUNIPERUS taxifolia Hooker & Arnold
          1841   Luchu Juniper. Tree to 10m or spreading shrub.   10m,Z9   Japan Is.

- - var. *luchuensis* (Koidz.) Satake
          1962   Grass-green foliage; prostrate habit; good ground cover. Very
prone to die-back in the foliage.   Japan

JUNIPERUS thurifera Linnaeus.
          1753   Spanish Juniper.   20m,Z9   Spain

- - var. *gallica* De Loiney   1897   No longer distinguished within the species.   B,D,K

JUNIPERUS tibetica Komarov
          1924   Tibetan Juniper. Now includes *JUNIPERUS distans* and
JUNIPERUS potaninii. (per Silba, 1984).   30m,Z6   W. China

JUNIPERUS turkestanica Komarov
          1924   Now known as *JUNIPERUS pseudosabina* var. *turkestanica.*

JUNIPERUS turkomanica B. Fedtsh
          1932   Now merged in *JUNIPERUS excelsa* var. *polycarpos.*

JUNIPERUS urbaniana Pilger & Exmau
          1926   Now merged in *JUNIPERUS barbadensis* (per Silba, 1984).

JUNIPERUS utahensis (Engelmann) Lemmon
          1890   Now merged in *JUNIPERUS osteosperma* (per Silba, 1984).

- - var. *megalocarpa* (Sudworth) Sargent
          1919   No longer distinguished within the species.

JUNIPERUS virginiana Linnaeus
          1753   Pencil Cedar, Eastern Red Cedar.   12-30m,Z9   U.S.A.

- - **'Albospica'** Beissner   1909   Branchlets tipped with white; rather tender. ('Albospicata').   B,K

- - 'Aquarius' Hort. Amer.   Growth compact, foliage blue-green. **O.** A mutation on 'Hetz'
on the Lake County Nurs.

- - 'Argentea' Carrière   1855   Clone no longer identifiable.   France

- - 'Argentovariegata' Sénéclauze
          1868   A listed name. NIC.   France

- - 'Aurea' Nelson   1866   Dark green foliage, tips bronze; spreading. NIC.   B   U.K.

- - 'Aurea Elegans' Beissner   1891   An ascending form with golden-variegated branchlets. NIC.   B   Germany

- - 'Aureospica'   1889   Bright-yellow branchlets in spring. NIC. ('Aureospicata')   B,D   Germany

- - 'Aureovariegata' Knight & Perry
          1851   A listed name. No longer identifiable.   U.K.

- - 'Black Green' Hort. Amer.
          1984   An unacceptable listed name.

- - **'Blue Arrow'** H.J. van de Laar
          1990   In "Dendroflora 27". As 'Skyrocket', but darker blue-grey
foliage. **O.** Tesselaar Nurs, Niagara-on-the-Lake, Ontario.   Canada

- - 'Blue Banff' Hort. Now listed under *JUNIPERUS scopulorum*.

- - **'Blue Cloud'** Welch 1979 Glaucous-grey foliage; long 'whiskery' shoots. G,W Holland

- - 'Blue Mountain' Hort. Holland
1969 A listed name. No further information.

- - 'Blue Rapids' Hort. Amer.
1972 A listed name. Found in Wisconsin in 1920.

- - **'Boskoop Purple'** H.J. Grootendorst
1965 In "Nurs. Cat". **O.** A sport of 'Hillii'; narrow form, purplish-
brown in winter. B,K,R,W Holland

- - 'Brodie' Hort. 1963 A listed name. No information.

- - **'Burkii'** Slavin 1932 Burk Red Cedar. Steel blue foliage in autumn; Columnar
form, dense, compact habit ascending branches. B,D,G,K,W U.S.A.

- - 'Burkii Compacta' Hort. Amer.
1986 An illegit. listed name.

- - **'Canaertii'** Sénéclauze 1868 Deep green, profuse blue berries; a small compact, pyramidal
tree bearing many blue berries. **O.** Found by Canaert
d'Hamale at Mechelen. B,D,G,K,W Belgium

- - **'Carolina'** H.J. van de Laar
1983 In "Dendroflora 20". A squat shrub with ascending shoots and
grey-green adult foliage. W Holland

- - **'Chamberlaynii'** (1) Carrière
1855 A pendulous tree with long, slender shoots; a female clone.
('Chamberlainii'). B,D,H,K,W Europe

- - 'Chamberlaynii' (2) H.G. Hillier
1964 In "Dwarf Conifers". See 'Pendula Nana'. B,D,H,K,W Hort.U.K.

- - 'Cinerascens' Carrière 1855 No longer identifiable. NIC. B,K Hort. France

- - var. *crebra* Fernald & Griscom
1935 A rather slender, regional variant found in North Eastern
U.S.A. B,K,W U.S.A.

- - 'Cunninghamii' Beissner 1904 Silvery-white variegated form. **O.** Cunningham, Edinburgh.
NIC. B Scotland

- - 'Cupressifolia' (1) Kammerer
1932 In "Bull. Morton Arb". Conical tree with soft, yellow-green
foliage. B,D,K,W3 U.S.A.

- - **'Cupressifolia'** (2) Kumlein
1946 Now known as 'Hillspire'.Compact, conical; dark green
whipcord foliage. **O.** D. Hill Nurs, Dundee, Ill. U.S.A.

- - 'Cylindrica' Kumlein 1936 Column Red Cedar. No longer identifiable. U.S.A.

- - 'Damnii' Hort. Amer. Name changed to 'Silver Spreader'.

- - **'Deforest Green'** Wyman
1963 In "Amer. Nurs 117". Similar to 'Canaertii' but foliage deeper
green. B,W3 U.S.A.

- - 'Dioica' Beissner 1887 NOM. NIC.

- - **'Dumosa'** Carrière 1855 A compact, globose shrub. An early selection, still in
circulation in U.K. B,D,W U.K.

- - **'Elegantissima'** Hochstetter
1882 Broadly conical; Foliage yellow-green, tips golden. B,K,R,W3 Germany

- - 'Emerald Sentinel' Hort. Amer.
1986 A listed name for a quick-growing columnar clone.

- - 'Erecta' Sénéclauze   1868 A clone with numerous upright branches forming a narrow cone. NIC.

France

- - 'Fairview' Hort.   Now listed under *JUNIPERUS chinensis*.

- - **'Fastigiata'** Hesse   1933 Bluish-green foliage; columnar. O. and I. H.A. Hesse Nurs, Weener-on-Ems.

B,K,W   Germany

- - 'Filifera' Bailey   1923 I. D. Hill Nurs, Dundee, Ill.

B,D,K   U.S.A.

- - **'Fiore'** Thomsen   1986 Similar in appearance to 'Fairview', better shape and more easily propagated. L. Thomsen's Nurs, Skalborg, Denmark. O. Fiore Nurs, Ill. (1954).

G,W3   U.S.A.

- - **'Frosty Morn'** Hort   .1981 A listed name for a semi-prostrate plant; silver-blue in summer, tinged bronze-purple in winter. ('Frosty Morning' is incorrect).

G

- - 'Gigantea' Hort. Ireland   Reported from the National Botanic Garden, Dublin.

- - **'Glauca'** Carrière   1855 A dense, columnar form; silvery-grey foliage.

B,D,G,K,W   France

- - 'Glauca Argentea' Sénéclauze
1868 A very vigorous tree, a beautiful silvery-green. NIC.

France

- - 'Glauca Hetzii' Hort.   See 'Hetz'.

- - 'Glauca Pendula' Beissner
1909 A shrub with grey foliage. NIC.

B,K

- - 'Glenn Dale' Hort. Amer.   1986 A listed name. (Glendale?).

- - **'Globosa'** Beissner   1891 Bright-green foliage; dwarf, dense, rounded habit.

B,D,G,H,K,W   Germany

- - **'Golden Spring'** H.J. van de Laar
1990 In "Dendroflora 27". A mutation from 'Grey Owl' with new foliage yellow. O. H.J. van den Top, Barnveld.

Holland

- - **'Goldspire'** Int. Con. Reg.
1985 An upright conical tree. Leaves golden-yellow.

- - 'Greenspire' Hort. Amer.   1980 O. and I. Lincoln Nurs, Inc., Grand Rapids, Mich.

G   U.S.A.

- - 'Green Spreader' Hort. Amer.
1986 A listed name for a spreading plant with threadlike foliage.

- - **'Grey Owl'** Den Ouden   1949 A semi-prostrate bush with silvery-grey foliage. I. F.J. Grootendorst & Sons Nurs, Boskoop (1949), O. Gebr. Caam, Oudenbosch.

B,D,G,K,W   Holland

- - **'Grey Rock'** Sheridan   1962 In "Nurs. Cat". A grey-green upright form. I. Sheridan Nurs, Oakville, Ontario, (1960).

- - 'Helle' Hort.   See *JUNIPERUS chinensis* 'Spartan'.

G,K

- - 'Henryi' Hort. Amer.   1984 An illegit. listed name.

- - **'Hetz'** Wyman   1963 (Under *JUNIPERUS chinensis*.)A large shrub with spreading branches and glaucous foliage. O. Fairview Evergreen Nurs, Fairview, P.A. (1920). Still widely listed under *JUNIPERUS* x *media*; it is possibly a hybrid.

W   U.S.A.

- - 'Hetz Glauca' Hort.   Superfluous name for the preceding item.

- - **'Hillii'** Kumlein   1944   In "Nurs. Cat". A compact column; grey-green in summer, purple-plum in winter, **L.** D. Hill Nurs, (as 'Pyramidalis Hillii').   B,G,K,R,W   U.S.A.

- - **'Hillspire'** Wyman   1963   In "Amer. Nurs **117**". A broadly conical form; dense, dark green foliage. **O.** D. Hill Nurs, Dundee, Ill.   B,K   U.S.A.

- - 'Holme's Yellow' Hort. Amer.   1984   A listed name. No information.

- - 'Horizontalis' Hornibrook   1939   A prostrate plant that can no longer be identified, so the name should not be used.   B,H,K,W

- - 'Horizontalis Glauca' Kumlein   1946   A widespreading (not procumbent) bush with stiff brs and rugged, bright blue foliage.**I.** D. Hill Nurs. Dundee, Ill. **O.** Found on a high, coastal cliff in Maine by Prof. Sargent.   K   U.S.A.

- - **'Humilis'** Hornibrook   1939   Deep sea-green appearance; a diminutive dwarf, bushy. **L.** Loddiges Nurs, Hackney, London (1826).   B,H,W   U.K.

- - 'Hutilm' Hort.   1964   A listed name. No information.

- - 'Hydro Green' Hort.   A broadly conical form and rugged outline. Dark green foliage.

- - **'Idyllwild'** Monrovia   1986   In "Nurs. Cat". A strong-growing conical tree with dark green foliage. **L.** Monrovia Nurs, Azusa, Cal.   U.S.A.

- - 'Interrupta' (Carrière) Beissner   1891   A compact dwarf shrub. NIC.   B   France

- - 'Keteleerii' Hort.   See *JUNIPERUS chinensis* 'Keteleerii'.

- - 'Kim' Hort. Holland   1992   A listed name, without description.

- - 'Kobendzii' Hort. Poland   1958   A small tree lacking in vigour. **O.** Arose as a seedling at the Körnickie Arb. (1932). NIC.   B,K   Poland

- - **'Kobold'** Den Ouden/Boom   1965   Bluish-green appearance; dwarf, globular dense habit.   B,K,R,W   Holland

- - **'Kosteri'** Jaeger & Beissner   1884   Grey-blue to purplish in winter; dwarf, bushy form. Formerly *JUNIPERUS* x *media* 'Kosteriana'.   B,D,H,K,W   Germany.

- - 'Kosteriana'   See 'Kosteri'.

- - 'Lebritonii'   1975   In "Nurs. Cat". Raraflora Nurs, Feasterville, PA.

- - 'Lemon Hill' Hort.   See *JUNIPERUS* x *media* 'Lemon Hill'.?   G

- - **'Manhattan Blue'** Scott ex Wyman   1963   In "Amer. Nurs **117**". Dark blue-green foliage; compact pyramidal form.   B,K,R,W   U.S.A.

- - 'Matthews Blue' Hort. Germany   1983   **L.** Horstmann Nurs, Schneverdingen, without description.

- - 'McCabei' Hort. Amer.   1986   An illegit. listed name. No further information.

- - 'Microphylla' Sénéclauze   1868   Slender, pyramidal bush with branches spreading, twisted. **O.** Bonamy Frères.   B   France

- - **'Monstrosa'** Carrière 1867   Likened to a squat, flat 'Globosa' with many 'witches brooms'.   B,K,W   France

- - 'Moonglow' Hort.   1983   Now listed under *JUNIPERUS scopulorum*.   G

- - 'Nana' Nelson	1866 "A dwarf variety". No longer identifiable as a clone.	B	U.K.
- - **'Nana Compacta'** De Vos.	1887 Greenish-blue to purple in winter; globose, but more irregular in outline than 'Globosa'.	B,K,W	Holland
- - 'Nana Nivea' Beissner	1891 A bushy dwarf-form with whitish foliage. NIC.	B	Germany
- - 'Nova' Hort. Germany	1983 A listed name, without description.		
- - 'Nutans' De Vos	1875 A form raised by C. de Vos, Hazerwoude, near Boskoop.NIC.	B	Holland
- - 'Pendula' Lawson	1852 Now only useful as a Group name.	B,K	
- - **'Pendula Nana'**	1935 Grey-green mat; prostrate in habit unless trained up early. A dwarf form. **L.** Hillier's Nurs, Winchester.	B,K,W	U.K.
- - 'Pendula Viridis' Gordon	1862 A clone no longer identifiable.	B,K	U.K.
- - 'Plumosa Argentea' De Vos	1887 A tender form with young growth silvery white. **O.** Raised by H. van Nes of Boskoop. NIC.	B,K	Holland
- - 'Plumosa Nivea' Beissner	1891 A slow-growing form with white foliage in Spring. NIC.	B	Germany
- - 'Polymorpha' Beissner	1891 A form with peculiar foliage. NIC.	B	Germany
- - 'Pom Pom' Hort. Amer.	1975 In "Nurs. Cat". Raraflora Nurs, Feasterville, PA.		
- - **'Pseudocupressus'** Bull. Morton Arb.	1932 New foliage colour pronounced; narrowly columnar.	B,K,R,W3	U.S.A.
- - **'Pumila'** Den Ouden	1949	B,W	Holland
- - **'Pyramidalis'** Carrière	1867 A name now only of value used in a collective sense.	B,D,K,W	France
- - 'Pyramidalis Glauca' Beissner	1877 A clone forming a broadly conical tree, with glaucous leaves. NIC.	B	Germany
- - 'Pyramidalis Hilli' Kumlein	1936 Hill Pyramidal Red Cedar. See 'Hillii'.		U.S.A.
- - 'Pyramidalis Viridis' Beissner	1877 A clone with leaves more scale-like, and so producing a green effect. NIC.	B	Germany
- - **'Pyramidiformis'** Kumlein	1922 Hill Dundee Juniper. A narrowly conical clone, dark green. **O.** and **I.** D. Hill Nurs, Dundee, Ill.	B,D,G,K,W	U.S.A.
- - 'Reptans' Beissner	1896 Named for a horizontally creeping plant in the Botanic Garden, Jena that died c.1914.	B,D,H,K,W	Germany
- - 'Richmond' Hort. Amer.	1964 A listed name.		
- - 'Robusta Green'	1983` See *JUNIPERUS chinensis* 'Robusta Green'?	K	
- - **'Schottii'** Gordon	1875 Grey-green foliage; upright pyramidal habit.	B,D,K,R,W	U.K.
- - **'Sherwoodii'** Sherwood	1948 In "Amer. Nurs". **O.** Sherwood Nurs.	B,K,W	U.S.A.
- - var. *silicicola* (Small) Silba	1984 Found in coastal areas and swany dunes. Formerly known as *JUNIPERUS silicicola*.		

- - **'Silver Spreader'** Monrovia
  1955 In "Nurs. Cat". Spreading; Silvery-green foliage. **O.**
        Monrovia Nurs, Azusa, Cal.   B,K,R,W   U.S.A.

- - 'Skyrocket' Hort.   Here listed under *JUNIPERUS scopulorum*.   B,G,K,W

- - 'Sparkle' Hort. Amer.   1988 A listed name. Mitsch Nurs, Auora, OR. ('Sparkling
                                      Skyrocket'?).

- - 'Staver Blue' Hort. Amer.   A listed name for a conical form with silver-blue foliage.

- - 'Tabuliformis' (Schneider) Hornibrook
  1939 Named for a flat-topped plant in Allard's Arboretum, Angers,
        long since dead. NIC.   B,H   France

- - **'Triomphe d' angers'** De Vos
  1874 Dark, bluish-green foliage sprinkled with white; conical,
        tender. Variegated form.   B,D,K,W   France

- - **'Tripartita'** De Vos   1867 A large strong, spreading bush, green to dull purple in winter.   B,D,G,H,K,W   Holland

- - 'Tripartita Aureovariegata' Beissner
  1891 A mutation of the previous item with golden-yellow foliage.
        NIC.   B,H   Germany

- - 'Tripartita Nana' H.G. Hillier
  1964 Superfluous synonym for 'Nana Compacta'.   U.K.

- - 'Turicensis' Fröbel ex Beissner
  1896 A free-fruiting conical tree with scale-like foliage. **O.** Fröbel
        Nurs, Zurich. NIC.   B   Switzerl.

- - 'Variegata' Loudon ex Lawson
  1852 Foliage with a white variegation. NIC.   B   U.K.

- - 'Variegata Aurea' Carrière
  1855 Same as last item, but a golden variegation. NIC.   B   France

- - 'Venusta' Rehder in Bailey
  1915 A narrowly columnar form with predominantly adult foliage.
        L. Ellwanger and Barry, Rochester, N.Y. NIC.   B   U.S.A.

- - 'Versicolor' Beissner   1909 A graceful light green plant with yellow variegation. **O.**
                                     Probably C.G. Overeynder Nurs, Boskoop. NIC.   B   Holland

- - **'Vinespire'**   1968 Dark green summer foliage; tall upright, columnar form.
                                     Canadian Hort. Council.   Canada

- - 'Vuyk' Hort. Holland   1968 L.J. Konijn in "Sortimentsliste". NOM.

- - 'Walter'   1964 A listed name.

- - 'Whitegreen'   1964 A listed name.

JUNIPERUS wallichiana (Hooker F.) E. Thomas ex Parlatore
  1868 Wallich Juniper. Not to be confused with *JUNIPERUS
        indica*, which is a low spreading bush.   20m,Z6   Himalayas

- - 'Manococca'   A listed name.   D

- - 'Prostrata' Hornibrook   1932 Named for a plant in Mr. Gerald Loder's garden at
                                     "Wakehurst", Sussex, that died. NIC.   B,H   U.K.

JUNIPERUS zeidamieusis Komarov
  1924

KETELEERIA Carrière (1856)

Pinaceae

A small genus allied to *Abies*, confined to Eastern Asia, not yet fully studied by botanists and rare in Western cultivation.

KETELEERIA davidiana (Bertrand) Beissner.
                1891 In "Handbuch Nadel". David Keteleeria.   10-50m,Z7   China

- - var. *chien-peii* (Flous) Cheng & L.K.Fu
                1978 A geographical form differing in the foliage.   R   China

KETELEERIA evelyniana Masters.
                1903 Now merged in *KETELEERIA davidiana* by some authorities.

KETELEERIA formosana Hayata in "Gar.Chron."
                1908 Taiwan Keteleeria. Now merged in *KETELEERIA davidiana*,
                by some authorities (per Silba, 1984).

KETELEERIA fortunei (Murray) Carrière
                1866 In "Revue Horticole". Fortune Keteleeria.   25m,Z8   China

KETELEERIA oblonga Cheng & L.K. Fu
                1975 A rare species, with long cones. Included in *KETELEERIA*
                fortunei by some authorities.   Z9   China

LAGAROSTROBUS Quinn (1982)

Podocarpaceae

A genus containing two species, formerly included in *DACRYDIUM*. There are no recorded cultivars.

LAGAROSTROBUS colonsoi (Hooker) Quinn.
                Westland Pine.   30m,Z8   N.Z.

LAGAROSTROBUS franklinii (Hooker f.) Quinn.
                1982 Huon Pine.   30m,Z8   Tasmania

LARIX Miller (1754)

Pinaceae

A Genus of deciduous trees widely distributed throughout the western hemisphere and of great value to mankind in the production of timber.

LARIX americana		Now known as *LARIX laricina*.		
LARIX chinensis Beissner	1896	Now merged in *LARIX potaninii*. (per Silba, 1984).		
LARIX dahurica Lawson	1836	Now known as *LARIX gmelinii*.		
LARIX decidua Miller	1754	In "Gar. Dict. (Abridged Ed) **4, 2**". Formerly known as *LARIX europaea*. European Larch.	25-35m,Z2	Europe
- - f. *adenocarpa* Borbas	1904	A form with peculiar cones, found by Borbas in Tirol in 1904. NIC.	B,K	
- - 'Alba' West	1770	Clone no longer identifiable; name for sporadic colour variants.	B,K	
- - 'Cervicornis' Beissner	1891	Named for a low shrub found on Mt. Semmering. NIC.	B,H,K	Austria
- - 'Compacta' Lawson	1836	Named for a tree having numerous brittle branches, raised from seed by A. Gorrie, Annat Gardens, Yorkshire.	B,G,H,K	U.K.
- - 'Conica' Sénéclauze	1868	Named for a tree with upcurved branches raised from seed. NIC.	B,K	France
- - **'Corley'** H.G. Hillier	1971	In "Hillier's Manual". A small bush raised from a witch's broom found by R.S. Corley.	G,K,R,W3	U.K.
- - 'Curvifolia' Sénéclauze	1868	Named for a plant with small, narrow, curved leaves. Found on the Sénéclauze Nurs, Bourg Argental. Loires. NIC.	B	France
- - **'Fastigiata'** Sénéclauze	1868	A columnar clone. like a Lombardy poplar. O. Sénéclauze Nurs, Bourg Argental, Loires.	B,D,K,W3	France
- - 'Flore Alba' Hort. Amer.	1964	Reported from Rochester Parks. N.Y.	D	U.S.A.
- - f. *glauca* Hort.	1865	Group name for sporadic colour variants.	B	
- - 'Globus' Hort. Germany	1992	A listed name. L. L. Konijn Nurs, Ederveen.		
- - 'Harz' Hort. Germany	1978	L. Horstmann.		
- - 'Hexenbodele' Hort. Germany	1992	In "Nurs. Cat".		
- - 'Julian's Weeper' Hort. Australia	1990	A very pendulous clone that requires stem training. **L.** Yamina Rare Plants Nurs. Monbulk. Australia. (1982).		
- - 'Kalous' Hort. Czechoslovakia	1990	Slow-growing low spreading open plant without leader. **O.** From a witch's broom. L. Libo Nurs, Baexem, Holland.		
- - 'Kellermannii' Lawson	1852	A dwarf monstrosity. I. Lawson & Son Nurs, Edinburgh. NIC.	B,H,K	Scotland
- - 'Kornik' Hort. Czechoslovakia		O. The Dendrological Institute at Kornik (near Poznan).		
- - **'Krejci'** J. Kazbal	1989	In "Amer. Conif. Soc. Bull. **6**".		U.S.A.
- - 'Langfenn' Hort. Germany	1983	Strong growing bush form, shoots 15-20 cms. **O.** and **I.** G. Horstmann, Schneverdingen, Germany.		

- - 'Laxa' Lawson   1836   In "Nurs. Cat". A vigorous spreading selection on the Lawson & Son Nurs, Edinburgh. NIC.   B   Scotland

- - **'Little Bogle'** Hort. Australia
     1990   A dwarf upright form with a leader. **O.** and **I.** Yamina Rare Plants Nurs, Monbulk, Australia.

- - 'Lombarts' Den Ouden   1949   A selection with glaucous foliage. L. Lombarts Nurs, Dedemsvaart. NIC.   B   Holland

- - 'Mit Drehwuchs' Hort. Germany
     1992   In "Nurs. Cat". G. Horstmann, Schneverdingen.

- - 'Multicaulis' Schröder   1894   Named for a tree with crowded leaves and branchlets. **O.** Schröder in Moscou. NIC.   B   Germany

- - 'Nana' Hort. Germany   1990   An illegit. listed name.   Germany

- - 'Nukmitz' Hort. Germany
     1992   In "Nurs. Cat".

- - 'Oberforster Karsten' Hort. Germany
     1990   Low growing spreading plant. Shoots 5-10 cms, long, pendulous. L. Horstmann Nurs, Schneverdingen, Germany.

- - **'Pendula'** Lawson   1836   A pendulous form that has arisen more than once, but still rare in cultivation. Reported from Cambridge Botanic Garden, U.K. (1971).   B,D,G,K.W3   U.K.

- - 'Pendulina' Hort. Russia   Growth wide at first, ascending from several stems at base. Only one tree in Leningrad Botanic Garden.   K   Russia

- - 'Pesek' Hort. Germany   1983   Semi-dwarf form. Annual growth to 20 cms. **O.** and **I.** Horstmann Nurs, Schneverdingen, Germany.

- - var. *polonica* (Raciborski) Ostenfeld & Larsen
     1930   Polish Larch.   B,D,K,W   Poland

- - 'Pyramidalis' Slavin   1932   In "Rep. Conif. Conf". **O.** Ellwanger & Barry (1908). NIC.   B,K

- - 'Repens' Lawson   1836   A clone with unusually long brs. No longer identifiable.   B,H,K   U.K.

- - 'Rittner Horn'   1992   In "Nurs. Cat".

- - f. *rubra* West   1770   No longer distinguished within the species.   B

- - 'Solden' Hort. Germany   1992   In "Nurs. Cat".

- - 'Steinplatte' Hort. Germany   A listed name. **O.** and **I.** G. Horstmann, Schneverdingen, Germany.

- - 'Tortuosa' K. Koch   1873   Branches twisted. NIC.   B

- - **'Varied Directions'** S. Waxman
     1985   In "Int. Pl. Prop. Soc. Bull". A tree of normal vigour but with an erratic branch system. **O.** Dr. S. Waxman, Univ. of Connecticut, Storrs, CT.   U.S.A.

- - 'Verkade's Witchbroom' Hort. Amer.
     1986   An illegit. listed name.

- - 'Viminalis' Valk   1925   In "Yaarb. Ned. Dendrol Ver". Named for an extremely pendulous form that turns up occasionally.   B,K   Holland

- - 'Virgata' Schneider   1892   A monstrous form with snake-like branches that occasionally turns up. NIC.   B,K

LARIX x _eurokurilensis_ Rohm. & Dimpflm.
1952 In "Zeitschr. For. Gen". A hybrid: _LARIS decidua_ x _LARIX gmelinii_ var. _japonica_.

- - 'Pentata' Hort. Germany   1983 Strong growing. Annual growth to 40 cms. Leading shoot pendulous unless stem trained. **O.** and **I.** Horstmann Nurs. Schneverdingen, Germany.

LARIX x _eurolepis_ Henry   1919 A hybrid: _LARIX decidua_ x _LARIX kaempferi_. (In "Int. Con. Reg".) Dunkeld Larch. (The name _LARIX henryana_ is accepted by some authorities as having priority. See also _LARIX marschlinsii_).   U.K.

- - 'Ardennes Weeping'   1992 Strongly pendulous plant, needs stem-training or top grafting for best effect. Exhibits characteristics of the two parents in equal amounts.

- - 'Domino' Hort. Anglia   1989 Open growing robust little plant. New leaves light green but blue-green by late summer. Scion roots out easily and becomes a very tight bush. **O.** Treborth Nurs, Bangor, N. Wales. **I.** Kenwith Nurs, Bideford, Devon.

- - **'Gail'** G. Haddow   1989 "Int. Con. Reg". (1992). Very dwarf multi-leadered little bush branches and branchlets fan forming. Annual growth 2.5 cms. Leaves light green. Derived from seed of _LARIX decidua_ 'Corley' hand pollenated by _LARIX kaempferi_. **O.** and **I.** Kenwith Nurs, Bideford, Devon. (Clone 1).   U.K.

- - **'Julie'** G. Haddow   1989 "Int. Con. Reg". Same details as 'Gail' but in growth rate only 1.5 cm. (Clone 2).   U.K.

LARIX europaea DC ex Lambert
1805 Now known as _LARIX decidua_.

LARIX gmelinii (Ruprecht) Kuzeneva
1854 Dahurian Larch.   Russia

- - 'Dwarf Form' Hort.   1992 An illegit. name.

- - var. _japonica_ (Regel) Pilger
1926 Kurile Larch. A rare geographical variant.   B,D,G,K,W   Siberia

- - var. _olgensis_ Henry   1930 Olga Bay Larch. Now merged in var. _japonica_ by some botanists. (per Silba, 1984).   B,D,W3

- - var. _principis-rupprechtii_ (Mayr) Pilger
1926 Prince Rupprecht's Larch.   B,D,K,W   China

- - f. _prostrata_ (Regel) Hornibrook
1939 Name used for an ecological variant.   B,H,K,W

LARIX griffithii F. Hooker   1854 Himalayan Larch.   20m,Z7   Asia

LARIX griffithiana (Lindley & Gordon) Carrière
1855 Here listed as _LARIX griffithii_.

- - var. _mastersiana_ (Rehder & Wilson) Silba.
1984 Master's Larch.   China

LARIX x henryana. Rehder   1919 A name possibly having priority over _LARIX leptolepis_.

LARIX himalaica Cheng & L.K. Fu
1975 Now merged in _LARIX potaninii_ (per Silba, 1984).

LARIX kaempferi (Lambert) Carrière.
1856 Japanese Larch. Formerly known as _LARIX leptolepis_   30m,Z2   Japan

- - 'Aureovariegata' Beissner

1899 Leaves with an irregular golden variegation. **O.** B.W. Dirken Nurs, Ouden Bosch.   B,K

- - **'Bambino'** Hort. Germany

Dwarf globose bush of very compact growth. **O.** and **I.** G. D. Bohlje, Westerstede, Germany. (At first circulated as 'Hexenbesen').

- - 'Bederkesa' Hort. Germany

1989 A listed name.

- - **'Blue Ball'** H.J. van de Laar

1990 In "Dendroflora 27". Globose dwarf bush, pendulous habit. **O.** K. Dierks Nurs, Bad Zwischenahn.   Germany

- - **'Blue Dwarf'** H.J. van de Laar

1987 In "Dendroflora 24". Slow-growing; quite robust low growing plant. L. J. zu Jeddeloh Nurs, Oldenburg.   Germany

- - **'Blue Haze'** H.G. Hillier   1971 In "Hillier's Manual". A selected clone with bluish foliage.   W3   U.K.

- - **'Blue Rabbit'** Den Ouden/Boom

1965 A narrowly conical form with beautiful glaucous foliage. **O.** L. Konijn Nurs, Tempelhof.   B,G,K,R,W3   Holland

- - 'Blue Rabbit Weeping' Hort. Holland

1986 Normally grown as a standard with slightly rising main branches and branchlets decurving from the branches.

- - **'Cruwys Morchard'** G. Haddow

1987 Low growing spreading form with short branches radiating all round the plant. In "Nurs. Cat". Kenwith Castle Nurs, Bideford, Devon. **O.** The same.   W3   U.K.

- - **'Cupido'** H.J. van de Laar

1990 In "Dendroflora 27". Dense globose dwarf; leaves very small, blue-grey. **O.** From a witch's broom by A. van Nijnatten Nurs, Zundert.   Holland

- - **'Dervaes'** Den Ouden   1949 A somewhat pendulous form with glaucous foliage. **O.** C. de Conink-Dervaes Nurs, Maldeghem.   B,K,W3   Belgium

- - **'Diane'** Horstmann   1983 In "Nurs. Cat". A form with contorted branchlets. Becomes a small tree as a grafted plant.. **O.** Found by G.D. Bohlje in 1974 near Westerstede, Oldenburg.   W3   Germany

- - 'Dumosa' Hornibrook   1939 An attractive, roundish blue. Recorded from Diedorf. NIC.   H

- - 'Elizabeth Rehder' Hort. Hungary

Very compact with many side branchlets. Foliage outstandingly silver-blue. Reported from Windsor Great Park, Berks.

- - 'Ganghoferi' Schwerin   1863 Named for a fastigiate tree found in the forestry garden at Diedorf. NIC.   B,K   Germany

- - 'Georgengarten' Hort. Germany

1978 From a witch's broom found in the Park of that name in Hanover. Quite strong growing.   G

- - **'Grant Haddow'** G. Haddow

1986 Upright, irregular growing to 50 cm in ten years. Some years producing clusters of growth at branch ends. **O.** and **I.** Kenwith Nurs, Bideford, Devon.

- - 'Green Pearl' Hort. Holland

1991 Globose dwarf form with short green leaves recurving from the branchlets giving the plant a green appearance. **I.** H. Kepers, Breda. L. Kenwith Nurs, Bideford, Devon.

- - **'Grey Pearl'** H.J. van de Laar
1989 In "Dendroflora 26". Dwarf globose bush with leaves growing closely up the branchlet stems showing silver-grey undersides giving the plant a grey appearance. O. André van Nijnatten Nurs, Zundert.   Holland

- - 'Haverbeck' Hort. Germany
1983 Low, wide growing thick shoots up to 10 cms long, marked with white resin. O. and I. From a witch's broom found by G. Horstmann, Schneverdingen, Germany.

- - **'Hobbit'** Hillier
1991 In 'Hillier's Manual". Tight globose to conical plant packed with small fine branchlets. A slow-growing dwarf raised from a witch's broom found by Stan Dolding (1960).

- - 'Inversa' Den Ouden
1949 A strongly pendulous tree. O. and I. Pierre Lombarts Nurs, Zundert. NIC.   B,K   Holland

- - 'Jakobsen's Hexenbesen' Arne Vagn Jakobsen
1991 Dwarf form in the shape of a miniature tree, a tiny miniature tree on own roots. O. and I. Arne Jakobsen, Denmark.   Denmark
- - 'Jakobsen's Pyramid' Arne Vagn Jakobsen
1985 Semi-fastigiate to narrowly conical slow-growing tree. O. and I. Arne Jakobsen, Denmark.   Denmark

- - 'Kaskade' G. Bohme
1991 O. and I. Wolter Kohler, Pirna, Germany.

- - 'Kazbal' Hort. Czechoslovakia
1989 L. Libo Nurs, Baexem, Holland. Name without description.

- - **'Little Blue Star'** H.J. van de Laar
1989 In "Dendroflora 26". A low, more or less globose bush. Leaves short, blue-grey. O. A. van Nijnatten Nurs, Zundert.   Holland

- - 'Lollipop' Hort. Holland.   L. L. Konijn & Co., Ederveen.

- - 'Lombarts' Den Ouden
1949 A spreading and pendulous form. O. and I. Pierre Lombarts Nurs, Zundert. NIC.   B   Holland

- - f. *minor* Murray
1862 Bush-form or forms, from seed. No longer identifiable.   B,D,K,W

- - 'Nana' Hort. Anglia
A dwarf plant with dense, globose habit. Distributed by Hillier's Nurs, Winchester, Hants.   R,W2   U.K.

- - **'Pendula'** Beissner
1896 An interesting tree if allowed to develop a leader. O. H.A. Hesse Nurs, Weener-on-Ems.   B,D,G,K,R   Germany

- - 'Prostrata' Beissner
1909 Named for a spreading seedling on the estate of Kneiffat Nordhausen. NIC.   B,G,K   Germany

- - 'Pyramidalis Argentea' Kobendza
1952 Named for a tree found in the Vjardowski Parkat, Warsaw. NIC.   B,K   Poland

- - **'Varley'** Welch
1979 A very slow-growing dwarf raised from a witch's broom found by M.J. Varley near Ormskirk, Lancashire in 1968.I. The Wansdyke Nurs, Devizes, Wilts.   W2   U.K.

- - 'Wehlen' Krüssmann
1979 A dwarf, spreading but compact plant. O. A witch's broom found by G. Horstmann on Luneberg Heath.   K   Germany

- - 'Wolterdingen' Krüssmann
1979 A dwarf plant of irregular habit and growth; foliage blue-green. O. A witch's broom found by G. Horstmann.   K,R   Germany

LARIX kamtchatica (Rupprecht) Carrière
1855 Now known as *LARIX gmelinii* var. *japonica.*

LARIX laricina (Duroi) K. Koch
    1773 Tamarack Larch.   20-30m,Z2   N. Amer.

- - 'Arethusa Bog' Hort. Amer.
    1970 Upright growing, lower branchlets very crowded, thin,
          twiggy, dark red brown upper branches thicker and stronger
          growing. Some branches decurving. Foliage bright mid green.
          O. H. Elkins, Michigan, U.S.A. **I.** G. Horstmann,
          Schneverdingen, Germany. (1983).

- - 'Aurea' Sénéclauze   1868 Named for a seedling with its young foliage yellow, found on
          the Sénéclauze Nurs, Bourg Argental, Loires. NIC.   B,K   France

- - **'Deborah Waxman'** S. Waxman
    1988 In "Int. Pl. Prop. Soc. Bull". An upright dwarf with crowded,
          ascending branches. **O.** S. Waxman, Univ. of Connecticut,
          Storrs, CT.   U.S.A.

- - 'Girard Dwarf' Hort. Amer.
    1991 In "Nurs. Cat". Rich's Foxwillow Pines, Woodstock, Ill.

- - 'Glauca' Hort. Sweden   1907 Named for a tree with steel-blue foliage in the Botanic
          Garden at Stockholm. NIC.   B,K   Sweden

- - **'Hartwig Pine'** Hort. Amer.
    1975 Description as 'Arethusa Bog' but no decurving branches. **O.**
          H. Elkins, Michigan, U.S.A. **L.** Horstmann Nurs,
          Schneverdingen, Germany.

- - f. *lutea* Den Ouden/Boom
    1965 Named for a tree bearing yellow flowers found in Clearwater
          County, PA. NIC.   B,K   U.S.A.

- - **'Newport Beauty'** S. Waxman
    1988 In "Int. Pl. Prop. Soc. Bull". A slow grower, foliage bluish-
          green. It is reported that semi-mature plants suffer partial die-
          back. **O.** S. Waxman, Univ. of Connecticut, Storrs, CT.   U.S.A.

- - **'Oxen Pond'** Int. Con. Reg.
    1989 A prostrate form with ground-hugging branches. **O.** A
          sporting branch found in the Memorial University Botanic
          Garden, St. Johns, Newfoundland.   Canada

- - f. *parvistrobus* Den Ouden/Boom
    1965 A local variant with short leaves and peculiar cones found in
          Linesville, Crawford County, PA.   B,K   U.S.A.

LARIX leptolepis (Siebold & Zuccarini) Gordon
    1858 Now known as *LARIX kaempferi*.

LARIX lyalli Parlatore   1863 Sub-alpine Larch.   25m,Z3   N. Amer.

LARIX x **marschlinsii** Coaz
    1917 In "Schweiz. Zeitschr. For". LARIX kaempferi x LARIX
          sibirica or LARIX decidua. (See LARIX eurolepis).

LARIX mastersiana Rehder & Wilson
    1914 Now known as *LARIX griffithii* var. *mastersiana*.

LARIX occidentalis Nuttall 1849 Western Larch.   25-40m,Z7   U.S.A.

LARIX x **pendula** (Solander) Salisbury
    1807 Possibly *LARIX decidua* x *LARIX laricina*. (x *pendulina*).

- - 'Contorta' Browicz & Bugala
    1958 Named for a tree with branches and branchlets twisted, found
          in the Körnickie Arboretum in 1931. NIC.   B,K   Poland

- - **'Repens'** Henry   1915   Named for a mat-forming (unless stem-trained) clone derived from a tree at Henham Hall, Halesworth, Sussex.   B,K   U.K.

LARIX potaninii Batalin   1893   Chinese Larch.   50m,Z7   China

LARIX principis-rupprechtii Mayr
    1906   Here listed as *LARIX gmelinii* var. *principis-rupprechtii*.

LARIX russica (Endlicher) Sabine & Trautvetter
    1884   Formerly known as *LARIX sibirica* Siberian Larch.   25-30m,Z2   Siberia

- - 'Conica' Hort. Amer.   1990   An illegit name. Conical tree with upright branches; foliage light green. L. Iseli Nurs. Boring, OR.

- - 'Fastigiata' Schelle   1909   Habit columnar. NIC.   B   Germany

- - 'Glauca' Schelle   1909   Leaves glaucous. NIC.   B   Germany

- - 'Graupa' Hort. Germany   1993   Dwarf upright bushy plant with very thin twiggy branchlets. **O.** Botanic Garden, Jakutsk, Siberia. **I.** Graupa Forest Garden, Pillnitz, Dresden.

- - 'Longifolia' Schelle   1909   Leaves unusually long. NIC.   B   Germany

- - 'Pendula' Schelle   1909   A pendulous tree. NIC.   B   Germany

- - 'Robusta' Schelle   1909   Growth unusually vigorous. NIC.   B   Germany

- - 'Tharandt' Hort. Germany
    1992   A listed name.

- - 'Tittlebachii' Schelle   1909   Named for a tree with cones white even when young. NIC.   B   Germany

LARIX sibirica Ledebour   1833   Now known as *LARIX russica*.

LARIX speciosa Cheng & Fu
    1975   Burmah Larch. Now merged in *LARIX griffithii* (per Silba, 1984).

LARIX sudetica Domin   1930   Now known as *LARIX decidua* var. *polonica* (per Silba, 1984).

LARIX sukaczewii Dylis   1945   Now merged in *LARIX russica* (per Silba, 1984).

LEPIDOTHAMNUS Philippi (1880)

Podocarpaceae

A genus containing three species, early recognised but for many years submerged in *DACRYDIUM*, but the distinction is once again recognised.

LEPIDOTHAMNUS fonkii Philippi
          1860 Chilean Rimu.   30m,Z8   Chile

LEPIDOTHAMNUS intermedius   15m,Z8   N.Z.

LEPIDOTHAMNUS laxifolius (Hooker f.) Quinn
          1982 A prostrate or erect shrub.   Spr.,Z8   N.Z.

- - **'Blue Gem'**   A tiny, sprawling plant that builds up into a low mound. Blue grey, turning to purple in winter.

- - **'Green Cascade'** C.P. Leach
          1992 A low, spreading plant with pendulous branches. Foliage at first yellow-green, descending. **O.** Found at Archer's Pass by W. Brockie, of the Otari Native Plants Bot. Gar. Wellington. It is probably a hybrid: *LEPIDOTHAMNUS intermedius* x *LEPIDOTHAMNUS laxifolius.*

LIBOCEDRUS Endlicher (1847)

Cupressaceae

A genus at one time comprised of 13 species; depleted in recent years by the transference of several species into the new genera *PILGERODENDRON, PAPUACEDRUS, CALOCEDRUS* and *AUSTROCEDRUS*. This leaves 5 species only in *LIBOCEDRUS* of which only 2 are hardy in cool temperate zones.

LIBOCEDRUS arfakensis (Gibbs) Li.
         1953 Now known as *PAPUACEDRUS arfakensis.*

LIBOCEDRUS austro-caledonica Brongniart & Grisebach
         1871 Not hardy.

LIBOCEDRUS bidwillii F. Hooker
         1867 Pahutea   20m,Z8   N.Z.

LIBOCEDRUS chevalier Buchholz
         1949 Not hardy.

LIBOCEDRUS chilensis (D. Don) Endlicher
         1847 Now known as *AUSTROCEDRUS chilensis.*

LIBOCEDRUS decurrens Torrey
         1853 Now known as *CALOCEDRUS decurrens.*

LIBOCEDRUS formosana Florin
         1930 Now known as *CALOCEDRUS formosana.*

LIBOCEDRUS macrolepis Bentham & Hooker
         1880 Now known as *CALOCEDRUS macrolepis..*

LIBOCEDRUS papuana F. Mueller
         1889 Now known as *PAPUACEDRUS papuana.*

LIBOCEDRUS plumosa (D. Don) Sargent
         1896 Kawaka.   N.Z.

LIBOCEDRUS torricellensis Sclect. & Laut.
         1913 Now known as *PAPUACEDRUS torricellensis.*

LIBOCEDRUS uvifera Pilger
         1926 Now known as *PILGERODENDRON uviferum.*

LIBOCEDRUS yateensis Guillaume
         1949 Not hardy.

METASEQUOIA Miki ex Hu and Cheng (1941)

Taxodiaceae

A monotypic genus of deciduous trees allied to *Taxodium* and *Glyptostrobus,*, differing therefrom in that the deciduous shoots, buds, leaves and cone-scales are in opposite pairs, not spirally arranged.

METASEQUOIA glyptostroboides Hu and Cheng

1941 Dawn Redwood.		40m,Z5	China
- - **'Emerald Feathers'**		W3	
- - **'Green Mantle'** Hort. Anglia			
1989 A listed name.			
- - **'Moerheim'** Krüssmann 1983		K,W3	Holland
- - **'National'** Reg'd. Arn. Arb.			
1963 Compact, narrowly columnar habit. **I.** U.S.Nat. Arb, Washington, DC. **O.** Merrill, U.S. Nat. Arb. (1950).		B,K,W3	
- - 'Nitschke Cream' Hort. Australia			
A seedling raised by P.C. Nitschke, Holmdorf with new growth cream-coloured.			
- - **'Sheridan Spire'** Sheridan			
1976 A narrowly columnar selection with bright green foliage. Good autumn colouring. **O.** Sheridan Nurs, Oakville. Ontario. (1968).		W3	Canada
- - **'Vada'** Krüssmann 1983 A listed name.		K,W3	Holland

MICROBIOTA Komarov (1923)

Cupressaceae

A monotypic genus long known but only recently become widely known in cultivation.

MICROBIOTA decussata Komarov

1923 A prostrate, juniper-like shrub: foliage similar to *Thuja*.		Russia
- - 'Jacobsen' Horstmann	1990 Very dwarf, globular bush with thin fine branches and foliage. **O.** Found as a mutation by Arne Vagn Jakobsen, Denmark. **I.** Horstmann Nurs, Schneverdingen.	Germany
- - 'Sinclair' G. Haddow	1992 Slow growing form with half the foliage deep gold, interesting in winter when the gold foliage is overlaid with a purple sheen. **O.** Occurred as a mutation in the garden of Terry Sinclair, N.Wales. **I.** Kenwith Nurs, Bideford, Devon.	U.K.

MICROCACHRYS Hooker f. (1845)

Podocarpaceae

A monotypic genus consisting of a low shrub that is found only in Tasmania.

MICROCACHRYS tetragona Hooker f.
1845 A low spreading shrub with bright scarlet fruits.   Tasmania

MICROSTROBUS Garden and Johnson (1951)

Podocarpaceae

A genus of two shrubby species from Australia/Tasmania, formerly called *Pherosphaera*.. Rare in the wild and rarer still in cultivation.

MICROSTROBUS fitzgeraldii (F. Mueller) Garden and Johnson
1951 Small bushy shrub with slender shoots and pale-green
incurved leaves, not tightly appressed. In the wild restricted to
one small area in the Blue Mountains, New South Wales.   Australia

MICROSTROBUS niphophilus Garden and Johnson
1951 Similar to last, but leaves thicker, much more distant and
appressed to the branchlets, in some respects nearer to
Microcachrys. High regions of Tasmania.   Tasmania

PAPUACEDRUS Li (1953)

Cupressaceae

A group of three species at one time separated from *Libocedrus* but not now considered distinct. (per Silba, 1984). None is hardy in cool temperate regions.

PARASITAXUS De Laubenfalls

Podocarpaceae

A monotypic genus from New Caledonia; remarkable as being the only parasitic conifer. Rare "in the wild" and probably not in cultivation.

PHYLLOCLADUS C. and A. Richard

Podocarpaceae

A curious genus with flattened branches (cladodes) acting as leaves. Five species, but only one is hardy in U.K.

PHYLLOCLADUS alpinus Hooker f.
1853 Mountain Celery Pine. A small shrub in U.K., strikingly unusual. Found throughout South Island and in scattered populations at higher altitudes in North Island. Now considered to be a sub species of *Asplenifolius* by some authorities.   N.Z.

- - 'Cockayne's Blue' N. Sampson
1992 A dwarf blue form selected and introduced by Omahanui Nurs.   N.Z.

- - 'Silver Blades' H.G. Hillier
1971 In "Hillier's Manual". No longer propagated, being considered insufficiently distinctive.

PHYLLOCLADUS asplenifolius Labillardiese.
Confined to small scattered populations in Tasmania. Slow growing but relatively hardy.   Tasmania

PHYLLOCLADUS glaucus Carrière
Confined to the Northern part of the North Island. Unlikely to be hardy in temperate regions.   N.Z.

PHYLLOCLADUS hypophyllus Hooker
Tree to 30m. Phillipines, Indonesia, Papua New Guinea.   Phillipines

PHYLLOCLADUS trichomanioides
Tree 15-20m. North Island and northern parts of South Island.   N.Z.

P I C E A Dietrich (1824)

Pinaceae

The Spruces are an important genus of between thirty and forty species of forest trees, all native in the cool and mountain areas of the northern hemisphere. Like the Firs, *Abies*, the nomenclature used by early writers was much confused, so older conifer books should be used with caution.

PICEA abies (L.) Karsten 1881 Norway Spruce. Formerly known as *PICEA excelsa* Link, *ABIES excelsa* Poiret *ABIES communis* and several other names. Widely grown for use as Christmas trees. 40-50m,Z2 Europe

- - **'Aarburg'** Van Gelderen
1965 In "Dendroflora **11-12**". A rather bizarre bushy form without leader, many spreading or pendulous branches. **I.** Haller Nurs, Aarburg. K Switzerl.

- - 'Abbeyleixensis' Hornibrook
1939 A dwarf seedling with new growth like ostrich feathers; found at Abbeyleix, Co Leix. NIC. B,H,K Ireland

- - 'Acicularis' 1973 Reported from Plant Research Inst., Canada Dept. Agriculture, Ottowa, Ontario.NOM.

- - **'Acrocona'** Fries 1890 Develops red cones at tips of branches even on young plants. It occurs sporadically, near Uppsala. B,G,K,R,W2 Sweden

- - 'Acrozwerg' Hort. Germany
1990 A dwarf form of 'Acrocona'. ('Acrocona Nana'). The name is now to be 'Pusch'.

- - f. *acuminata* (Beck) Dallimore & Jackson
1966 Sporadic tree form with peculiar cones. No longer distinguished within the species (per Silba, 1984). B,K Europe

- - 'Acutissima' Beissner 1891 Named for a tree in Stockholm Botanic Garden (1879) NIC. B,K Sweden

- - f. *alba* Borkhausen 1800 A sporadic form with whitish foliage suggestive of a fir. Germany

- - 'Alingsas' Hort. Sweden 1988 L. J.W. Spingarn in "Amer. Conif. Soc. Bull. **5**.(4)". NOM. O. Tage Lundell of Helsingborg. Sweden

- - var.*alpestris* (Bruegger) Krüssmann
1972 Alpine Spruce. Compact local form from Graubuenden Alps. K Switzerl.

- - f. *apiculata* (Beck) Krüssmann
1972 Sporadic local form with peculiar cones. B,K Europe

- - 'Araucarioides' Beissner
1905 A form with curious foliage, aptly named suggestive of *ARAUCARIA araucana*. NIC. Discovered by Saachy at Kámon. B,K Hungary

- - 'Archangelica' Lawson ex Sénéclauze
1868 Dwarf form of unrecorded origin. NIC. B,H,K U.K.

- - **'Archer'** Hort. Anglia 1985 Dwarf form from a witch's broom. Reported from Windsor Great Park, Berks. **O.** J.W. Archer of Farnham. U.K.

- - 'Argentea' Beissner 1891 A clone not now identifiable. Seedlings with whitish colouration occur. NIC. B,K Germany

- - 'Argentea Pendula' Hort. Germany
1987 Reported from Forstbot. Gart.. Tharandt. Dresden.

- - **'Argenteospica'** Beissner
1891 Tree with young foliage tipped white. **O.** H.A. Hesse Nurs, Weener-on-Ems. ('Argenteospicata'). B,K Germany

- - **'Arnold Dwarf'** Hort. Amer.
  1986 A listed name for a broadly conical compact dwarf; foliage mid-green. **O.** Arnold Arboretum, Mass.

- - 'Asselyn' Hort. Amer. See 'Compacta Asselyn'.

- - 'Attenuata' Carrière 1855 Strong growth with slender branches and incurved leaves. NIC. B France

- - **'Aurea'** Carrière 1855 Leaves bright yellow, especially in spring. Such coloured seedlings occasionally turn up. B,K,R France

- - 'Aurea Horstmann' Hort. Germany
  1983 An illegit. listed name.

- - 'Aurea Jacobsen' Hort. Germany
  1983 An illegit. listed name for a selection with the upper side only of the leaf a golden-yellow.

- - **'Aurea Magnifica'** (1) Beissner
  1891 A broader, lower selection of 'Aurea'. A good yellow. B,G,K Germany

- - **'Aurea Magnifica'** (2) Krüssmann
  1960 A lower, broader clone than 'Aurea', with horizontal branches. **I.** Ottolander & Hooftman Nurs, Boskoop, (1899). Holland

- - **'Aurescens'** Slavin 1932 Leaves yellow at first, becoming yellowish-green. Named for a tree discovered at Westbrook Gardens, L.I., N.Y. B,K U.S.A.

- - 'Barnes' Hort. Amer. 1970 L. Hillside Nurs, Lehighton, PA. NOM.

- - **'Barryi'** Beissner 1891 Robust but compact, conical form; but not a dwarf. In some American nurseries confused with 'Clanbrassiliana'. B,H,K U.S.A.

- - **'Beissneri'** Hornibrook 1939 Clone with monstrous branches and stiff leaves. B,H,K,W2 Germany

- - **'Bennett's Miniature'** Reg'd. Arn. Arb.
  1967 Diminutive form from a witch's broom. Reg'd by W.M. Bennett, Christianberg, Virginiana. **O.** The same (1965). ('Bennett's Compact'). K U.S.A.

- - 'Bergman's Flat Top' Hort. Amer.
  1986 A listed name. Fred Bergman of Raraflora, Feasterville, PA. listed several clones ('Midget'. 'Monstrosa'. 'Striped-leaf' and others) named after himself, but at the sale of the nursery after his decease they were lost sight of).

- - 'Berry Gardens' Hort. Amer.
  1990 A very slow-growing form with dark green leaves and conspicuous buds. (formerly distributed as 'C.L.U. Berry').

- - 'Blue Cameo' Hort. Amer. See 'Kellerman's Blue Cameo'.

- - 'Bohemica' Hort. Germany
  1987 Reported from Forstbotan. Gart., Tharandt, Dresden.

- - 'Bonitz' Horstmann 1978 In "Naamlijst . . .". Strong-growing but compact, conical bush. Formerly known as "No. 43". Possibly NIC. Germany

- - var. *borealis* The Finnish Spruce. No longer distinguished within the species.

- - 'Brevifolia' von Kunste 1867 A name now in loosely use for various clones. W

- - 'Brevifolia Argentea' Hornibrook
  1923 Slow, conical; foliage yellowish-white. NIC. W2 U.K.

- - 'Bruff' Hort. Anglia 1985 Reported from Windsor Great Park. Berks. U.K.

- - 'Bruka' Hort. Germany   1983   A listed name for a plant raised from a witch's broom found in Sweden.

- - 'Capitata' Bailly 1889 Large buds in clusters. **O.** Croux Nurs, Sceaux.	B,G,H,K,W2	France

- - 'Capitata' Bailly   1889   Large buds in clusters. **O.** Croux Nurs, Sceaux.   B,G,H,K,W2   France

- - var. *carpathica* Loudon   1838   A local variant from Carpathian Mts. NIC.   B,K   Europe

- - 'Cellensis' Schiebler   1903   Golden variegated dwarf, fine heath-like branches. **O.** Schiebler, Celle.   B,H,K   Germany

- - f. *chlorocarpa* Purkyne   1877   Sporadic variant with unripe cones green.   B,K   Germany

- - 'Cincinnata' Hesse   1897   In "Nurs. Cat". Small tree with weeping branches. Still listed in U.S.A.   B,K   Germany

- - 'Cinderella' Hort. Anglia   1989   Dwarf, slow-growing plant with ascending branches and branchlets, leaves short, glaucous grey-green. Plant at Royal Hort. Soc., Gardens, Wisley.

- - 'Clanbrassiliana' (1) Lawson   1836   The first dwarf form to be named and still one of the best. Planted in 1798, the mother plant still flourishes. L. Loddiges Nurs, Hackney, (as *PINUS clanbrassiliana*) (1820).   B,G,H,K,R,W   Ireland

- - 'Clanbrassiliana' (2) Beissner   1891   A mistake in identification.

- - 'Clanbrassiliana Elegans' (1) Hornibrook   1923   An early mistake, causing much confusion. Now known as 'Elegans'.   B,H,W

- - 'Clanbrassiliana Elegans' (2) Lawson   1851   In "Plants of the Fir Tribe". Differing in the colour of the leaves, which is pallid green. NIC.

- - 'Clanbrassiliana Plumosa'   1909   A form with stout, twisted leaves. NIC.   B,H,K,W2   Germany

- - 'Clanbrassiliana Stricta' Loudon   1838   A quick-growing form of fastigiate habit. The clone in production may not be identical with Loudon's plant.   B,K,W2   Ireland

- - 'Clanbrassiliana Variegata' Nelson   1866   "The variegated form". NIC.   B,H

- - 'C. L.U. Berry' Hort. Amer.   Now known as 'Berry Gardens'.

- - f. *coerulea* Breinig ex Beissner   1891   A colour form occasionally found 'in the wild'.   B,K,R   Sporadic

- - 'Cohassett' Hort. Amer.   1992   From a witch's broom by Joe Stupka. Very dense small dwarf. Deep-green cinnamon coloured buds. L. Rarafolia Nurs, Kintersville, PA.

- - f. *columnaris* (Jacques) Rehder   A botanical designation for variants with columnar habit and short, more-or-less horizontal branches.   B,K   Sporadic

- - 'Columnaris' Hort.   Name in use for several selections, so of no current value in a clonal sense.

- - 'Columnaris Acuminata' Oudemans   1931   Named for a tree with peculiar cones, found on the Putten Estate, Gelderland.   B   Holland

- - 'Columnaris Fuchs' Hort. Germany   1983   An illegit. name. No longer listed.

- - f. *compacta* Rehder — 1949 In "Bibliography". A botanical designation covering all the forms of compact habit. — W3 — Sporadic

- - 'Compacta' Hornibrook — 1923 An early selection of f. *compacta*. The name is loosely used in the trade for several compact clones. — H

- - **'Compacta Asselyn'** Hornibrook
  1939 A denser and more compact form. Still listed. — B,H,K — Holland

- - 'Compacta Nana' Hort. Anglia
  1985 An illegit. name. Reported from Windsor Great Park, Berks.

- - 'Compacta Pyramidalis' Beissner
  1891 A broadly conical dwarf form resembling 'Ohlendorffii'. — B,H — Germany

- - 'Compressa' Schwerin — 1903 Named for a plant found in the Forest garden at Diedorf, near Augsburg, NIC. — B,H,K — Germany

- - 'Concinna' Carrière — 1855 A conical shrub with fastigiate branches. NIC. — B,K — Germany

- - **'Congesta'** Hort. Anglia — 1984 A dwarf globe shaped plant some parts being quite congested with growth. O. Royal Botanic Garden, Edinburgh. L. Kenwith Nurs, Bideford, Devon.

- - **'Conica'** Endlicher — 1847 Another dwarf selection that has been lost sight of. NIC. — B,H,K,W2 — France

- - 'Conica Elegans' Forbes — 1839 Elegant tree with silvery leaves. O. Smith Nurs, Monkwood, near Ayr. — Scotland

- - 'Contorta' Hort. Amer. — 1985 An illegit. name for a semi-compact form with contorted branches.

- - 'Conwentzii' Wittrand — 1912 Named for a tree with a curious, pendulous habit. NIC. Such monstrosities occasionally turn up. No longer identifiable. — B — Sporadic

- - 'Corbit' Hort. Amer. — 1986 A listed name. See 'Jack Corbit'.

- - f. *corticata* Schroet — 1898 Sporadic form with noticeably thick bark. — B — Europe

- - 'Costickii' Hort. Amer. — 1986 An illegit. name for an upright dwarf-form.

- - **'Cranstonii'** Carrière — 1855 A tree with branches similar to 'Virgata'. O. Cranston Nurs, Hereford. — B,G,K,R — U.K.

- - **'Crippsii'** Cripps — 1875 In "Nurs. Cat". Kenwith Nurs, Bideford. An old form with yellow-green foliage. Squat conical shape. — B,H,K — U.K.

- - **'Cruenta'** Horstmann — 1978 In "Naamlijst . . .". Slow-growing; young growths bright red, soon fading. L. Horstmann Nurs, Schneverdingen. O. Received by Tage Lundell, Helsingborg, from an unrecorded Swedish Botanical Garden. Formerly listed as 'Clone 2'. ('Crusita'). — Sweden

- - 'Crusita' Hort. Anglia — A mistake. See 'Cruenta'.

- - **'Cupressina'** Thomas — 1908 Widely planted columnar tree, probably several clones in cultivation. — B,G,K,R — Germany

- - 'Decumbens' Hornibrook
  1923 A dwarf, spreading form; not always found true in cultivation. NIC. — B,H,K,W2 — U.K.

- - f. *deflexa* Tyskiearez — 1934 Sporadic variant with peculiar cones. — B,H,K — Poland

- - 'Densa' Carrière — 1867 A compact, conical selection. — B,K — France

- - 'Denudata' Carrière — 1854 A slow-growing form with branches as 'Cranstonii'. NIC. — B,K — France

- - 'Depressa' Berg   1887 Named for a strongly pendulous tree in the Botanic Gardens, Geneva. NIC.   B,K   Switzerl.

- - 'Dicksonii' Beissner   1891 Similar to 'Cranstonii' but shoots red and foliage dense. NIC.   B,K   Germany

- - 'Diedorfiana' Schwerin   1903 Named for a tree with yellowish leaves in the Forest garden at Diedorf, near Augsburg. NIC.   B,K   Germany

- - **'Diffusa'** Hornibrook   1923 A good form, low, spreading, yellow-green leaves. Still listed in the U.K.   B,G,H,K,W2   U.K.

- - 'Dippenhall' D.W. Hatch   1980 A dwarf form, squat conical wide blue-green leaves. **I.** Chantry Nurs, Honiton. (Pungens variety?).   U.K.

- - **'Doone Valley'** Hillier   1971 In "Hillier's Manual". Diminutive form raised from a witch's broom. **O.** Found by J.W. Archer of Farnham.   U.K.

- - 'Drew Kellerman' Hort. Amer.
     1982 See 'Kellerman's Blue Cameo'.

- - 'Dumosa' Carrière   1855 Name loosely used for several clones.   B,H,K,W2   France

- - 'Dumpy' Hort. Anglia   1985 A very tight form, raised from a witch's broom found on 'Pygmaea'. **O.** and **I.** Red Lodge Nurs, Chandlers Ford, Hants, about 1970.

- - **'Echiniformis'** Beissner   1891 "The Hedgehog Spruce". A bushlike form with long and needle-like leaves,   B,H,R,W   Germany

- - 'Echiniformis Glauca'   1987 Reported from Forstbotan. Gart. Tharandt, Dresden.

- - **'Effusa'** Hillier   1971 In "Hillier's Manual". A dwarf spreading plant recommended by Hillier for a small rock-garden.   U.K.

- - **'Elegans'** Forbes   1839 "Knight's Dwarf Spruce". One of the earliest selections, with uniformly fine leaves. Frequently confused by authors with 'Clanbrassiliana'. ('Clanbrassiliana Elegans').   B,H,K,W2   U.K.

- - **'Elegantissima'** De Vos   1867 A tree-form with golden-yellow shoots in Spring, fading by late Summer. **O.** C. de Vos Nurs, Hazerwoude. NIC.   B   Holland

- - **'Ellwangeriana'** Beissner
     1891 A dwarf, conical to upright form. Named for a tree in Highland Park, Rochester, N.Y.   B,H,K,W2   U.S.A.

- - 'Emsland' Horstmann   1983 In "Nurs. Cat". Dwarf form with radial foliage; stiff habit. **O.** Germer in Emsland.   G   Germany

- - 'Engadin' Horstmann   1983 In "Nurs. Cat". Coarse foliage similar to 'Pachyphylla'. **O.** Witch's broom found by Horstmann at Engadin.   Germany

- - 'Eremita' Carrière   1855 A coarse, open tree. NIC.   B,K   France

- - f. *erythrocarpa* Purkyne   1877 Cones purple, ripening to red. NIC.   B,K   Sporadic

- - 'Eva' Horstmann   1978 In "Nurs. Cat". A globose dwarf. **O.** A witch's broom found by Tage Lundell, Helsingborg.   Sweden

- - 'Evaluators' Hort. Amer.   1985 Reported by Iseli Nurs, Boring, OR. NOM.

- - 'Fahndrich' Horstmann   1983 In "Nurs. Cat". Extremely dwarf. **O.** A witch's broom found at Fahndrich, Menzigen.   Germany

- - 'Falcata' Wray   1912 Named for a tree in the palace of the Prince of Lippe with leaves sickle-shaped and turning upwards. NIC.   B,K   Germany

- - 'Falcato-viminalis' Schwerin
     1919 Tree with peculiar branch-formation. (var. *bella*).   B,K   Germany

- - 'Farnsburg' Hort. Holland
    1979 A small, pendulous or sprawling tree. I. C. Esveld Nurs, Boskoop. O. Seedling from 'Inversa' by R. Haller, Aarburg.   G   Switzerl.

- - 'Fastigiata' Hort.   See 'Pyramidata'.

- - **'Finedonensis'** Paul ex Gordon
    1862 Tree with leaves creamy-yellow at first. O. Seedling at Finedon Hall, Northampton.   B,K,R   U.K.

- - **'Formanek'** Svoboda   1906 Attractive slow-growing weeper. I. Wansdyke Nurs, Devizes, Wilts, U.K.(1970). O. Seedling raised by V. Formanek at Pruhonice.   G,W2   Czechosl.

- - 'Four Winds' D.W. Hatch
    1980 Dwarf similar to 'Echiniformis' but leaves incurved. Globose but old plants squat conical. O. and I. Ken Potts, Four Winds Nurs, Alice Holt, Surrey.   U.K.

- - 'Freiberg' Hort. Germany
    1992 L. Horstmann Nurs, Schneverdingen.

- - **'Frohburg'** H.J. van de Laar
    1973 In "Dendroflora 10". Upright and vigorous but strongly pendulous branches. O. Seedling from 'Inversa'. A. Haller Nurs, Aarburg.   G,K,R   Switzerl.

- - 'Gigantea' Loudon   1838 A vigorous selection. NIC. O. Smith of Ayr Nurs.   B   Scotland

- - 'Glauca Fastigiata' Hort. Amer.
    1972 Reported from Longwood Gardens, Kennett Square, PA. Name possibly illegit.

- - 'Globe' Hort. Anglia   1985 An unacceptable name. Wansdyke Nurs, Devizes.

- - 'Globosa' Hornibrook   1939 Named for a tree that develops numerous globose witch's brooms. NIC.   B,H   Germany

- - 'Globosa Compacta' Hort. Amer.
    1987 An illegit. listed name.

- - 'Globosa Nana' Hornibrook
    1939 A form referred to by Hornibrook. No longer identifiable.   H,K,W2   U.K.

- - f. *glomerulans* Krüssmann
    1955 A sporadic monstrous form.   B,K   Finland

- - **'Goblin'** H.J. van de Laar
    1988 In "Dendroflora 25 and 27". Dwarf sub-globose compact form. Stiff habit; bright green, slender leaves, appressed as in 'Ohlendorffii'. O. Mutation found by H.Geese, Boskoop.   Holland

- - 'Gracildam' R. Crutz   1985 In "Amer. Conif. Soc. Bull. 3". A diminutive bush. O. Ed. Lohbrunner of Victoria, B.C, Canada.

- - 'Gracilis' Hort. Amer.   1986 An illegit. listed name for an undescribed dwarf form.

- - **'Gregoryana'** John Jefferies
    1856 In "Ornamental Trees and Shrubs". One of the earliest recorded dwarf cultivars; needle-like radial leaves throughout the whole plant.   B,G,H,K,W2   U.K.

- - 'Gregoryana Parsonsii'   See 'Parsonsii'.

- - 'Gregoryana Veitchii'   See 'Veitchii'.

- - 'Gudula' P.A. Schmidt   1987 In "Beitrage zur Geholzkunde". NOM.

- - 'Gymnoclada' Hornibrook

1939 A spreading dwarf with unusual foliage. O. A seedling found at Ede. NIC.	B,H,K,W2	Holland

- - 'Haga' Hort. Sweden

1981 Flat topped to globose plant. O. Found as a witch's broom by Tage Lundell. L. Kenwith Castle Nurs, Bideford, Devon.		

- - 'Hauenstein' G. Horstmann

1983 In "Nurs. Cat". Globose dwarf-form. O. A witch's broom found by Fritz Hauenstein Nurs.		Switzerl.

- - 'Haugk' P.A. Schmidt 1987 In "Beitrage zur Geholzkunde". NOM.

- - 'Helene Cordes' Frahm

1898 Open, globose bush; foliage light yellow. Named for a plant in the Frahm Nurs, Elmshorn.	B,K	Germany

- - f. *hercynica* Hort. ex Beissner

1891 Named for a tree found by Al. Braun near Lerchenfelt in Harz.	B,K	Germany

- - 'Highlandia' Slavin

1923 A densely growing dwarf form similar to 'Pumila'. O. Highland Park, Rochester, N.Y.	B,H,K,W2	U.S.A.

- - 'Hildburghausen' Hort. Germany
    1990 L. G. Bohme.

- - 'Hillside Dwarf' Hort. Amer.
    1970 Reported from Hillside Gardens, Lehighton, PA.

- - **'Hillside Upright'** Hort. Amer.

1970 A semi-dwarf, dense, conical tree with foliage dark green; large buds. O. A witch's broom found by Layne Ziegenfuss; as last item.	G

- - 'Himfa' Barabits

1965 In "Magyar Fenyóújdonságok". O. Elemér Barabits, (1935).	Hungary

- - **'Holmstrup'** Jensen

1943 In "Nurs. Cat". A broadly conical dwarf. O. Asger M. Jensen Nurs, Holmstrup. ('Holmstrupii').	B,K	Denmark

- - **'Hopen'** G. Horstmann

1983 In "Nurs. Cat". Habit similar to *PICEA abies* 'Nidiformis', but growth slower. (formerly known as "No. 34".	Germany

- - 'Horizontalis' R. Smith

1864 A spreading plant of irregular growth. NIC.	B,W2	U.K.

- - **'Hornibrookii'** P. Den Ouden

1937 In "Naamlijst . . . ". A low, spreading form found by M. Hornibrook.	B,H,K,W2	U.K.

- - **'Humilis'** Beissner

1891 A very compact form with short leaves cushion shaped, older plants conical.	B,K,R,W2	Germany

- - 'Humphrey's Gem' Hort. Amer.
    1986 A listed name. NOM.

- - 'Hystrix' Hornibrook

1923 A loose, straggling dwarf-form. NIC?	B,G,H,K,W2	U.S.A.

- - var *integrisquama* Carrière
    1855 A local population with peculiar cones.

- - 'Intermedia' Carrière

1867 A loose-growing tree, intermediate between 'Virgata' and 'Pendula'. NIC.	B,K	France

- - 'Interrupta' Beissner

1907 Named for a monstrous tree found by chief-forester Pollich near Willingen. Augsberg. NIC.	B,K	Germany

- - **'Inversa'** Gordon

1862 A weeping form, still in cultivation. O. R. Smith Nurs, Worcester, (as 'Inverta').	B,G,K,R,W2	U.K.

- - **'Iola'** L.C. Hatch   1988 In "Conifer Database". Tree with contorted branches. **L.** Hillside Gardens, Lehighton, PA. (1970).   U.S.A.

- - 'Jack Corbit'. Hort. Amer.   A dense irregular bush.

- - 'Jane's Seedling' Hort. Germany
      1992 **L.** Horstmann Nurs, Schneverdingen.

- - 'Jarna' Hort. Sweden   1973 A plant with coarse leaves raised by Tage Lundell that died before it could be propagated.

- - 'Jarmila' Kazbal   1989 In "Amer. Conif. Soc. Bulletin 6".   Hungary

- - **'Kalmthout'** R. de Belder
      1969 In "R.H.S. Journ. **94**". Habit as *PICEA abies* 'Nidiformis' but of very much stronger growth, reaching tree-size.   W2   Belgium

- - **'Kámon'** Bánó ex Barabits
      1965 In "Magyar Fenyóújdonságok". Dwarf, with blue-green foliage. **O.** Raised from witch's broom on tree of *PICEA abies* 'Cranstonii' at Kámon Arboretum, (1955).   K,R,W2   Hungary

- - **'Kellerman's Blue Cameo'** L.C. Hatch
      1985 In "Rererence Guide". A dense, low, bun-shape plant; leaves wide; terminal buds in clusters.   U.S.A.

- - **'Kingsville Fluke'** L.C. Hatch
      1985 In "Reference Guide". Irregular semi-dwarf with large winter buds. **L.** from Hillside Gardens, Lehighton, PA. (1970).   U.S.A.

- - 'Kirkpatrick' Hort. Amer.   1991 A listed name for an irregular, upright dwarf.

- - **'Kluis'** L.C. Hatch   1985 In "Reference Guide". Dwarf, dense, leaves very short. **O.** Seedling raised by R. Croshaw of N.J.   U.S.A.

- - 'Kluson' Hort. Holland   1982 A listed name.   Czechosl.

- - 'Knaptonensis' Hornibrook
      1923 Flat, cushion-shaped. **O.** A witch's broom found by M. Hornibrook. NIC.   B,H,K,W2   U.K.

- - 'Kral' Hort. Germany   1992 A listed dwarf form. **L.** Horstmann Nurs, Schneverdingen.

- - 'Krasickiana'   1987 Reported from Forstbotan. Gart, Tharandt, Dresden. NOM.

- - 'Krickii' Hort. Holland   1982 An illegit. listed name.

- - **'Krockling'** G. Horstmann
      1985 In "Nurs. Cat". Dwarf; conical habit; needles short and appressed. **O.** Tage Lundell, Helsingborg.   Sweden

- - 'Laxa' A.C. Mitchell   1972 In "Conifers in the British Isles". Named for a plant in the Royal Botanic Gardens, Kew. NIC.   U.K.

- - 'Lemoniana' Hort. ex Lawson
      1851 "Lemon's Dwarf Spruce". NOM. NIC.   U.K.

- - 'Lincoln' Hort. Amer.   1986 A listed name. No information.

- - **'Little Gem'** Den Ouden/Boom
      1965 A slow-growing mutation from 'Nidiformis'. **O.** F.J. Grootendorst & Sons Nurs, Boskoop.   B,G,K,R,W2   Holland

- - 'Little Joe' Hort. Amer.   1985 A listed name for a conical dwarf. **O.** Layne Zeigenfuss.

- - **'Lombartsii'** P. Lombart
      1935 In "Nurs. Cat". An open, conical tree. **O.** Pierre Lombarts Nurs, Zundert, ('Lombarts').   B   Holland

- - **'Loreley'** D.M. van Gelderen
    1975 In "Dendroflora **11-12"**. A slow-growing, pendulous form. **I.** F.J. Grootendorst & Sons Nurs, Boskoop.   K   Holland

- - **'Lovik'** G. Horstmann   1978 In "Nurs. Cat". Slow, irregular bush. **O.** From a witch's broom found by Tage Lundell, Helsingborg.   Sweden

- - 'Lubecensis' Rose   1903 Form with small leaves, golden-yellow in Spring. **O.** W. Rose, Lubeck. NIC.   B,K   Germany

- - 'Lynne Kellerman' Hort. Amer.
    1985 A listed name. No information.

- - 'Magnifica' Beissner   1891 See. 'Aurea Magnifica'.

- - 'Malena' Hort. Holland   1990 Reported from Arboretum Trompenburg, Rotterdam. A good compact form; needles very small. **O.** Mr. A.G. Hauenstein, Rafz, (1985).   Switzerl.

- - **'Mariae Orffi'** Hesse   1936 Dwarf bun-forming with small, yellow-green leaves. **I.** H. A Hesse Nurs, Weener-on-Ems, Germany. **O.** Found near Unteralting, north of Ammerlake, ('Mariae Orffiae'). Normally grafted - it is a shy rooter.   B,K,W2   Germany

- - **'Maxwellii'** (1) Maxwell   1860 "Maxwell's Dwarf Spruce". A dense bush; globose to conical rigid, deep green leaves. **O.** Maxwell Nurs, Geneva, N.Y. about 1853.   B,H,K,W2   U.S.A.

- - 'Maxwellii' (2) Beissner   1891 See 'Pseudomaxwellii'.

- - 'Medio-aurea' Carrière   1867 A yellow variegated form. **O.** Morel Nurs, Bergny, (Oise).   B   France

- - **'Merkii'** Beissner   1884 A compact-growing, irregular pyramid. Similar to 'Nana Compacta'.   B,H,K,W2   Germany

- - 'Microphylla' Carrière   1855 Several clones are probably in cultivation under this descriptive name. NIC.   B,K,W2

- - 'Microsperma' (1). Masters
    1891 In "Kew Handlist". NOM. Conical, branches fan-forming.   W2   U.K.

- - 'Microsperma' (2) Rehder in Bailey
    1923 In "Cult Evergreens". A dense, compact conical bush with bright green thick leaves.   B,H,K   U.S.A.

- - 'Mikulasovice' Hort. Germany
    1992 L. Horstmann Nurs, Schneverdingen.

- - 'Millstream Broom' Hort. Amer.
    1985 Now known as 'Witches' Brood'.

- - 'Miniata' Forbes   1839 In "Pinetum Woburnense". Extremely dwarf: slender, erect branches. **O.** Dicksons Nurs, Chester. NIC.   U.K.

- - 'Minima' Hort. Amer.   1986 L. Hillside Gardens, Lehighton, PA. (1970). NOM. Possibly the following.

- - 'Minuta' T.C. Maxwell   1860 In "Nurs. Cat". Quite dwarfish and compact. NIC.   U.S.A.

- - 'Minutifolia' Grootendorst ex Hornibrook
    1939 A bush-form with very short leaves. **O.** F.J. Grootendorst & Sons Nurs, Boskoop.   B,H,K,W2   Holland

- - **'Monstrosa'** Loudon   1838 A monstrous plant lacking branches and long stout leaves. NIC.   B,K   U.K.

- - 'Moscowensis' Hort. Sweden
  1973 An illegit. listed name for a slow-growing upright bush/small tree with coarse dark-green leaves. New foliage dark red lasting 2-3 weeks, turning to green. **O.** Raised by Tage Lundell from a witch's broom from an unrecorded Swedish Botanical Garden. (Formerly No. 1).

- - 'Moskowika' Hort. Germany
  1983 A listed name for a 'Viminalis'-type plant with red young growths.

- - **'Motala'** G. Horstmann 1978 In "Nurs. Cat". A low, spreading bush, with foliage of the 'Pachyphylla' type. **O.** Witch's broom found by an unrecorded friend of Tage Lundell at Motala. Sweden

- - 'Mrs Cesarini' See *PICEA pungens* 'Mrs. Cesarini'.

- - **'Mucronata'** Loudon 1842 A conical bush, becoming a tree in time. **O.** Found in the Trianon Gardens, Versailles. B,H,K,W2 France

- - 'Multnomah' Hort. Amer.
  1986 See 'Sherwood's Multnomah'. ('Multimah').

- - 'Mutabilis' Carrière 1867 Young shoots creamy-yellow, becoming green. **O.** André Leroy Nurs, Angers. NIC. B,K France

- - 'Nana' (1) Carrière 1867 A rather coarse, dense large bush, often with protruding coarse shoots. NIC. France

- - 'Nana' (2) Gordon 1875 A dwarf, cushion-like plant, seldom over 30 cm. high. U.K.

- - 'Nana Compacta' H.A. Hesse
  1950 A dense, compact, globose bush, buds numerous and conspicuously red. Branches fan-forming, similar to 'Ohlendorffii' but leaves darker green. B,G,W2 Germany

- - 'Nestoides' Hort. Amer. Reported from Arnold Arb. Jamaica Plain, Mass.

- - **'Nidiformis'** Beissner 1907 A low, spreading bush, often with a central, neat-forming depression. **O.** Rulemann Grisson Nurs, Sasselheide near Hamburg. B,G,H,K,R,W2 Germany

- - 'Nidiformis Broom' Hort. Germany
  1992 An illegit. name. **L.** Horstmann Nurs, Schneverdingen.

- - f. *nigra* Loudon 1887 A vigorous form with long, thick, dark green leaves. NIC. B,K Sporadic

- - **'Norrkoping'**. G. Haddow
  1988 In "Nurs. Cat". Slow-growing, leaves at first yellow, dislikes wind but established plants do not scorch in sun. **O.** Tage Lundell, Helsingborg. **L.** Kenwith Nurs, Bideford, Devon.

- - **'Novy Dvur'** G. Bohme 1990 Found as a witch's broom in Czechoslovakia by G. Bohme. Dwarf globular plant with light glaucous-green leaves. Germany

- - 'Obergartner Bruns' Hort. Holland
  1986 Now renamed "Will's Zwerg". G

- - subsp. *obovata* (Ledebour) Hulten
  In "Flora Europea 1", (1986). Here listed as a distinct species.

- - **'Ohlendorffii'** Späth 1904 A dense broadly conical bush, foliage yellowish-green; radial or semi-radial. **O.**Th.Ohlendorff of Hamburg. **I.** Späth Nurs, Berlin (1904). ('Ohlendorfii'). B,G,H,K,W2 Germany

- - 'Oldhamiana' Welch 1966 A dwarf form; foliage as 'Mucronata'. W2 U.S.A.

- - 'Orks' Hort. Germany Extreme dwarf; foliage as 'Gregoryana' but coarser long tapered buds. **O.** Tage Lundell, Helsingborg. Sweden

- - **'Ottsjo'** G. Horstmann   1978   In "Nurs. Cat". Slow-growing form, leaves thick, similar to 'Pachyphylla' but faster growing. **O.** A witch's broom found at Ottsjo in N.Sweden by Tage Lundell of Helsingborg, ('Ottsno').   Sweden

- - **'Pachyphylla'** Hornibrook
   1923   Dwarf upright with flat branches and thick four-sided dark green leaves.   B,G,H,K,W2   U.K.

- - f. *palustris* Berg   1887   An ecological state due to swampy conditions. NIC.   B,K

- - **'Parsonsii'** Rehder   1927   A loose straggling bush. Some needles are radial on top of the plant similar to 'Gregoryana' but most are pectinate leaves lighter green. **O.** Parson's Nurs, Flushing, N.Y. ('Gregoryana Parsonii').   B,H,K,W2   U.S.A.

- - **'Parviformis'** Maxwell   1874   In "The Horticulturist . . . 29". Extremely slow, low-growing clone. The true clone is possibly no longer identifiable.   B,K,W2   U.S.A.

- - 'Peer Gynt Wagn' Hort. Germany
   1992   L. Horstmann Nurs, Schneverdingen.

- - f. *pendula* Rehder   1949   A botanical designation covering all pendulous clones.   W2

- - **'Pendula'** Booth ex Lawson
   1836   A clone of the last, NIC.   B,W2   U.K.

- - 'Pendula Bohemica' Krüssmann
   1972   Named for a pendulous tree found "in the wild" (1910). **I.** State Nurs, Zehusice.   K   Czechosl.

- - 'Pendula Harrachii'   1987   Reported from Forstbotan. Gart. Tharandt, Dresden, NOM.

- - **'Pendula Major'** Sénéclauze
   1868   A strong-growing pendulous tree. Still listed. **O.** Simon-Louis Nurs, Metz-Plantieres.   B,G,K   France

- - 'Pendula Monstrosa' Beissner
   1909   Similar to preceding entry.   B,K   Germany

- - **'Petra'** Hort. Holland   1990   Dwarf upright, new leaves very pale green later dark green. L. Libo Nurs, Baexam.

- - 'Petrowskoensis' Schröder
   1899   A seedling raised in the Moscow Arb. gardens.   B,H   Russia

- - **'Phylicoides'** Carrière   1855   An open, conical small tree with small leaves widely spread. Still in cultivation.   B,G,H,K,W2   France

- - 'Pirna' Hort. Germany   1990   Small globose form from a witch's broom. **O.** Walter Kohler. L. G. Bohme.

- - 'Plicatilis' Sénéclauze   1868   A small spreading bush with small curved leaves. NIC.   B   France

- - 'Plumosa' Schröder   1899   A densely branched, pendulous shrub. Raised in the garden of the Agricultural Univ. Moscow.   B,K   Russia

- - f. *procumbens* Rehder   1949   A botanical designation covering all procumbent to prostrate forms.   W2

- - **'Procumbens'** Carrière   1855   A clone of the last entry that forms a wide spreading flat-topped plant with horizontally spreading leaves foliage yellowish-green, widely planted.   B,G,K,R,W2   France

- - 'Prostrata' Silva Tarouca   1913   A name of no clear application.   Germany

- - **'Pruhoniceana'** Weltz and Hahn
   1938   A tree with snake-like leaves. **O.** Named for a tree in the park at Pruhonice by the head gardener, Weltz.   B,K   Czechosl.

- - **'Pseudo-Maxwellii'** Hornibrook
  1923 Plants and material of Maxwellii imported from U.S.A. to
  Europe change their characteristics to become upright plants
  with short mid-green leaves, pectinate on side shoots.   H,K,R,W   U.S.A.

- - **'Pseudo-prostrata'** Hornibrook
  1939 A vigorous, prostrate clone, the irregularly borne leaves give
  a wild look. At one time this was distributed in the U.K. as
  'Procumbens'.   B,H,K,W2   U.K.

- - **'Pumila'** R. Smith   1874 A more or less low, wide-spreading bush with foliage a grass-
  green.   B,H,K,R,W2   U.K.

- - 'Pumila Argentea' Hornibrook
  1939 Named for it's whitish foliage. Now a small tree with normal
  foliage. NIC.   B,H,K,W2   U.K.

- - **'Pumila Glauca'** Veitch   1881 Similar to the following but numerous white stomata give a
  slight glaucous sheen.   B,H,K,W2   U.K.

- - **'Pumila Nigra'** Beissner   1891 A widespreading low bush with foliage dark-green.   B,G,H,K,R,W2   Germany

- - **'Pumilio'** Sénéclauze   1868 A diminutive form, leaves three sided. NIC.   W2   France

- - 'Pusch' Hort. Germany   1987 Reported from Arboretum der Humboldt Univ. Berlin.

- - 'Pustertal' G. Horstmann
  1978 In "Nurs. Cat". Named for an extremely pendulous tree at
  Pustertal, South Tyrol.   Austria

- - **'Pygmaea'** Loudon   1838 A very early selection, still widely planted. A very slow
  growing plant, growth dense and shoots widely varying in
  vigour.   B,G,H,K,W2   U.K.

- - 'Pygmaea Hauenstein' Hort. Germany
  1983 An illegit. name. Now to be 'Hauenstein'.

- - *pyramidalis* (1) Carrière   1855 See f. *pyramidata*.

- - **'Pyramidalis'** (2) T.C. Maxwell
  1874 In "The Horticulturist . . . 29". Probably replacing earlier
  clones lost to cultivation. See f. *pyramidata*.

- - 'Pyramidalis Gracilis' (1) Beissner
  1891 A small dense conical form with fine growth and reddish
  buds. NIC.   B,K   Germany

- - 'Pyramidalis Gracilis' (2) Slavin
  1932 A compact dense almost globose plant received from M.
  Hornibrook. NIC.

- - 'Pyramidalis Robusta' Beissner
  1891 A compact conical form; thick winter buds.   B,K   Germany

- - f. *pyramidata* (Carrière) Rehder
  1919 In "Journ. Arnold Arb". A botanical designation covering a
  group of now indistinguishable clones.   G   France

- - 'Ramosa' Krüssmann   1960 Named for a low-growing dwarf form found in the Jura Mts.
  (1903). NIC.   B,K   Switzerl.

- - 'Raymontii' Carrière   1870 Named for a much-branched, columnar tree exhibited in Paris
  (1867). NIC.   B   France

- - 'Reclinata' Hort. Canada   1987 Reported from Plant Res. Inst., Ottawa, Ontario. O. Louis
  Frères.   France

- - 'Recurvata' Hort. Amer.   1979 Reported from Arnold Arboretum, Mass. A form with dark
  green foliage.   U.S.A.

- - **'Reflexa'** Carrière — 1890 — A vigorous clone. If left alone, it forms a low mass of tumbling shoots: if stem-trained a tree with long, up-sweeping branches. — B,G,H,K,W2 — France

- - **'Remontii'** R. Smith — 1874 — An erect conical bush; with a neat outline, leaves short, mid-green. — B,G,H,K,W2 — U.K.

- - **'Repens'** Simon-Louis — 1898 — A wide-spreading form, with regular horizontal branching, building height up in centre of old plants. — B,G,H,W2 — France

- - **'Ringwood'** Hort. Anglia — 1987 — A listed name.

- - **'Rothenhausii'** Hahn — 1938 — Named for a tree found as a sport by Prince Hohenlohe-Langenburg, at Rothenhausen. Later removed to Pruhonice. ('Rothenhaus'). Different accounts of it's origin are found. — B,K — Czechosl.

- - **'Rubra Spicata'** Hillier — 1981 — In "Hillier's Manual". Young shoots scarlet. Leaves obtuse with tiny stomata lines visible. I. Wansdyke Nurs, Devizes, Wilts, U.K. in 1973. O. Tage Lundell received scions from the Botanic Garden at Gothenburg. — G

- - **'Rydal'** Hort.Sweden — Dwarf form with young foliage scarlet-red. O. A witch's broom found by Tage Lundell of Helsingborg. (Formerly listed as No.1). — Sweden

- - **'Saint James'** J.W. Spingarn
1967 — In "Nurs. Cat". Very dwarf bun-shaped plant. Yellow-green leaves, noticeably red buds in Spring. O. Johnson Rare Plants Nurs, Sayville, N.Y. — U.S.A.

- - **'Saint Mary's Broom'** Hort. Anglia
1986 — See *PICEA pungens* 'Saint Mary's Broom'. A name may not be re-used within the same genus, so must be replaced.

- - **'Salen'** Hort. Sweden — O. A witch's broom found by Tage Lundell of Helsingborg. — Sweden

- - **'Sargentii'** Hornibrook — 1923 — Original plant in Arnold Arboretum. As grown in Holland it is a spreading plant close to 'Pumila Nigra'. — B,H,K,W2 — U.S.A.

- - **'Seglora'** G. Horstmann — 1978 — Dwarf, conical; yellow-green foliage held radially. O. A witch's broom found by Tage Lundell of Helsingborg, Sweden. I. Horstmann Nurs, Schneverdingen. — Sweden

- - **'Shelesnowii'** Schröder — 1899 — A dense conical plant with large winter buds. NIC. — B,H — Germany?

- - **'Sherwood Gem'** Hort. Amer.
1979 — Reported from Arnold Arboretum. Possibly the same as following entry.

- - **'Sherwoodii'** Reg'd. A.A.N
1949 — In "Woody Plant Register, No.1". A flattened globose plant with a rugged outline. R. Sherwood Nurs, Portland, OR. O. The same. ('Sherwood's Multnomah'). — B,K,W2 — U.S.A.

- - **'Sherwood's Multnomah'** Hort. Amer.
Commercial equivalent of 'Sherwoodii' and now the name in general use. — U.S.A.

- - **'Siberica'** Carrière — 1855 — An unidentifiable clone. NIC. — B,K — France

- - **'Silva Taronca'** Hort. Germany
1987 — Probably a superfluous synonym for 'Pruhoniceana'.

- - **'Späthulifolia'** Hornibrook
1923 — A low growing form with ends of leaves wider than is normal. NIC. — B,H,K — U.K.

- - f. *squarrosa* (Jacobach) Krüssmann
1955 — A variant differing only by its unusual cones. NIC. — B,K

- - 'Stricta' Hort. Amer.   1979 Reported from Arnold Arboretum. NIC.

- - f. *strigosa* (Christ) Dallimore & Jackson
    1948 A curious local form resembling a larch. NIC.   B,K   Switzerl.

- - 'Svaty Jan' Hort. Germany
    1992 L. Horstmann Nurs, Schneverdingen.

- - 'Swanson's Unknown' Hort. Amer.
    1987 An unsatisfactory listed name.

- - 'Tabulfonius' T.H. Fries   1890 A prostrate or low spreading form with leaves in horizontal planes. It has turned up more than once.

- - **'Tabuliformis'** Carrière   1865 Dwarf, leaves horizontal; growth builds up in flat layers.   B,G,H,K,W2   France

- - 'Tenuifolia' Smith ex Loudon
    1842 An open, spreading plant; leaves thin. NIC.   B   U.K.

- - 'Thompsonii' Den Ouden/Boom
    1965 A regularly conical selection. **O.** Reputedly raised by M.Thompson, Skalborg. *PICEA pungens* 'Thomsen'.   B   Denmark

- - **'Tompa'** Hort. Holland   1987 Conical light-green reminiscent of *PICEA glauca* 'Conica'. **O.** and **I.** Konijn Nurs, Ederveen.

- - 'Treblitsch' Hort. Holland
    1988 See *PICEA omorika* 'Treblitsch'.

- - f. *triloba* Krüssmann   1955 A minor variant with some cone-scales deeply lobed. NIC.   B,K   Europe

- - 'Tuberculata' Schroet.   1898 Named for a curious tree in a garden near Kerkrade, Limburg, NIC.   B,K   Holland

- - **'Tufty'** Welch   1979 A diminutive form with tiny upright yellow-green leaves. **I.** Wansdyke Nurs, Devizes, Wilts. **O.** Found by J.W. Archer of Farnham, Surrey.   U.K.

- - f. *turfosa* Lingelsh   1916 A local variant, no longer distinguished within the species. NIC.   B,K

- - 'Ultental' Hort. Germany   1992 L. Horstmann Nurs, Schneverdingen.

- - 'Uwarowii' Beissner   1884 Named for a peculiar tree found in a forest near Poretschy, 30km from Moscow.   B   Russia

- - 'Van Bemmel' Hort.Holland
    1990 A listed name. **O.** and **I.** Le Feber & Co., Boskoop. Named for the finder. ('Van Bemmel's Dwarf').

- - 'Variegata' Forbes   1839 A variegated form noted in 1839 but no longer known to be in cultivation. NIC.   B   U.K.

- - 'Vassar Broom' Hort. Amer.
    1985 A listed name. No further information.

- - **'Veitchii'** Rehder   1927 Similar to 'Gregoryana' but looser and faster growing, leaves radial only on top of plant. Leaves on the sides semi-radial to pectinate. ('Gregoryana Veitchii').   B,G,H,K,W2   U.K.

- - 'Verkade's Dwarf' Hort. Amer.
    1986 A listed name for a tree propagated from a witch's broom.

- - 'Verni-purpureis' Hort. Sweden   Superfluous name for 'Rubra Spicata'.

- - 'Viminalis' Caspar   1878 A tall loose, open tree. Found by Alstroemer in the neighbourhood of Stockholm. NIC.   B,G,K   Sweden

- - **'Virgata'** Jacques   1853 "Snake-bark Spruces".A clone is still in cultivation under this name.   B,G,K,R   France

- - 'Virgata Hexenbesen' Hort. Germany
1988 Dwarf form from a witch's broom found on 'Virgata'. **O.** and **I.** Carsten Nurs, Varel.

- - **'Wagner'** L.C. Hatch 1985 In "Reference Guide". Very dwarf and congested; subglobose. **L.** Hillside Nurs, Lehighton, PA.(1970) NOM. ('Wagneri').   W2   U.S.A.

- - 'Wansdyke Miniature' Den Ouden/Boom
1965 A mistake. No such plant has ever existed. See *CHAMAECYPARIS lawsoniana* 'Wansdyke Miniature'.

- - **'Wartburg'** D.M. van Gelderen 1975 In "Dendroflora **11-12**". A pendulous form that requires stem training, rather thick coarse foliage and noticeably orange young branches. **O.** A selection made by Haller of Switzerland. ('Waartburg').   G,K,R   Switzerl.

- - Watzlawik' Tesche and Watzlawik
1975 At first incorrectly distributed as 'Echiniformis'. NOM.

- - **'Waugh'** H.G. Hillier 1964 In "Dwarf Conifers". A slow-growing coarse plant of no great distinction.   B,K,W2   U.K.

- - 'Wells Green Globe' R.L. Fincham
1983 In Coenosium Gars. "Nurs. Cat". A tight, globose form.   U.S.A.

- - **'Will's Zwerg'** Krüssmann 1972 Dense, conical to 2m; leaves bright green. **I.** Hans Wills. Nurs, Barmstedt, Holstein. **O.** Found on the Bruns Nurs, Westerstede, by the foreman and named for him.   G,K,W2   Germany

- - 'Wilson' Hort. Amer. 1986 An illegit. listed name. No further information.

- - 'Winkelmoos' Hort. Germany
1992 **L.** Horstmann Nurs, Schneverdingen.

- - **'Witches' Brood'** R.L. Fincham 1983 In Coenosium "Nurs. Cat". Globose at first, becoming conical; fine, light green foliage, ostrich-feather-shaped branches. **L.** Hillside Gardens, Lehighton, PA., (1970) (As 'Millcreek Broom'). **O.** Raised by H.Lincoln Foster from seed taken from a witch's broom. (Also known as 'Millstream Broom').   U.S.A.

- - 'Zala' Hort. Hungary   A listed name.

- - 'Zdena' J.Kaspal 1987 In "Amer. Conif. Soc. Bull. **4**".

- - 'Ziegelweg Hexenbesen' Hort. Germany
1992 **L.** Horstmann Nurs, Schneverdingen, without description.

PICEA ajanensis Fischer ex Trautvetter & Meyer
1856 Now known as *PICEA jezoensis*.

- - var. *microsperma* Beissner
1909 Now known as *PICEA jezoensis* var. *hondoensis*.

PICEA alba Link 1831 Now known as *PICEA glauca*.

PICEA albertiana Stewardson-Brown
1907 See *PICEA glauca* var. *albertiana*.

PICEA alcoquiana Parlatore
1868 Alcock Spruce. Now known as *PICEA bicolor*.

PICEA amabilis Douglas 1836 Now known as *ABIES amabilis*.

PICEA ascendens Patschke
    1913 Now known as *PICEA brachytyla*.

PICEA asperata Masters   1906 Dragon Spruce. The Chinese counterpart of the Norway
    spruce *PICEA abies*.   20-30m,Z6   China

- - var. **aurantiaca** Masters   1906 By some authorities now treated as a separate species. (per
    Rushforth, 1987).

- - **'Glauca'** H.A. Hesse   1936 In "Nurs. Cat". Foliage glaucous; Growth otherwise normal.   B   Germany

- - var. **heterolepis** (Rehder & Wilson) Cheng ex Rehder
    1940 Formerly regarded as a distinct species.   B

- - 'Hunnewelliana' Hornibrook
    1923 A dwarf plant raised at the Wellesley Pinetum. Mound shaped
    with grey-green leaves. Rare.   B,H   U.S.A.

- - var. **notabilis** Rehder & Wilson
    1914 Not now distinguished within the species.   B

- - 'Pendula' Hort. Amer.   1987 An illegit. listed name.

- - var. *ponderosa* Rehder & Wilson ex Sargent
    1914 Not now distinguished within the species by some authorities
    (per Silba, 1984).   U.S.A.

- - var. *retroflexa* (Masters) Boom
    1965 Now treated as a separate species (per Rushforth, 1987).   R

PICEA aurantiaca Masters   1906 Now treated as a separate species by some authorities (per
    Rushforth, 1987).   R

PICEA balfouriana Rehder & Wilson
    1914 Balfour Spruce.   25-30m,Z5   China, Tibet

- - var. *hirtella* Rehder & Wilson & Cheng
    Now known as a distinct species by some authorities (per
    Rushforth,1987).   R

PICEA balsamea Loudon   1838 Now known as *ABIES balsamea*.

PICEA bicolor (Maximowicz) Mayr
    1890 Alcock's Spruce. Formerly known as *PICEA alcoquiana*.   25-30m,Z6   Japan

- - var. *acicularis* Shirawasa & Kayana
    1913 Now known as *PICEA shirasawa* (per Rushforth, 1987).   R

- - **'Howell's Dwarf'** Welch   1985 A dwarf form becoming popular. I. Vermeulen Nurs, N.J.   G,W2   U.S.A.

- - 'Howell's Dwarf Tigertail' Hort. Amer.
    Superfluous name for 'Howell's Dwarf'.

- - **'Prostrata'** Welch   1979 A low spreading plant. L. Pruhonice Arboretum.   G,W2   Czechosl.

- - var. *reflexa* Shirawasa & Koyama
    1913 A local variant, differing only in minor respects.   B,R

PICEA bifolia Murray   1875 Now known as *ABIES lasiocarpa*.

PICEA brachyphylla (Maximowicz) Gordon
    1875 Now known as *ABIES homolepis*.

PICEA brachytyla (Franchet) Pritzel
    1900 Northern Sargent Spruce.   20m,Z7   China

- - var. *complanata* (Masters) Cheng ex Fu
    1934 Southern Sargent Spruce. A minor variant, not now
    recognised by most authorities.   30-40m   China etc.

- - f. *latisquamata* Stapf   1922 No longer distinguished within the species.

- - var. *rhombisquama* Stapf
                                 1922 No longer distinguished within the species.

PICEA x *brewentalis* Krüssmann
                                 1979 An alleged hybrid: *PICEA breweriana* x *PICEA orientalis*
                                       'Nutans'.   K

PICEA breweriana Watson
                                 1855 Brewer's Weeping Spruce.   20-40m,Z5   U.S.A.

- - 'Hexenbesen Wustemeyer' Hort. Germany
                                       A listed name. **O.** Raised from a witch's broom found by W.
                                       Wustemeyer in 1978. A better name should be suggested.

- - **'Pompon'** Reuter   1978 **O.** Witch's broom found by W. Wustemeyer. (1978).   Germany

PICEA cephalonica Loudon
                                 1839 Now known as *ABIES cephalonica*.

PICEA chihuahuana Martinez
                                 1942 Chichuaha Spruce.   30m,Z7   Mexico

PICEA columbiana Lemmon
                                 1897 Now known as *PICEA engelmannii*.

PICEA complanata Masters
                                 1896 Now known as *PICEA brachytyla*.

PICEA concolor Gordon   1858 Now known as *ABIES concolor*.

PICEA crassifolia Komarov
                                 1923 Tsinghai Spruce; Quinhai Spruce.   20-25m,Z5   China

PICEA engelmannii (Parry) Engelmann
                                 1853 Engelmann Spruce.   20-40m,Z3   N. Amer.

- - 'Argentea' Beissner   1891 Silvery-grey foliage. Similar forms turn up from seed. See
                                       also 'Glauca'.   B,D,K,R   U.S.A.

- - 'Argyrophylla' Sudworth   1897 A superfluous name for 'Argentea'.

- - 'Banff' Hort. Germany   1992 From a witch's broom. **L.** Horstmann Nurs, Schneverdingen.

- - **'Blue Cheops'** Hort. Amer.
                                 1964 Broadly conical; foliage glaucous grey. **O.** Seedling on
                                       Bloomer's Nurs, Fremington, N.J.   U.S.A.

- - 'Candida' Hort.   A listed name for a selection with long, bluish leaves.

- - 'Columbiana' Lemmon   1897 Indistinguished from 'Microphylla'.

- - 'Compact' Hort. Anglia   A listed name for a dwarf conical plant with glaucous foliage.
                                       Faster growing than *PICEA pungens* 'Montgomery'.

- - **'Fendleri'** Henry   1912 Named for a pendulous tree at Kew of uncertain identity.
                                       Possibly found in Mexico by Fendler (1847). NIC.   B,D,K,R   Mexico

- - **'Glauca'** (R. Smith) Beissner
                                 1887 Leaves glaucous blue. A common deviant. (Other names
                                       loosely used in this group are 'Argentea', 'Argyrophylla', and
                                       'Candida', 'Griseifolia, none now having any clonal value).   B,D,G,K,R

- - 'Glauca Pendula' Beissner
                                 1899 Similar to previous entry but with pendulous branches. NIC.   B

- - 'Glauca Virgata' Hort. Germany
  1990 An illegit. listed name. Growth as *PICEA abies* 'Virgata'.
  NIC.

- - 'Hoodie' Hort. Amer.   1991 **L.** Iseli Nurs, Boring, OR.

- - 'Jasper' Hort. Germany   1992 From a witch's broom. **L.** Horstmann Nurs, Schneverdingen.

- - 'Kohout' Hort. Germany   1992 From a witch's broom. **L.** Horstmann Nurs, Schneverdingen.

- - var.***mexicana*** (Martinez) Silba
  1984 Mexican Spruce.   25-30m,Z7   Mexico

- - 'Microphylla' Hesse ex Beissner
  1891 Dwarf form with small leaves. ('Minutifolia').   B,D,H,K   Germany

- - 'Pendula' Hort. Amer.   1984 An illegit. listed name.

- - 'Pungens' Hort. Amer.   1979 Reported from Arnold Arboretum, Jamaica Plain. Mass.   U.S.A.

- - **'Schovenhorst'** H.J. van de Laar
  1966 In "Naamlijst . . .". NOM.   Holland

- - **'Snake'** Van Gelderen & van Hoey Smith
  1987 A bizarre form found as a seedling by Dr Illa Martin.
  Illustrated in "Conifers".   G   Holland

- - **'Tulendeena'** Hort. Australia
  1983 From a witch's broom. **O.** P. Nitschke.

- - **'Vanderwolf's Blue Pyramid'** Vermeulen
  1971 In "Nurs. Cat". Compact form with fastigiate branch system.
  (Incorrectly distributed as 'Glauca' 1969/70.) **I.** Vermeulen
  Nurs, Neshanic Station, N.J.   U.S.A.

PICEA excelsa Link   1841 Now known as *PICEA abies*.

PICEA falcata (Rafinesqe) Suringar.
  1927 Now known as *PICEA sitchensis*.

PICEA farreri Page & Rushforth
  1980 Burman Spruce, Farrer Spruce.   30m,Z8   Burmah

PICEA x *fennica* (Regel) Komarov
  1863 A natural hybrid: *PICEA abies* x *PICEA obovata.*

PICEA firma Gordon   1858 Now known as *ABIES firma*.

PICEA gemmata Rehder & Wilson
  1914 Tapaoshan Spruce.   20-40m,Z6   W.China

PICEA glauca (Moench) Voss
  1908 White Spruce. (Formerly known as *ABIES alba,* and under
  other names).   15-25m,Z2   N. America

- - 'Acutissima' Beissner   1891 Named for an old tree in a park at Worlitz. NIC.   B   Germany

- - 'Alberta Blue' Hort. Anglia
  1990 Occurred as a blue sport on 'Albertiana Conica' at the Bos
  Nurs, (1977). **O.** Bos Nurs, Surrey. **I.** Bressingham Gardens,
  Diss, Norfolk, (1993).

- - **'Alberta Globe'** H.M. Grootendorst
  1968 In "Dendroflora 5". **O.** C. Streng Jnr., Boskoop. ('Albert
  Globe').   G,R,W2   Holland

- - var. ***albertiana*** (S. Brown) Sargent
  1919 Alberta White Spruce.   50m,Z2   N.Amer.

- - **'Albertiana Conica'** Bailey
1933 In "The Cultivated Evergreens", p. 60. This is the well known
'Conica' of the trade.   H,W2   U.S.A.

- - 'Arenson's Blue' Hort. Europe
1990 A mistake for the next entry.

- - **'Arneson's Blue Variegated'** R.L. Fincham
1989 In Coenosium "Nurs. Cat". A blue form of Alberta spruce
with new growth light pale-blue and other foliage grey-blue.   U.S.A.

- - 'Aurea' Nelson   1866 Vigorous; leaves browny-yellow above.   B,D,G,K   U.K.

- - 'Aureospicata' Den Ouden
1949 Now listed as *PICEA mariana* 'Aureospicata'.   B,K

- - 'Aureovariegata' Beissner
1898 Named for a seedling with gold leaves raised in Germany.
NIC.   B   Germany

- - **'Bill Archer'** L.C. Hatch
1988 In "Conifer Database". A dwarf, mounded plant raised from a
witch's broom.   Hort. U.K.

- - 'Black Hills'   1987 Reported from Forstbot. Gart. Tharandt, Dresden.

- - **'Blue Planet'** H.J. van de Laar
1990 In "Dendroflora **27**". A flattish globe; growth dense and
regular. **O.** H. Kruse, Bad Zwischenahn from a sport on
'Echiniformis Glauca'.   Germany

- - 'Blue Wonder' Hort. Germany
1992 'Conica'-form with good blue colour which occurred as a
sport. O. and I. Kordes Nurs, Bilsen/Holstein, Germany.

- - 'Bluff' Hort. Amer.   1992 A listed name without description. **L.** Rarafolia Nurs,
Kintersville, PA.

- - 'Brevifolia' Hort. Amer.   1983 Name illegit. A tree with very small leaves. **L.** Hillside Nurs,
Lehighton, PA (1970).

- - 'Caerulea' Hort.   See 'Coerulea'.   B

- - 'Canadensis' T.J. Cole   1987 **L.** in "Woody Plant Source List". NOM. Name illegit?

- - 'Cecilia' Welch   1979 A slow growing,dense, upright plant with blunt ended silvery-
grey leaves; established older plants have much bluer leaves.
I. J.W. Spingarn, then of Baldwin, N.Y. **O.** A witch's broom
found by Greg Williams near the Skippack highway. The
name 'skippack' was never registered, and the present name is
now in general use.   D,W2   U.S.A.

- - 'Coerulea' Nelson   1866 "Blue foliage". Such colour forms turn up occasionally. NIC.   B,G,K   U.K.

- - 'Coerulea Hendersonii' Dallimore & Jackson
1923 See 'Hendersonii'.   D

- - 'Coerulea Hudsonii' Dallimore & Jackson
1923 see 'Hudsonii'.

- - 'Compacta' Dallimore & Jackson
1923 An unidentifiable dwarf selection. NIC.   B,D   U.K.

- - 'Compacta Gracilis' Breinig ex Beissner
1891 Not now distinguishable from the previous item.   H

- - 'Compressa' Beissner   1891 A dense, glaucous blue dwarf.   B,H   Czechosl.

- - f. *conica* Rehder   1920 Now considered to be a cultivar. See 'Albertiana Conica'.   D   U.S.A.

- - 'Conica' Hort.   This name is widely in use but the cultivar name 'Albertiana
                                   Conica' has priority.   B

- - **'Cupido'** H.J. Van de Laar
                        1986 In "Dendroflora **24**". NOM.   Holland

- - **'Cy's Wonder'** G. Bentham
                        1981 A listed name for a compact green globose to conical form.
                              Foliage like 'Conica' but coarser. L. G.Bentham, Victoria,
                              B.C.   Canada

- - var. *densata* Bailey   1933 The Black Hills Spruce. See next entry.   B   U.S.A.

- - 'Densata' Bailey   1933 A slow growing, dense tree; very hardy. **O.** Raised from
                                       collected seed by Black Hills Nurs, Dakota.   B   U.S.A.

- - **'Dent'** Hort. Amer.   1985 A large tree with foliage splashed with creamy variation. **L.**
                                       Coenosium Gar. Aurora, OR.

- - 'Eagle Rock' Hort. Amer.
                        1992 A listed name without description. **L.** Rarafolia Nurs,
                              Kintersville, PA.

- - **'Echiniformis'** Carrière 1855 A popular dwarf, with dense, greyish foliage, older
                                       established plants are much bluer.   B,D,G,H,K,W2 France

- - **'Ed. Hurle'** L.C. Hatch   1988 In "Conifer Database". A diminutive sport from 'Albertiana
                                       Conica'.   U.S.A.

- - 'Elegans Compacta' Krüssmann
                        1972 A narrowly conical mutation of 'Albertiana Conica'. **O.**
                              Jehusice State Nursery, (1950).   K,R   Czechosl.

- - **'Elf'** G. Bentham   1982 In "Dwarf Conifer Notes **2**". A very diminutive squat, conical
                                       sport from 'Albertiana Conica'. **L.** Wm. Goddard, Floravista
                                       Gardens, Vancouver Is., B.C.   Canada

- - 'Ericoides' Hort. Amer.   An illegit. listed name. Similar in growth to 'Echiniformis' but
                                       looser.

- - 'Fastigiata' Carrière   1867 Habit narrowly conical. **O.** Sénéclauze Nurs, Bourg Argental,
                                       Loires.   B   France

- - **'Fort Ann'** R.L. Fincham
                        1983 In Coenosium Gar. "Nurs. Cat". Growth rapid; Branches few
                              and gnarled. Leaves grey-blue and upcurved on both sides of
                              branches.   U.S.A.

- - 'Fuiri Ogon' Hort. Amer.   Name now to be 'Rainbow's End'.

- - 'Girard Dwarf Pyramid' L.C. Hatch
                        1985 In "Reference Guide". A Dwarf, conical plant with annual
                              growth 8mm. ('Girard's Montrosa Nana').   U.S.A.

- - 'Globe' Hort. Canada   1987 An unacceptable listed name.

- - 'Globulosa' Schwerin   1927 A dwarf, globose form raised by Count von Schwerin. NIC.   B   Germany

- - 'Gnom' Krüssmann   1972 A mutation from 'Conica'. Same origin as 'Elegans Compacta'
                                       (before 1960).   K,R   Czechosl.

- - 'Gnome' Hort. Canada   1982 Raised from a mutation on 'Albertiana Conica'. **O.** Wm.
                                       Goddard of Floravista Gardens, Vancouver Is. B.C. **Canada**.
                                       It should not be confused with the previous entry.

- - 'Goldilocks' Hort. Amer.   1992 Yellow mutation of 'Albertiana Conica' reported not to burn
                                       in full sun. More information is required.   U.S.A.

- - 'Gracilis' Breinig ex Beissner
                1891 A conical dwarf; branches stiffer than 'Nana'. NIC.   B   Germany

- - 'Gracilis Compacta' Krüssmann
                1972 An illegit. listed name not appearing in 1983 edition.

- - **'Hendersonii'** Dallimore & Jackson
                1923 Young shoots horizontal, becoming pendulous. ('Coerulea
                      Henderson').   B,K   U.K.

- - 'Hexenbesen Uwe' Hort. Germany
                1992 A listed name without description. **L.** Horstmann Nurs,
                      Schneverdingen.

- - **'Hillside'** R. L. Fincham 1983 In Coenosium Gar. "Nurs. Cat". A compact, globose plant. **O.**
                      Hillside Nurs, Lehighton, PA. (1970).   U.S.A.

- - 'Hirthals Gelbnadelig' Hort. Germany
                1992 A listed name without description. **L.** Horstmann Nurs,
                      Schneverdingen.

- - **'Hudsonii'** Späth   1891 In "Nurs. Cat". Bushy habit; glaucous foliage. NIC.   B   Germany

- - 'Intermedia' (1) Carrière   1867 A vigorous tree; possibly a hybrid with *PICEA mariana*. **O.**
                      Sénéclauze Nurs, Bourg Argental, Loires. NIC.   B   France

- - 'Intermedia' (2) Hort. Amer.
                1985 An illegit. listed name for propagands of strong, reversed
                      shoots on 'Albertiana Conica'.

- -**'Ity Bity'** L.C. Hatch   1988 In "Conifer Database". A slow-growing mutation from var.
                      albertiana ('Pixie group'). **O.** Iseli Nurs, Boring, OR.   U.S.A.

- - **'Jean's Dilly'** P.Haladin 1987 In "Amer. Conif. Soc. Bull. **5**". A mutation of 'Albertiana
                      Conica' which is fastigiate and somewhat slower. Named in
                      memory of Jean Iseli of Boring, OR.   U.S.A.

- - **'Jone's Flat Top'** Hort. Amer.
                1985 A listed name. **L.** Twombly Nurs, Monroe, Conn.   U.S.A.

- - **'Laurin'** Arnold ex Krüssmann
                1972 Another very dwarf mutation from 'Albertiana Conica'. **I.** R.
                      Arnold, Alveslohe, Holstein. **O.** The same.   G,K,R,W2   Germany

- - **'Lilliput'** Welch   1979 A diminutive plant, similar to a miniature 'Albertiana Conica'
                      O. Le Feber and Co., Boskoop.   G,W2   Holland

- - 'Little Gem' Hort. Canada
                1987 In "Woody Plant Source List". Name unacceptable. (per
                      ICNCP Art. 50).

- - **'Little Globe'** Verkade 1968 Registered at Arnold Arboretum by Verkades Nurs. Wayne,
                      N.J. **O.** A witch's broom found in the Waterford Works at
                      Wayne, N.J. (1959).   W2   U.S.A.

- - 'Minima' (1) Sénéclauze   1868 A diminutive conical bush. **O.** From seed on the Sénéclauze
                      Nurs, a similar plant was found in the garden of Gambier
                      Parry, near Gloucester, U.K. NIC.   B,H   France

- - 'Minima' (2) Hort.Amer.   1986 An illegit name for an extremely slow-growing mutation
                      found on 'Albertiana Conica' on the Iseli Nurs. (1982).

- - 'Monstrosa' Dallimore & Jackson
                1923 Branches abnormally loose. NIC.   B   U.K.

- - 'Mrs Cesarini' Hort.   Now listed under *PICEA pungens*.

- - 'Nana' Carrière   1855 A conical or globose bush. Growth dense.   B,H   France

- - 'Nana Compacta' Hort. Amer.
1979 Reported from Arnold Arboretum, Jamaica Plain, Mass.   U.S.A.

- - 'Nana Glauca' Beissner   1891 Similar to previous item, save for colour.   B,H   Germany

- - 'Palececk' Hort. Germany
1992 A listed name without description. L. Horstmann Nurs,
Schneverdingen.

- - **'Paul's Dwarf'** L.C. Hatch
1988 In "Conifer Database". A diminutive mutation from
'Albertiana Conica'. O. Found on Iseli Nurs, Boring, OR.   U.S.A.

- - f. *'parva'* (Victorin) Fernald & Weatherby
1932 An ecological low-growing form found in alpine areas.   B,K

- - 'Pendula' Carrière   1867 Named for a pendulous tree found by Carrière in Trianon
Park, Versailles. Similar plants turn up.   B,K   France

- - 'Piccolo' Hort. Holland   1987 Reported as a sport on 'Conica'. Dwarf conical, foliage a little
coarse. I. Le Feber & Co., Boskoop.

- - 'Pinsapoides' Van der Elst
1897 A somewhat monstrous plant. O. van der Elst, Tottenham
Nurs, Dedemsvaart. NIC.   B,K   Holland

- - **'Pixie'** R.L. Fincham   1982 In Coenosium "Nurs. Cat". A slow growing conical selection
from 'Albertiana Conica' dark-green leaves with prominent
round buds. O. Wm. Goddard, Floravista Gardens,
Vancouver Is., B.C.   Canada

- - var. *porsildii* Raup   1947 Not now distinguished within the species (per Rehder, 1949).   B,K   Canada

- - 'Procumbens' Meyer   1934 A low growing selection (of the f. *parva* type). NIC.   B   Germany

- - 'Pyramidalis Compacta' Hort. Anglia
1985 An illegit. listed name.

- - **'Rainbow's End'** Hort. Amer.
1978 O. A mutation on 'Albertiana Conica' on which new growth is
often creamy-yellow. Found by Don Howse on Iseli Nurs,
Boring, OR, (1978).   U.S.A.

- - **'Sander's Blue'**   1986 A selection of 'Albertiana Conica' with blue foliage, variable
and somewhat unstable.   U.S.A.

- - **'Sander's Fastigiate'** Iseli
1985? In "Nurs. Cat". A slow-growing selection from 'Albertiana
Conica' with very fastigiate branching system when young. I.
Iseli Nurs, Boring, OR.   U.S.A.

- - 'Skippack' Hort. Amer.   This is the raiser's (unpublished) name:see 'Cecilia'.

- - 'Tabuliformis' Slavin   1932 Named for a flat-topped plant in the Highland Park,
Rochester, N.Y. NIC.   U.S.A.

- - **'Tiny'** Welch   1979 A diminutive mutation from 'Albertiana Conica'. I. W.H.
Rogers Nurs, Chandlers Ford, Hants. O. The same.   W2   U.K.

- - **'Tiny Temple'** Iseli   1985 A slow-growing selection from 'Albertiana Conica' ('Pixie
group'). O. Iseli Nurs, Boring, OR, (1960).   U.S.A.

- - 'Variegatospicata' Beissner
1898 Tree with an irregular whitish variegation. NIC.   B   Germany

- - **'Wild Acres'** R.L. Fincham
1983 In Coenosium "Nurs. Cat". L. Hillside Nurs, Lehighton, PA
(1970).   U.S.A.

- - 'Woerlitzensis' Späth   1890   In "Nurs. Cat". An ascending form raised in Woerlitz, near Dessau. NOM.   B   Germany

- - **'Zucherhut'** H.J. van de Laar
    1987   In "Dendroflora **24**". Yet another dwarf green mutation, hopefully the last, of 'Albertiana Conica'. **I.** Gebr. Van Vliet, Boskoop. **O.** A witch's broom found in Germany. Since *PICEA glauca* 'Albertiana Conica' is the "Zucherhut-Fichte" in Germany, the name is confusing and another name should be found. (ICNCP Rec. 31A (h).).

PICEA glehnii (Fr. Schmidt) Masters
    1880   Sakhalin Spruce; Aka-ezo-matsu.   30m,Z6   E. Asia

- - 'Aurea' P.Smith ex Beissner
    1891   Upper side of leaves. yellow in summer. **O.** P.Smith Nurs, Bergdorf near Hamburg. NIC.   Germany

- - 'Chitose-maru' Hort. Japan
    1976   A flat topped dwarf form with leaves arranged radially, showing stomatic lines, buds are red.

- - 'Donry-maru'.Hort.Germany
    1978   A listed name for a witch's broom. **L.** Horstmann Nurs, Schneverdingen.   Hort. Japan

- - 'Sasamo' Hort. Japan   1986   A dwarf form.

- - 'Sasanosei' Hort. Amer.   1986   Dwarf with dark green foliage and turned branches. **L.** J.W. Spingarn, L.I., N.Y.

- - 'Sato-sei' Hort.Japan   A dwarf form.

- - 'Shimezusei' Hort.Japan   1986   Dwarf with bluish foliage in layers. Slower growing than 'Sasanosei'. **L.** J.W. Spingarn, L.I., N.Y.

- - 'Yatsubusa' Hort.Amer.   1990   An unsatisfactory name for a slow-growing upright plant of dense habit. **L.** Iseli Nurs, Boring, OR.

- - 'Yosana' Hort. Japan   1988   A listed name for an upright form with dark green congested foliage. Received from Japan by G. Horstmann.

PICEA grandis Douglas & Loudon
    1838   Now known as *ABIES grandis.*

PICEA heterolepis Rehder & Wilson
    1914   Now known as *PICEA asperata* var. *heterolepis.*

PICEA hirtella Rehder & Wilson
    1914   16m,Z5   China

PICEA holophylla (Maximowicz) Gordon
    1876? Now known as *ABIES holophylla.*

PICEA homolepis (Siebold & Zuccarini) Gordon
    1858   Now known as *ABIES homolepis.*

PICEA **x** *hurstii* De Hurst   1938   A hybrid: *PICEA engelmannii* x *PICEA pungens.*   K   Hort.

PICEA intercedens Nakai   Now known as *PICEA koraiensis* var. *intercedens.* (per Silba, 1984). (See Rushforth, 1987).

PICEA jezoensis (Siebold & Zuccarini) Carrière
    1855   Yezo Spruce. Formerly known as *ABIES menziesii.*   30m,Z4   Asia N.

The indiscriminate use by European writers of the names Ezo. Yedo. Yezo etc. for the two species native to the (at that time) Yezo Island, has caused much confusion. ('Eso-aka-matsu' = The red Spruce from Yezo) A name first mentioned by Mayr in 1890 is the Japanese vernacular name for *PICEA glehnii.* Selections that are either dwarf or used in Bonsai manufacture in Japan are now listed under that species.

- - var. *ajanensis* (Fisher) Cheng et Fu
    1978 (See Rushforth, 1987).

- - 'Chinese Marll' Hort. Germany
    1992 A listed name. L. Horstmann Nurs, Schneverdingen.

- - 'Chitosemaru' Hort. Amer.
    1988 Compact form. L. Mitsch Nurs, Oregon, PA.

- - 'Gurt' Hort. Germany   1992 A listed name without description. L. Horstmann Nurs,
    Schneverdingen.

- - var. **hondoensis** (Mayr) Rehder
    1915 Hondo Spruce.

- - var. *komarovii* (V.Vassil) Cheng et Fu
    1978

- - 'Landis' Hort. Canada   1981 A listed name. L. G. Bentham, Victoria, B.C.

- - var. *microsperma* (Lindley) Cheng et Fu
    1978

- - 'Mrs. Cesarini'   See *PICEA pungens*.

- - 'Nana' Hort. Amer.   1986 An illegit. listed name.

- - 'Yatsubusa' Hort. Canada 1981 A dwarf form, very slow-growing with short yellow-green
    leaves. L. G. Bentham, Victoria, B.C.

- - 'Yosawa' Hort.   1983 A miniature selection. In "Nurs. Cat". Horstmann Nurs,
    Schneverdingen.   G

PICEA komarovii V. Vassil 1950 Now known as *PICEA jezoensis* var. *komarovii*.

PICEA koraiensis Nakai   1919 Northern Korean Spruce.   15-25m,Z5   Korea

- - var. **intercedens** (Nakai) Lee
    1966 Southern Korean Spruce; Tonai Spruce.   8-10m.   Korea

PICEA koyamai Shirawasa 1913 Koyama Spruce.   10-20m,Z6   Japan

- - var. *koraiensis* (Nakai) Liou & Wang
    1955 Now known as *PICEA koraiensis*.

PICEA kukunaria Wenderoth
    1851 Now known as *ABIES cephalonica*.

PICEA likiangensis (Franchet) Pritzel
    1900 Likiang Spruce.   25-30m,Z6   China

- - var. **balfouriana** (Rehder & Wilson) Hillier
    1932 Balfour Spruce. Now known as *PICEA balfouriana* by some
    authorities (per Rushforth, 1987).   G,R

- - var. *hirtella* (Rehder & Wilson) Cheng ex Chen.
    1937 By some authorities now listed as *PICEA hirtella*. (per
    Rushforth. 1987).   R

- - var. *linzhiensis* Cheng et Fu
    1975 Not now distinguished within the species by some authorities.
    (Per Silba, 1984).

- - var. *montigena* (Masters) Cheng ex Chen.
    1937 Northern Likiang Spruce. By some authorities now listed as
    PICEA montigena. (per Rushforth, 1987).   R

- - var. *purpurea* (Masters) Dallimore & Jackson
    1923 Now known as *PICEA purpurea*.   R

- - 'Purpurea Compacta' Hort. Anglia
　　　　　　　　1985 An illegit. listed name.

- - var. *rubescens* Rehder & Wilson in Sargent
　　　　　　　　1914 See Rushforth, (1987).　　　　　　　　　　　　　　　R

PICEA x *lutzii* Little　　　　1953 A natural hybrid: *PICEA glauca* x *PICEA engelmannii*.?

PICEA mandshurica Nakai
　　　　　　　　1943 In "Journ. Jap. Bot. **19**".

PICEA mariana (Miller) Britton, Sterns & Poggenburg
　　　　　　　　1888 Black Spruce. Formerly known as *ABIES nigra* and under
　　　　　　　　　　　other names.　　　　　　　　　　　　　1-20m,Z2　　N. America

- - 'Argenteovariegata' Beissner
　　　　　　　　1891 A white variegated form raised by H.A.Hesse Nurs, NIC.　B,G,K　　　Germany

- - **'Aurea'** Beissner　　　1891 Leaves shining golden-yellow. **O.** as previous entry. NIC.　B,K,R

- -'Aureovariegata' Beissner　1909 A golden-yellow variegated form.**O.** as previous entry. NIC.　B,R,W2

- - **'Beissneri'** Rehder　　1915 A broad shrub. Leaves coarse, steel blue.　　　　B,K,R,W2

- - **'Beissneri Compacta'** Hesse
　　　　　　　　1954 In "Nurs. Cat". Dwarf compact round topped with fine
　　　　　　　　　　　foliage. **O.** W.A.Hesse Nurs, Weener-on-Ems.　　B,H,K,R,W2　Germany

- - 'Corbit' Hort. Amer.　　1986 A listed name for a slow-growing conical tree with blue-green
　　　　　　　　　　　foliage.　　　　　　　　　　　　　　　　　　　　　U.S.A.

- - **'Doumetii'** Carrière　1855 A widely planted selection, slow-growing, conical with coarse
　　　　　　　　　　　silvery leaves. **O.** Found by Carrière in the garden at Chateau
　　　　　　　　　　　de Baleine, Moulins.　　　　　　　　B,G,H,K,R,W2 France

- - 'Empetroides' Krüssmann
　　　　　　　　1955 A dwarf prostrate form found on Mount Sterling, Quebec.
　　　　　　　　　　　NIC.　　　　　　　　　　　　　　　　　B,K　　　　Canada

- - **'Ericoides'** Bean　　1914 A slow growing shrub; leaves being very small, narrow,
　　　　　　　　　　　almost heath-like.　　　　　　　　　　　　B,H,K,W2　U.S.A.

- - **'Fastigiata'** (Carrière) Rehder
　　　　　　　　1915 Conical and very slow-growing. **O.** Raised by Briot at the
　　　　　　　　　　　Trianon Gardens, Versailles.　　　　　　　B,H,K,W2　France

- - 'Globosa' Hort. Amer.　1986 An illegit. listed name for a dense, globose selection.

- - 'Golden' Hort. Amer.　　　　An unacceptable listed name for a slow growing plant with
　　　　　　　　　　　the new foliage yellow.

- - **'Nana'** Beissner　　1894 A very slow-growing globose to broadly conical bush, leaves .
　　　　　　　　　　　blue-green. Widely planted.　　　　　　　B,G,H,K,W2　Germany

- - 'Pendula' Schwerin　　1903 Branches extremely pendulous. Raised by Gaughofer in the
　　　　　　　　　　　Forest garden at Diedorf, near Augsburg.　　B,K　　　Germany

- - 'Pendula Variegata' Hornibrook
　　　　　　　　1923 Similar to the preceding entry, but leaves yellow variegated;
　　　　　　　　　　　I. Little and Ballentyne Nurs, Carlisle.　　B,H　　　U.K.

- - 'Procumbens' Hort. Amer.
　　　　　　　　1986 An illegit. listed name, presumably descriptive.

- - **'Pumila'** W.M. Barron　1875 In "Nurs. Cat". A strong-growing, spreading plant. No longer
　　　　　　　　　　　identifiable.　　　　　　　　　　　　　　B,H,K,W2　U.K.

- - **'Pygmea'** Welch　　1966 A very diminutive form. 'Nana' in miniature.　　R,W　　　U.K.

- - 'Reath's W.B.' Hort. Amer.

    1980 A listed name. L. J.W. Spingarn, L.I., N.Y.

- -'Ruddigore' Welch	1979	Name suggested for the plant wrongly described by Hornibrook as 'Ericoides'.	W	U.K.
- - 'Semiprostrata' Krüssmann	1955	A form having the same origin as 'Empetroides' and difficult to distinguish therefrom.	B,K	Canada
- - 'Viminalis' Sénéclauze	1868	A form with thin branches and short, crowded leaves. O. Sénéclauze Nurs, NIC.	B	France
- - 'Virgata' Rehder	1901	Sparcely branched as *PICEA abies* 'Virgata'.	B	U.S.A.
- - 'Wellspire' Hort. Amer.	1991	A flat, columnar form, foliage as the species. A good accent plant said to be only 3ft wide at base when 10 years old. L. Wells Nurs, Mt. Vernon, Washington.		
- - 'Witch's Broom' D.W. Hatch	1980	A plant propagated from a witch's broom found in Austria. Dwarf, low-growing, light grey-blue fine leaves. Suitable name is required.		

PICEA x *mariorika* B.K. Boom

    1959 A hybrid: *PICEA mariana* x *PICEA omorika*.   B

- - 'Gnom' Welch	1979	Unquestionably a hybrid. O. J. zu Jeddeloh Nurs, Oldenburg.	K,W2	Germany
- - 'Kobold' Krüssmann	1972	A hybrid: *PICEA mariana* 'Doumetii' x *PICEA omorika*. A dense, globose bush. O. J. zu Jeddeloh Nurs, Oldenburg.	K,W2	Germany
- - 'Machala' H.M. Grootendorst	1971	In "Dendroflora 24". O. Machala, Jehusice.	G,K,W2	Czechosl.
- - 'Tremonia' Welch	1979	Name suggested for a globose bush in Westfalen park, Dortmund-Brunninghausen.	W2	Germany

PICEA maximowiczii Regel ex Masters

    1880 Japanese Bush Spruce.   25m,Z4?   Japan

- - var. *senanensis* Hayashi 1969 Senan Spruce. (per Silba, 1984).   Japan

PICEA mexicana Martinez 1962 Now known as *PICEA engelmannii* var. *mexicana*. (per Silba, 1984).

PICEA meyeri Rehder & Wilson

    1914 Meyer Spruce.   W. China

PICEA montana (Schurl) Kondratjuk

    1958 East Carpathian Spruce.

PINUS montigena Masters 1906 Candelabra Spruce. By some authorities listed as *PICEA likiangensis* var. *montigena*. (per Silba, 1984).   Z5   China

PICEA morinda (Loudon) Link

    1841 Now known as *PICEA smithiana*.

PINUS morrisonicola Hayata

    1908 Taiwan Spruce. A species close to *PICEA wilsonii*.   Z8   Taiwan

PICEA x *moseri* Masters 1901 A hybrid: *PICEA jezoensis* x *PICEA mariana*. Raised 1901 by Moser, Versailles.   France

PINUS neoveitchii Masters 1903 Hupeh Spruce.   8-15m,Z7

PICEA nobilis (Douglas) Loudon

    1838 Now known as *ABIES procera*.

- - var. *magnifica* Nelson   1866 Now known as *ABIES magnifica*.

PICEA *nordmanniana* (Steven) Loudon
                                  1842 Now known as *ABIES nordmanniana*.

PICEA *notabilis* Rehder & Wilson ex Sargent
                                  1914 Now merged in *PICEA asperata*. (per Silba, 1984).

PICEA x *notha* Rehder   1939 A hybrid: *PICEA glehnii* x *PICEA jezoensis*. **O.** Arnold Arb.
                                        Jamaica Plain, Mass.   Hort. U.S.A.

PICEA *obovata* Ledebour   1833 Siberian Spruce. In "Flora Europea". This is now treated as a
                                        sub-species of *PICEA abies*.   35m,Z2   Asia

- - var. *alpestris* (Brugger) Henry
                                  1912 Not now distinguished within the species. (per Silba, 1984).   B

- - var. *coerulea* Tigerstedt   Foliage blue-green.   K   Altar Mtns.

- - var. *fennica* (Regel) Elwes & Henry
                                  1912 Finnish Spruce.   B.K   Finland

- - 'Glauca' Hort. Anglia   1986 An illegit. listed name. Possibly a clone of var *coerulea*.

PICEA *omorika* (Pancic) Purkyne
                                  1877 Serbian Spruce.   30-40m,Z5   Yugoslavia

- - 'Alpestris' Hort. Amer.   1986 A listed name. See *PICEA obovata alprestris*.

- - 'Arendal' Hort. Germany   1983 L. Horstmann Nurs, Schneverdingen.

- - **'Aurea'** Krüssmann   1979 Normal habit; foliage a persistent yellow. **O.** G. Bos & Sons,
                                        Boskoop.   K   Holland

- - 'Bad Bewensen' Hort. Germany
                                  1992 A listed name. L. Horstmann Nurs, Schneverdingen.

- - **'Berliner's Weeper'** Welch
                                  1979 NOM. A remarkably fastigiate selection and a rapid grower.
                                        O. Ben Berliner of L. Is., N.Y. ('Berliner's Weeping').   R.,W2   U.S.A.

- - 'Borealis' Schwerin   1929 Possibly a natural hybrid with *PICEA abies*.   B   Germany

- - 'Buchtmann' Hort. Germany
                                  1992 A dwarf form. L. Horstmann Nurs, Schneverdingen.

- - 'de Ruyter' Den Ouden   1949 Mr de Ruyter writes (12 Feb. 1974) "Named for a plant never
                                        propagated and later destroyed in a gale". NIC.   B

- - **'Denella'** H.J. van de Laar
                                  1986 In "Naamlijst . . .". NOM.   Holland

- - **'Expansa'** Den Ouden   1949 Named for a wide-spreading plant at Arboretum
                                        Trompenburg, Rotterdam. Probably a cultivariant.   B,G,K,W2   Holland

- - 'Fassei' Schwerin   1929 Similar to 'Borealis'. NIC.   B   Germany

- - 'Fennica' Hort. Amer.   1986 Possibly *PICEA obovata* var. *fennica*.

- - 'Freya' Hort. Holland   1990 Dwarf, conical, coarse grey-blue foliage. **O.** A seedling
                                        selected by Gebroeders Meeuwissen. Zundert. (1980).

- - **'Frohnleiten'** Krüssmann
                                  1972 An irregular dwarf shrub. **O.** Frohnleiten Alpengarten.
                                        ('Frohleiten').   K,R   Austria

- - 'Gnom' Krüssmann   1972 See *PICEA* x *mariorika* 'Gnom'.

- - 'Hexenbesen' Hort.Amer.   1989 A more acceptable name should be found.

- - 'Hillier's Gold' Hort. Anglia
                              1985 Reported from Windsor Great Park, Berks.

- - 'Linda' Hort. Holland   1992 Listed name for a slender grower. **O.** Raised from seed by
                                    Gebr. Meeuwissen, Zundert.

- - 'Microphylla' Hort. Amer.   An illegit. listed name.

- - 'Minima' Krüssmann   1979 An illegit. listed name. Now known as 'Minimax'.   K

- - 'Minimax' Hort. Germany
                              1985 A very dwarf form, flat topped cushion shaped. Developed
                                    from a witch's broom on 'Nana'. **O.** and **I.** J.zu Jeddeloh,
                                    Oldenburg.

- - **'Nana'** H.M. Grootendorst in Hornibrook
                              1939 A dwarf conical form. **O.** Goudkade Nurs, Boskoop.   B,G,H,K,W2   Holland

- - **'Pendula'** Schwerin   1920 Name now of value only in a collective sense.   B,G,K,R   Sporadic

- - **'Pendula Bruns'** Hort. Germany
                                    A name for an extremely pendulous clone. **I.** Bruns Nurs, Bad
                                    Zwischenahn, (c. 1955).   G   Germany

- - 'Pendula Kuck' Hort. Germany
                              1983 A listed name for a pendulous plant. **O.** Kuck, Oldenburg. **L.**
                                    Horstmann Nurs, Schneverdingen.

- - 'Pendula Major' Hort. Anglia
                              1985 Reported from Windsor Great Park, Berks.

- - **'Pimoko'** R. Reuter   1984 In "Amer. Conif. Soc. Bull.". A globose plant with short
                                    needles. **O.** From a witch's broom found by W. Wustemeyer
                                    of Schermbeck.   G,K,R   Germany

- - **'Professor Lanjouw'** H. J. van de Laar
                              1986 In "Naamlijst . . .". Named for a tree in the Utrecht Botanic
                                    Garden in honour of Professor Lanjou of Utrecht University.
                                    NOM.   Holland

- - 'Raraflora' Hort. Amer.   1975 A listed name. **L.** Raraflora Nurs, Feasterville, PA.

- - 'Schneverdingen' Hort. Germany
                              1991 Tight, conical bush from a witch's broom. **O.** and **I.**
                                    Horstmann Nurs, Schneverdingen.

- - **'Treblitsch'** P.A.Schmidt
                              1987 In "Beitrage zur Geholzkunde". A very compact cushion
                                    shaped form with coarse foliage. **I.** Weisenburg Nurs. **O.**
                                    raised from a witch's broom found in the park at Treblitsch,
                                    Belgen. ('Treblitschensis'). (1977).   Germany

- - 'Tremonia' Hort. Germany
                              1983 **L.** G.Horstmann, Schneverdingen. **O.** A witch's broom found
                                    in the Romberpark, Dortmund.   Germany

PICEA orientalis (Linnaeus) Link
                              1847 Oriental or Caucasian Spruce.   40-50m,Z5   Asia Minor

- - **'Atrovirens'** Beissner 1911 Leaves shining dark green. **O.** H.den Ouden Nurs. Boskoop.
                                    I. 1935.   B,K,R   Holland

- - **'Aurea'** Otto   1873 Shining golden-yellow foliage, the colour persisting
                                    throughout the year. **O.** H.A. Hesse Nurs, Weener-on-Ems.   G,K,R,W2   Germany

- - **'Aurea Compacta'** (1) Jeddeloh ex Krüssmann
                              1979 See 'Wittboldt'.   G,K,R   Germany

- - 'Aurea Compacta' (2) Hort. Amer.
      See *PICEA orientalis* 'Skylands'.

- - 'Aurea Compacta Pendula' Hort. Amer.
      1985 See 'Skylands'.

- - **'Aureospicata'** Beissner 1909 Young foliage creamy-yellow, becoming dark green during
      the summer. N.B. Not the same as 'Aurea'. B,W2 Germany

- - **'Barnes'** R.L. Fincham 1989 In "Nurs. Cat". Reliably dwarf, forming a nest-like shape. U.S.A.

- - 'Bergman's Gem' Hort. Amer.
      1980 A cushion shaped later conical dwarf. Leaves mid green to
      dark green in autumn. L. Kristick Nurs, Wellsville, PA.

- - **'Bergman's Spreading'** L.C. Hatch
      1988 In "Conifer Database". Dark green, spreading habit,
      ('Bergman's Repens'). U.S.A.

- - 'Compacta' Krüssmann 1972 Named for a broadly conical plant exhibited at Dortmund by
      Hillier's Nurs. in 1969. An illegit. name. K

- - 'Compacta Aurea' Hort. Amer.
      1985 See 'Skylands'.

- - 'Compacta Pendula' Hort. Amer.
      1985 An illegit. but (presumably) descriptive name.

- - **'Connecticut Turnpike'** L.C. Hatch
      1988 In "Conifer Database". A selected compact green clone. U.S.A.

- - 'Doverside Pendula' Hort. Anglia
      1976 Slow-growing tree with strongly pendulous side branches.
      Blackish-green leaves. L. Hillier's Nurs, Winchester.

- - **'Early Gold'** Welch 1979 Flushes two weeks earlier than 'Aureospicata'. I. Vermeulen
      Nurs. G,K,R,W2 U.S.A.

- - **'Eese'** Den Ouden/Boom
      1965 A very dwarf densely globose form. I. H den Ouden Nurs,
      Boskoop. B Holland

- - 'Glauca Compacta' Hort. Ireland
      1989 Reported from the National Botanic Garden, Dublin. Ireland

- - **'Gowdy'** Wyman 1961 Habit narrowly columnar. Leaves small, rich green. B,W2 U.S.A.

- - **'Gracilis'** A. Kort 1903 In "Nurs. Cat". A dense tree to 6m, light green. O. and I.
      A.Kort, Kalmthout. B,K,W2 Belgium

- - 'Gracilis Nana' Hort. Anglia
      1905 See 'Nana'.

- - 'Gracilis Nigra' Hort. Anglia
      1981 See 'Nana'.

- - 'Hatch's W.B. No.2'   See 'Reynolds'.

- - 'Inversa' Hort. Amer. 1986 An illegit. listed name.

- - 'Kenwith' G. Haddow 1988 In "Nurs. Cat". Very dwarf globose form, light-green foliage.
      O. and I. Kenwith Nurs, Bideford, Devon.

- - 'Kolaga' Hort. Amer. 1982 A dwarf plant. L. Iseli Nurs, Boring, OR. ('Nana Kolaga',
      'Nana Kologa').

- - 'Landis' Hort. Canada 1981 A listed name without description. G. Bentham, Victoria, BC.

- - 'Martin' Hort. Amer. 1986 A listed name. No further information.

- - **'Mount Vernon'** L.C.Hatch

  1985 In "Reference Guide". A slow-growing dense, mounded
       dwarf.   U.S.A.

- - **'Murphy'** D.W. Hatch   1980 Very dwarf cushion to globose form with mid-green leaves.
       O. Found as a witch's broom by Mike Murphy. **I.** Chantry
       Nurs, Honiton. ('M3 W.B. No.l').   U.K.

- - **'Nana'** Carrière   1891 Several slow-growing clones, varying in habit from squat,
       globose to conical are grown under this name or under
       combinations with the epithets 'Compacta' or 'Gracilis' that
       are impossible to distinguish from published descriptions.
       New names for worthwhile distinctive clones should be found.   B,H,K,W2

- - 'Nana Compacta' Hort.   1988 An illegit. name. See the previous item.

- - 'Nana Pendula' H.G. Hillier
                               1964 An illegit. name. See 'Weeping Dwarf'.

- - **'Nigra'** Helene Bergman 1965 In "Plants and Gardens **21**". Open and irregularly conical;
       leaves small, dark green.   U.S.A.

- - 'Nigra Compacta' Hort. Amer.
                               1985 An illegit. listed name.

- - **'Nutans'** Niemetz   1905 A dense irregular bush. NIC. **I.** H.A. Hesse Nurs, Weener-on-
       Ems. **O.** Niemetz, Temesvár.   B,K,R   Hungary

- - **'Pendula'** Schwerin   1920 The name is now used loosely for any pendulous clone.

- - **'Pygmaea' (1)** Beissner 1887 In "Conif. Ben". A mistake for *PICEA abies* 'Ohlendorffii'.   H

- - **'Pygmaea' (2)** Welch   1979 An illegit listed name. Named for a diminutive plant at
       Wansdyke Nurs, Devizes, Wilts, received from R.S. Corley.
       (See 'Wansdyke').   W2   U.K.

- - 'Pygmaea Glauca' R.Smith
                               1874 As *ABIES orientalis pygmaea glauca*. NOM. NIC.   H   U.K.

- - 'Raraflora Fluke' Hort. Amer.
                               1986 Possibly the same as 'Raraflora'. **L.** F. Bergman, Raraflora
       Nurs, Feasterville, PA. (1966).

- - 'Repens' Hort. Amer.   1986 An illegit. listed name. Possibly 'Bergman's Spreading'.

- - **'Reynolds'** D.W. Hatch 1980 Low spreading plant with dark-green needles as a graft,
       tightly conical dwarf when rooted out. **O.** Witch's broom
       found by Bernard Reynolds. **I.** Chantry Nurs, Honiton. ('M3
       W.B. No. 2', 'Hatch's W.B. No.2').   U.K.

- - 'Semivirgata' Schwerin   1910 A loose 'snake form' tree found by Count von Schwerin in a
       park at Archen. NIC.   B   Germany

- - 'Silver seedling' Hort.Holland
                               1990 A good colour form. **L.** L.Konijn Nurs, Lunteren.

- - **'Skylands'** Welch   1979 Name suggested for a golden-yellow plant of outstanding
       colour, found at Skyland Farm, N.J. (Now Ringwood State
       Park). Syn. 'Aurea Compacta'.   G,R,W2   U.S.A.

- - 'Sulphur Flush' D. van Klaveren
                               1981 In Wansdyke "Nurs. Cat". Sulphur-yellow young shoots
       fading to yellowish-green.   U.K.

- - 'Summergold' Hort. Germany
                               1992 A listed name.

- - 'Tom Thumb' Hort. Amer.
　　　　　　 1990　Dwarf globose form with very small leaves, outer foliage
　　　　　　　　　golden. L. J.W. Spingarn, West Redding, Conn. ('Tom
　　　　　　　　　Thumb Gold').

- - 'Viminalis' Schwerin　　1932　Named for a spreading tree in the park at Henneburg near
　　　　　　　　　Schachen-on-Bodensec. NIC.　　　　　　　　　　B　　　　Germany

- - 'Wansdyke' D. van Klaveren
　　　　　　 1981　In Wansdyke "Nurs. Cat". Dark green with yellow sheen.　　　　　U.K.

- - 'Weeping Dwarf' Den Ouden/Boom
　　　　　　 1965　A compact slow-growing form with pendulous side branches
　　　　　　　　　received by Hillier's Nurs. from an unrecorded Dutch Nurs.
　　　　　　　　　('Nana Pendula').　　　　　　　　　　　　　　B,W2　　U.K.

- - 'Wittboldt' Jeddeloh ex Krüssmann
　　　　　　 1979　A seedling selection with the upper side of the leaf yellow. O.
　　　　　　　　　K. Wittboldt-Muller Nurs, Verden-Eitze.　　　　　　　　　Germany

PICEA pichta Loudon　　1838　Now known as *ABIES sibirica*.

PICEA pindrow (D. Don) Loudon
　　　　　　 1838　Now known as *ABIES pindrow*.

PICEA pinsapo (Boissier) Loudon
　　　　　　 1838　Now known as *ABIES pinsapo*.

PICEA polita (Siebold & Zuccarini) Carrière
　　　　　　 1855　Tigertail Spruce.　　　　　　　　　　　20-30m,Z6　　Japan

- - 'Hergest Croft' Hort. Anglia
　　　　　　 1978　Slow-growing upright form with short thick sharp leaves. L.
　　　　　　　　　Wansdyke Nurs, Devizes, Wilts.

PICEA ponderosa (Rehder & Wilson) Lacassagne
　　　　　　 1914　Now merged with *PICEA asperata* by some authorities. (per
　　　　　　　　　Silba, 1984).

PICEA pungens Engelmann
　　　　　　 1875　Colorado Spruce. Formerly known as *ABIES menziesii*.　　30-45m,Z2　　Western U.S.A.

- -'Albivariegata' Schwerin　1920　Leaves pale glaucous blue. NIC.　　　　B　　　　Germany

- - 'Arcuata' Schwerin　　1920　Named for an open tree with green foliage in the Count von
　　　　　　　　　Schwerin park at Wendisch-Wilmersdorf. NIC.　　　　B,K　　Germany

- - 'Argentea' Rosenthal　　1887　Useful only as a collective name for selections with a silvery-
　　　　　　　　　white foliage.　　　　　　　　　　　　　　B,D,K　　Austria

- - 'Atriviridis' Schwerin　　1920　Named for a tree with conspicuously dark green leaves NIC.
　　　　　　　　　('Atroviridis').　　　　　　　　　　　　　B,K　　Germany

- - 'Aurea' Niemetz　　1905　Yellowish colour is best during the winter. O. Raised by
　　　　　　　　　Niemetz, Temesvár.　　　　　　　　　　　B,D,G,K　　Hungary

- - 'Baby Blueyes' U.S. Plant Patent 5457
　　　　　　 1985　Dense, upright semi-dwarf; foliage sky-grey. I. Holden Nurs,
　　　　　　　　　Silverton, OR. O. A selected seedling (1972).　　　　　U.S.A.

- - 'Bakkeri' Hort. Amer.　　See 'Royal Knight'.

- - 'Bakeri' Bailey　　1933　A clone with long, deep blue leaves. O. Found by Ellery
　　　　　　　　　Baker, Hiti Nurs, Pomfret, Conn.　　　　　　　B,K　　U.S.A.

- - 'Bastion' H.J. van de Laar
　　　　　　 1983　In "Dendroflora 20". Globose form with short, blue-grey
　　　　　　　　　foliage. O. From seed by P. Bakhuyzen & Sons, Boskoop.　　　Holland

- - 'Bialobok' Hort. Poland   1992   Young needles in spring soft-yellow, becoming silvery-blue.
I. The Kornick Arboretum and named for Prof. S. Bialobok, Kornick.

- - 'Bismarck' Hort. Germany
    1984   See 'Furst Bismarck'. **L.** Jeddeloh Nurs, Oldenburg.

- - 'Blaukissen' Hort. Germany
    1992   A listed name. **L.** Horstmann Nurs, Schneverdingen.

- - 'Blue Bun' Hort. Amer.   1986   A listed name. No further information.

- - 'Blue Candlestick' Hort. Amer.
    1992   A listed name. Rarafolia Nurs, Kintersville, PA.

- - 'Blue Mist' Hort. Amer.   1986   A mistake for 'Prostrate Blue Mist'.

- - 'Blue Spreader' Hort. Amer.
    1986   An unaccceptable name.

- - **'Blue Trinket'** H.J. Grootendorst
    1969   In "Dendroflora 6". A compact, conical form with rather coarse leaves.**O.** and **I.** Konijn and Co Nurs, then of Reeuwijk.   K,G,W2   Holland

- - 'Brady' Hort. Amer.   1982   A listed name without description. **L.** Iseli Nurs, Boring, OR.

- - 'Caerulea' Hort. Amer.   1988   An illegit. listed name. No further information.

- - 'Colorado Blue' Hort. Germany
    1983   A witch's broom. Horstmann Nurs, Schneverdingen.

- - **'Columnaris'** Schelle   1909   A columnar form, short, spreading branches. Such forms arise from time to time.   B,K   Germany

- - f. *compacta* Rehder   1916   Dwarf Colorado Spruce. The name was raised for a single clone but is a botanical designation covering all such compact forms from seed.   B,D,H   U.S.A.

- - **'Compacta'** Rehder   1916   A slow growing clone with horizontal branch system and dark green foliage. It was raised from seed at Harvard Botanic Gardens, (1863). See full account in Welch (1979).   B,K,W2   U.S.A.

- - 'Compacta Glauca' Hort.   See 'Glauca Compacta'.

- - 'Compacta Thume' Hort. Amer.
    1986   See 'Thuem'.

- - **'Copeland'** L.C. Hatch   1985   In "Reference Guide". A conical tree with foliage intense blue; twigs whitish. ('Coplane').   U.S.A.

- - 'Corbet' Hort. Amer.   1986   A listed name. But see *PICEA Abies* 'John Corbit'.

- - 'Dietz Prostrate' Hort. Amer.
    1985   A listed name. No further information.

- - 'Diversifolia' Hort. Germany
    1964   **L.** Eiselt in "Nadelgehölze", but no longer listed.

- - **'Donna's Rainbow'** R.L. Fincham
    1989   In Coenosium Gard. "Nurs. Cat". A dwarf, spreading mound. **O.** Iseli Nurs, Boring, OR.   U.S.A.

- - **'Edith'** H.J. van de Laar   1990   In "Dendroflora 27". Broadly conical, compact bush. **O.** M. Barabits, Sopron. (1985).   Hungary

- - **'Egyptian Pyramid'** Vermeulen
    1985   Dwarf; dense, broad, ripening blue cones. **L.** Vermeulen and Son Nurs, Neshanic Station, N.J.   U.S.A.

- - **'Elegantissima'** R.L. Fincham
1985 An illegit. name. In Coenosium Gard. "Nurs. Cat". Young leaves white.

- - **'Emerald Cushion'** R.L. Fincham
1983 A diminutive clone with emerald green foliage. Not of good constitution.   U.S.A.

- - **'Endtz'** Entz
1933 A dense, conical tree with horizontal branches. Foliage blue. O. L.J. Endtz Nurs, Boskoop. (1925).   B,G,K,R   Holland

- - **'Erich Frahm'** Timm
1950 In "Nurs. Cat". Very regularly conical; foliage conspicuously glaucous.   B,K   Germany

- - 'Fastigiata' Hort. Canada   1987 In "Woody Plant Source List". Name probably illegit.

- - **'Fat Albert'** Int. Con. Reg.
1981 Dense, conical habit due to multiple buds; foliage blue colour as 'Moerheim'. Registered by Iseli Nurs, Boring, OR.   G   U.S.A.

- - 'Fat Albert Hexenbesen ' Hort. Germany
1992 A witch's broom. L. Horstmann Nurs, Schneverdingen.

- - **'Flavescens'** Niemetz   1905 Leaves whitish-yellow. NIC.   B,K   Germany

- - **'Formidable'** Iseli   1985 In "Nurs. Cat". Dwarf and globose but larger than 'Globosa'; foliage blue-green. I. Iseli Nurs, Boring, OR.   U.S.A.

- - 'Fox Tail' Hort. Amer.   See 'Iseli Foxtail'.

- - **'Furst Bismarck'** Weisse
1887 A vigorous, regularly symmetrical tree with bright blue foliage. (Misdescribed by Den Ouden/Boom).   B,K   Germany

- - 'Gelbtreibend' Hort. Germany
1992 A listed name without description.

- - **'Girard Dwarf'** L.C. Hatch
1985 In "Reference Guide". Dwarf; mounded; foliage very blue; leaves short.   U.S.A.

- - 'Girardii' Hort. Amer.   See 'Girard Dwarf'.

- - **f.*glauca*** Beissner   1891 A botanical designation that includes all the selected colour forms in garden cultivation. Intermediate forms turn up in the seed beds and are sometimes offered for sale under the following names.

- - 'Glauca' Hort.   Horticultural equivalent of the previous item. This term may no longer be used in any new cultivar name nor be added on to a valid old one. Now useful only as a group name.   B

- - 'Glauca Aurea' Hort. Amer.   Now renamed 'Maigold'.

- - 'Glauca Bacherii' Hort. Canada
1987 An illegit. listed name. Probably ='Bakkeri' the former name for 'Royal Knight'.

- - 'Glauca Compacta' (1) Van Nes
1913 In "Nurs. Cat". C.B. van Nes and Son (Blaaw & Co.) A superfluous synonym for 'Koster' q.v. ('Glauca Compacta Koster') (1908).   B   Holland

- - 'Glauca Compacta' (2) Hort. Amer.
Name often misapplied in the trade to 'Thuem'!

- - 'Glauca Globosa' H.G. Hillier
1964 A dense globular bush with foliage as rich a blue as in 'Kosteri'.   G,K,W   U.K.

- - 'Glauca Intense' Hort. Canada
         1987 An illegit. listed name.

- - 'Glauca Moerheimii' Hort.   See 'Moerheim'.   D

- - **'Glauca Nana'** Hesse   1962 In "Nurs. Cat". (1961-62) A dwarf forming a flattened globose plant with horizontal branching and glaucous grey foliage. **I.** Le Feber and Co.,Boskoop (1955). **O.** Arith. Kluys Nurs, Boskoop (1937).   W2   Germany

- - **'Glauca Pendula'** (1) Koster ex Beissner
         1891 A clone with pendulous branches and shoots; leaves falcate. **O.** Koster and Co.,Boskoop (1895), ('Kosteriana').   B,D,G,K   Holland

- - 'Glauca Pendula' (2) Hort. Cultivariants resulting from propagations from side shoots. Such plants may throw up a leader and form a monstrous specimen not entitled to this or any other cultivar name.

- - **'Glauca Procumbens'** H. den Ouden & Son
         1924 See note under ('Glauca Prostrata').   B,D,G,H,K

- - **'Glauca Prostrata'** Beissner
         1906 See the following note.   B,H   Germany

Although the previous two entries are well-established names in the trade, all such plants are clearly cultivariants (per Welch, 1966) of unrecorded glaucous clones. Similarly spreading plants, propagated from lateral shoots of a "named form" do not constitute new clones, (since they are unstable and apt to become arboreal). Such must retain the clonal name but should be distinguished commercially by a note, not forming part of the name, but descriptive of the actual plant, such as the additional word (prostrate) e.g. 'Hoopsii' (prostrate).

- - 'Glaucescens' Sudworth   1897 A superfluous name for 'Glauca'.   U.S.A.

- - 'Globe' Hort. Canada   1982 An unacceptable listed name. **L.** Iseli "Nurs. Cat". (1990). **O.** Wm Goddard.

- - 'Globosa'(1) H. den Ouden
         1949 See 'Glauca Nana'.   B   Holland

- - 'Globosa'(2) Hort.   See 'Glauca Globosa'.   G

- - 'Globosa'(3) Hort.   Frequently misapplied to 'Montgomery' (and probably also to other clones in circulation).

- - 'Globosa Formidable' Hort. Amer.
         See 'Formidable'.

- - **'Gloria'** D.W. Hatch   1987 In Chantry "Nurs. Cat". Honiton, Devon. A dwarf flat-topped plant with blue needles. Named in honour of his wife.   U.K.

- - 'Goldie' Hort. Amer.   Now known as 'Walnut Glen'.

- - **'Gotelli's Broom'** Welch
         1979 A small flat-topped plant that originated with a witch's broom in the Gotelli Conifer collection.   W2   U.S.A.

- - 'Green Fox' Hort. Amer. 1985 A listed name.

- - 'Green Globe' Hort. Amer.
         1988 An unacceptable name and not a very descriptive one.

- - 'Green Spire' Hort. Amer.
         1985 A listed name for a selection similar to 'Iseli Fastigate' but green in colour.

- - 'Grey Cone' Hort. Germany
         1973 An unacceptable name for a tree found by Heindrick Bruns in Westerstede, Germany.

- - **'Henry Fowler'** L.C. Hatch

    1988 In "Conifer Database". Dense compact, symmetrical tree with bluish-green leaves. **O.** Found as a seedling by Henry Fowler (c.1960).   U.S.A.

- - **'Hillside'** Iseli   1990 In "Nurs. Cat". Dense, globose. Bluish-grey leaves.

- - **'Hoopsii'** Hoops ex H.J. Grootendorst

    1958 In "Nurs. Cat". A dense conical tree; foliage conspicuosly glaucous.   B,G,K,R   Germany

- - **'Hoto'** Krüssmann   1979 A vigorous clone. Dullish blue foliage. **I.** A. Hoodgendorn and Gebr.Van Tool, both of Boskoop.   K,G,R   Holland

- - **'Hunnewelliana'** Hornibrook

    1923 Slow-growing at first, but eventually tree-like. **I.** Framingham Nurs, Mass. (Still listed in U.S.A).   B,H,K,W2   U.S.A.

- - **'Iseli Fastigiate'** Int. Con. Reg.

    1981 A narrowly fastigiate tree; foliage colour as 'Moerheimii'. Registered by Iseli Nurs, Boring, OR. **O.** The same (1963).   G   U.S.A.

- - 'Iseli Fat Albert'   See 'Fat Albert'.

- - **'Iseli Foxtail'** Int. Con. Reg.

    1981 Branches twisted; foliage peculiar. Registered by Iseli Nurs, Boring, OR. **O.** The same (1965). ('Foxtail').   G   U.S.A.

- - 'Iseli Prostrate Blue Mist'   See 'Prostrate Blue Mist'.

- - 'Iseli Snowkiss' Hort. Amer.   See 'Snow Kiss'. ('Snowkist').

- - 'Jean Iseli' Hort. Amer.   1992 Dwarf which grows like a birds nest. **O.** Ed Wood. **I.** Coenosium, Boring, OR.

- - "Kaibab" Hort. Amer.   A word of uncertain application, possibly used for seedlings.

- - **'Kleinood Luusbarg'** Den Ouden /Boom

    1965 A spreading dwarf. Named for a plant in the garden of Mrs. E. Muchmayer, Hamburg-Risen. ('Luusbarg').   B,G,K   Germany

- - 'Kluis' Hort.Amer.   1989 A listed name for a compact, conical plant; needles coarse. **O.** Dudi Kluis.?

- - **'Koenig Albert'** Weiss   1887 In "Nurs. Cat". Foliage very pale. NIC.   B   Germany?

- - **'Koster'** Blaauw   1901 In "Nurs. Cat". The well-known "Koster's Blue Spruce". A group of very similar clones selected and distributed by Blaauw and Co. **O.** Arie Koster Nurs, Boskoop. (1885).('Kosteri').   B,G,K,R   Holland

- - 'Kosteri Pendula' Bean   1908 In "Kew Bull.". See 'Glauca Pendula'.

- - 'Kosteriana' Masters   1903 In "Kew Handlist of Conif.". See 'Glauca Pendula'.

- - 'Koster Prostrate' Hort.   See Notes under 'Glauca Prostrata'.

- - **'Lombarts'** Lombart   1935 In "Nurs. Cat". A strong-growing selection with bluish-white foliage. **O.** Pierre Lombart's Nurs, Zundert.   B,K   Holland

- - **'Lucky Strike'** H.J. van de Laar

    1983 In "Dendroflora 20". Irregular, open tree with dark green glossy foliage; coning heavily even when very young. **I.** Gebr. van Vliet Nurs, Boskoop (1983). A seedling of unrecorded parentage.   G   Holland

- - 'Lutea' Hort. Amer.   1986 An illegit. listed name. Said to be a paler yellow than 'Walnut Glen'.

- - 'Maigold' Hachmann   1988 In "Nurs. Cat". Young foliage a strikingly pale yellow in
                                      May, becoming blue green. **O.** Hachmann, Barmstedt in
                                      Holstein.   Germany

- - **'Max'** L.C. Hatch   1988 In "Conifer Database". NOM.   U.S.A.

- - 'Microphylla' Schwerin   1922 Named for a tree with short leaves found by Count Schwerin.
                                      NIC.   B,K,R   Germany

- - **'Mission Bay'** Int. Con. Reg.
                                1981 Normal conical habit and growth; foliage steel-blue
                                      throughout year. Registered by F. J. Crowe, San Diego, Cal.
                                      I. The same. **O.** Ralph Jack, Silver Falls, OR.   U.S.A.

- - **'Mission Blue'** Krüssmann
                                1979 A very quick-growing clone selected at the Mission Gardens,
                                      Techny, Ill.   K   U.S.A.

- - **'Moerheim'** Ruys   1912 In Moerheim "Nurs. Cat". A slender, conical tree; blue colour
                                      retained throughout the winter. **O.** Royal Moerheim Nurs,
                                      Dedemsvaart.   B,G,K   Holland

- - **'Möll'** P. Möll ex Krüssmann
                                1955 A slow growing conical plant with greyish-green foliage.   B,K,W2   Germany

- - **'Montgomery'** Teuscher 1949 The popular dwarf with blue foliage. The mother plant is now
                                      in the New York Botanical Garden.   B,G,K,R,W2 U.S.A.

- - 'Morden' Hort. Canada   1977 A dense form; foliage blue. NIC. See "Int. Con. Reg." (1985).
                                      'Morden Blue' is a superfluous name.

- - 'Mrs. Cesarini' Hort. Amer.
                                1981 Previously listed under either *PICEA abies, PICEA glauca* or
                                      PICEA jezoensis. Originally found as a witch's broom by Joe
                                      Cesarini when at Long Island? For many years the foliage
                                      was difficult to positively identify. Dwarf, globose to flat-
                                      topped plant with blue-green leaves. Noticeable orange brown
                                      buds in spring. **I.** J.W. Spingarn, L.Is., N.Y.

- - 'Nana' Hort. Amer.   1986 An illegit. name of no clear application. (Also are 'Nana
                                      Compacta' and 'Nana Pendula').

- - 'Neugebauer' P.A. Smith   1987 In "Beitrage zur Geholzkunde".

- - **'Oldenburg'** Int. Con. Reg.
                                1981 Narrowly conical; growth dense; foliage steel-blue. **I.** J. zu
                                      Jeddeloh Nurs, Oldenburg. **O.** The same, a selected seedling
                                      (1955).   G,K   Germany

- - **'Omega'** H.J. van de Laar
                                1983 In "Dendroflora 20". A close, conical habit; silvery-grey
                                      leaves and yellow-brown young shoots. Readily develops a
                                      good leader and starts into growth very late.   G   Germany

- - 'Pendens' (1) Sudworth   1897 Superfluous name for 'Glauca Pendula'.

- - 'Pendens' (2) Hort.Amer.   1989 A prostrate plant reported from Arnold Arb. Jamaica Plain.
                                      Mass.

- - 'Pendula' Schwerin   1920 Named for an unrecorded tree. NIC   B,K   Germany

- - 'Perpendicularis' Schwerin
                                1920 A sporadic form with slender, pendulous branches. NIC. B   Russia etc.

- - 'Porcupine' Hort. Amer.   1991 A listed name for an irregular, tightly congested bun with a
                                      nice blue coloured foliage. **O.** Richard Bush.

- - 'Procumbens' Hort.   1987 See notes following 'Glauca Procumbens'.

- - 'Professor Bialobok'   1992 Reported from the Botanical Garden in Wroclaw.   Poland

- - 'Prostrata' Hort.   See 'Glauca Prostrata'.

- - **'Prostrate Blue Mist'** Int. Con. Reg.
      1981 Prostrate habit; Annual growth 75mm; foliage as 'Moerheim' in colour but leaves half as long. **O.** Iseli Nurs, Boring, OR, (1965).   U.S.A.

- - 'Pumila' Hahn   1940 A compact globose form; leaves very glaucous. **O.** Eisenberg Nurs. NIC.   B,K   Czechosl.

- - 'Regalis' Schwerin   1920 A form with peculiar branch formation. NIC.   B   Austria

- - 'Retroflexa' Hort. Anglia 1982 Probably a mistake for *PICEA retroflexa*.

- - 'R.H. Montgomery' Hort.   Now to be 'Montgomery' q.v.

- - **'Richardson'** L.C. Hatch
      1985 In "Reference Guide". Foliage very blue at first but tinged yellow 2nd year; stems thick.   U.S.A.

- - **'Rovelli's Monument'** Van Klaveren
      1981 Narrowly columnar to 10m. Found by Humphrey Welch in the one-time famous Rovelli Frères Nurs, at Pallanza.   Italy

- - 'Royal Blue' Hort. Amer. 1979 Reported from Arnold Arboretum.

- - **'Royal Knight'** Vermeulen
      1983 In "Nurs. Cat". Vermeulen and Son, Neshanic Station, N.J. **I.** The same. **O.** J. C. Bakker and Sons, St Catherines, Ontario.   Canada

- - **'Saint Mary's Broom'** R.L. Fincham
      1983 In Coenosium "Nurs. Cat". Dense, dwarf conical plant; foliage very glaucous.   G   U.S.A.

- - 'Schloss Herrenstein' Hort. Germany
      1992 A listed name. **L.** Horstmann Nurs, Schneverdingen.

- - **'Schovenhorst'** Van Nes
      1962 As 'Koster', but stiffer habit.   B,K   Holland

- - 'Schwartz' Krüssmann   1983 Reported from Arnold Arboretum. Mass. **L.** Hillside Nurs, Lehighton, PA. (1970). ('Swartzii').   K   U.S.A.

- - "Select" Hort. Amer.   A descriptive adjective used in nursery catalogues for un-named, unpublished private selections thought by the selector to be worth offering for sale. Not a cultivar name.

- - "Select Blue"   See previous item.

- - 'Sherwood Prostrate Koster' Hort. Amer.
      1985 A cultivariant propagated from a clone of the 'Koster' group.

- - "Shiner" Hort. Amer.   A similar term to "Select" (above), used for selected seedlings. Not a cultivar name.

- - 'Snow Cushion' Hort. Amer.
      1986 A listed name. No further informtion.

- - **'Snowkiss'** Int. Con. Reg.
      1981 Conical habit and colour as 'Hoopsii' but needles as 'Moerheimii' in size. Registered by J. Iseli. **I.** Iseli Nurs, Boring, OR. (1981). **O.** The same (1965).   G   U.S.A.

- - "Special" Hort.   See note under "Select", above.

- - **'Spek'** Spek ex den Ouden
     1933 A vigorous clone with dull blue foliage. **I.** Jan Spek Nurs,
       Boskoop.   B,K,R   Holland

- - 'Spekii' Hort.   See 'Spek'.

- - 'Stanley Gold' Hort. Amer.
     1991 A selection with golden foliage. Brighter than 'Aurea'. **O.**
       Larrie Stanley.

- - 'Straw' Hort. Amer.   1992 In "Nurs. Cat". Rarafolia Nurs, Kintersville, PA.

- - 'Sunshine' Hort. Amer.   1990 A listed name for a selection with young growth lemon-
       yellow.

- - 'Tabuliformis' Beissner   1909 A flattened shrub. **O.** Ordnung of Eisenburg Nurs.   B   Czechosl.

- - 'Teton' Hort. Amer.   1993 In the"A.C.S. Mag. Bull. Vol. **10.** No. l".At the present time a
       collective name for thirteen different clones found in Teton
       Grove, Wyoming by D. Hermsen, Farley, Iowa and
       subsequently investigated by Jerry Morris, Lakewood,
       Colorado and Justin C. "Chub" Harper of Hidden Lake
       Gardens. Some cultivars to be introduced in the near future.

- - **'Thomsen'** Thomsen   1932 In "Nurs. Cat". A symmetrical tree with foliage silvery-blue.
       O. Found by Thomsen in a garden at Lancaster, PA, U.S.A. **I.**
       Thomsen Nurs. (then of Mansfield, PA.) (Since 1934, of
       Skalborg).   B,K,R   Denmark

- - **'Thuem'** Welch   1979 A broad, compact form of a good blue colour. Similar to
       'Montgomery', but a faster grower with longer leaves. Often
       offered as 'Glauca Compacta'.   W2   U.S.A.

- - 'Tiffen Blue' Hort. Canada   See following item.

- - **'Tiffin'** Reg'd. C.O.P.F. Reg.
     1976 Slow-growing tree with compact, regular growth and good
       blue colour. **I.** Kenneth V. Tiffin of Midhurst, Ontario.   Canada

- - **'Virgata'** Beissner   1909 A 'snake branch' form. **O.** Masek Nurs, Turnau. NIC.   B,K   Czechosl.

- - 'Viridis' Regel   1883 Leaves green. NIC.   B,D,K   Russia

- - **'Vissneriana'** (1) Visser   1934 A vigorous grower with long dark blue leaves. **O.** Seedling
       raised by L.C. Visser Nurs, Pressbaum.   Austria

- - 'Vissneriana' (2) Hort.Amer.
     1970 **L.** Hillside Nurs, Lehighton, PA. NOM.

- - **'Vuyk'** Vuyk   1912 In "Nurs. Cat". A vigorous clone with long silvery blue leaves
       greyish in winter. **O.** T. Vuyk and Son, Boskoop. (1912).   B,K   Holland

- - **'Walnut Glen'** Hort. Amer.
     1985 A listed name for a tree with golden-yellow young growth.
       (Formerly listed as 'Goldie').   U.S.A.

- - 'Waterloo' Hort. Amer.   1992 In "Nurs. Cat". Rich's Foxwillow Pines, Woodstock, ILL.

- - **'Yvette'** Iseli   1985 In "Nurs. Cat". An irregular dwarf mound. Jean Iseli named
       this for his youngest daughter.

- - 'Ziegler' Hort.Amer.   1986 A listed name.

- - 'Zilke' Hort. Amer.   1986 A listed name.

PICEA pungsaniensis Vyeki ex Schenk.
     1939 A rare species allied to *PICEA koraiensis.*   N.Korea

PICEA purpurea Masters	1906	Purple-cone Spruce. Formerly listed as *PICEA likiangensis* var *purpurea*.	30m,Z5,K China
PICEA retroflexa Masters	1906	A species close to *PICEA asperata*, of which it is by some authorities listed as a variety.	20m,Z6,K
PICEA robertii Vipper		A species intermediate between *PICEA schrenkiana* and *PICEA glehnii*.	
PICEA rubens Sargent	1896	Red Spruce: The name refers to the small reddish brown cones. (Formerly known as *PICEA rubra*).	25m,Z3 East N. Amer.
- - 'Coerulea' Loudon	1838	Leaves glaucous. NIC.	B
- - 'Crista-galli' Hornibrook	1923	A dwarf cockscomb-like bush found by M. Hornibrook. NIC.	B,H
- - 'Grandfather Mountains' New name.	1992	Raised from a witch's broom found by G. Horstmann in Grandfather Mountains, U.S.A in 1979. Formerly listed as 'Hexenbesen'.	U.S.A.
- - 'Monstrosa' Hort. Amer.	1986	An illegit. name raised for a tree having its twigs partly fused together.	
- - **'Nana'** Den Ouden/Boom	1965	A very slow-growing broadly conical plant raised from seed in the Gimborn Arboretum. (1908). NIC.	B,K,W2 Holland
- - 'Pendula' Carrière	1867	Branches pendulous. NIC.	B France
- - 'Pocono' Welch	1979	Named for a seedling found by Layne Zeigenfuss on the Pocono Mountains in 1966. Dwarf cushion shape, short grey-green leaves.	R,W2 U.S.A.
- - 'Virgata' Rehder	1907	A snake-branch tree found at the base of Mount Hopkins, Mass. (1893) I. Arnold Arboretum. NIC?	B,D,K
PICEA rubra (Du Roi) Link	1831	See *PICEA rubens.*.	
PICEA x *saaghyi* Gayer	1929	A hybrid: *PICEA jezoensis* x *PICEA glauca*. Raised at Kámon, Hungary.	Hungary
- - 'Walter Kohler' Bohme	1990	A dwarf conical form with silvery blue leaves raised from seed of the original tree by Walter Kohler of Pirna.	
PICEA sargentiana Rehder & Wilson in Sargent		See *PICEA brachytyla.*	
PICEA schrenkiana Fischer & Meyer	1842	Schrenk Spruce.	30-40m,Z5 Russia,China
- - 'Glauca' Bailey	1933	Leaves glaucous green. NIC.	B U.S.A
- - **'Globosa'** Schelle	1985	A large globose shrub. Known since 1885, but still in cultivation.	B,H,R,W2 Czechosl.
- - var. *tianschanica* (Ruprecht) Cheng & S.H. Fu	1980	A foliar variant.	Eastern Asia.
PICEA shirasawae Hayashi		Shirasawa Spruce. A very rare species. Formerly known as *PICEA bicolor* var *shirasawae*.	20-30m,Z6 Japan
PICEA shrenkiana		See *PICEA schrenkiana.*	
PICEA sitchensis (Bougard) Carrière	1855	Sitka Spruce. Formerly known as *ABIES menziesii*.	60m,Z6
- - 'Aurea' Hort. Amer.	1989	Outstanding for colour, but prone to sunburn.	

- - 'Blue Yosh' Hort. Amer. 1982 A listed name. **L.** Iseli Nurs, Boring, OR.

- - 'Christine Berkau' Hort. Germany
  1983 A dwarf conical plant with bright silvery-blue growth, raised
  from a witch's broom by G. Horstmann.

- - **'Compacta'** Den Ouden 1949 A compact, broadly conical dwarf, to 2m. Reported from
  Arboretum Trompenburg. B,K,R Holland

- - f. *crispa* Antoine 1840 A minor variation in the cone scales. NIC. B Austria

- - 'Fastigiata' Nelson 1866 "Branching fastigiate". NIC. B U.K.

- - 'Gelert' Hort. Anglia 1989 A dwarf mound forming plant. **O.** and **I.** Richard Watson,
  Treborth Nurs, Wales.

- - 'Glauca' Hort. Anglia Reported from Edinburgh Botanic Gardens.

- - 'Hoodie' Hort. Amer. A listed name.

- - 'Innellan Gold' Hort. Anglia
  1985 A listed name.

- - 'Microphylla' Hort. Ireland
  1923 A listed name for a plant found "in the wild". NIC. B,H,K Ireland

- - 'Midget' Hort. Holland 1987 "Dendroflora **24**". A superflous synonym for 'Tenas'. (Note
  that the citation "No.1" is incorrect).

- - 'Mirage' Hort. Holland 1987 **L.** Konijn and Co. in "Sortimentslijst". Upright and open with
  branches pendulous. NIC.

- - 'Nana' (1) Nelson 1866 Name given to a plant which has never been traced,
  presumably lost to cultivation. B,H U.K.

- - 'Nana' (2) Hort. Holland 1986 Quite a loose open dwarf plant propagated in Holland. Origin
  unknown. G

- - 'Ottmanns' Hort? 1991 Dwarf globose plant, quite robust with longer light-blue
  leaves showing silver reverse, maybe difficult to tell apart
  from 'Silberzwerg'.

- - **'Papoose'** G. Bentham 1981 In "Dwarf Conifer Notes **2**". Dwarf, forming a flat topped
  little plant, showing glaucous underside of leaves. Slower
  growing than 'Tenas' and smaller in all it's parts. (Formerly
  No. 1). **O.** Found on Vancouver Is. and given to Parks Dept.
  in Victoria. **I.** Wm. Goddard, received at Wansdyke Nurs,
  Devizes, U.K. in 1979. See also 'Tenas'. R Canada

- - 'Point Loma Cowboy' Int. Con. Reg.
  1981 Slow growing and irregular. **O.** Fred J. Crowe, San Diego,
  Cal. U.S.A.

- - 'Renken' Hort? 1991 Dwarf squat conical. Leaves short and light-blue not showing
  silver reverse.

- - 'Schermbeck' Hort. Germany
  1992 **L.** Horstmann Nurs, Schneverdingen.

- - **'Silberzwerg'** Hort. Germany
  1990 A small conical dwarf plant. **L.** J. zu Jeddeloh Nurs. U.S.A.

- - 'Speciosa' Beissner 1891 A form with glaucous blue needles. B,K Holland

- - **'Strypemonde'** van Hoey Smith
  1979 A dwarf form that arose as a witch's broom on the
  Strypemonde Estate. Conical with irregular shape and
  particularly good silver-blue colour. **L.** Kenwith Nurs,
  Bideford, Devon. G,K,R,W2 Holland

- - 'Sugarloaf' Hort. Amer.   1992 Miniature tree. Discovered at Sugarloaf Mountain. Broadly conical and dense. **I.** Buccholz & Buccholz Nurs, Gaston, OR.

- - 'Tannhoft' Hort. Germany

                1992 **L.** Horstmann Nurs, Schneverdingen.

- - **'Tenas'** G. Bentham   1981 In "Dwarf Conifer Notes **2**". Similar to 'Papoose' at first (and having the same origin) but eventually making a larger plant. (Formerly No. 2).   R   Canada

- - 'Trinket' Hort. Holland   1987 In "Dendroflora **24**". (In error). A superfluous synonym for 'Papoose' (Note the citation No.2 is incorrect).

- - **'Upright Dwarf'** Hort. Amer.

                1972 An unacceptable name for a plant listed by Watnong Nurs.

- - 'Virgata' Hort. Amer.   1989 An illegit. listed name for a snake-branch tree.

PICEA shrenkiana   See *PICEA schrenkiana*.

PICEA smithiana (Wallich) Boissier

                1884 West Himalayan Spruce. (Formerly known as *PICEA morinda).*   40m,Z6   S.E. Asia

- - **'Ballarat'** Hort. Australia 1993 Raised from a witch's broom. A very dense, clump-forming plant. **O.** P.C. Nitschke, **I.** John Emery, Drue Wholesale Nurs.

- - 'Monstrosa' Carrière   1869 Named for a curious tree in the Municipal Nurs, Paris. NIC.   B   France

- - var. *nepalensis* Franco   A local variant found in west Nepal.   R

- - 'Pendula' Sénéclauze   1868 An unidentifiable deviant.   B   France

PICEA spinulosa (Griffith) Henry

                1906 Sikkim Spruce.   25+m,Z7   Himalayas

PICEA tianschanica (Ruprecht) Cheng & S.H. Fu.

                1980 See under *PICEA schrenkiana*.

PₐCEA tonaiensis Nakai   A species close to *PICEA koraiensis*.

PICEA torano Koehne   1893 Now known as *PICEA polita*.

PICEA veitchii (Lindley) Murray   Now known as *ABIES veitchii*.

PICEA vulgaris Link   Now known as *PICEA abies*.

PICEA watsoniana Masters

                1906 (See PICEA wilsonii).

PICEA webbiana (Lindley) Loudon

                Now known as *ABIES spectabilis*.

PICEA wilsonii Masters   1903 Wilson Spruce.   15-20m,Z5   E. Asia

PILGERODENDRON Florin (1930)

Cupressaceae

A monotypic genus from Chile for many years included in *Libocedrus*.

PILGERODENDRON uviferum (Pilger) Florin
        1930 Patagonian Pilgerodendron. (Formerly known as
           LIBOCEDRUS uvifera) (Pilger).   8-15m,Z7   S. Amer.

P I N U S Linnaeus (1753)

Pinaceae

The Pines form a large genus of nearly one hundred species, many of forest-tree size, distributed widely throughout the northern hemisphere, although some species have a very restricted habitat. Some species are variable from seed and several are prone to develop witch's brooms, so in some cases there is a large number of cultivars, many being sufficiently slow-growing to rank as "dwarf-forms". The nomenclature of such a large group is difficult and many changes have been made over the years. The classification of some species, especially those occurring in the Mexican area is still unresolved. The listings here follow Silba (1984) or Rushforth (1987) except where otherwise stated. Since all the *Pinaceae* were included in *Pinus* by Linnaeus and have only acquired their present names over a long period, very many cross-references are listed, but an exhaustive synonymy has not been attempted.

PINUS abies Linnaeus   1753 Now known as *PICEA abies*.

PINUS alba Aiton   1789 Now known as *PICEA glauca*.

PINUS albicaulis Engelmann
        1863 Whitebark Pine. 2n.   15m,Z4   Rocky Mts.

- - 'Algonquin Pillar' Hort. Canada
        1987 L. T. J. Cole in "Woody Plant List". NOM.

- - **'Flink'** Hort. Germany   1978 A dwarf form raised from seed from a witch's broom by G.
           Horstmann of Schneverdingen. Upright growing. One year
           shoots densely covered with dark brown pubescence.   K,R   Germany

- - 'Landis' Hort. Canada   1981 L. Gordon Bentham, Victoria. Without description.

- - 'Nana' Hillier   1964 An illegit. name for 'Noble's Dwarf'.

- - **'Noble's Dwarf'** Den Ouden/Boom
        1965 A dwarf, shrubby upright form with compact habit. Leaves
           grey-green, shoot pubescence not noticeable. O. James Noble
           collection, San Francisco.   B,R,W2   U.S.A.

- - 'Number One Dwarf' Hort. Amer.
        1987 Dwarf growing upright form. Maximum 2" per year. Listed
           E.A. Cope and some American Nurs. A better name should be
           found. (1S Witch's Broom).   U.S.A.

PINUS amamiana Koidzumi
        1924 A rare species differing from *PINUS armandii* in minor
           respects. Not now distinguished within that species by some
           authorities. (per Silba, 1984).0   40m,Z8   Japan

PINUS apulcensis Lindley   1839 Apulco Pine. 5n. Formerly listed as *PINUS pseudostrobus*
           var. *apulcensis*.   40m,Z9   Mexico

PINUS araragi Siebold   1844 Now known as *TSUGA sieboldii*.

PINUS aristata Engelmann ex Parry & Engelmann
     1862 Bristlecone Pine. Famous for the specimens (var. *longaeva*) in Arizona 4,900 years old.   5-15m   U.S.A/Mexico

- - 'Baldwin Dwarf' J.W. Spingarn
     1971 L. J.W. Spingarn, Long Is. N.Y. Now renamed 'Cecilia'.   W2

- - **'Cecilia'** J.W. Spingarn   1979 Young plants globular, eventually leader forming. Leaves white spotted with resin as in the species. Dwarf seedling found by J. W. Spingarn then of Long Is. N.Y. and named for his wife.   K,W2   U.S.A.

- - 'Little Mound' Hort. Canada
     1981 L. Gordon Bentham, Victoria. Without description.

- - var. *longaeva* (Bailey) Little
     1979 Western Bristlecone Pine. By some authorities listed as *PINUS longaeva* Bailey (1970), (per Rushforth, 1987).   K,R   U.S.A.

- - 'Ossorio Variegated' Hort. Amer.
     1988 L. Mitsch Nurs, Aurora, OR. Without description.

- - **'Sherwood Compact'** Krüssmann
     1983 Dwarf form with tight growth and ascending habit. Leaves much shorter than the species and very few white resin spots.   K   U.S.A.

- - 'Woods' Hort. Amer.   1991 L. Arboretum Trompenburg, Rotterdam, Holland.

PINUS arizonica (Engelmann) Shaw
     1909 Arizona Pine. Now known as *PINUS ponderosa* var. *arizonica*.   Mexico

- - var. *stormiae* Martine   1948 A minor variant of uncertain standing.   N.E. Mexico

PINUS armandii Franchet   1884 Armand Pine, Chinese White Pine.   40m,Z7   China etc

- - var. *amamiana* Koidzumi
     1924 Amm pine. Recognised as a distinct species by some authorities. (per Rushforth, 1987).   K,R

- - var. *mastersiana* Hayata   1908 Not now distinguished within the species by some authorities (per Silba, 1984).   K,R

PINUS attenuata Lemmon   1892 Knobcone Pine. 3n.   10-25m,Z7   U.S.A/Mexico

PINUS x *attenuradiata* Stockwell & Richter
     1946 An artificial hybrid: *PINUS attenuata* x *PINUS radiata*.   B

PINUS ayacahuite Ehrenberg & Schlechtendal
     1838 Mexican White Pine. 5n.   25-35m,Z7   Mexico etc

- - var. *brachyptera* (Engelmann) Shaw
     1909 Now known as *PINUS strobiformis* (per Silba, 1984).   B,D,K

- - var. *strobiformis* Lemmon
     1892 Now known as *PINUS reflexa* (per Rushforth, 1987).   B

- - var. *veitchii* (Roezl) Shaw
     1909 A regional variant with larger seeds. No longer disting-uished within the species by some authorities (per Rushforth, 1987).   B,K,R

PINUS balfouriana Jeffrey ex A. Murray
     1853 Northern Foxtail Pine. 5n. Differs from other Foxtail Pines by the absence of white resin dots.   10-15m,Z6   California

- - subsp. *austrina* (Mastrogiuseppe & Mastrogiuseppe) Silba
     1984 Southern Foxtail Pine. 5n. A local minor variant.   S. California

- - 'Dwarf Form' J.W. Spingarn   Conical dwarf to one metre, shapely bush tightly clothed with foliage.

PINUS banatica Georgescu & Ionescu
1936 Now treated as a regional variant of *PINUS nigra*.

PINUS banksiana Lambert
1803 Jack Pine. 2n. Shrub or broadly conical tree. Hardy but of little ornamental value. It has produced a number of garden cultivars.   10-20m,Z2   N.E. America

- - 'AA2' Hort. Amer. 1991 Plant in Arboretum Trombenburg, Rotterdam. **L.** Horstmann Nurs, Schneverdingen.

- - 'Al Johnson' Hort. Amer.
1990 A listed name. Further information requested.

- - 'Annae' Schwerin 1909 Leaves partly yellowish-white. NIC   B,K   Germany

- - 'Arctis' No information.

- - **'Chippewa'** Welch 1979 Irregular low bush. **O.** and **I.** Raised by Alfred Fordham at Arnold Arboretum.   W2   U.S.A.

- - 'Compacta' Hort. 1986 Illustration in "Conifers". Probably an illegit. name.   G

- - 'Elkin's Dwarf' Hort. Amer.
1967 Now listed as 'Tucker's Dwarf'.

- - 'Fastigiata' Hort. Amer. 1986 An illegit. listed name. Information requested.

- - 'Flach Creeper' Hort. Germany
1992 A listed name, without description.

- - 'Hexenbesen' Hort. Germany
1992' Dwarf tight bush with short twisted yellow-green leaves. **L.** Horstmann Nurs, Schneverdingen.

- - 'H.J.Welch' Hort. Anglia 1980 An illegit. name for a low-growing bush. **L.** Wansdyke Nurs, Devizes, Wilts, U.K. **O.** A seedling at Minnesota Bot. Gar. by A.G. Johnson and sent to H.J. Welch in 1974.   U.S.A.

- - **'Manomet'** Welch 1979 Dwarf, globose as young plant but later leader forming and conical. **O.** As 'Chippewa'.   W2   U.S.A.

- - 'Nana' Hort. Amer. 1986 An illegit. listed name. NOM.

- - **'Neponset'** Welch 1979 Low, flat-topped and spreading; leaves persistent. **O.** As 'Chippewa'.   W2   U.S.A.

- - 'Nidiformis' Hort. Germany
1992 A listed name, without description.

- - 'Pendula' Hort. Amer. 1991 In "Nurs. Cat". Foxborough Nurs, Maryland. ('Weeper').

- - 'Repens' Hort. Germany 1992 A listed name, without description.

- - **'Schoodic'** Welch 1979 Prostrate, mat-forming, needles short. **O.** As 'Chippewa'.   W2   U.S.A.

- - **'Tucker's Dwarf'** Hort. Germany
1978 Tage Lundell of Sweden received scions from Harry Elkins who suggested the name. It is probably the same as 'Elkin's Dwarf'. Small globose bush tightly covered with small shoots and leaves.   G   U.S.A.

- - **'Uncle Fogy'** Reg'd. Arnold Arb.
1970 Small contorted tree. **R.** A.G. Johnson, Minneapolis. 'Fogey' was a mistake, later corrected by Johnson.   W2   U.S.A.

- - 'Watt's Golden' Hort. Amer.
1986 A listed name.

- - 'Weeper' Hort. Amer.   1980 O. J.W. Spingarn, Long Is., N.Y. ('Pendula').

- - 'Westhawk Lake' Hort. Germany
1991 A listed name, without description.

- - 'Winipek' Hort. Germany
1991 A listed name, without description.

- - **'Wisconsin'** Welch   1979 Dense, rounded bush. **O.** As 'Chippewa'.   W2   U.S.A.

PINUS bhutanica Grierson, Long & Page
1980 Eastern Himalayan Pine, Bhutan Pine. A recently described
species from Bhutan.   25m,Z9   Bhutan

PINUS brachyptera Engelmann
1848 Now known as *PINUS ponderosa* var. *scopulorum*.

PINUS bracteata D. Don   1837 Now know as *ABIES bracteata*.

PINUS brutia Tenore   1811 Calabrian Pine. By some authorities listed as *PINUS halepensis* var. *brutia*. (See Silba, 1984).   10-15m   Turkey etc.

- - var. *eldarica* (Medwediew) Magini & Tulst.
1886 Eilar Pine. A geographical variant. Here listed as a species.   12-15m   USSR

- - var. *pityusa* (Steven) Silba
1986 Black Sea Pine. A geographical variant, here listed as a
species. (pithyusa).   8-20m   Ukraine

- - var. *pyramidalis* Selik   A sporadic variant with columnar habit.

- - var. *stankewiczii* (Sukaczev) Fomin
1914 See *PINUS stankewiczii*.

- - 'Susan Forreyan' G. Haddow
1992 Dwarf globular bush. **O.** Raised from witch's broom seed by
S. Forreyan, Leicester. **I.** Kenwith Nurs, Bideford, Devon.

PINUS bungeana Zuccarini ex Endlicher
1847 Lacebark Pine. 3n.   20m,Z4   China

- - 'B Dwarf' Hort. Amer.   Small upright bushy plant. Leaves mid green, slightly
incurved. Buchholz Nurs, Gaston, OR. Correct name
required.

- - 'Diamant' Hort. Germany
1990 Dwarf form with short straight yellow-green leaves. **O.** A
witch's broom found in the Diamant Nurs, Duisburg. **I.**
Jeddeloh Nurs, Oldenburg.   Germany

- - 'Fastigiate' Hort. Amer.   1975 L. Raraflora Nurs, Feasterville, PA, without description.

- - 'Rowe' Hort. Amer.   1988 L. Mitsch Nurs, Aurora, OR, without description.

PINUS canadensis Linnaeus
1753 Now known as *TSUGA canadensis*.

PINUS canariensis C. Smith
1825 Canary Island Pine. Not hardy in U.K.   24-40m,Z9   Canary Is.

- - 'Jericho' Hort. Australia   1993 O. Peter Nitschke.

- - 'Pete's Pygmy' Hort. Australia
1993 O. Peter Nitschke.

- - 'Zulu' Hort. Australia   1993 O. Peter Nitschke.

PINUS caribaea Morelet	1851 Caribbean Pine. 3n. Not hardy in U.K.	10-40m,Z10 Cuba

- - var. **bahamensis** (Grisebach) Barret ex Golfari
1962 Bahaman Pine. 3n.
Bahamas

- - var. *hondurensis* (Sénéclauze) Barret ex Golfari
1962 A local variant no longer distinguished within the species by
some authorities.
S

PINUS catarinae Robert-Passini
1981 Now merged in *PINUS remota* (per Silba,1984).
S

PINUS caucasica Fischer   Not now distinguished within *PINUS sylvestris*.

PINUS cedrus Linnaeus   1753 Now known as *CEDRUS libani*.

PINUS celakofskiorum Ascherson & Graebner
A hybrid: *PINUS sylvestris* x *PINUS mugo* var. *pumilio*.
Europe

PINUS cembra Linnaeus   1753 Arolla Pine, Swiss Stone pine. A conical tree. 5n.   25-40m,Z5   Central Europe

- - 'Alba' Nelson   1866 "The very white form". NIC.

- - 'Argentea' Schelle   1909 Superfluous name for 'Glauca' (1) NIC.

- - 'Aurea' Hort. ex Fitschen in Beissner
1930 Doubtfully distinct from the following entry.
G,K

- - **'Aureovariegata'** Sénéclauze
1868 Foliage in parts a golden-yellow. Narrowly upright form.
Yellow brightest in winter. Still listed in U.K. **O.** and **I.**
Sénéclauze Nurs, Bourg Argental, Loires.
B,K,R,W2   France

- - **'Barnhourie'** G. Haddow
1987 In "Nurs. Cat". Dwarf narrowly upright form with dark green
leaves. **O.** Selected by Miss E. King, Dalbeattie, Scotland. **I.**
Kenwith Nurs, Bideford, Devon.
U.K.

- - 'Bennett Dwarf' Hort. Amer.
1975 A listed name. Raraflora Nurs, Feasterville, PA.

- - 'Blaue Form' G. Horstmann
1978 **L.** Watnong Nurs, N. Jersey.
Germany

- - 'Blauspinne' Hort. Holland
1986 A listed name. Information requested.

- - 'Blue Mops' Hort. Holland
1986 A listed name. Information requested.

- - **'Blue Mound'** G. Bentham
1987 "Dwarf Conifer Notes". Original plant mound shaped,
propagations conical; foliage a good blue. **O.** and **I.**
Floravista Gardens, Vancouver Is., B.C.
Canada

- - 'Broom' Hort. Amer.
1986 In "Nurs. Cat". Dwarf bushy plant with a leader, leaves dark
green. **O.** unknown. **I.** M. Kristick.

- - **'Chalet'** Vermeulen
1972 In "Nurs. Cat". Dense, rounded column; soft bluish-green. **O.**
and **I.** Vermeulen Nurs, Neshanic Station, N.J.
R,W2   U.S.A.

- - **'Chamolet'** L.C. Hatch
1988 In "Conifer Database". Slow-growing, columnar selection.
U.S.A.

- - var. *chlorocarpa* (1) Beissner
1899 A sporadic variant with yellow-green cones.
B,WI,W2

- - var. *chlorocarpa* (2) H.G. Hillier
1964 Now known as *PINUS pumila* 'Compacta'.

- - 'Chlorocarpa' Hort. Europe   See previous item.   W1

- - 'Columnaris' Hellemänn   1897 Named for a plant found by Hellemänn in Moorende. Now
used loosely for several clones.   Germany

- - 'Compacta' Hort.   A name of no clear application or present value.

- - **'Compacta Glauca'** Den Ouden/Boom
1965 Compact grower; foliage glaucous blue, otherwise normal. **O.**
Frets & Zonen Nurs, Boskoop.   B,G,K   Holland

- - 'Fastigiata' F.G. Meyer   1963 In "Plant Explorations". A superfluous synonym for 'Stricta'.

- - 'Glauca' Nelson   1866 "The very glaucous form". Similar forms turn up and are in
cultivation.   B,K   U.K.

- - 'Glauca Compacta' Hort. Germany
1990 An illegit. listed name. Further information requested.

- - 'Globe' Hort. Holland   Now known as *PINUS pumila* 'Globe'.   B,K,W

- - 'Helvetica' Forbes   1839 A spreading, open form with large cones. NIC.   U.K.

- - 'Inverleith' G.Haddow   1985 In "Nurs. Cat". Upright bushy dwarf pine to 1 metre in 30
years. **O.** Selected by Miss E. King, Dalbeattie, Scotland
1933 and donated to the Royal Botanic Gardens, Edinburgh.
I. Kenwith Nurs, Bideford, Devon.   W2   Scotland

- - 'Japonica' Nelson   1866 "The Japanese form". NIC.   U.K.

- - **'Jermyns'** H.G. Hillier   1971 Extremely dwarf bushy little plant with pale silver-blue
incurved leaves. **O.** and **I.** Hillier's Nurs. (Listed by H.G.
Hillier in 1964 as *PINUS pumila* 'Jermyns', in error but later
corrected by him in his Manual of Trees & Shrubs).   W2

- - 'Kairamo' Schwerin   1926 Named for a pendulous tree in the garden of A. O. Kairomi in
Pekola. NIC.   B,K   Finland
- - 'King's Dwarf' G. Haddow
1989 In "Nurs. Cat". **O.** Selected seedling by Miss E. King in 1933
of Dalbeattie, Scotland. Very dwarf squat conical bush. **I.**
Kenwith Nurs, Bideford, Devon.   U.K.

- - 'Landis' Hort. Canada   1981 L. Gordon Bentham, Victoria, Canada.

- - 'Monophylla' Carrière   1855 A tree carrying most of its leaf-bundles tightly closed. NIC.   B,K,R   France

- - 'Nana' Gordon   1815 Dwarf, upright, compact with blue-grey needles. A definite
cembra form. Listed in the Lawson Nurs. Cat, Edinburgh,
Scotland.   U.K.

- - 'Pendula' Nelson   1866 "The slender, drooping-branched form". NIC.   B,K,R   U.K.

- - 'Prostrata' Hort. Amer.   1986 An illegit. listed name.

- - var. *pumila* Pallas   1784 Now known as *PINUS pumila*.   W2

- - var. *pygmaea* Loudon   1838 Now known as *PINUS pumila*.

- - 'Pygmaea' Hort. Amer.   1986 See *PINUS pumila* 'Pygmaea'.   W2

- - 'Pyramidalis' Hort. Anglia
1985 Reported from Windsor Great Park, Berks. Probably a
superfluous name for 'Columnaris'.

- - 'Roughills' G. Haddow   1991 In "Nurs. Cat". **O.** Selected seedling by Miss E. King (1933)
of Dalbeattie, Scotland. Dwarf stronger growing, dark green
leaves. **I.** Kenwith Nurs, Bideford, Devon.   U.K.

- - var. *sibirica* Loudon   1830 Now known as *PINUS sibirica*.   B

- - **'Silver Sheen'** Vermeulen

    1985 In "Nurs. Cat". Slow, conical form; silver-blue, white stomata. L. Vermeulen and Son Nurs, Neshanic Station, N.J.   U.S.A.

- - **'Stricta'** Carrière

    1855 Slender column; fastigiate branch-system like a Lombardy poplar. This distinguishes it from 'Columnaris'.   B,G,K,R   France

- - **'Variegata'** R. Smith

    1864 Having some of its leaves a pale straw colour. NIC, but similar forms appear.   B,K   U.K.

- - **'Viridis'** Sénéclauze

    1868 Named for a tree on the Sénéclauze Nurs, Bourg Argental, Loires. NIC.   B   France

PINUS cembroides (1) Newberry

    1857 Now known as *PINUS albicaulis.*

PINUS cembroides (2) Zuccarini

    1852 Mexican Pinyon Pine, 2 or 3n.   5-15m,Z7   Mexico

This is one of a group of related pines in Mexico, the classification of which is the subject of botanical debate. The classification here follows Rushforth, (1987).

- - 'Albovariegata' Schwerin   1910 Named for a plant found by Count von Schwerin in a seedbed, with much of its foliage white. The clone in cultivation with its foliage speckled white is not the same.   B   Germany

- - 'Blandsfortiana' V. Gibbs

    1932 Named for a curiosity that was never propagated. NIC.   B,H,K   U.K.

- - var. *edulis* (Engelmann) Jones

    1891 Here accepted as a species, *PINUS edulis.*(per Rushforth, 1987).   B,D,K,R   Mexico

- - 'Glauca' Hort. Anglia   1985 Reported from Windsor Great Park, Berks. Name probably illegit.

- - 'Juno' G. Haddow   1987 Slow growing selection with outer half of leaves cream coloured. O. and I. Kenwith Nurs, Bideford, Devon.

- - subsp. **lagunae** (Robert-Passini) Bailey

    1981 A minor variant with a limited habitat.   R   Mexico

- - var. *monophylla* (Torrey) Voss

    1908 One-needle Pine. Here accepted as a species.   R   Mexico

- - subsp. **orizabensis** Bailey

    1983 Another minor variant with a restricted habitat.   Mexico

- - var. *parryana* (Engelmann) Voss

    Now known as *PINUS quadrifolia.*   B,R

- - var. *quadrifolia* (Parlatore) De Laubenfels

    1984 Here listed as *PINUS quadrifolia*   R   Mexico

- - var. *remota* Little   1966 Now known as *PINUS remota.*   R   Mexico

PINUS cephalonica (Loudon) Endlicher

    1847 Now known as *ABIES cephalonica.*

PINUS chiapensis (Martinez) Andrésen

    1964 Chiapas Pine. 5n. By some authorities regarded as a variety of *PINUS strobus.*   S   Mexico

PINUS chihuahuana Engelmann

    1848 Chihuahana Pine.

PINUS clausa (Chapman ex Engelmann) Vasey & Sargent

    1880 Southern Sand Pine. Low spreading tree, seldom seen in cultivation.   5-7m,Z7   S.East U.S.A.

- - var. *immuginata* D.B.Ward
  1961 Northern Sand Pine. A local variant now accepted as a
  distinct species.   R

PINUS *concolor* Parlatore in De Candolle
  1868 Now known as *ABIES concolor*.

PINUS *contorta* Douglas ex Loudon
  1838 Shore Pine. 2n. Rushforth (1987) treats vars. *bolanderi*,
  latifolia, murrayana and *contorta*, (the typical form) as
  subspecies.   25m   U.S.A.

- - 'Aurea' Hort. Amer.   A mistake for *PINUS contorta* 'Frisian Gold'.

- - 'Asher' G. Haddow   1992 Quite strong growing dwarf form with ascending branches.
  Leaves on the current years branches decreasing in length to
  the apex. **O.** and **I.** Richard Watson, Treborth Nurs, Bangor,
  N. Wales.

- - 'Banff' Hort. Germany   1983 A listed name.

- - var. *bolanderi* Lemmon   1894 Mendicino Shore Pine. A shrubby, local form, not now
  distinguished within the species.   S

- - 'Compacta' Hort. Europe   1986 An illegit. name for a shrubby form illustrated in the book
  "Conifers".   G,R

- - 'Conica Pygmaea' Hort. Amer.
  1970 An illegit. name. L. F.W. Bergman, Feasterville, PA. NOM.

- - **'Frisian Gold'** Krüssmann
  1979 Leaves bright golden-yellow. Not quite hardy. Found as a
  witch's broom at the Jeddeloh Nurs. **O.** Jeddeloh Nurs,
  Oldenburg.   G,K,R,W2   Germany

- - 'Goldchen' Welch   1979 The name arose as a result of a misunderstanding. 'Frisian
  Gold' is the correct name.   W2

- - "Hindu Pan" Hort. Amer.   Commercial term used for certain artificially trained trees. Not a
  cultivar name.

- - **'Inverewe'** R. Fulcher   1988 In "Roy. Hort. Soc. Journ. **105**(10)". Conical habit, medium
  vigour; patches of golden-yellow foliage.   U.K.

- - 'Jasper' Hort. Germany   1983 L. G. Horstmann, Schneverdingen.

- - var. *latifolia* Engelmann ex Watson
  1871 Rocky Mountain Lodgepole Pine. The inland form of the
  species.   B,K   Rocky Mts.

- - 'Minima' Hort. Amer.   1986 An illegit. name of uncertain application.

- - var. *murrayana* (Greville & Balfour) Engelmann
  1879 Sierra Lodgepole Pine. (*murrayensis*).   K   Mexico, U.S.A.

- - 'Pendula' Hort. Europe   1986 An illegit. name for a plant illustrated in the book "Conifers". G

- - **'Rustic'** L.C. Hatch   1988 In "Conifer Database". Growth contorted and irregular;
  leaves thick, dark green.   U.S.A.

- - 'San Bernadino'   **O.** A witch's broom found by J.R.P. van Hoey-Smith.   Holland

- - 'San Francisco' Hort. Germany
  1983 L. G. Horstmann, Schneverdingen.

- - 'Sonora Pass' Hort. Germany
  1983 Rather stiffly branched little plant. Leaves held at 45o to the
  branchlets. L. G. Horstmann, Schneverdingen.

- - **'Spaan's Dwarf'** Welch	1979 Squat or globose dwarf; thick, upstanding branches; short dark green leaves.	G,R,W2	U.S.A.
- - 'Spaan's Globe' Hort. Amer.	A listed name.		
- - 'Taylor's Goldtip' Hort. Amer.	Name changed to 'Taylor's Sunburst'.		
- - **'Taylor's Sunburst'** J. Iseli	1982 In "Nurs. Cat". L. Iseli Nurs, Boring, OR.		U.S.A.
- - 'Tioga Pass Hexenbesen' Hort. Germany	1992 A listed name, without description.		
- - 'Treborth' G. Haddow	1992 Very dwarf, globe shaped form with dark green leaves. O. Richard Watson, Treborth Nurs, Bangor, N. Wales. I. Kenwith Nurs, Bideford, Devon.		
PINUS cooperi Blanco	1949 Cooper Pine. 5n.	30m,Z7	Mexico
- - var. *ornelasii* (Martinez) Blanco	1950 A vigorous form with minor differences in foliage and cones.		
PINUS coulteri D. Don	1836 Coulter Pine, Big-cone Pine. Remarkable for the enormous cones.	15-25m, Z8	S. West U.S.A.
PINUS cubensis Sargent	1862 Cuban Pine. 2n. By some authorities listed as *PINUS occidentalis* var. *cubensis*.	S	
PINUS culminicola Andrésen & Beaman	1961 Cerro Potosi Pinyon Pine. A shrub. 5n.	4m,Z6	U.S.A./Mexico
PINUS dabeshanensis Cheng & Law	1975 Dabieshan Pine. A species near to *PINUS armandii*.	30-40m,Z9	E. China
PINUS dalatensis de Ferre	1960 Dalat Pine. By some authorities listed as *PINUS wallichiana* var. *dalatensis*.	S	
PINUS densa (Little & Dorman) Gaussen	1960 South Florida Slash Pine; Dade Pine. Formerly known as *PINUS elliotii* var. *densa*.	S	
PINUS densata Masters	1906 Gaoshan Pine. 2 or 3n. An uncommon species close to *PINUS tabulaeformis*.	30m,Z7	China
PINUS densiflora Siebold & Zuccarini	1842 Japanese Red Pine. 2n.	20-30m,Z5	China/Japan

"Akamatzu" being the Japanese name for the Red Pine, it should properly not be used as part of a cultivar name, but several descriptive cultivar names (such as 'Cristata', 'Oculus-draconis') are in use in several other species so the use is condoned here to avoid confusion. Some of the Japanese vernacular names given by Mayr may not be synonyms in the present-day sense. Many of the following have never reached western cultivation and may no longer be known in Japan under these or any names.

- - f. *aggregata* Nakai in Kobayashi	1975 In "Matsu-zukan". (Text in Japanese).		
- - **'Aka-bandaisho'** Mayr	1890 A particular clone of 'Globosa'. (in cultivation under this name in U.S.A.).	W2	Hort. Japan
- - 'Aka-fuiri' Mayr	1890 A synonym of 'Variegata'.	W2	Hort. Japan
- - 'Aka-Hitoba-no-matsu' Mayr	1890 A synonym of 'Monophylla'. (Hitotsuba-matsu).	W2	Hort. Japan
- - 'Akasemmosho' Mayr	1890 A synonym of 'Tortuosa'.	W2	Hort. Japan
- - 'Aka-senmo-matsu' Mayr	1890 A synonym of 'Tortuosa'.	W2	Hort. Japan

- - **'Akebono'** Kobayashi   1975 In "Matsu-zukan". Leaves tipped with yellow, turning green later. L. L.C. Hatch in "Conifer Database 1988".   Hort. Japan

- - **'Albo-terminata'** Mayr   1890 Tips of the leaves yellowish-white.   B   Hort. Japan

- - **'Alice Verkade'** Welch   1979 A multiple-stemmed, semi-dwarf form. I. Verkade Nurs, Wayne, N.J. O. The same.   G,K,R,W2   U.S.A.

- - **'Anguina'** Kobayashi   1975 Snake Pine. A clone with twisted, snake-like branches.   Hort. Japan

- - 'Arakaba-sho' Mayr   1890 A synonym of 'Tortuosa'.   Hort. Japan

- - **'Argentea'** Kobayashi   1975 In "Matsu-zukan".   Hort. Japan

- - **'Argenteovariegata'** Dallimore & Jackson
                                1923 Patches of silvery-white leaves.   B,D   Hort. Japan

- - 'Asamamatsu' Mayr   1890 A synonym of, or a clone of f. *asamensis*.   Hort. Japan

- - **'Asamensis'** Mayr   1890 Dwarf, growth distorted and stunted.   B   Hort. Japan

- - **'Aspera'** Mayr   1890 A dwarf form; bark grey, abnormally thick and cracked.   B   Hort. Japan

- - **'Aurea'** Mayr   1890 Patches of light-golden foliage.   B,D,K,R   Hort. Japan

- - 'Aureopendula' Kobayashi
                                1975 In "Matsu-zukan". Probably a mistake for 'Aureovariegata Pendula'.

- - **'Aureovariegata'** Dallimore & Jackson
                                1923 Patches of golden-yellow leaves.   Hort. Japan

- - **'Aureovariegata Pendula'** Mayr
                                1890 Pendulous, leaves golden-yellow. A monstrosity produced by grafting scions of 'Aurea' onto a tree of 'Pendula'.   B   Hort. Japan

- - **'Aurescens'** Kobayashi   1975 In "Matsu-zukan". Foliage yellowish.   Hort. Japan

- - 'Bandai-sho' Mayr   1890 A synonym of 'Octo-partita'.   Hort. Japan

- - **'Barbata'** Mayr   1890 Leaves irregularly twisted.   B   Hort. Japan

- - 'Bergman' L.C. Hatch   1988 In "Conifer Database". O. F. Bergman. Raraflora, Feasterville, PA.   U.S.A.

- - 'Burke' Hort. Amer.   1988 Red variegated seedling. L. Mitsch Nurs, Aurora, OR.

- - **'Chuya-matsu'** Welch   1979 A clone of 'Variegata' with leaves white at the base, green towards the tip.   Hort. Japan

- - **'Cristata'** Kobayashi   1975 Some branches fasciated like a cockscomb.   W2   Hort. Japan

- - 'Elmwood Compact'   1991 In "Nurs. Cat". Rich's Foxwillow Pines, Woodstock, Illinois.

- - 'Enko-sho' (1) Mayr   1890 A synonym of 'Longiramea'.   Hort. Japan

- - 'Enko-sho' (2) Hort. Amer.
                                1988 Described as a tree of moderate size and weeping habit.   W2

- - f. *erecta* Krüssmann   1983 Possibly a natural hybrid: *PINUS densiflora* x *PINUS thunbergii*.   K   Korea

- - 'Erecta' Hort. Anglia   1984 Reported from the Royal Botanic Gardens, Kew, as *forma erecta*.

- - var. *funebris* (Komarov) Liou & Wang
                                1955 Sikhote Red Pine.   6-12m.   Korea; China

- - 'Ganseki-matsu' Mayr   1890 A synonym of 'Aspera'.

- - **'Globosa'** Mayr · 1890 Dwarf, semi-globose. Similar forms turn up from seed, e.g. 'Alice Verkade'. · B,G,K,W2 · Hort. Japan

- - 'Goblin's Nest' Welch · 1979 See 'Tengu-su'.

- - **'Griffith Prostrate'** L.C. Hatch
  · 1988 In "Conifer Database". Dwarf, globose; foliage bright green. · U.S.A.

- - 'Hai-iro-matsu' Welch · 1979 Leaves turn from the normal green to greyish-yellow. · W2 · Hort. Japan

- - 'Hase-matsu' Mayr · 1890 A synonym of 'Mōllis'.

- - **'Heavy Bud'** Welch · 1979 A clone similar to 'Alice Verkade' but distinguished by its large brown buds in winter. I. Vermeulen and Son Nurs, Neshanic Station, N.J. · W2 · U.S.A.

- - 'Hebe-matsu' Welch · 1979 A synonym of 'Anguina'. In cultivation in U.S.A. as 'Hebe'. · W2 · Hort. Japan

- - **'Hospitalis'** Mayr · 1890 Leaves half the normal length. · B · Hort. Japan

- - 'Ippon-matsu' Mayr · 1890 A synonym of 'Monophylla'. · B,W2 · Hort. Japan

- - **'Jane Kluis'** L.C. Hatch · 1988 In "Conifer Database". A globose dwarf form with fresh-green straight leaves and conspicuous buds. Possibly a hybrid: *PINUS densiflora* x *PINUS nigra*. O. Kluis Nurs. · U.S.A.

- - **'Jano-me'** Mayr · 1890 A synonym of 'Oculus Draconis'. (But it is in cultivation under this name in U.S.A.). · W2 · Hort. Japan

- - 'Jim Cross' Hort. Amer.
  · 1991 Very congested, flat topped dwarf globe, it's reddish bark being a good contrast to the bright green needles. 3 ft in 15 years. In "Nurs. Cat". Rarafolia, Kintersville, PA. ('Jim Cross 168').

- - 'Kakuyo-sho' Mayr · 1890 A synonym of 'Hospitalis'. · W2 · Hort. Japan

- - 'Kokin-sho' Mayr · 1890 A synonym of 'Rubroaurea'. · W2 · Hort. Japan

- - 'Koyomatsu' Hort. Amer. Leaves white-banded, tinged pink.

- - **'Laver's Broom'** L.C. Hatch
  · 1988 In "Conifer Database". Dwarf, globose habit, bright green. · U.S.A.

- - **'Little Christopher'** Hort. Amer.
  · 1991 Rounded globular umbrella-like head. Bright green colour. ('Rezek Seedling').

- - 'Longiramea' Mayr · 1890 Head leader erect, branches few. · B · Hort. Japan

- - **'Low Glow'** S. Waxman · 1990 In "Int. Pl. Prop. Soc. Bull.". A witch's broom seedling; a low mound with short needles; bright yellow-green foliage. O. S. Waxman at the University of Connecticut, Storrs, CT. · U.S.A.

- - 'Mini Kin' Hort. Germany
  · 1992 L. Horstmann Nurs, Schneverdingen. Without description.

- - **'Mitsuba-akamatsu'** Welch
  · 1979 A synonym for *PINUS densiflora* f. *subtrifoliata*. · W2

- - **'Mōllis'** Mayr · 1890 Leaves long, slender, greyish-green. · B · Hort. Japan

- - **'Monophylla'** Mayr · 1890 One-leaved. · B · Hort. Japan

- - 'Nishiki-akamatsu' Welch
  · 1979 A synonym of 'Aspera'. · W2

- - **'Octo-partita'** Mayr · 1890 With buds in clusters of eight. · B · Hort. Japan

- - **'Oculus-draconis'** Mayr 1890 "Dragon's Eye". Leaves form alternately green and yellow rings, viewed from above. B,G,K,R Hort. Japan

- - 'Oculus-draconis' 1975 'Eechee', 'Nee', 'Sun', and 'Shee'. These forms listed by Fred Bergman in Additions page. Further information required.

- - **'Oculus-draconis Pendula'** Mayr 1890 A pendulous variant from the last. Hort. Japan

- - 'Ogon-akamatsu' Mayr 1890 A synonym of 'Aurea'. W2 Hort. Japan

- - 'Ogon-shibore' Welch 1979 A synonym of 'Aurescens'. W2 Hort. Japan

- - 'Ori-tsuru' Mayr 1890 A synonym of 'Recurva'. W2 Hort. Japan

- - f. *parviphylla* Uyeki in Kobayashi 1975 In "Matsu-zukan". Hort. Japan

- - **'Pendula'** Mayr 1890 Habit pendulous or prostrate. B,G,H,K,R Hort. Japan

- - 'Pendula Oculus-draconis' A mistake for 'Oculus-draconis Pendula'.

- - **'Prolifera'** Mayr 1890 Cones densely set. B Hort. Japan

- - 'Prostrata' Hort. See 'Pendula'.

- - **'Pumila'** Den Ouden/Boom 1965 Dwarf shrub to 4 m, young shoots bluish-green. I. H.A. Hesse Nurs, Weener-on-Ems, (1930). B,W2 Germany

- - 'Pygmaea' Hort. Anglia 1985 An illegit. name. reported from Windsor Great Park, U.K.

- - 'Rata' Hort. Amer. 1989 A listed name for a flat-topped, dwarf-form; needles short.

- - **'Recurva'** Mayr 1890 Leaves malformed and curved backwards. B Hort. Japan

- - 'Rezek Seedling' Hort. Amer. 1990 Now to be known as 'Little Christopher'.

- - **'Rubroaurea'** Mayr 1890 Leaves reddish with yellow margins. B Hort. Japan

- - 'Ryo-no-higo' Mayr 1890 A synonym of 'Barbata'. Hort. Japan

- - 'Sagari-matsu' Mayr 1890 A synonym of 'Pendula'. Hort. Japan

- - 'Sekka-akamatsu' Kobayashi 1975 In "Matsu-zukan", a synonym of 'Cristata'. W2 Hort.

- - 'Shidare-akamatsu' Mayr 1890 A synonym of 'Pendula'. W2 Hort. Japan

- - 'Shidare-janome-matsu' Welch 1979 A synonym of 'Oculis-draconis Pendula'. W2 Hort. Japan

- - 'Shidare-ogon-akamatsu' Welch 1979 A synonym of 'Aurea Pendula'. W2 Hort. Japan

- - 'Shiraga-matsu' Welch 1979 A synonym of 'Variegata'. W2 Hort. Japan

- - 'Soft Green' Hort. Amer. 1990 An unacceptable listed name, that should be replaced.

- - f. *subtrifoliata* Hurusawa in Kobayashi 1975 In "Matsu-zukan". Hort. Japan

- - **'Sunburst'** S. Waxman 1989 In "Int. Pl. Prop. Soc. Bull.". A vigorous tree marked by bright-yellow, extra long needles around each terminal bud. O. S. Waxman at the University of Connecticut. Storrs, CT. U.S.A.

- - 'Tagyo-sho' See 'Tanyosho'.

- - 'Tanyo-akamatsu' Welch   1979 A selection with very short leaves. See *PINUS densiflora* var. *parviphylla* Uyeki.   W2   Hort. Japan

- - **'Tanyosho'** Hort.   A commercial equivalent of 'Umbraculifera'.   Hort. Japan

    'Tanyosho Compacta', 'Tanyosho Pygmy', 'Tanyosho Dwarf', 'Tanyosho Special' and 'Tanyosho Witch's Broom' are undocumented names listed in U.S.A., all presumably seedlings or derivatives from 'Tanyosho'.

- - 'Tatejima-akamatsu' Hort. See 'Vittata'.

- - 'Tengu-su' Kobayashi   1975 See Welch, p301 (1979).   W2   Hort. Japan

- - **'Tigrina'** Mayr   1890 Leaves blotched like a tiger's coat.   B   Hort. Japan

- - 'Tora-fu akamatsu' Hort.   See 'Tigrina'.   W2   Hort. Japan

- - **'Tortuosa'** Mayr   1890 Leaves distorted.   B   Hort. Japan

- - 'Tsuma-jiro akamatsu' Hort.   A synonym of 'Albo-terminata'.   Hort. Japan

- - **'Umbraculifera'** Mayr   1890 Small tree forming a rounded crown, vaguely suggesting an umbrella.   B,D,G,H,K   Hort. Japan

- - 'Umbraculifera Nana'   1992 An illegit. name for a slower grower than the previous item. **O.** Le Feber, Boskoop.

- - 'Utsukushi-akamatsu' (1) Mayr
          1890 A synonym of 'Albo-terminata'.

- - 'Utsukushi'(2) Kobayashi
          1975 See Welch p301 (1979).   W2

- - **'Variegata'** Mayr   1890 Leaves variegated.   B   Hort. Japan

- - **'Vittata'** Kobayashi   1975 In "Matsu-zukan".   Hort. Japan

- - 'Witch's Broom No.7' Hort. Amer.
          1991 In "Nurs. Cat". Iseli Nurs, Boring, OR, PA. New name required.

- -'Yatsubusa-akamatsu' Mayr
          1890 A synonym of 'Octo-partita'.   W2   Hort. Japan

- - 'Zyo-no-mi' Hort. Amer.   A listed name.

PINUS devoniana Lindley   1839 Michoacan Pine. 4n (variable). Formerly known as *PINUS michoacana* (per Rushforth, 1987).   25m,Z9   Mexico?

PINUS x *digenea* Beck   A natural hybrid: *PINUS sylvestris* x *PINUS uncinata*.   K   Europe

PINUS discolor Bailey & Hawkesworth
          1979 Border Pinyon Pine. Species with bi-coloured leaves. 3n (variable).   5-10m,Z7   Mexico, U.S.A.

PINUS divaricata (Aiton) Dumont de Courset
          1811 Name possibly having priority over the name *PINUS banksiana* (which, however, is retained here).   W3

PINUS douglasiana Martinez
          1943 Douglas Pine. 5n. A rare species close to *PINUS pseudostrobus*. Not hardy in U.K.   Z9   Mexico

PINUS durangensis Martinez
          1942 Durango Pine. 5n.   20-40m   Mexico

PINUS echinata Miller   1768 Shortleaf Pine. 2n (rarely 3).   25-30m,Z7   U.S.A.

- - 'Clines Dwarf' Welch   1979   A dwarf form that was never propagated and is now dead. (The name is used in U.S.A. for a prostrate, spreading clone, possibly the following).

- - 'Nana' Hort. Amer.   1972   An illegit. name. I. Raraflora, Feasterville, PA. U.S.A.

PINUS edulis Engelmann   1848   Colorado Pinyon Pine, Rocky mountain Pinyon Pine 2n.   6-15m,Z8   Mexico/U.S.A.

- - var. *fallax* Little   1968   A rare local variant not now distinguished within the species by some authorities.   R

PINUS eldarica Medwediew
    1903   Eilar Pine. A rare species, close to *PINUS brutia*, of which species some authorities treat as a variety. (per Silba, 1984).   Russia

- - **'Christmas Blue'** Monrovia
    1986   In "Nurs. Cat". Symmetrical, conical tree with long, blue needles. L. Monrovia Nurs, Azusa, Cal.   U.S.A.

PINUS elliotii Engelmann   1880   Slash Pine. (elliottii).   10-30m,Z9   U.S.A.

- - var. *densa* Little & Dorman
    1952   Dade Pine. Now recognised as a distinct species. (per Silba, 1984).   K

PINUS engelmannii Carrière
    1854   Apache Pine, Arizona Long-leaf Pine. 3n (rarely 5).   15-35m.   U.S.A./Mexico

- - var. *blancoi* (Martinez) Martinez
    1948

PINUS escarina (Risso) Loudon
    1838   Now known as *PINUS pinaster* 'Aberdoniae'.

PINUS estevesii (Martinez) Perry
    1982   Esteves Pine. Formerly known as *PINUS pseudostrobus* var. *estevesii* (per Silba, 1984).   Mexico

PINUS excelsa Wallich ex D.Don
    1824   Now known as *PINUS wallichiana*.

PINUS fenzeliana Handel-Mazzetti
    1931   Fenzel Pine. 5n. A species allied to *PINUS parviflora*.   50m,Z8   China

PINUS flexilis James   1823   Limber Pine. 5n.   10-15m,Z4   Canada, U.S.A.

- - **'Albovariegata'** Schwerin
    1910   Green leaves and white ones intermixed. O. D. Count von Schwerin from seed collected in Arizona. (1907).   B   U.S.A.

- - 'Bergman Dwarf' Hort. Amer.
    1985   Slow-growing, upright, compact. L. L.C. Hatch in "Reference Guide". NOM.

- - 'Brevifolia' Hort. Amer.   1972   Reported from Longwood Gardens, Kennett Square, PA.

- - 'Compacta' Hort. Amer.   1986   An illegit. listed name.   U.S.A.

- - 'Elmwood Foxtail' Hort Amer.
    1991   A listed name.

- - 'Extra Blue' Hort. Amer.   1985   An unacceptable listed name for an asymmetrical tree with very blue colour.(Art. 31A(g) ICNCP).

- - **'Fastigiata'** R.M. Nordine
    1961   In "Int. Plant Prop. Soc Proc. **11**".   U.S.A.

- - **'Firmament'** H.J. van Gelderen

      1982 In "Dendroflora 19". Name to replace the following illegit. name. **I.** J.D. zu Jeddeloh Nurs. Oldenburg.   G,K,R   Germany

- - 'Glauca' (1) Hort. Germany   Now known as 'Firmament'.

- - 'Glauca' (2) Hort. Amer.   An illegit. name for a different but similar selection.

- - 'Glauca Compacta' Hort. Amer.

      1968 An illegit. name for an unrecorded clone.

- - 'Glauca Pendula' Hort. Anglia

      1970 **L.** Hillier and Son Nurs, Winchester. NOM.

- - 'Glenmore' Hort. Amer.   1949 See 'Glenmore Silver'.   B,G,K,R

- - 'Glenmore Dwarf' Hort. Anglia

      1970 Very slow-growing upright bush with incurved grey green leaves. **L.** Hillier and Sons Nurs, Winchester.   W2

- - **'Glenmore Silver'** Woody Pl. Reg. No. 2.

      1950 Leaves very long, intensely blue. **O.** and registered by Robert E. More. **I.** Scott Wilmore Nurs, Wheatridge, Col. (as 'Glenmore').   B,K   U.S.A.

- - 'Globosa' Hort. Amer.   1985 An illegit. listed name for an unrecorded, slow-growing, sub-globose clone.

- - 'Gracilis' Hort. France   1970 Mme. C. Testu in "Conifères de nos Jardins".

- - 'Hexenbesen' Horstmann

      1992 **L.** Horstmann Nurs, Schneverdingen.

- - **'Nana'** J.R. Noble   1951 In "Calif. Hort. Soc. Journal". Dwarf bushy form. **O.** Found by James Noble in the Sierra Nevada Mts (1947).   B,K,R,W2   U.S.A.

- - **'Pendula'** Welch   1979 A strong-growing, spreading tree. **O.** Vermeulen and Sons Nurs, Neshanic Station, PA, (1941).   G,K,W2   U.S.A.

- - 'Pendula Glauca' Hort. Amer.   A listed name. Probably a superfluous name for 'Glauca Pendula'.

- - 'Pygmaea' Hort. Germany

      1972 An illegit. listed name. **O.** J. zu Jeddeloh Nurs, Oldenburg, (1965).

- - var. *reflexa* Engelmann   1882 Not now distinguished within the species.

- - 'Reflexa' Hort. Anglia   1970 A listed name. NOM. Possibly same as previous item.

- - **'Scratch Gravel'** Reg'd. Arn. Arb.

      1970 Erect, broad, robust tree. Registered by A.V. Berg (1969). **O.** Named for a tree found in the wild in 1963.

- - 'Semivirgata' Schwerin   1932 A gaunt, open tree. **O.** Found on the Count von Schwerin Estate, Wendisch-Wilmersdorf.   B   Germany

- - 'Shadow's Blue' Hort Amer.

      1991 In "Nurs. Cat". Iseli Nurs, Boring, OR.

- - 'Temple' Hort. Amer.   1986 A listed name for a conical, slow-growing tree. May be a superfluous name for the following.

- - **'Tiny Temple'** J. Vermeulen

      1972 In "Nurs. Cat". Name suggested by the shape of the buds. **O.** Vermeulen Nurs, Neshanic Station. N.J.   K,R   U.S.A.

- - **'Vanderwolf's Pyramid'** J. Vermeulen
1972 In "Nurs. Cat". Makes a narrowly conical specimen; foliage
dark blue-green. **I.** Vermeulen and Son Nurs. Neshanic
Station, N.J.   G   U.S.A.

- - 'Witch's Broom No.1' Hort. Amer.
1984 An unacceptable name. Very slow-growing cushion shaped,
later squat conical. Short straight leaves at 45o. **L.** Kristick
Nurs, Wellsville, PA.   U.S.A.

- - 'Witch's Broom No.2' Hort. Amer.
1984 An unacceptable name. Very slow growing globose to
conical, thin silvery blue leaves, slightly incurved. **L.** Kristick
Nurs, Wellsville, PA.   U.S.A.

PINUS funebris Komarov   1901 Now known as *PINUS densiflora* var. *funebris.* (per Silba,
1984).

PINUS gerardiana Wallich ex D. Don
1832 Chilgoza Pine, Gerard Pine. Bark less spectacular than in *P.
bungeana.* 3n.   25m,Z7   Himalayas

- - 'Khyber Pass' G. Haddow
1992 Dwarf conical plant grown from seed collected in the Khyber
Pass. **O.** and **I.** Kenwith Nurs, Bideford, Devon.

PINUS glabra Walter   1738 Spruce Pine. 2n.   25-30m,Z9   U.S.A.

- - 'Globosa' Hort. Anglia   1985 An illegit. name. Reported from Windsor Great Park, Berks.   U.K.

PINUS glauca Moench   1785 Now known as *PICEA glauca.*

PINUS gordoniana Hartweg
1847 Possibly a subspecies of *PINUS montezumae.* (per Rushforth,
1987).   Mexico

PINUS greggii Engelmann ex Parlatore
1868 Gregg Pine. 3n.   10-15m,Z7   Mexico

PINUS griffithii M'Clelland in Griffith
1854 Now known as *PINUS wallichiana.* There are several
cultivars.

PINUS x *hakkodensis* Makino   A natural hybrid. *PINUS parviflora* x *PINUS pumila.* One
particular clone appears to be in cultivation with pale
powder-blue leaves. **L.** J.W. Spingarn, Long Is., N.Y. (1982).   Japan

PINUS halepensis Miller   1768 Aleppo Pine. 2n.   20m,Z8   Mediterr.

- - 'Brevifolia' Carrière   1867 Branches crowded; leaves few and irregular. NIC.   B   France

- - var. *brutia* (Tenore) Elwes & Henry
1910 Now regarded as a distinct species. *PINUS brutia.*(per Silba,
1984).   B,D   E. Mediterr.

- - var. *eldarica* Medwediew   Here listed as *PINUS brutia* var *eldarica.* (per Silba, 1984).

- - **'Kapunda'** Hort. Australia
1979 A weeping or prostrate form found as a seedling on the
roadside at Kapunda. Quite vigorous. **I.** P.C. Nitsche,
Hahndorf, S. Australia. **O.** The same.   Australia

- - 'Nana' Hort. Germany   1990 An illegit. listed name for a dwarf form raised from a witch's
broom found in the Spanish province of Catalonia.

- - var. *pityusa* (Steven) Gordon
1858 Here listed as *PINUS brutia* var. *pityusa.* (per Silba, 1984).
(pithyusa).   B,D

- - 'Rotundata' Carrière   1867 Branches, very short and uniform. Leaves short NIC.   B,H   France

- - var. *stankewiczii* (Sukaczew) Fitschen
    1930 Here listed as *PINUS brutia* var. *stankewiczii*. (per Silba, 1984).   B,D   Crimean Penin.

- - 'Variegata' Carrière   1867 Yellowish-white variegation, not constant. NIC?   B   France

PINUS halepensi-pinaster Saporta
    1889 A natural hybrid: *PINUS halepensis* x *PINUS pinaster*.   France

PINUS hartwegii Lindley   1839 Hartweg Pine. 3 to 5n.   30-35m,Z7   U.S.A.

PINUS heldreichii Christ   1863 Heldreich Pine (Often confused with *PINUS leucodermis*, q.v.) 2n.   20m,Z6   Balkans

- - 'Aureospicata' Hort.   See *PINUS leucodermis* 'Aureospicata'.   B

- - 'Compact Gem' Hort.   See *PINUS leucodermis* 'Compact Gem'.   B

- - var. *leucodermis* (Antoine) Markgraf ex Fitschen
    1930 Now known as *PINUS leucodermis*. (per Rushforth, 1987).   B,R

- - 'Pygmy' Hort.   See *PINUS leucodermis*. 'Pygmy'.   B

PINUS henryi Masters   1902 Henry Pine. 2n. A species close to *PINUS massoniana*.   Z8   Hupeh

PINUS herrerai Martinez   1940 Herrera Pine. Now included in *PINUS teocote*. (per Silba, 1984).   Z10   Mexico

PINUS himekomatsu Miyabe & Kudo
    1930 South Japanese White Pine. See *PINUS parviflora*.   Japan

PINUS x holfordiana A.B. Jackson
    1933 A hybrid: *PINUS ayacahuite* x *PINUS wallichiana*. It arose spontaneously in Westonbirt Arboretum, Tetbury, Glos.   B,R   U.K.

PINUS x hunnewelli Johnson
    1952 A hybrid: *PINUS parviflora* x *PINUS strobus*. Probably raised in the Hunnewell Arboretum, Mass.   R   U.S.A.

PINUS hwangshanensis Hayata   Hwangshan Pine. A newly described and rare species, close to *PINUS taiwanensis*. 2n.   Z8   China

PINUS inops (1) Aiton   1879 Now known as *PINUS virginiana*.

PINUS inops (2) Bongard   1853 Now known as *PINUS contorta*.

PINUS insularis Endlicher   1847 An alternative name for *PINUS kesiya* (per Rushforth, 1987).

- - var. *yunnanensis* (Franchet) Silba
    1986 Yunnan Pine. Treated as a distinct species by some authorities.   Mexico

PINUS jaliscana Perez de la Rosa
    1983 Jalisco Pine.   10-12m,Z9   Mexico

PINUS jeffreyi Greville & Balfour ex A. Murray
    1853 Jeffrey Pine. 3n.   50m,Z6   U.S.A.

- - var. *deflexa* (Torrey) Lemmon   Differs in bearing smaller leaves and cones.   D

- - 'Glauca' Hort. Germany   1990 An illegit. listed name.

- - **'Joppi'** H.J. van de Laar   1990 In "Dendroflora 27". Dense, globose plant with long twisted lvs. O. P. Vergeldt, Lotum, and named for his eldest son.   Holland

- - 'Yellow Form' Hort. Holland
    1991 Listed with photograph in the book "Conifers" by D.M. van Gelderen and J.R.P. van Hoey Smith.

PINUS johannis M.F.Robert
1978 Johan Pine. 3n. A shrub or small, multi-stemmed tree.   3-4m,Z7   Mexico

PINUS juarensis Lanner   1974 Not now distinguished within *PINUS cembroides* var.
quadrifolia (per Silba, 1984).

PINUS kesiya Royle ex Gordon   Khasi Pine. 3n. Listed by some authorities as *PINUS*
insularis. (per Silba, 1984). (spelling varies).   Asia

- - var. *langbianensis* (Cheval) Gaussen
A local form with unusually broad leaves and cones.   R

PINUS kochiana Klotzsch   1849 Not now distinguished within *PINUS sylvestris.*

PINUS koraiensis Siebold & Zuccarini
1844 Korean Pine. 5n.   20-50m,Z3   Korea etc.

- - 'Avogadro' Hort. Amer.   Probably the same as next entry..

- - **'Avogagio'** L.C. Hatch   1988 In "Conifer Database". Medium size, conical tree; foliage
very dense.   U.S.A.

- - 'Bergman' Hort. Amer.   1974 Upright almost fastigiate dwarf with dark blue-grey leaves. In
winter conspicuous dark red buds. **O.** Raraflora Nurs,
Feasterville, PA. **I.** M. Kristick Nurs, Wellsville, PA.

- - 'Brookside Variegated'   1988 L. Mitsch Nurs, Aurora, OR.

- - 'Chosen-fuiri matzu' Mayr
1890 A synonym of 'Variegata'.

- - **'Compacta Glauca'** H.G. Hillier
1971 In "Hillier's Manual". Vigorous but compact upright form
with some nearly fastigiate branches and conspicuously
glaucous leaves.   K,R

- - 'Dragon Eye' R. Fincham
1987 Upright growing bush with mop heads of recurved leaves,
leaves sometimes coloured with pale cream bars. **L.**
Coenosium Gardens, Lehighton, PA.

- - 'Dwarf Form' Hort. Amer.
1982 **L.** Iseli Nurs, Boring, Oregon. Slow-growing upright form.

- - 'Glauca' Hort. Holland   An illegit. name, now replaced by 'Silveray'.

- -'Jack Corbit' Hort. Amer.   1986 A listed name.

- - 'Kamurogoyo' Mayr   1890 A synonym of 'Tortuosa'.

- - 'Morris Blue' Hort. Amer.
1992 Six ft at six years old. L. Buccholz Nurs, Gaston, OR.

- - 'Nana' Hort. Amer.   1986 An illegit. listed name.

- - 'Select Blue' Hort.Canada
1981 In "Nurs. Cat". G. Bentham, Victoria, B.C.

- - 'Shibamichi' J.zu Jeddeloh
1980 Slow-growing, narrowly upright bush with pale silver blue
leaves. **O.** Shibamichi Nurs, Japan. **I.** J. zu Jeddeloh Nurs,
Oldenburg.

- - **'Silveray'** H.J. Grootendorst
1979 In "Dendroflora **19**". An upright-growing tree-shaped bush
with light silver blue leaves. **I.** F.J. Grootendorst Nurs,
Boskoop (1978). **O.** Unrecorded.   G,K,R   Holland

- - 'Silverlining' Hort.Anglia 1992 In "The Plant Finder".

276

- - 'Tabuliformis' Hort. Amer.   An illegit. listed name.

- - **'Tortuosa'** Mayr   1890 With contorted foliage.   B,K,R,W2   Hort. Japan

- - **'Variegata'** Mayr   1890 Leaves variegated.   B,D,K,R   Hort. Japan

- - **'Winton'** H.G. Hillier   1964 In "Dwarf Conifers". A large bush wider than high, with long glaucous leaves. Possibly a hybrid with *PINUS pumila*. **O.** Hillier and Son Nurs, Winchester.   B,R,W2   U.K.

PINUS krempfii (Lecompte) A. Cheval
Krempf Pine. A rare pine with distinctive foliage.   15-30m,Z10   S. Vietnam

- - var. *poilanei* Lecompte   1921 Doubtfully distinguishable within the species.   D

PINUS kwantungensis Chen ex Tsiang
1964 Kwantung Pine, Guangdon Pine. 5n. Not hardy in U.K.   30m,Z8   China

PINUS lambertiana Douglas
1827 Sugar Pine. 5n.   50-60m,Z7   U.S.A.

PINUS langbianensis A. Cheval
1944 Now listed under *PINUS insularis* (per Silba, 1984).   Mexico

PINUS laricio of some authors   Corsican Pine. See *PINUS nigra* subsp. *laricio*.   Europe

PINUS latteri Mason   1849 A little known tree species. May be identical with *PINUS merkusii* (per Silba, 1984).   N. Vietnam

PINUS lawsonii Roezl ex Gordon
1862 Lawson Pine. 3-5n.   20-25m,Z9   Mexico

PINUS leiophylla Schiede & Dieppe
1832 Smooth-leaf Pine. 5n.   15-30m,Z7   Mexico

- - var. *chihuahuana* (Engelmann) Shaw
1909 Now listed as *PINUS chichuaha*.   R

PINUS leucodermis Antoine
1868 Bosnian Pine. Not to be confused with the allied species *PINUS heldreichii* 2n.   30m,Z6   Balkans

- - **'Aureospicata'** Hesse   1955 In "Nurs Cat". Slow-gowing; leaves yellow-tipped. **O.** and **I.** H.A. Hesse Nurs, Weener-on-Ems.   B,G,K,R,W2   Germany

- - **'Compact Gem'** H.G. Hillier   1964 In "Dwarf Conifers". Dark green, compact form, at one time distributed as 'Compacta' or as 'Dwarf form'.   G,K,R,W2   U.K.

- - 'Creamy' Hort. Amer.   1982 In "Nurs. Cat". Iseli Nurs, Boring, OR.

- - 'Fastigiate' Hort. Amer.   1985 An illegit. listed name.

- - 'Gold Tip' Hort. Amer.   An unacceptable listed name.

- - **'Green Bun'** Hort. Amer.
1982 A listed name. Reported from Iseli Nurs, Boring, OR.

- - **'Green Shag'** Hort. Amer.
1982 A listed name. Reported from Iseli Nurs, Boring, OR.

- - 'Groen' Hort. Germany   1987 An unacceptable listed name.(Art. 31A (g). **L.** Jeddeloh Nurs. Oldenburg, Germany.

- - **'Horak'** Czechoslovakia 1986 **L.** H.J. van de Laar in "Naamlijst . . .". NOM. **O.** and **I.** K. Horak, Bystrice.

- - **'Malink'** Hort. Germany   A dwarf upright form with mid green leaves. **O.** Wustemeyer Nurs.   Germany

- - 'Minaret' Hort. Holland   1992   **O.** and **I.** Le Feber & Co., Boskoop.

- - 'Pygmaea' Krüssmann   1962   See 'Pygmy'.

- - **'Pygmy'** Den Ouden/Boom

1965	Cushion shaped slow-growing dwarf with short leaves to 2.5 cms.	B,K,R,W2	Germany

- - **'Satellit'** D.M. van Gelderen

1971	In "Dendroflora **8**". A small, fastigiate tree with dark green foliage. **I.** Konijn Nurs, Reeuwijk. **O.** Found in the Gimborn Arboretum, Doorn.	G,K	Holland

- - 'Schmidtii'   Since the plant is named after its finder, there is no case for Germanising the spelling.   K

- - **'Smidtii'** Pilat

1964	Very slow growing globose eventually conical, leaves to 4 cms. **I.** Pruhonice Arboretum, Czechoslavakia. **O.** Found in the wild by Eugene Smidt. (1926).	G,R,W2	Czechosl.

- - 'Zwerg Schneverdingen' Hort. Germany

1991   Very compact growing globular dwarf form with short very dark green needles. **O.** and **I.** Horstmann Nurs, Schneverdingen.

PINUS michoacana Martinez

1944	Michoacan Pine. Now known as *PINUS devoniana*. (per Rushforth 1987).		Mexico

- - var. *cornuta* Martinez   1044   Now known as *PINUS wincesteriana*. (per Rushforth 1989).   R

PINUS monophylla Torrey & Fremont

1845	Single-leaf Pinyon Pine. 1n. Formerly known as *PINUS cembroides* var. *monophylla*.	5-10m,Z9	U.S.A./Mexico

- - var *edulis* (Engelmann) M.E. Jones

1891	Colorado Pinyon Pine. Now recognised as *PINUS edulis*. (Per Rushforth, 1987).	R	

- - **'San Bernadino'** Hort. Holland

1971	Found by J.R.P. van Hoey-Smith at San Bernadino, California.		U.S.A.

- - **'Tioga Pass'** Hort. Germany

1986	A selection with compact growth and blue leaves. **O.** and **I.** Jeddeloh Nurs, Oldenburg. **O.** Found near Tioga Pass, Yosemite.	G	U.S.A.

PINUS montana Miller   1768   Now known as *PINUS mugo*.

PINUS montezumae Lambert

1832	Montezuma Pine. 5n. This name is often loosely applied in U.K. cultivation to several other Mexican species.	30m,Z8	C. America

- - var *hartwegii* Lindley in Engelmann

1847	Now known as *PINUS hartwegii*. (Per Silba, 1984). Often cultivated in U.K. as *PINUS montezumae*.	D,K	

- - var *lindleyi* Loudon   1883   A name of uncertain application.   D,K

- - f. *macrocarpa* Martinez

1948	Possibly synonymous with *PINUS wincesteriana*. (Per Rushforth, (1987).	K,R	

- - var *rudis* (Endlicher) Shaw

1909   Now known as *PINUS rudis*.   D,K

PINUS montezumae x *PINUS patula* A.C. Mitchell

1972	A hybrid discovered at Fota, Co. Cork.		Ireland

PINUS monticola Douglas ex D. Don

	1832 Western White Pine. 5n.	35m,Z7	N. America

- - **'Ammerland'** Krüssmann

1929 A strong-growing clone with silvery-blue needles. **I**. Jeddeloh
Nurs, Oldenburg.   G,K   Germany

- - **'Chad'** L.C. Hatch   1988 In "Conifer Database". A compact, upright plant; leaves blue.

- - 'Glauca' Hort. Germany   See *PINUS monticola* 'Skyline'.

- - 'Minima' Lemmon   1888 A name for trees with abnormally small cones.   K,R,W2

- - 'Ondulata' Hort. Germany Growth slow; needles short, thick and curled. **O**. Wustemeyer Nurs,
Schermbeck, Germany, (1960).

- - 'Pendula' Krüssmann   1979 Illegit. name for a very pendulous form from a tree found in a
forest near Schermbeck. **O**. J.zu Jeddeloh, Oldenburg.   G,K,R

- - 'Raraflora' Hort. Amer.   1980 Dwarf upright growing with branches in tiers. Leaves short
mid-green. **L**. Originally listed by Raraflora in 1980
catalogue as Pygmaea.

- - **'Rigby's Weeping'** Hort. Amer.
1986 Strongly pendulous, (needs stem straining); leaves soft, pale
green. **L**. Iseli Nurs, Boring, OR., U.S.A.

- - **'Skyline'** D.M. Gelderen   1982 In "Dendroflora **19**". A medium, upright-grower with blue-
grey leaves.   G,K   Holland

- - 'Windsor Dwarf' G.Haddow
1993 A dwarf plant in Windsor Great Park, Berks, U.K. Flat
topped, spreading leaves held closely round the shoots, buds
as the species. **L**. Kenwith Nurs, Bideford, Devon.   U.K.

PINUS morrisonicola Hayata

	1908 Taiwan (Formosan) White Pine. 5n.	25-30m,Z8	Taiwan

PINUS mugho Poiret   1804 Now known as *PINUS mugo*.

PINUS mughus Scopoli   1772 Now known as *PINUS mugo*.

PINUS mugo Turra   1764 Mugo Pine. Dwarf Mountain Pine [=*PINUS montana* Miller
(1768) in part; *PINUS mughus* Scopoli (1772); *PINUS
mugho* Poiret (1804)].   Europe

This species is frequently confused with *PINUS uncinata*, the Mountain Pine. *PINUS mugo* var. *rotundata*, *PINUS
uncinata* var. *rotundata* and *PINUS uncinata* var. *rostrata* are intermediate forms, possibly natural hybrids.

- - 'Allen's Seedling' Hort. Amer.
1986 A listed name for a globose dwarf. ('Allen').

- - **'Allgau'** H.J. Grootendorst
1977 In "Dendroflora **13-14**". Compact, globose to upright form
with short leaves. **O**. Found by Gebr. van den Nieuwendijk in
the Allgauer Alps, Zuid Duitsland.   K   Germany

- - 'Almhutte' Hort. Germany
1983 A listed name. Horstmann Nurs, Schneverdingen, Germany.

- - 'Alpenglow' Hort. Canada
1986 Growth dwarf, vigorous, compact. A good rooting clone.

- - 'Arneson's Gold' Hort. Amer.
1985 A listed name. Mitsch Nurs, Boring OR, (1988).

- - 'Arpad' Hort. Hungary   1992 A dwarf form. **O**. Found by M. Barabits, Sopron, Hungary.

- - 'Aurea' Hort. Amer.   1982 An illegit. name for an open bush with long, twisted leaves,
                                       bright golden-yellow in winter. L. Iseli Nurs, Boring, OR.

- - 'Aureovariegata' Schelle   1909 Now listed under *PINUS uncinata*.   B

- - 'Big Tuna' Iseli   1990 A broadly conical, dense dwarf with thick, blue-green
                                       needles. O. and I. Iseli Nurs, Boring, OR.   U.S.A.

- - **'Blue Globe'** Hort. Holland
                                1986 L. H.J. van de Laar in "Naamlijst . . .". NOM.

- - 'Bohlkens Zwerg' Hort. Germany
                                1983 L. Horstmann Nurs, Schneverdingen, Germany.

- - 'Bonsai' Hort. Germany   1983 O. and I. Kramer Nurs, Oldenburg, Germany. L. Horstmann
                                       Nurs, Schneverdingen, Germany.

- - 'Brevifolia' Hort.   Probably several clones in cultivation under this, now illegit.
                                       name. See 'Kissen'.   K

- - 'Brownie' Hort. Anglia   1992 A listed name.

- - 'Bubikopf' Hort Germany
                                1988 A dwarf, short-needled form.. I. Hachmann Nurs.

- - **'Bucco'** Hort. Holland   1986 A very compact, dwarf plant. O. Selected seedling of var
                                       pumilio raised by Th. Streng of Boskoop.

- - **'Carsten'** Hachmann   1988 In "Nurs.Cat".L. Hachmann Nurs, Barmstedt-in-Holstein.
                                       Dwarf form turning rich golden in winter. O. Erwin Carsten,
                                       Varel, Germany. I. Hachmann Nurs, Barmsted in Holstein.   Germany

- - **'Champ'** G. Haddow   1986 Extremely dwarf cushion seedling of Pumilio. O. and I.
                                       Kenwith Nurs, Bideford, Devon.   U.K.

- - 'Columnaris' Hort. Anglia
                                1984 An illegit. listed name for a slow-growing, dense, conical
                                       plant with radial foliage.

- - **'Compacta'** (1) D. Hill ex Bailey
                                1923 Globose, dense form; slender, bright green leaves. O. D. Hill
                                       Nurs, Dundee, Ill.   D,H,K,R,W2   U.S.A.

- - 'Compacta' (2) Hort. Germany
                                1954 See *PINUS mugo* 'Hesse'.

- - **'Corley's Mat'** Welch   1979 Popular mat-forming clone. I. Wansdyke Nurs, Devizes,
                                       Wilts. O. Selected seedling by R. S. Corley of High
                                       Wycombe.   R,W2   U.K.

- - 'Dolomiten' Hort. Germany
                                1983 A listed name. Horstmann Nurs, Schneverdingen.

- - 'Dunajec' Hort. Holland   1992 A listed name for a flat spreading form. O. A witch's broom
                                       found by M.M. Bömer of Zundert, Holland.

- - **'Elfengren'** Hort. Amer. 1986 Growth compact; good colour. O. Selected at Oregon State
                                       University.   U.S.A.

- - 'Ellie B' Hort. Amer.   1986 A listed name. J.W. Spingarn, Long Is., N.Y.

- - **'Emerald Tower'** Hort. Amer.
                                1985 A listed name for an upright, slow-grower; foliage dark green.

- - 'Eschrich' Hort. Germany
                                1993 Witch's Broom. L. Horstmann Nurs, Schneverdingen.

- - 'Esveld' Hort. Holland.   See next item.

- - **'Esveld Select'** Esveld   1979   In "Nurs. Cat". Forms a flat-topped bun; foliage similar to 'Mops' but growth slower. **O.** and **I.** Esveld Nurs, Boskoop.   G   Holland

- - **'Fastigiate'** Buccholz   1992   Compact little bush, dark green foliage, columnar habit unique for *mugo*. 6 ft x 2 ft in ten years.

- - 'Fischleinboden' Horstmann
       1983   L. Horstmann Nurs, Schneverdingen.

- - 'Fisherii' Forbes   1839   Listed as a *PINUS mugo pumilio* form. NIC.   U.K.

- - 'Flat Top' Hort. Amer.   See 'Iseli Flat Top'.

- - **'Frisia'** Krüssmann   1982   Compact upright growing, densely twiggy bush, leaves moss-green. **I.** Jeddeloh Nurs, Oldenburg, (1970). **O.** Found by G. Krüssmann near Bergen.   G,K   Holland

- - 'Frohling's Gold' Hort. Amer.
       1988   In "Nurs. Cat". Mitsch Nurs, Aurora, OR.

- - 'Gallica' Fitschen in Beissner
       1930   A strong-growing, hardy selection introduced by Joh. Rafn-Kopenhagen. NIC.   B

- - 'Glendale' Hort. Amer.   1987   A listed name. Difficult to distinguish from *PINUS contorta* 'Spaan's Dwarf'.   G

- - **'Gnom'** Den Ouden   1937   A widely grown dwarf form; old plants upright to conical. **O.** Den Ouden and Son Nurs, Boskoop. ('Gnome' is incorrect).   B,D,G,H,K,W2   Holland

- - 'Goldspire' Hort. Amer.   1990   A listed name for a dwarf; golden-yellow candles in Spring.

- - **'Green Candle'** E.A. Cope
       1986   In "Native . . . Conifers . . . ". Dwarf, globose; foliage dark green. Young shoots thick, frequently carrying flowers.

- - **'Green Shadow'** Hort. Holland
       1986   H.J. van de Laar in "Naamlijst. . .". NOM.

- - 'Hedgehog' Hort. Canada
       1981   L. Gordon Bentham, Victoria, B.C. Without description.

- - 'Helvetica' Den Ouden/Boom
       1965   A broad globose form, **L.** Hooftman Nurs, Boskoop, (1951) NIC.   B   Holland

- - 'Henry' Hort. Holland   1990   Reported from Trompenburg Arboretum, Rotterdam.

- - **'Hesse'** Den Ouden/Boom
       1965   Dwarf, globose; leaves dark green, twisted. **I.** H.A. Hesse Nurs, Weener-on-Ems. (As 'Compacta', 1954). **O.** The same (1940).   B,K,R,W2   Germany

- - 'Hoersholm' Jakobsen   1990   Slow-growing form of var *mughus* with well variegated gold-green leaves in summer. **O.** and **I.** Arne Vagn Jakobsen, Denmark.

- - 'Horstmann Dwarf' Horstmann
       1983   **O.** and **I.** Horstmann Nurs, Schneverdingen.

- - **'Humpy'** Welch   1979   Slow-growing bun-form with dark green leaves. **O.** Draijer Nurs, Heemstede.   G,K,W2   Holland

- - 'Ironside' Hort. Amer.   1988   In "Nurs. Cat". Mitsch Nurs, Boring, Oregon.

- - **'Iseli Flat Top'** Iseli   1985   In "Nurs. Cat". A low bun; very dense, tight form. It deserves a better name. **L.** Iseli Nurs, Boring, OR.   U.S.A.

- - **'Iseli White Bud'** Iseli   1985 In "Nurs. Cat". Dwarf, bun-forming; leaves short; young shoots pure white. **O.** and **I.** Iseli Nurs, Boring, OR.   U.S.A.

- - **'Jacobsen'** G. Haddow   1987 In "Nurs. Cat". Slow-growing, low bun-form, possibly a hybrid with *PINUS nigra.* (per Haddow, 1987). **O.** Arne Vagn Jacobsen, Denmark. **I.** Kenwith Nurs, Bideford, Devon.   U.K.

- - 'Janovsky' Hort. Anglia   1990 A listed name.

- - **'Jeddeloh'** Welch   1979 Similar to 'Corley's Mat but coarser growth. **I.** Jeddeloh Nurs, Oldenburg, Germany. (1946). **O.** Found in Arboretum von Doorn.   Holland

- - 'Joséphine Leney' Hort. Anglia
    1992 Reported from Windsor Great Park, Berks, without description.

- - 'Karsten's Wintergold'   See 'Carsten'.

- - **'Kissen'** Welch   1979 Slow-growing globular selection of var. *pumilio.* **O.** Jeddeloh Nurs, Oldenburg. (Formerly distributed as 'Brevifolia').   G,K,R,W2

- - 'Klosterkotter' Hort. Holland
    1992 A listed name. **L.** Wiel Linssen, Baexam, Holland.

- - **'Knapenburg'** Welch   1979 A squat, spreading bush, eventually upright, dense but irregular; leaves short and dark green. **O.** and **I.** Draijer Nurs, Heemstede.   K,W2   Holland

- - **'Kobold'** Den Ouden/Boom
    1965 Rounded bush. **I.** Hooftman Nurs, Boskoop, (1955).   B,K,W2   Holland

- - **'Kokarde'** Reinold ex Krüssmann
    1955 Dwarf, with several upright stems of no fixed pattern, leaves yellow variegated. **O.** Reinold Nurs, Dortmund, (1952).   B,K,R,W2   Germany

- - **'Krauskopf'** Hachmann   1988 In "Nurs. Cat". Dense, low-spreading irregular growth; leaves bright green. **I.** Hachmann Nurs, Barmstedt-in-Holstein.   Germany

- - 'Kruger's Liliput' Hort.   See 'Lilliput'.

- - **'Laarheide'** Hort. Holland
    1986 H.J. van de Laar in "Naamlijst . . .". NOM.

- - **'Laurin'** Nathebusch ex Reuter
    1984 In "Amer. Conif. Soc. Bull. **1.**". Compact, hemispherical plant of very slow growth. **O.** Sass Nurs, Elmshorn, (1928).   Germany

- - **'Lilliput'** Hort. Germany
    1985 A broadly conical small bush; short needles. **L.** J. zu Jeddeloh Nurs, Oldenburg, Germany ('Kruger's Lilliput'?).

- - 'Mala Falica' Hort. Germany
    1983 A listed name. No further information.

- - 'Maleton' Hort. Holland   1992 In "Nurs. Cat". Libo Nurs, Baexam.

- - **'Marand'** Hort. Holland   1986 Tall-growing selection with yellowish young needles. **L.** H.J. van de Laar, in "Naamlijst. . . .".

- - **'March'** Hort. Amer.   1980 In "Nurs. Cat". A dense, squat plant selected in U.S. National Arboretum. **I.** J.W. Spingarn, Long Is., N.Y.   U.S.A.

- - 'Mayfair Dwarf' Hort. Amer.
    1986 A listed name.

- - **'Minikin'** H.J. van de Laar
    1983 In "Dendroflora 20". Slow-growing dwarf with short leaves. **I.** Gebr. Van Vliet, Boskoop, (1983).   Holland

- - 'Mini Mops' Bruns   1988   A listed name for a diminutive form. Raised from a witch's broom on 'Mops'. **L.** Bruns Nurs, Bad Zwischenan.   Germany

- - **'Misty'** J. Emery   1989   In "Con. Soc. Australia Newsletter **5**".A dense compact bush; with young growth lemon yellow in Spring. **O.** Cedar Lodge Nurs, Sulphur Creek, Australia. **L.** Yamina Rare Plants, Monbulk, Victoria.

- - 'Mitsch Mini' Hort. Amer.
    1989   A very dwarf low-spreading form with mid green twisted leaves and comparatively long winter buds. **O.** and **I.** Mitsch Nurs, Aurora, OR.

- - **'Mops'** Hooftman   1951   In "Nurs. Cat". A popular globose dwarf. **O.** H.F. Hooftman, Boskoop.   B,G,K,R,W2   Holland

- - var. *mughus* (Scopoli) Zenari
    1921   Now known as *PINUS mugo*.   G,K

- - 'Mumpitz' Carsten   1988   Globular eventually conical slow-growing dwarf with long rich green needles. **O.** and **I.** Carsten Nurs, Varel, Germany.

- - 'Nana' Loudon ex Gordon
    1858   A very dwarf form allegedly found in the Styrian Alps. No longer identifiable.   B

- - 'Nymphenburg' Hort. Germany
    1992   A listed name.

- - **'Ophir'** H.J. van de Laar   1975   In "Dendroflora **11-12"**. Compact, flat topped plant with foliage pale yellow in winter. **O.** K.J. Kraan, Waddinxveen.   Holland

- - 'Oregon Jade' Hort. Amer.
    1986   A listed name. Growth dwarf, compact.

- - 'Oregon Pixie' Hort. Amer.
    1986   Possibly same as previous entry.

- - **'Pal Maleter'** D.M. van Gelderen
    1982   In "Dendroflora **19"**. Multi-stemmed or with a single leader. Leaves dark green with outer half light yellow. **O.** Raised from seed by Van der Poel at Hazerwoude, (1965).   G   Holland

- - **'Paul's Dwarf'** Iseli   1986   In "Nurs. Cat". A diminutive cushion shaped plant; very short needles. **O.** and **I.** Iseli Nurs, Boring, OR.   U.S.A.

- - 'Pendula' Schelle   1909   Pendulous clone of var. *rostrata*. NIC.   B   Germany

- - **'Picobello'** H.J. van de Laar
    1990   In "Dendroflora **27"**. Tight globose; leaves short and dark green. **O.** K. Dierks Nurs, Bad Zwischenhahn.   Germany

- - 'Pigglemee' Kortmann   Globe shaped dwarf bush with short straight needles. Occurred as a sport on 'Mops'. **O.** and **I.** P.J. Kortmann, Biezen, Boskoop.   Holland

- - **'Pincushion'** (1) Welch   1979   Low, bun-forming plant. **O.** F. Bergman, Raraflora Nurs, Feasterville, PA.   U.S.A.

- - 'Pincushion' (2) Hort. Australia
    1990   A low, bun-shape plant. **O.** Yamina Rare Plants, Monbulk, Victoria.

- - 'Prostrata' Hort. Amer.   1985   An illegit. listed name for an unrecorded prostrate clone. **L.** Iseli Nurs, Boring, OR.

- - 'Pudgy' Hort. Amer.   1992   In "Nurs. Cat". Rarafolia Nurs, Kintersville, PA.

- - var. *pumilio* (Haenke) Zenari
    1921 A low, spreading shrub. From this botanical variety, numerous selections have been made and named.   B,D,H,K

- - 'Pygmy' Hort. Anglia
    1985 An unacceptable name. Reported from Windsor Great Park, Berks.   U.K.

- - 'Pyramidalis' Hort. Amer.
    An illegit. name for an unrecorded pendulous clone.

- - 'Rautal' Hort. Germany
    1983 A listed name. Horstmann Nurs, Schneverdingen, Germany.

- - 'Reher' Hort. Germany
    1983 A listed name for a witch's broom. L. Horstmann Nurs, Schneverdingen, Germany.

- - 'Rezek' Hort. Amer.
    1990 In "Nurs. Cat". M. Kristick, Wellsville, PA.

- - 'Rigi' D.M. van Gelderen
    1982 In "Dendroflora 19". An upright bush with dark green leaves. O. Draijer Nurs, Heemstede.   G,K   Holland

- - **'Rock Garden'** L.C. Hatch
    1988 In "Conifer Database". A dwarf of picturesque habit. A better name should be found.   U.S.A.

- - **'Roger's Weeping'** Hort. Amer.
    1985 A listed name for a procumbent plant.

- - var. *rostrata* (Antoine) Gordon
    1858 Here listed under *PINUS uncinata* with which it may be a hybrid.   B   Europe

- - var. *rotundata* Link
    1827 Another tree-forming variant showing affinity with *PINUS uncinata*.   B

- - 'Rushmore' Hort. Anglia
    A small dwarf form originating at Robinson's Nurs, Knockholt, Kent. L. D. Sampson, Oakdene Nurs, Heathfield, E. Sussex.

- - 'Schneeberg' Horstmann
    1992 L. Horstmann Nurs, Schneverdingen, Germany.

- - 'Sherwood Compact' Hort. Amer.
    1986 A listed name for a globose dwarf form.

- - 'Shon Ilse' Hort. Germany
    1983 L. Horstmann Nurs, Schneverdingen, Germany.

- - 'Skylands 2$' Hort. Amer.
    1992 In "Nurs. Cat". Rarafolia Nurs, Kintersville, PA, U.S.A.

- - **'Slavinii'** Hornibrook
    1923 Dense, low-growing form. O. Raised by B.H. Slavin of Rochester, N.Y.   B,D,K,W2   U.S.A.

- - **'Spaan'** Welch
    1979 A low, spreading plant with tiny leaves. A curiosity: raised by Joe Spaan.   W2   U.S.A.

- - 'Spaan's Pygmy' Hort. Amer.
    Superfluous name for 'Spaan'.

- - 'Sponi' Hort. Amer.
    1986 An illegit. listed name for a mounded dwarf, faster-growing than 'Gnome'.

- - 'Stapeley' Hort. Anglia
    1990 L. Wansdyke Nurs, Devizes, Wilts., U.K.

- - 'Sunshine' Hort. Holland
    1992 A listed name.

- - **'Sylvia'** Hort. Holland
    1986 L. H.J. van de Laar in "Naamlijst . . .". NOM.

- - 'Teeny' Hort. Canada
    1986 A listed name for a very diminutive form. O. Ed. Lohbrunner of Vancouver Is. B.C.   Canada

- - **'Trompenburg'** Welch 1979 A slow-growing, spreading bush. **O.** Arboretum
Trompenburg, Rotterdam.   G,W   Holland

- - 'Tyrol' Hort. Amer. 1986 A listed name for an upright, open dwarf.

- - 'Uelzen' Horstmann 1983 **L.** Horstmann Nurs, Schneverdingen.

- - 'Umbraculifera' Hort. Amer.
1986 An illegit. listed name for a globose dwarf with needles long,
except around the buds. **L.** Iseli Nurs, Boring, OR.   U.S.A.

- - var. *uncinata* Ramond ex de Candolle
1808 Now known as *PINUS uncinata*.

- - **'Valley Cushion'** Mitsch
1982 In "Nurs. Cat". Low-growing form with short, yellow-
variegated leaves. **L.** Mitsch Nurs, Aurora, OR. **O.** Dr
Tichnor.   U.S.A.

- - 'Variegata' Nelson 1866 "The variegated form". NIC.   B,K   U.K.

- - 'Virgata' Schroeter 1903 A snake-branch form found by Dr C. Schroeter in Switzerland
in 1902.   B,K   Switzerl.

- - **'Well's Columnar'** L.C. Hatch
1988 In "Conifer Database". A columnar form with coarse foliage.   U.S.A.

- - 'White Bud' Hort. Amer. 1985 See 'Iseli White Bud'.

- - 'White Tip' Hort. Anglia 1985 Reported from Windsor Great Park, Berks. Small cushion-
shaped plant with very short dark green leaves.

- - 'Winter Gold' Welch 1979 Dwarf multi-stemmed bush, leaves short, dark green,
extremities of leaves goldish in winter.   G,K,R,W2

- - 'Winter Sun' Hort. Australia
1990 Gold-tipped needles in winter. **O.** Yamina Rare Plants,
Monbulk, Victoria.

- - 'Winzig' Hort. Germany
A listed name for a very dwarf cushion shaped plant with
small leaves - looks rather similar to 'Minikin'.

- - 'Yaffle Hill' Hort. Amer. 1990 A mistake for *PINUS nigra* 'Yaffle Hill'.

- - 'Yellow Point' Hort.
See the following entry.

- - 'Yellow Tip' Hort. Holland
1986 H.J. van de Laar in "Naamlijst . . .". Similar to 'Gnom' but
with leaf-tips yellow in Spring.

- - **'Zundert'** H.J. van de Laar
1987 In "Dendroflora **24**". Small bush with leaves light-golden
yellow in winter; buds conspicuously resinous. **O.** S. van
Nijnatten, Zundert, (1977).   Holland

- - 'Zwergkugel' Hort. Germany
1983 Dwarf globe, multi-budded with very short leaves. **O.** and **I.**
Horstmann Nurs, Schneverdingen, Germany. (a better name
required for such a beautiful plant). When rooted out from the
grafting stock this really is a tiny plant for the connoisseur.

PINUS muricata D. Don 1837 Bishop Pine.   10-20m,Z8   West U.S.A.

- - var. *borealis* Axelrod 1983 A geographical variant with minor differences. (per
Rushforth, 1987).   R

- - var. *cedrosensis* J.T. Howell
1941 Not now distinguished within the species. (per Silba, 1984).

- - var. *remorata* Duffield   1952   Now treated as a separate species. (per Rushforth, 1987).   R

- - var. *stantonii* Axelrod   1983   Not now distinguished within the species. (per Silba, 1984).

PINUS x *murraybanksiana* Righter & Stockwell
                1949   A hybrid: *PINUS banksiana* x *PINUS contorta* var.
                      latifolia..   B,K

PINUS nelsonii Shaw   1904   Nelson Pinyon Pine. A rare, bushy species. Apparently 1n,
                              but in reality 3n.   9m,Z9   Mexico

PINUS nigra Arnold   1785   The European Black Pines. 2n.   40m,Z4   Europe

This is a difficult group of pines to classify. It consists of several geographical variants that over the years have been recognised at different levels and under a great variety of names. This has been the source of much confusion, in the past as is clear from the following table. In the Checklist, following Rushford (1987), the main variations are now listed as sub-species.

Popular Name	Austrian Pine	Corsican Pine	Crimean Pine	Pyrenean Pine
As species	*nigra* Arnold (1785) *austriaca* Hoess (1825) *maritima* (Koch) (1837)	*laricio* Poiret (1804)	*pallasiana* D.Don in Lambert *caramanica* Bosc & Delamare	*pyrenaica* Lapayrouse *cebennensis* Hort. ex Gordon
As sub-species	*nigra* (Arn.) Novak (1926)	*laricio* (Poiret) Maire *croatica* Lovril (1971-2)	*pallasiana* (Lambert) Holmboe *salzmannii*	*salzmannii* (Dunal) Franco
As (botanical) variety.	*nigra* Harrison *austriaca* (Hoess) Badoux (1910)	*calabrica* (Loudon) Schneider *corsicana* (Loudon) Hyl. (1953) *maritima* (Aiton) Melville (1958) *poiretiana* (Loudon) Schneider (1913)	*caramanica* (Loudon) Rehder (1927) *pallasiana* (Lambert) Schneider	*cebennensis* (Gren. & Godr.) Rehder (1922) *pyrenaica* Grenier & Godron (1856)
Confusing Cross references	*P. laricio* vars. *P. nigricans* Host. (1831)	*P. laricio* vars. *P. nigra* vars.	*P. caramanica* *P.caramaniensis* *P. corsica* vars. *P. laricio* vars. *P. pallasiana* *P. romana*	*P. laricio* vars. *P. monspeliensis* *P. salzmannii*

PINUS NIGRA

The regional groups within the species *PINUS nigra* are recognisable as follows:-

The Austrian Pine. Central Europe. Tree with domed crown shoots pale buff turning shiny green and then brown. Buds squat conical brown overlaid with white scales. Leaves stiff very dark green. Here listed as sub-species *nigra*. (the "typical" form of the species).

The Corsican Pine. Tall vigorous conical open tree, shoots buff to pale brown, grooved, second year dark brown, buds thin conical to sharp point, red-brown overlaid with white resin. Leaves light green sparse. Here listed as sub-species *laricio* (Poiret) Maire.

The Crimean Pine. Balkans to Asia Minor. Tree often multi-stemmed, shoots yellow-green then orange-brown buds white-brown with grey conical tip. Leaves appressed to shoot at base, thick stiff dark shiny green or grey-green. Here listed as sub-species *pallasiana* (Lambert) Holmboe.

The Pyrenean Pine. S.W. France, Pyrenees, Central and Eastern Spain. Dome headed tree, shoot fissured and strongly orange-brown, leaves long grey-green. Buds cylindrical with conical top covered in white resin. Here listed as sub-species *salzmannii* (Dunal) Franco.

The Dalmatian Pine. Small tree, slow-growing, young shoots very red then brown, short leaves. Small scattered populations down Yugoslavian coast. Here listed as sub-species *dalmatica* (Vis.) Franco.

- - 'Arnold Sentinel'	1988 A dense selection of var. *pyramidata*. **O.** Selected at Arnold Arboretum, Jamaica Plain, Mass.		U.S.A.
- - **'Aurea'** Beissner	1909 Leaves pale yellow. **O.** Found in the wild by Ilsemann in Nylas Forest.	B,G,K,R	Hungary
- - 'Aureospicata' F.G. Meyer	1963 Possibly a mistake for *PINUS leucodermis* 'Aureovariegata'.		Holland
- - var. *austriaca* (Hoess) Badoux	1910 Here regarded as the "typical" form, ie. subsp. *nigra*.		Europe
- - **'Balanica'** L.C. Hatch	1988 In "Conifer Database". Possibly a mistake for a recently introduced clone of the following.	K	
- - var. *balcanica* Fitschen in Beissner	1930 Cushion-shaped dwarf form found in the Balkan region.	B,H,K,W2	Balkans
- - var. *banatica* Schenk ex Kirchner	1864 An uncommon local variant. See "The Plantsman, **2**". (1981).		
- - 'Bergen' G. Horstmann	1983 A slow-growing form, similar to 'Helga' raised from a witch's broom found by G. Krüssmann in Bergen, Holland.		
- - **'Black Prince'** D.W. Hatch	In "Nurs. Cat". One of the smallest of the Nigra forms, introduced by Don Hatch, forming a dense little pyramid. **O.** Chantry Nurs, Honiton, Devon.		
- - 'Bobby McGregor' M. McGregor	1988 Dwarf form with branchlets nearly appressed to the stem. Short twisted grey-green leaves. **I.** and **L.** Kenwith Nurs, Bideford, Devon.		
- -'Bright Eyes' Int. Con. Reg.	1983 A conical bush with light-green leaves and white winter buds. Registered by Don Hatch, Chantry Nurs, Honiton, Devon. **I.** The same (1979). **O.** From a witch's broom found by B. Reynolds at Horsell Common, Woking, Surrey.		U.K.

- - 'Buda' Hort. Hungary   1992   A listed name. Libo Nurs, Baexam, Holland.

- - 'Bujotii' Carrière   1867   Tree with leader, no branches but branchlets only growing
pendulously down the trunk, probably never distributed. NIC.   B,H,K,   France

- - var. *calabrica* (Loudon) Schneider
      1838   Not now distinguished within *PINUS nigra* subsp. *laricio*.

- - 'Caperci's Golden Cream' Hort. Amer.
      1986   A listed name. No information.

- - var. *caramanica* (Loudon) Rehder
      1927   Crimean Pine. See division note.   B,D,K   Crimea

- - var.*cebennensis* (Grenier & Godron) Rehder
      1949   The Pyrenean Pine. Here listed as sub-species.   B,D,K

- - 'Cebennensis Nana' Carrière
      1855   A slow-growing dwarf form of picturesque appearance, grey-
green leaves, noticeably red brown young branchlets. **L.**
Kenwith Nurs, Bideford, Devon.

- - 'Columnaris' Schwerin   1907   Columnar; branches short, up-curved. Found by Hartmann in
Cyprus. NIC.   B,G,K   Cyprus

- - 'Compacta' Hort. Amer.   1986   An illegit. listed name. No information.

- - 'Contorta' Carrière   1855   A slow-growing spreading shrub with twisted leaves.   B   U.S.A.

- - var. *corsicana* (Loudon) Hyl
      1953   The Corsican Pine. 2n. See division note.

- - subsp. *croatica* Lovril   1971   Not now distinguished within the species. (per Silba, 1984).

- - subsp. **dalmatica** (Visiana) Franco
      Dalmatian Pine. A small tree, rare in cultivation.   4-7m   Yugoslavia

- - 'Falcata' Schelle   1909   A plant with distorted foliage, probably never distributed.
NIC.   B   Germany

- - 'Frank' Hort. Amer.   1988   Compact form that grows naturally similar to
'Hornibrookiana' but at a slower rate I. Mitsch Nurs, Aurora,
OR, PA. L. Coenosium Nurs, OR.

- - **'Geant de Suisse'** H.J. van de Laar
      1981   In "Dendroflora 18.". A spreading clone with dense, dark
green foliage. **I.** P.J. Kortmann Nurs, Boskoop, Holland. **O.**
Found in the Botanic Garden, Geneva.   G.K   Switzerl.

- - **'Globosa'** R.M. Nordine   1961   In "Plant Prop. Soc. Proc. **11**". A medium-size, globose form.   G,K,W2   U.S.A.

- - 'Goldfingers' R. Watson   1990   A slow-growing form of Corsican Pine making an upright
miniature tree. Leaves bright yellow when planted in full sun.
O. and **I.** Treborth Nurs, Bangor, N. Wales.

- - 'Hatchlands' Hort. Anglia
      1985   A plant in Windsor Great Park, Berks, without description.

- - **'Helga'** G. Krüssmann   1983   Very slow-growing dwarf upright form; short, fresh-green
needles and contrasting white buds. **O.** Found as a witch's
broom in a 60 year old plantation of *PINUS nigra* var. *nigra*
by Dr Simon, Marktheidenfeld, Germany, (1965).

- - 'Herk Osterreich' Hort. Ireland
      1985   Reported from J.F. Kennedy Park, Co. Wexford, Ireland.

- - 'Hornibrook' Hort.   A mistake for the following.

- - 'Hornibrookiana' Slavin

                1932 A well-tried dwarf form. **O.** A witch's broom found in Seneca
                     Park, Rochester, N.Y.   B,D,G,H,K,W2 U.S.A.

- - 'Horstmann's Creeper' Hort. Germany
                1983 In list as 'repens' form.

- - f. *hornotina* Beck   1890 A local variant in lower Austria that ripens seed in 1 year.   K   Germany

- - 'Jacobsen' G. Haddow   1988 In "Nurs. Cat". Slow, low-growing bush; possibly a hybrid
                         with *PINUS mugo*. **O.** Kenwith Nurs, Bideford, Devon.   U.K.

- - 'Jeddeloh' Krüssmann   1979 A slow-growing miniature tree form. **O.** J. zu Jeddeloh Nurs,
                         Oldenburg, (1955).   K,R   Germany

- - 'Koekelare' Herbignat   1953 In "Bull. Soc. Roy. Forestiere". A selection of value in
                         forestry.   B   France

- - subsp. *laricio* (Poiret) Maire   Corsican Pine. Differs from subsp. *nigra* by its vigour, open
                         crown and light grey foliage.

- - 'Magnifica' Schwerin   1920 Named for a tree in a park at Brunswick. NIC.   B   Germany

- - var. *maritima* (Aiton) Melville
                1958 Now known as *PINUS nigra* subsp. *laricio*.   B,D

- - 'Meylan' Hort. Germany   1983 A listed name. Horstmann Nurs, Schneverdingen.

- - 'Molette' Hort. Hungary   1990 Young plants appear to be fastigiate. A clone of var.
                         pyramidata raised by M. Barabits, Sopron.

- - 'Monspeliensis' Hort. Amer.
                1986 An illegit. listed name.

- - 'Monstrosa' Carrière   1867 A monstrous plant found in the Sénéclauze Nurs, Bourg
                         Argental, Loires. NIC.   B,D,H,K,W2   France

- - 'Moseri' Moser   1900 Globose form, turning yellowish in winter. The yellow is best
                         when Nigra is used as understock. Still widely planted.**O.**
                         Moser Nurs, Versailles.   B,H,K,R,W2   France

- - 'Nana' (1) Carrière   1985 See 'Cebennensis Nana'.   B,K,W2   France

- - 'Nana' (2) Hornibrook   1939 Based on a broadly pyramidal tree formerly at Wageningen,
                         and found by H.J. Grootendorst. Now again in production.   H   Holland

- - 'Nana' (3) Krüssmann   1979 A mistake for *PINUS nigra* 'Schovenhorst'.   K

- - 'Nana' (4) Hort. Holland 1982 A mistake for *PINUS nigra* 'Strypemonde'.

- - 'Nana Wurstle' Hort. Germany
                1990 An illegit. name. See 'Wurstle'.

- - subsp. *nigra* Hort.   Austrian Pine. Branching coarse, foliage dark green. The
                         "typical" form of the species, excluding all other sub-species.

- - 'Obelisk' Hort. Germany   A narrowly columnar clone of var. *pyramidata*. See also
                         'Molette'. Young plants are very fastigiate.

- - subsp. *pallasiana* (Lambert) Holmboe
                The Crimean Pine.

- - 'Pendula' Carrière   1855 No longer identifiable.   B,D,K   France

- - 'Petra' Hort. Germany   1986 Dwarf form from a witch's broom. **O.** Eschrich. **I.** and **L.**
                         Horstmann Nurs, Schneverdingen.

- - 'Pierrick Bregeon' H.J. van de Laar
                1992 In "Dendroflora **29**". A new dwarf of the Corsican Pine. **O.**
                       and **I.** H. Bregeon, Renens, Switzerland.

- - var. *poiretiana* Antoine	1840	Not now distinguished within subsp. *laricio*.		
- - 'Prostrata' Beissner	1903	A prostrate plant, lacking a leader. NIC.	B,D,H,K	Germany
- - 'Pumila Aurea' Beissner	1891	A dwarf form with yellowish leaves. NIC.	B,K	Germany
- - f. *pygmaea* Rauch ex Gordon	1858	Low, spreading form with small globose cones.	B,W2	Italy
- - 'Pygmaea' (1) (Carrière) Rehder	1855	A dwarf, globose form no longer identifiable.	B,D	
- - 'Pygmaea' (2) Beissner	1891	Globose to conical dwarf form; leaves at the tips of the shoot *gehauft*. This is *PINUS sylvestris* 'Globosa Viridis' of the trade but is now recognised as a Nigra form once again.	Not as B	Germany
- - 'Pygmaea' (3) Hornibrook	1923	Same as last entry. The yellow form described by Hornibrook is *PINUS nigra* 'Moseri' under which name it is now listed.	H	
- - 'Pyramidalis' Slavin	1932	Named for a tree in the Durand-Eastman Park, Rochester, N.Y.	B,D,K	U.S.A.
- - f. *pyramidata* A. Acatay	1955	A columnar local variant found in the Tansavli region. I. Meyer, Tonisvort,	K	Turkey
- - 'Pyramidata' Carrière	1855	A broad, pyramidal shrub. No longer identifiable.	B,K	France
- - **'Schovenhorst'** Welch	1979	A squat shrub with short light green leaves held closely round the buds. O. A witch's broom found on the Schovenhorst Estate, Putten.	W2	Holland
- - 'Skyborn' R. Watson	1987	Slow-growing form with very thick branches, large buds and long stiff leaves. O. and I. Treborth Nurs, Bangor, N. Wales.		
- - 'Spingarn' Hort. Anglia	1985	Dwarf globose to conical plant with twisted dark green leaves. L. Kenwith Nurs, Bideford, Devon.		
- - **'Strypemonde'** Welch	1979	Foliage dark green; buds light grey. O. Reported from the Strypemonde Estate.	G,K,R,W2	Holland
- - 'Sylvit' Hort. Holland	1990	Listed name for a fastigiate form. O. M. Barabit of Sopron, Hungary.		
- - **'Talland Bay'** G. Haddow	1988	In "Nurs. Cat". From a witch's broom, named for its place of finding and described as similar to 'Wurstle' with small tufts of leaves. I. Kenwith Nurs, Bideford, Devon.		U.K.
- - 'Tenuifolia' Hort. Amer.	1986	An illegit. name.		
- - 'Trompenburg' Hort. Holland	1982	A mistake for *PINUS nigra* 'Strypemonde'.		
- - **'Variegata'** Lawson ex Gordon	1858	Green and straw-coloured leaves intermingled.	B,K,R	U.K.
- - 'Villetta Barrea' Nageli	1929	A local strain found in Abruzzo, of value in forestry.	B	Italy
- - **'Wurstle'** Hort. Germany	1983	A slightly faster growing version of the so-called *PINUS sylvestris* 'Globosa Viridis', i.e., *PINUS nigra* 'Pygmaea' with small leaves in tufts produced later in the year. O. Wurstle Nurs, Munich.	G	Germany
- - **'Yaffle Hill'** Welch	1979	A globose form with dark green leaves. Found in the garden at "Yaffle Hill", Broadstone, Dorset. Home of Mr. Charles Carter of Poole.		U.K.

- - 'Zlatiborica' Adam ex Beissner
1909 A golden-yellow form. NIC?　　　　　　　　　　　　　B,K　　　Serbia

PINUS *novo-galiciana* Caravajal　A recently named species with a limited habitat in Jalisco, possibly referable to *PINUS strobiformis*. (per Rushmore, 1987).　　　　　　　　　　　　　　　　　　　Mexico

PINUS *oaxacana* Mirov　1958 Oaxaca Pine. A species allied to *PINUS strobiformis*, but distinct in the cones.　　　　　　　　　　40m,Z9　　Mexico

PINUS *occidentalis* Swartz
1788 West Indian Pine. A tropical species allied to *PINUS caribaea*.　　　　　　　　　　　　　　Z10　　W. Indies

- - var. *baorensis* Silba　1984 Hispaniola Pine. A newly described variety.

- - var. *cubensis* (Sargent) Silba
1984 By some authorities treated as a species. (per Rushforth, 1987).　　　　　　　　　　　　　　　Z10　　Cuba

PINUS *oocarpa* Scheide ex Schlechtendal
1838 Egg-cone Pine. A descriptively-named tropical species with foliage similar to *PINUS patula*. 5n. Neither the species nor the foliage variants, vars. *manzanoi, microphylla, ochoterai or trifoliata* are in cultivation in cool temperate zones.　30m,Z9　　Peru

PINUS *pallasiana* Lambert　Crimean Pine. Here listed as *PINUS nigra* var.*caramanica*.

PINUS *palustris* Miller　1786 Longleaf Pine. Species marked by large white buds and open habit. 3n.　　　　　　　　　　　　25-30m,Z9　U.S.A.

PINUS *parviflora* Siebold and Zuccarini
1844 Japanese White Pine. 5n.　　　　　　　　20m,Z5　　Japan

This species is by some authorities treated as two species *Pinus himekomatsu* Miyabe and *PINUS pentaphylla* Miyabe and Kudo. It is widely used in Japan in the "manufacture" of Bonsai, and an enormous number of names are in use, many nothing more than private distinctions for use within the nurseries engaged in this trade. Others are true cultivar names in the western sense. Names selected by Welch (1979) provisionally for botanical recognition as *formae* are here treated as provenances in a forestry sense. On present information, the status of many names is not possible to determine. Some names undoubtedly are superfluous, and many clones must be indistinguishable. The inclusion of the word "goyo" (=Five-needle pine) in names is contrary to the Cultivar Code and the hyphenation used varies.

Descriptions of plants in this section are fraught with problems due to the fact that use of a wide variety of understocks produces very different looking plants in vigour, leaf length and colour and growth habit. Where possible descriptions have been taken from plants on their own roots or from plants grafted on *PINUS strobus* from which *P. parviflora* cultivar roots out readily but we are aware that some plants have been grafted on *P. wallichiana, P. peuce, P. thunbergii, P. contorta* and others.

- - 'AA Special No. I' Hort. Amer.　Upright dwarf form with short, thick dark-blue needles. O. Selection by A.J. Fordham at Arnold Arboretum, Boston.

- - 'AA Special No. 2' Hort. Amer.　See 'Al Fordham'.

- - **'Adcock's Dwarf'** C.R. Lancaster
1966 In "Gard. Chron". Globose dwarf with short recurving mid-green leaves. I. Hillier and Sons Nurs. Winchester. O. Raised from seed by G. Adcock, Head Propagator.　　G,K,W2　　U.K.

- - 'Aija' Hort. Anglia　1970 L. Hilliers Nurs in "Conifer Conf. List". NOM.

- - "aizu-goyo" W.N. Valavanis
1976 In "Japanese Five-needle Pines". A local provenance from the Prefecture of Fukushima.　　　　　　　　　　　Japan

- - "akashi-goyo" Hort. Japan
1976 A local provenance of Mt. Akashi, Shikoku Island.　　　Japan

- - 'Alba' Hort.　1976 L. W.N. Valavanis. NOM.

- - f. *albo-terminata* Mayr   1890   Having some yellow or white leaves.   Hort. Japan

- - 'Al. Fordham' Hort. Amer.
     1989   Very small dwarf with fine mid-green recurved needles. Raised at Arnold Arboretum and named for Al Fordham the Head propagator.

- - **'Ama-no-gawa'** W.N. Valavanis
     1976   Yatsubusa cultivar. Squat globose plant with dark-green, short, thick recurving needles.   Hort. Japan

- - 'Aoba jo' Hort. Amer.   1988   Narrow upright tree with short curly needles which are bright blue. **L.** Mitsch Nurs, Aurora, OR.

- - **'Aoi'** W.N. Valavanis   1976   A popular Yatsubusa cultivar with short, thick curving bluish needles; brown, bluntly pointed buds.   W2   Hort. Japan

- - **'Ara-kawa'** W.N. Valavanis
     1976   A clone with very rough bark; and thin straight dark-green leaves.   Hort. Japan

- - 'Asahi Zuro' Hort. Amer.   1988   A listed name. Mitsch Nurs, Aurora, OR.

- - "asama-goyo" Hort. Japan
     1976   Provenance of Nagano Prefecture with long thick needles and rough bark.   Japan

- - 'Aurea' Hort.   1976   A commercial equivalent of 'Ogon-goyo'.   Hort. Japan

- - **'Azuma-goyo'** Hort. Japan
     1976   Slow growing dwarf. Leaves silver blue, held forward round the buds on the shoot ends. ("Azuma-goyo" is from the Provenance of Fukushima and Yamagata Prefecture).   Japan

- - **'Azuma-ko-fuji'** W.N. Valavanis
     1976   A clone of "bandai-goyo". Stronger growing than 'Azuma-goyo'. Leaves dark blue-grey, trunk thick.   Hort. Japan

- - 'Baasch's Form' Hort. Amer.
     1976   See 'Brevifolia'(3).

- - **'Baldwin'** Hort. Amer.   1976   Curving blue needles, upright growing, branches upswept. **L.** J.W. Spingarn, Baldwin, Long, Is., N.Y.

- - 'Ban-dai' Hort. Amer.   1976   A clone of "Aizu-goyo".

- - "bandai-goyo"   1976   Provenance from Mt. Bandai, Fukushima Prefecture.   Japan

- - 'Barrie Bergman' Hort. Amer.
     1975   **O.** and **I.** Raraflora Nurs, Feasterville, PA.

- - **'Bergman'** Helene Bergman
     1965   In "Plants and Gardens". Dwarf plant wider than high with twisted blue needles and large buds. **O.** Raraflora Nurs, Feasterville, PA. Grafted plants are strong growing and upright. Propagation should be scion rooted whenever possible.   R,W2   U.S.A.

- - 'Bergman Aurea' Hort. Amer.
     1980   A listed name. Kristick Nurs, Wellsville, PA.

- - 'Bergman Sun' Hort. Amer.
     1980   A listed name. Kristick Nurs, Wellsville, PA.

- - 'Bergman's Challenger' Hort. Amer.
     1992   A listed name.

- - 'Bergman's Gold' Hort. Amer.
     1978   **L.** Wansdyke Nurs, Devizes, Wilts.

- - 'Blauer Engel' Hort. Germany
          1992 A listed name. **L.** Hachmann Nurs, Barmstedt in Holstien, Germany.

- - **'Blue Giant'** D.M. van Gelderen
          1982 In "Dendroflora **19**". A very vigorous selection with silver blue leaves. **O.** Gebr. van Vliet (1975).   K,R   Holland

- - 'Bo-jyo' W.N. Valavanis 1976 Yatsubusa cultivar. A slow-growing clone with thick, yellow-green, much twisted needles in open bundles.   Hort. Japan

- - **'Bonnie Bergman'** Hort. Amer.
          1975 Slow-growing form with ascending branches and leaves a shining pale blue-grey in summer. **I.** Into U.K. by Wansdyke Nurs, Devizes, Wilts. **O.** F.W. Bergman, Raraflora Nurs, Feasterville, PA, (1970). ('Bonny Bergman' is incorrect).   U.S.A.

- - 'Bonsai' Hort. Holland   1975 Now known as 'Negishi' in Holland.

- - **'Brevifolia'** (1) Mayr   1890 A narrowly-ascending form (of var. *himekomatsu*) with bluish-green foliage. **I.** Barbier et Fils, Orleans. See 'Ha-tzumari'.   B,D,G,H,K,W2 Hort. Japan

- - 'Brevifolia' (2) Mayr   1890 A selection of var. *pentaphylla* with short, thick needles.   Hort. Japan

- - 'Brevifolia' (3) Baasch's Form W.N. Valavanis
          1976 Dense, upright bush. Short, dark blue, curved leaves. **L.** Hillside Nurs, Lehighton, PA, (1970). NOM.   U.S.A.

- - 'Burke's Bonsai' Hort. Amer.
          1989 Upright growing plant with short twisted blue-grey needles. Selected by Joe Burke who has subsequently selected further clones suitable for Bonsai.

- - **'Cedar Lodge'** Hort. Australia
          1989 Creamy-white variegated form. **O.** Ron Radford, Cedar Lodge Nurs, Sulphur Creek, Australia.

- - "chichibu-goyo" Hort. Japan
          1976 Provenance of Tochigi Prefecture.   Japan

- - 'Cho-un' W.N. Valavanis 1976 An old Yatsubusa cultivar. NOM.   Hort. Japan

- - 'Cleary' Hort. Amer.   Strong growing, silver-blue leaves.

- - 'Compacta' Hort. Amer.   1986 An illegit. listed name.

- - "*corticosa*"   1976 A Latin adjective meaning "Coarse-bark". (=nishiki).

- - 'Dai-ho' W.N. Valavanis 1976 Yatsubusa cultivar. Light green-grey recurving needles, darkening. A selection from "nasu-goyo".('Tai-ho').   Hort. Japan

- - 'Dai-mon-ji' W.N. Valavanis
          1976 Yatsubusa cultivar much used for Bonsai. A selection from "shikoku-goyo".   Hort. Japan

- - 'Diaset-susan' G. Haddow
          1986 Conical, horizontally spreading branches. dark green leaves. Original plant in collection of the late Sir H.G. Hillier. In "Nurs. Cat". **L.** Kenwith Nurs, Bideford, Devon.   U.K.

- - 'Early Cone' Hort. Amer. 1991 An unacceptable listed name that should be replaced. Sets numerous large, blue green cones.

- - 'Eigoro-goyo' Mayr   1890 A clone of 'Brevifolia' (2), named for its originator. NIC.   Hort. Japan

- - **'Ei-ko'** W.N. Valavanis 1976 Yatsubusa cultivar. Dark green, short, thick needles. rough bark.   Hort. Japan

- - 'Ei-ko-nishiki' W.N. Valavanis
          1976 Bark of trunk becomes corky.   Hort. Japan

- - **'Ei-ryu'** W. N. Valavanis
          1976 Yatsubusa cultivar. Pale green, thick straight needles in open
bundles showing the white stomata. Small red buds.   Hort. Japan

- - 'Emperor' Hort. Amer.   1986 E.A. Cope in "Native . . . Conifers". Foliage Emerald green.
Quite fast growing.

- - var. *fenzeliana* Wu   1956 Not now distinguished within the species. (per Mirov, 1967).

- - 'Frick Estate' Hort. Amer.   Upright, leaves paler blue held at 45o to branches.

- - 'Fubuki Nishiki' Hort. Amer.
          1988 A listed name. Mitsch Nurs, Aurora, OR..

- - 'Fuiri-goyo' Y. Kobayashi et al.
          1975 Same as 'Shimofuri-goyo'.

- - **'Fukai'** G. Horstmann   1986 In "Nurs. Cat". Dwarf plant with leaves barred creamy white.
O. Tage Lundell, Helsingborg.   Sweden

- - 'Fukai Seedling' G. Haddow   Same origin as 'Fukai'. Probably the same plant.

- - 'Fukiju' Hillier & Sons   1970 In "Conifer Conf. List". Yatsubusa cultivar with short, thick
curved needles; buds whitish. ('Fuku-ju').   Hort. Japan

- - 'Fuku-ju-bi' W. N. Valavanis
          1976 Silver-blue needles. A selection of "ishizuki"
provenance.('Fuku-zu-mi'; 'Na-mori').

- - 'Fuku-no-kami' W. N. Valavanis
          1976 Yatsubusa cultivar. Dark green, thick, twisted needles.   Hort. Japan

- - "fukushima-goyo" Hort. Japan
          1976 Provenance of Fukushima Prefecture. One of the best natural
selections for Bonsai. Upright growing, radial branches,
shortish dark blue/silver-grey leaves.   W2   Japan

- - **'Fuku-zu-mi'** W. N. Valavanis
          1976 Yatsubusa cultivar. Low spreading dwarf plant with recurved
and twisted silver-blue needles. I. Into U.K. by Wansdyke
Nurs, Devizes, Wilts.   W2   Hort. Japan

- - 'Fu-shiro-goyo' W. N. Valavanis
          1976 Needles turn white in winter.   Hort. Japan

- - 'Futsumo' Hort. Amer.   1988 Fine green blue leaves, often slightly recurving. L. Mitsch
Nurs, Aurora, OR.

- - 'Gan-seki-sho' W. N. Valavanis
          1976 Bark has rough texture.   Hort. Japan

- - **'Gimborn's Ideal'** Den Ouden/Boom
          1960 Large, upright-branched shrub with long curved needles. I.
Konijn and Son, Ederveen, O. Found on van Gimborn Estate,
Doorn.   B,G,K,W2   Holland

- - **'Gimborn's Pyramid'** Den Ouden/Boom
          1965 Compact, broad bush with short dark blue/green curved
leaves. I. Konijn and Son, Ederveen. O. Found on van
Gimborn Estate, Doorn.   B,K,W2   Holland

- - 'Gin Yatsubusa' Hort. Amer.
          1980 Upright, moderate growing, branches sparse. leaves pale blue,
incurved. L. J.W. Spingarn, Long Is., N.Y.

- - 'Gi-on' W.N. Valavanis   1976 Yatsubusa cultivar. Dark green, thick, short needles.   Hort. Japan

- - **'Glauca'** Beissner   1909   Small tree with silver-blue curved leaves. Often has red flowers in Spring. Widely planted. More than one selection is in cultivation.   B,G,K,R,W2   Hort. Japan

- - 'Glauca Brevifolia' Hort. Amer.
      1986   See 'Brevifolia' (2).

- - 'Glauca Compacta' Hort. Amer.
      1986   An illegit. listed name.

- - 'Glauca Nana' Hort. Amer.
      1980   An acceptable name is required. Popular clone in U.S.A. dwarf tree-like form with blue-green curved needles. **L.** J.W. Spingarn, Long Is., N.Y.

- - 'Glauca Pendula' Hort. Amer.
      1972   Reported from Longwood Gardens, Kennett Square, PA.

- - 'Go-Gin' Hort. Amer.   1983   Long twisted needles, multiple buds. In "Nurs. Cat". Coenosium Gardens, Lehighton, PA.

- - 'Go-ko-haku' W.N. Valavanis
      1976   Yatsubusa cultivar. Silver-blue needles. Upswept branches with branchlets and foliage similarly grouped round the branches. A selection of "shikoku-goyo".   Hort. Japan

- - 'Go-ryo-haku' W.N. Valavanis
      1976   Yatsubusa cultivar. Yellow-green needles.   Hort. Japan

- - 'Gotelli' Hort. Amer.   1992   Dwarf form from the Gotelli Collection at the U.S. Dept. Agric., Washington, DC. **L.** Jeddeloh Nurs, Oldenburg. ('Gothelli').

- - 'Goykuri' Hort. Sweden   1979   **I.** Tage Lundell, Helsingborg.

- - 'Goyoku-sui' Hort. Anglia
      1986   A listed name.

- - 'Goyo Unkasai' Hort. Amer.
      1988   A listed name. Mitsch Nurs, Aurora, OR.

- - 'Gyok-kan' W.N. Valavanis
      1976   Yatsubusa cultivar. Grey-blue, short, thick straight needles. Strong grower.   Hort. Japan

- - 'Gyokkasen' Y. Kobayashi et al.
      1975   In "Matsu-zukan". Blue-green short thin leaves, similar to but much smaller than 'Kokonoe'. (Several spellings are found).   G,W2   Hort. Japan

- - 'Gyokuei' Hort. Sweden   1979   Dwarf upright bush with pale blue to grey incurved leaves. **I.** Tage Lundell, Helsingborg.

- - 'Gyo-ku-sen' W.N. Valavanis
      1976   Yatsubusa cultivar. Dwarf plant, blue-grey, short thick slightly recurving leaves.   Hort. Japan

- - 'Gyoku-sho-hime' W.N. Valavanis
      1976   Yatsubusa cultivar. Yellow-green, thick, twisted needles. ('Hagoromo').   W2   Hort. Japan

- - 'Gyo-ku-sui' W.N. Valavanis
      1976   Yatsubusa cultivar. Upright growing blue-green, medium thick, curved needles.   Hort. Japan

- - 'Hagoromo' Hort. Amer.   1976   Same as 'Gyoku-sho-hime'. (per Valavanis).

- - 'Hagoromo Seedling' Hort. Sweden
  1979 Dwarf globose to flat topped plant with medium length slightly incurved blue-green leaves. Quite outstanding. **I.** Tage Lundell, Helsingborg. **L.** Kenwith Nurs, Bideford, Devon.   G

- - **'Hakko'** W.N. Valavanis 1976 Yatsubusa cultivar. Dark green, short, twisted needles. **O.** Mr. Kaneko in Saimata Prefecture. ('Kaneko' is incorrect).   W2   Hort. Japan

- - 'Hakkodo-goyo' Hort.   1986 A mistake for *PINUS hakkodensis* Makino.   W2   Hort. Japan

- - 'Handsworth' Hort. Anglia
  1985 Reported from Windsor Great Park, Berks. Upright growing plant with silver-blue slightly recurved leaves.

- - 'Haru-ko-ro' W.N. Valavanis
  1976 Yatsubusa cultivar, becoming widely used. ('Shun-ko-ro').   Hort. Japan

- - 'Hatchichi' G. Haddow   1992 Very dwarf globose plant tightly furnished with branches and leaves. Leaves short, pale blue incurved. Named for Don Hatch. **O.** and **I.** Kenwith Nurs, Bideford, Devon.

- - **'Ha-tzumari-goyo'** Mayr
  1890 A commerical equivalent of 'Brevifolia' (1). (Ha-zumari'). A slow-growing upright form with dark blue/green fairly long curved needles.   W2   Hort. Japan

- - 'Heidelberger Schloss' G. Horstmann
  1983 In "Nurs. Cat". Slow-growing; green; bizarre habit.   Germany

- - 'Hikari' W.N. Valavanis 1976 Yatsubusa cultivar. Habit conical.   Hort. Japan

- - 'Hime-goyo-matsu' Welch
  1979 Same as 'Nana' and probably NIC.   W2   Hort. Japan

- - var *himekomatsu* Miyabe and Kudo
  1954 The form endemic to South Japan. Not now distinguished within the species.   Japan

- - 'Ho-ho' W.N. Valavanis 1976 Yatsubusa cultivar. Young growth yellow.   Hort. Japan

- - 'Ho-ju' W.N. Valavanis 1976 Yatsubusa cultivar. Blue-green, short needles. A selection from "fukushima-goyo".   Hort. Japan

- - 'Ho-ki' W.N. Valavanis 1976 Yatsubusa cultivar. Thin, yellow-green needles.   Hort. Japan

- - 'Ho-sho' W.N. Valavanis 1976 Yatsubusa cultivar. New shoots yellow. A selection from "shikoku-goyo".   Hort. Japan

- - 'Hyaku-man-goku' W.N. Valavanis
  1976 Yatsubusa cultivar. Needles silver-blue.   Hort. Japan

- - "hyuga-goyo" Hort. Japan
  1976 A provenance from Fukushima Prefecture.   Japan

- - **'Ibo-can'** Y. Kobayashi et al.
  1976 In "Matsu-zukan". (Illus.) Thick, long dark green leaves and rough bark.   W2   Hort. Japan

- - 'Ibo-can-nishiki' W.N. Valavanis
  1976 See 'Suna-kawa-nishiki'.   Hort. Japan

- - **'Ichi-no-se'** W.N. Valavanis
  1976 Yatsubusa cultivar. Dark green, slightly twisted needles.   W2   Hort. Japan

- - 'Ikari-goyo' Mayr   1890 A synonym of 'Recurva'.   Hort. Japan

- - 'Ikeda-sho' W.N. Valavanis
  1976 Ridged, corky bark. **O.** Mr. Ikeda.   Hort. Japan

- - **'Iri-fune'** W.N. Valavanis
  1976 Yatsubusa cultivar. Deep blue, white-flecked needles.   Hort. Japan

- - "ishizuchi-goyo" Hort. Japan
  1976 Provenance of Mt. Ishizuki, Shikoku Island.   Japan

- - 'Iwasaki' Hort. Amer.   1976 A listed Yatsubusa name.

- - 'Janome-ibokan-goyo' Hort. Amer.
  1986 A listed name.

- - 'Joe Burke' Hort. Amer.   1986 A listed name.

- - "joetsu-goyo" Hort. Japan
  1976 Provenance of Fukushima and Tochigi Prefectures.   Japan

- - 'Jo-ho' W. N. Valavanis   1976 Yatsubusa cultivar. Multiple buds. A selection from
  "shiobara-goyo".   Hort. Japan

- - 'Jyu-ji-seki' W. N. Valavanis
  1976 Yatsubusa cultivar. Needles thin.   Hort. Japan

- - 'Jyu-man-goku' W. N. Valavanis
  1976 Yatsubusa cultivar. Compact growth; needles short.   Hort. Japan

- - 'Jyu-roko-ra-kan' W. N. Valavanis
  1976 Yatsubusa cultivar. Yellow-green, thin, straight needles.   Hort. Japan

- - 'Ka-Ho' W. N. Valavanis 1976 Yatsubusa cultivar. A selection from "ishi zuchi-goyo". Blue-
  grey needles held closely round terminal shoots. ('Ka-hoo').   Hort. Japan

- - 'Kamuro goyo' Mayr   1890 A synonym of 'Tortuosa'. Leaves spiralling.   W2   Hort. Japan

- - 'Kane-ko' Hillier & Sons
  1970 In "Conifer Conference List". See 'Hak-ko'.   U.K.

- - 'Kan-zan' W. N. Valavanis
  1976 Yatsubusa cultivar.Deep-green needles. Rough bark.   Hort. Japan

- - 'Kiki-sui' W. N. Valavanis
  1976 Yatsubusa cultivar. Dark-green, thick, stiff, twisted needles.   Hort. Japan

- - 'Kin-dai-shi' W. N. Valavanis
  1976 Yatsubusa cultivar. Upright habit. A selection from "Akashi-
  goyo".   Hort. Japan

- - 'Kin-ka-cho' Hort. Amer.   1976 A listed Yatsubusa name.

- - 'Kin-kaku' W. N. Valavanis
  1976 Yatsubusa cultivar. Sometimes confused with 'Koko-no-e'.   Hort. Japan

- - 'Kin-po' W.N. Valavanis   1976 Yatsubusa cultivar. A mutation from 'Ka-ho'. ('Kin-sho').

- - **'Kiyomatsu'** T. Lundell   1986 Short, blue needles; dense and bushy. L. Horstmann Nurs,
  Schneverdingen.   Germany

- - 'Kluis seedling' Hort. Amer.
  1976 An acceptable name is required.

- - 'Koba-goyo' Mayr   1890 A clone of 'Brevifolia' (2).   W2

- - 'Kobe' G. Haddow   1986 Very slow-growing conical plant. Short straight thick yellow-
  green leaves. Plant in Royal Edinburgh Botanic Garden ex
  Kobe Arboretum, Tokyo. L. Kenwith Nurs. Bideford. Devon.   Hort. Japan

- - 'Kokonde' G. Haddow   1985 Plant in Windsor Great Park, Berks. Branches in regular
  tiers; short, curved, dark-green leaves. Similar to but faster
  growing than 'Koko-no-e'. L. Kenwith Nurs, Bideford, Devon.   Hort. U.K.

- - **'Koko-no-e'** W.N. Valavanis
  1976 Yatsubusa cultivar. Dark green, short curved needles. Upright with tiered branch system. ('Kokonoye'). W2 Hort. Japan

- - 'Kokonoye' Hort. Anglia 1970 L. Hillier & Sons in "Conifer Conf. List". NOM. Probably as previous item. R

- - 'Kokuho' Y. Kobayashi et al.
  1975 Yatsubusa cultivar. Yellow-green, straight, thin needles. Small plants globose, maybe conical later. ('Koku-how'). R.W2

- - 'Ko-raku' W.N. Valavanis
  1976 Yatsubusa cultivar. Yellow-green needles and compact upright habit. W2 Hort. Japan

- - 'Ko-rin' W.N. Valavanis 1976 Yatsubusa cultivar. Very diminutive clone. A selection from "fukushima-goyo". Hort. Japan

- - 'Kusu-dama' W.N. Valavanis
  1976 Yatsubusa cultivar. Very congested growth habit. Produces clumps of multiple buds. Hort. Japan

- - f. *laevis* Hayashi 1964 Very smooth bark: found on Mt. Apoi in Hokkaido and elsewhere. 'Todo-hada-goyo' is a superfluous name. W2 Japan

- - 'Landis' Hort. Canada 1981 L. Gordon Bentham, Victoria, Canada. (as 'Glauca Landis', Iseli Nurs, Boring, OR, 1982).

- - 'Levy' Hort. Amer. 1976 A listed name

- - 'Mai-tsuzumi' W.N. Valavanis
  1976 Yatsubusa cultivar. Dark-blue incurved needles. Hort. Japan

- - **'Meiko'** W.N. Valavanis
  1976 Yatsubusa cultivar. New shoots yellow-green. A selection from "shiobara-goyo'. Hort. Japan

- - 'Mei-o' W.N. Valavanis 1976 Yatsubusa cultivar. Bushy habit. Hort. Amer.

- - 'Michinoku' Hort. 1983 Globose; grey-green short leaves with a twist.

- - 'Mine-matsu' W.N. Valavanis
  1976 Yatsubusa cultivar. Yellow-green, thin needles. A selection of "shiobara-goyo".

- - **'Miyajima'** Mayr 1890 A clone similar to 'Brevifolia' (3), named for its place of origin. Probably same as following item.. W2 Hort. Japan

- - "miyajima-goyo" Hort. Japan
  1976 Provenance of Hiroshima Prefecture. Much used for Bonsai. Japan

- - "miyama-goyo" Hort. Japan
  1975 Provenance of Nagano Prefecture. Japan

- - "mizukami-goyo" Hort. Japan
  1976 Provenance of Nagano Prefecture. Japan

- - 'Momo-yama' W.N. Valavanis
  1976 Yatsubusa cultivar. Dark green, thick needles. A selection from "nasu-goyo". Hort. Japan

- - 'Morris Dwarf' Hort. Amer.
  1972 L. Watnong Nurs, Morris Plains, N.J. ('Watnong Dwarf'?). Low globose to spreading, leaves green with a twist.

- - 'Myo-jo' Hort. Amer. 1976 A Yatsubusa listed name.

- - 'Na-mori' Hort. Amer. 1976 A listed name. ('Fuku-ju-bi', 'Fuku-su-mi').

- - 'Nana' Carrière   1867   A weak plant, NIC. Re-use of the name is not permitted.   B,H   France

- - 'Naru-to' W.N. Valavanis
            1976   Yatsubusa cultivar. A selection from "azuma-goyo".

- - 'Na-shi' Hort. Amer.   1976   A listed name.

- - "nasu-goyo" Hort. Japan   1975   Provenance of Nasu district in Tochigi Prefecture. Upright
                                          fairly fast grower. Leaves silver-grey new leaves incurved,
                                          older leaves straight. Much used for Bonsai.   Japan

- - 'Nasu-musume' W.N. Valavanis
            1976   Yatsubusa cultivar. A selection of "nasu-goyo".

- - **'Negishi' (1)** W.N. Valavanis
            1975   Short curved silver-blue leaves with strong stomatic lines.
                                          Upright growing. Branching dense. (Syn. Bonsai). In order to
                                          avoid confusion in the future it might be sensible for this
                                          plant, the dwarf form 'Negishi', to revert to it's original U.S.A.
                                          name of 'Bonsai'.   G,K,W2   Hort. Japan

- - **'Negishi' (2)** H.J. van de Laar
            1975   In "Dendroflora **11-12**" I. Imported from Japan by W.J.
                                          Spaaren Nurs, Boskoop (1970). A very vigorous tree, not the
                                          same as last. (At first distributed as 'New seedling' or
                                          'Bonsai').   Hort. Holland

- - **'Negishi-goyo'** Mayr   1890   A synonym of 'Brevifolia' (2).   Hort. Japan

- - 'Nisbet's Gem' Hort. Anglia
            1985   A listed name. Possibly a mistake for *PINUS sylvestris*
                                          'Nisbet's Gem'.

- - **'Nishiki-goyo'** W. N. Valavanis
            1976   Straight, blue-green needles and coarse-textured bark.
                                          ('Corticosa').   W2   Hort. Japan

- - **'Oculus-draconis'** Mayr   1890   Bands of light yellow variegation on the leaves. ('Jano-me' is
                                          a synonym).   B   Hort. Japan

- - **'Ogon-goyo'** W. N. Valavanis
            1976   Needles golden-yellow. ('Aurea'). Slow-growing and not one
                                          of the robust growers.   Hort. Japan

- - 'Ogon-janome' Hort. Amer.
            1976   Very similar if not identical to 'Oculis-Draconis'.

- - 'O-kan' W. N. Valavanis   1976   Yatsubusa cultivar. Vigorous. Deep blue, straight, thick
                                          needles.   Hort. Japan

- - 'Oku-no-matsu' W. N. Valavanis
            1976   Yatsubusa cultivar. Short needles.   Hort. Japan

- - 'Oliver' Hort. Amer.   1982   L. Iseli Nurs, Boring, OR.

- - **'Oritsuru'** Mayr   1890   Commercial equivalent of 'Recurva'. (Ori-zuru').   W2   Hort. Japan

- - 'O-sho' Hort. Amer.   1975   A listed name. ('Tai-kan-o-kanmuri').

- - 'Ossorio Dwarf' Hort. Amer.   Very dwarf plant with short pale curly green leaves, older
                                          leaves darker.

- - 'Otori' W. N. Valavanis   1976   Yatsubusa cultivar. Deep-green needles. A selection from
                                          "nasu-goyo".   Hort. Japan

- - var. *pentaphylla* Mayr   1890   The form endemic to N. Japan. Not now distinguished within
                                          the species.   Japan

- - 'Pentaphylla Glauca' Hort.
      1986 Superfluous name for 'Glauca'.

- - 'Pest' Hort. Hungary   1992 A listed name. **O.** A selection by M. Barabits, Sopron.

- - 'Pumila' Hort. Amer.   1985 L.C. Hatch in "Reference Guide". Dwarf, upright, dense.

- - 'Pygmaea Daiyo Nishiki' Hort. Anglia
      1985 An illegit. listed name. See 'Dai-ho'.

- - 'Pygmaea Hagoromo' Hort. Anglia
      1985 An illegit. listed name. See 'Hagoromo Seedling'.

- - 'Pygmy Yatsubusa' Hort. Amer.
      1983 A congested dwarf form. In "Nurs. Cat". Coenosium Gardens, Lehighton, PA.

- - 'Recurva' Mayr	1890 Some leaves suddenly distorted. (See 'Oritsuru').	B		Hort. Japan
- - 'Rin-un' W. N. Valavanis	1976 Yatsubusa cultivar. Silver-blue needles. A selection from "azuma-goyo".			Hort. Japan
- - **'Ryo-ku-ho'** W. N. Valavanis	1976 Yatsubusa cultivar. Mid blue-silver needles. Upright,very slow-growing. A selection from "nasu-goyo".			Hort. Japan
- - **'Ryo-ku-sui'** W. N. Valavanis	1976 Yatsubusa cultivar. Compact habit.			Hort. Japan
- - **'Ryu-ju'** Y. Kobayashi et al.	1975 In "Matsu-zukan" (Illus.) Yatsubusa cultivar. Green needles, speckled white.	W2		Hort. Japan
- - **'Ryu-ka'** W. N. Valavanis	1976 Yatsubusa cultivar. Upright habit; deep blue needles. A selection from "nasu-goyo".			Hort. Japan
- - **'Ryu-sen'** W. N. Valavanis	1976 Yatsubusa cultivar. Vigorous. A selection from "nasu-goyo".			Hort. Japan
- - **'Sa-dai-jin'** Y. Kobayashi et al.	1975 In "Matsu-zukan" (Illus). Yatsubusa cultivar. Thin, blue, slightly twisted needles. A selection from "nasu-goyo".	W2		Hort. Japan
- - 'Sakı-shiro-goyo' W. N. Valavanis	1976 Needle tips white.			Hort. Japan
- - **'San-bo'** W. N. Valavanis	1976 Yatsubusa cultivar. Blue-green needles stiff and straight, sometimes speckled. A selection from "ishizuki-goyo".			Hort. Japan
- - **'Saphir'** Draijer	1982 In "Dendroflora **19**". Slow, irregular growth; leaves blue. **I.** Draijer Nurs, Heemstede. **O.** the same.	K,R		Holland
- - **'Schoon's Bonsai'** E. A. Stockmann	1983 In "Deutsche Baumschule **27"**. Blue-grey. **O.** Schoon's Nurs. From a witch's broom.	G		Germany
- - 'Seiryoden' Hort. Sweden	1979 A fast growing open plant presumably suitable mainly for bonsai. **I.** Tage Lundell, Helsingborg. L. Mitsch Nurs, Aurora, OR, (1988).			
- - 'Sen-ko' W.N.Valavanis	1976 Yatsubusa cultivar. Thick green twisted needles. A selection from "azuma-goyo".			Hort. Japan
- - 'Seto' W.N.Valavanis	1976 A corky-barked selection from"Shikoku-goyo".			Hort. Japan

- - 'Setsu-gek-ka' W.N.Valavanis
  1976 Yatsubusa cultivar. Dark blue-green, short, thick needles.
  ('Setsugetsuka').   Hort. Japan

- - 'Shiba-musume' W.N.Valavanis
  1976 Yatsubusa cultivar. Short, blue needles with white stomatic
  line.   Hort. Japan

- - 'Shi-ho' W.N.Valavanis   1976 Yatsubusa cultivar. Short needles as in 'Zui-ko'. A selection
  from "nasu-goyo".   Hort. Japan

- - 'Shika-Shima' W.N.Valavanis
  1976 Yatsubusa cultivar. Thick upright irregular growing bluish
  needles, sharply pointed. A selection from "nasu-goyo".   Hort. Japan

- - "shikoku-goyo" Hort. Japan
  1976 Provenance of Shikoku Island marked by short needles and
  rough bark. Illus. in "Matsu-zukan"   W2   Japan

- - 'Shimofuri' W.N.Valavanis
  1976 Straight, blue-green needles with white specks.   W2   Hort. Japan

- - 'Shimofuri-Goyo' Mayr   1890 A synonym of 'Variegata'. Illustration in "Matsu-zukan".   Hort. Japan

- - 'Shin-sen' Hort. Amer.   1976 Yatsubusa cultivar. A listed name.

- - "shiobara-goyo" Hort. Japan
  1976 Provenance of Tochigi Prefecture. Short, thin, light green
  needles. Popular bonsai material.   W2   Japan

- - 'Shi-on' W.N.Valavanis   1976 Yatsubusa cultivar. Dark yellow-green, twisted needles. A
  selection from "zao-goyo". A fast growing form with multiple
  buds.   Hort. Japan

- - 'Shirobana' Hort. Anglia   1970 Hillier and Son in "Conifer Conf. List". NOM.

- - 'Shiro-janome' W.N.Valavanis
  1976 'Shiro-raga goyo' Dwarf form with creamy-white variegation
  on dark green incurved leaves. Believed to be a clone from
  Shikoku Island.   Hort. Japan

- - **'Shizukagoten'** Hort. Anglia
  1976 Short dark silver-blue needles. I. Ex Japan by Wansdyke
  Nurs, Devizes, Wilts.

- - 'Shun-ko-ro' Hort. Amer.
  1976 A listed name. (Haru-ko-ro').

- - 'Shun-mei-kan' W.N.Valavanis
  1976 Yatsubusa cultivar. Silver-blue, short, thick needles. A
  selection from "nasu-goyo".   Hort. Japa

- - 'Shu-re' W.N.Valavanis   1976 Yatsubusa cultivar. Thin short silver blue needles and white
  buds. A selection of "fukushima-goyo".   Hort. Japan

- - 'Suna-kawa-nishiki' Hort. Amer.
  1976 See 'Ibo-can-nishiki'.

- - 'Tai-ho' Hort. Amer.   1976 See 'Dai-ho'.

- - "taiho-goyo" Hort. Japan
  1976 Provenance of Wakayama Prefecture.   Japan

- - 'Tai-kan' W.N.Valavanis   1976 Yatsubusa cultivar. Dark-green, thick, straight needles.   Hort. Japan

- - 'Tai-kan/O-kanmuri' Hort. Japan
  1976 See 'O-sho'.

- - 'Taizumi' Hort. Anglia   1970 L. Hillier and Son in "Conifer Conf. List". NOM.

- - "takane-goyo" Hort. Japan
  1976 Province of Nagano Prefecture.   Japan

- - 'Takara-game' W.N. Valavanis
  1976 A listed Yatsubusa cultivar.   Hort. Japan

- - 'Tano-Mano-Uki' Hort. Amer.
  1990 L. Kristick Nurs, Wellsville, PA.

- - **'Tempelhof'** H.J. Grootendorst
  1969 In "Dendroflora 6". A strong-growing tree with dark blue-
        silver leaves found in the Gimborn Arboretum, Doorn. **I.** L.
        Konijn Nurs, Ederveen, (1965).   B,G,K,R   Holland

- - "todo-hada-goyo" Hort. Japan
  1976 Provenance of Hokkaido and Central Honsu. Bark smooth,
        not flaky. See also f. *laevis*.   W2   Japan

- - 'Tone' Hort. Amer.   1988 Narrow small open tree with short needles. **L.** Mitsch Nurs,
                                       Aurora, OR.

- - 'Tortuosa' Mayr   1890 Needles twisted, branches contorted.   B   Hort. Japan

- - 'Tsai Cheng'   1988 A witch's broom. **L.** Mitsch Nurs, Aurora, OR.

- - 'Tsuma-jiro goyo' Mayr   1890 Commercial synonym of 'Albo-terminata'.   W2

- - **'U-dai-jin'** Y. Kobayashi et al
  1975 Yatsubusa cultivar. Thick, slightly twisted dark blue needles
        and small, long-pointed buds.   W2   Hort. Japan

- - **'Un-ryu'** W.N. Valavanis
  1976 Yatsubusa cultivar. Dark-green, thick, straight needles.   Hort. Japan

- - 'Variegata' Mayr   1890 Similar to *PINUS densiflora* 'Variegata'.   B,K,R   Hort. Japan

- - 'Venus' H.J. Grootendorst
  1965 In "Dendroflora 2". (as 'No. 73'). A large, grey bush. **O.** L.
        Konijn Nurs, Ederveen.   Holland

- - 'Wako' Hort. Amer.   1990 Narrowly upright form, ascending branches, short dark
                                      glaucous leaves. In "Nurs. Cat". Kristick Nurs, Wellsville,
                                      PA.

- - 'Watson' Hort. Amer.   1976 L. W.N. Valavanis. NOM.

- - 'Weeping' Hort. Amer.   1982 An unsatisfactory name. **O.** and **I.** Iseli Nurs, Boring, OR.
                                      May we suggest 'Iseli Weeping'?

- - 'Wells' Hort. Amer.   1986 L. E.A. Cope in "Native . . . Conifers . . .".

- - 'Ya-kumo' W.N. Valavanis
  1976 Yatsubusa cultivar. Yellow-green, thin needles.   Hort. Japan

- - "yamato-goyo" Hort. Japan
  1986 Provenance of Nara Prefecture. Long, thin recurved needles.   Japan

- - 'Yu-ho' W.N. Valavanis   1976 Yatsubusa cultivar. Prostrate habit. A selection from "Zao-
                                      goyo".   Hort. Japan

- - 'Yume-dono' W.N. Valavanis
  1976 Yatsubusa cultivar. Short, thick, dark green needles.   Hort. Japan

- - 'Za-o' W.N. Valavanis   1976 Yatsubusa cultivar. A selection from the following
                                      Provenance.   Hort. Japan

- - "zao-goyo" Hort. Japan   1976 Provenance of Miyagi and Yamagata Prefectures.   Japan

- - 'Zia-no-me' Hort. Amer.   1987 A listed name.

- - 'Zui-ho' W.N. Valavanis   1976 Yatsubusa cultivar. Similar to 'Zui-sho'.   Hort. Japan

- - 'Zui-ko' W.N. Valavanis   1976 Yatsubusa cultivar. Dark green, short, twisted leaves; small
    green buds.   W2   Hort. Japan

- - 'Zui-sho' W.N. Valavanis
    1976 Yatsubusa cultivar. Medium length green twisted needles. A
    seedling from "nasu-goyo". Much used for miniature Bonsai.   W2   Hort. Japan

PINUS patula Schiede & Deppe
    1831 Mexican Weeping Pine. Not hardy in U.K. 5n.   30-50m,Z8   Mexico

- - var. *longipedunculata* Loock ex Martinez
    1948 Now known as *PINUS oocarpa* var. *ochotereneri*. (per Silba,
    1984).

- - 'Zebrina' Dallimore & Jackson
    1966 Leaves striped green and yellow. Named for a tree found in
    Buenos Aires in 1948.   Brazil

PINUS pentaphylla Mayr   1890 Northern Japanese White Pine. Not now distinguished within
    PINUS parviflora.

- - var. *himeokomatsu* (Miyabe & Kudo) Makino
    1954 Southern Japanese White Pine. Now known as *PINUS*
    parviflora.

PINUS peuce Grisebach   1844 Macedonian Pine. 5n. Has affinity with *PINUS cembra*.   20-30m,Z5   Europe

- - **'Arnold Dwarf'** Welch   1979 Dense, upright bush. O. Arnold Arboretum. Formerly listed
    as 'Nana'.   R,W2   U.S.A.

- - 'Aurea' Hort. Amer.   1986 An illegit. listed name. Leaves attractive yellow, especially in
    winter.   G

- - 'Aureovariegata' Hort. Holland
    1968 Needles at first are yellow, fading to normal.   G

- - 'Glauca' Hort. Germany   1979 An illegit. listed name. L. Esveld Nurs, Boskoop. NOM.

- - 'Glauca Compact' Krüssmann
    1983 An illegit. listed name. O. J. zu Jeddeloh Nurs, Oldenburg.   K,R,W   Germany

- - 'Horstmann Zwerg'
    Very slow-growing plant, pale green leaves originated as a
    seedling. O. and I. Horstmann Nurs, Schneverdingen.

- - 'Nana' Hort. Amer.   1979 Now known as 'Arnold Dwarf'.

PINUS pinaster Aiton   1789 Maritime Pine, Sea Pine, Cluster Pine. 2n.   25-35m,Z7   Mediterr.

- - **'Aberdoniae'** Loudon   1839 A selection having paler-green leaves. Intro. from Nice by the
    Earl of Aberdeen (1825). (= var. *escarina* Risso ex Loudon
    (1838), 'Hamiltonii').   B,G,K   Italy

- - 'Atlantica' Dallimore & Jackson
    1966 A selection planted in certain coastal areas.   B   France

- - 'Jericho' Hort. Australia   1983 Raised from a witch's broom. No further information.

- - **'Lemoniana'** Dallimore & Jackson
    1923 Sir Charles Lemon's Pine. A form with ashy-grey foliage.
    NIC.   B,D,K   U.K.

- - f. *major* Nicholson   1900 In "Dict. Gar". Not now distinguished within the species.

- - f. *microcarpa* Herre   1928 A local variant with unusually small cones.   B   S.Africa

- - f. *minor* Loiseleur   1812 A local variant found on the west coast. NIC.   B,K   France

- - 'Monophylla' Nelson	1866 "Leaves single". NIC.		B	U.K.
- - 'Nana' (1) Nelson	1866 "The dwarf form". NIC.		B	U.K.
- - 'Nana' (2) Hornibrook	1939 A dwarf, semi-globose bush with short, thick leaves. Named for a plant found near Mandelieu, Alpes Maritimes.		B,H,K,W2	France
- - 'Pendula' Nelson	1866 "The pendulous form".		B	U.K.
- - f. *prolifera* Mottet in Nicholson	1896 Named for a monstrous tree with cones in clusters. NIC.		B	France
- - 'Tortuosa' Nelson	1866 "The twisted-branch form".		B	U.K.
- - 'Variegata' Forbes	1839 Leaves 1/3 normal size; variegated straw-yellow and white.		B,K,R	U.K.
PINUS pinceana Gordon	1858 Pince Pinyon Pine, Weeping Pinyon Pine. 3n.		12m,Z9	Mexico
PINUS pinea Linnaeus	1753 Stone Pine, Umbrella Pine. The latter name is suggested by the shape of the mature crown.			
- - 'Correvoniana' Hornibrook	1932 Named for a very slow growing plant in M. Correvon's garden near Geneva. NIC, (1910).		B,H,K	Switzerl.
- - 'Fragilis' Krüssmann	1972 Form with peculiar seeds.		K	Germany
- - 'Nana' Hort. Germany	1990 An illegit. listed name.			
- - 'Queensway' G. Haddow	1991 Plant from a witch's broom found by Dick van Hoey Smith at Queensway, Exeter University. Dwarf globose bush. Contains some juvenile foliage as a young plant. I. Kenwith Nurs, Bideford, Devon.			
PINUS pityusa Steven	1838 A rare species close to *PINUS brutia*, of which some authorities regard it as a variety. (per Silba, 1984).		20m,Z8	Turkey
PINUS ponderosa Douglas ex Lawson	1836 Ponderosa Pine. 3n (varies).		40m,Z4	N. Amer.
- - var. *arizonica* (Engelmann) Shaw	1909 Now known as *PINUS arizonica* (per Rushforth, 1987).		B,K,R	
- - 'Canyon Ferry' Reg'd. Arn. Arb.	1972 Name registered by C.V. Berg, Helena, Montana, for a dwarf plant found in the wild.		W2	U.S.A.
- - 'Crispata' Schwerin	1919 Named for a seedling with falcate leaves, raised by Count von Schwerin, Wendisch-Wilmersdorf. NIC.		B	Germany
- - var. *deflexa* Torrey	1859 A minor variant with dark coloured leaves and bark. NIC.		B	
- - 'Globosa' Hort. Germany	1986 Reported from U.S. Nat. Arb. Washington D.C.		G	
- - 'Hexenbesen' R. Reuter	1984 In "Amer. Conif. Soc. Bull. 1". An unsatisfactory name.O. A witch's broom found by G. Horstmann in the Rocky Mountains. (formerly listed as W.B. No.1).			Germany
- - var. *jeffreyi* Vasey	1875 Now known as *PINUS jeffreyi*.			
- - 'King Canyon'	A strong growing unsymmetrical tree with stiff shoots.O. Found in the Sierra Nevada, CAL. U.S.A. by J.zu Jeddeloh.			
- - 'Koolhaas No.l' Hort. Holland	1955 Named for a pendulous seedling found by Koolhaus (1910). NIC. O. Koolhaus Nurs.		B	Holland
- - f. *macrophylla* Shaw	1909 Now merged in *PINUS engelmannii*.		B	

- - f. *mayriana* Sargent	1897	Now merged in *PINUS engelmannii.*	B	
- - 'Pendula' Sargent	1878	A pendulous form early recorded but still rare in cultivation. I. J.zu Jeddeloh, (1990).	B,G,R	U.K.
- - subsp. *scopulorum* (Engelmann) S. Watson	1879	Rocky Mountains Ponderosa Pine, smaller leaves and cones.	B	U.S.A.
- - 'Tortuosa' Carrière?	1867	Branches, branchlets and leaves, contorted and twisted. NIC.	B	France
- - 'Twodot Columnar' Reg'd. Arn. Arb.	1969	A columnar form with upstanding branches. O. Found near Twodot, Montana.		
PINUS pringlei Shaw	1905	Pringle Pine. Not hardy in U.K.	15-20m,Z9	Mexico
PINUS pseudostrobus Lindley	1839	Smoothbark White Pine.	40m,Z8	Central Amer.
- - var. *alpulcensis* (Lindley) Shaw	1909	Apulco Pine. Here accepted as a species. (per Rushforth, 1987).	K,R	
- - var. *coatepecensis* Martinez	1948	Not now distinguished within the species (per Silba, 1984).		
- - var. *estevezi* Martinez	1948	Now known as *PINUS estevesii* (per Rushforth, 1987).	R	
- - var. *oaxacana* (Mirov) Harrison	1966	Now accepted as a distinct species, (per Silba, 1984).		
- - var. *tenuifolia* (Bentham) Shaw	1909	Not now distinguished within the species.	K	
PINUS pumila (Pallas) Regel	1859	Japanese Stone Pine, Dwarf Siberian Pine. Several cultivars were formerly listed under *PINUS cembra.* 5n.	4-6m,Z5	E. Asia
- - 'Barmstedt' Hachmann	1988	In "Nurs. Cat". A selection with long, twisted, silvery leaves. L. Hachmann Nurs, Barmstedt-in-Holstein.		Germany
- - 'Blaukissen' Hort. Germany	1988	O. and I. Hackmann Nurs, Barmstedt-in-Holstein.		
- - 'Blauspinne' H.J. van de Laar	1986	L. In "Naamlijst . . .". A slow growing blue, found on the neglected Pinetum on the De Belten Estate at Vorden. NOM.		Holland
- - 'Blue Mops' D.M. van Gelderen	1983	In "Dendroflora 20". Low-growing dense plant with short blue-grey foliage. O. Seedling on Konijn and Co. Nurs, Ederveen.		Holland
- - 'Blue Star' Hort. Germany	1990	A listed name for a weak-growing, upright clone.		
- - 'Brevifolia' Mayr	1890	A clone with very short leaves. In cultivation in 1890 in Japan as 'Aizu-goyo'. No longer identifiable.		Hort. Japan
- - 'Buchanan' G. Haddow	1990	Dwarf upright more conical form with short fine dark silver-blue leaves. O. Wm. Buchanan. I. Kenwith Nurs, Bideford, Devon.		
- - 'Chlorocarpa' (1) Beissner	1909	A plant with yellow-green cones, first noticed in 1887. NIC.	K	Germany
- - 'Chlorocarpa' (2) H.G. Hillier	1964	In "Dwarf Conifers". Compact bush distributed for many years under this name; now replaced by 'Compacta'.	G,W2	U.K.

- - **'Compacta'** H.G. Hillier 1971 In "Hillier's Manual". See also 'Chlorocarpa'. Dwarf globe shaped to flat topped, leaves mid-green. W2

- - 'H.J. Draht' Hort. Germany
1989 O. and I. Draht Nurs. L. Wiel Linssen, Baexam, Holland.

- - 'Draijer's Blue' D.M. van Gelderen
1983 In "Dendroflora 20". Holland

- - **'Draijer's Dwarf'** Welch
1979 Densely branched globose-form with long, blue-grey leaves. O. Draijer Nurs, Heemstede. G,K,R,W2 Holland

- - 'Dwarf Blue' Den Ouden 1954 Dwarf plant wider than high. Short blue incurved leaves. O. Hesse nurs, Weener on Ems, Germany. I. H. den Ouden & Son, Boskoop. B,K,W2 Holland

- - 'Glauca' Wm. Hooftman 1943 In "Nurs. Cat". See "Dendroflora 19".(1982). Bushy shrub with grey-blue leaves, upswept branches. B,G,K,W2 Holland

- - **'Globe'** Den Ouden 1949 Dwarf, globose. O. Found in the Gimborn Arboretum, Doorn. I. L. Konijn Nurs, Reeuwijk. G,K,W2 Holland

- - 'Hann Munden' Hort. Germany
1992 A listed name for a dwarf form with long, blue needles. O. Hann Munden in Germany.

- - 'Hillside' Hort. Amer. 1986 A listed name.

- - **'Jeddeloh'** J. zu Jeddeloh
1969 In "Nurs. Cat". Strong-growing, widespreading bush. O. Found in the Gimborn Estate by J. zu Jeddeloh. K,R Germany

- - 'Jermyns' H.G. Hillier 1964 See *PINUS cembra* 'Jermyns'. B,K,R,W2 U.K.

- - 'Klosterkoter' Hort. Germany
1988 L. Hachmann Nurs, Barmstedt-in-Holstein.

- - 'Knightshayes' G. Haddow
1990 In "Nurs. Cat". Low growing spreading plant with relatively short but thick silver-blue leaves. O. and I. Kenwith Nurs, Bideford, Devon.

- - 'Nana' Hort. Holland 1979 An old cultivar of unknown origin quite commonly seen on the Continent - there is a fine specimen in the Arboretum Trompenburg, Rotterdam. Globose semi-dwarf bush with typical *pumila* leaves which are green with silver-grey insides. G,K

- - 'Oosthoek' Hort. Holland
1982 See *PINUS pumila* 'Glauca'. See "Dendroflora 19." (1982).

- - 'Pinocchio' Hort. Germany
1988 L. Hachmann Nurs, Barmstedt-in-Holstein.

- - 'Pipistrella' Hort. Holland
1986 L. H.J. van de Laar in "Naamlijst . . .". A dwarf with blue foliage. O. Draijer Nurs, Heemstede. NOM. Holland

- - 'Prostrata' H.G. Hillier 1964 In "Dwarf Conifers". NOM. An illegit. name for a low mounding plant with silver grey leaves. K U.K.

- - 'Pygmaea' Hornibrook 1939 A plant which is doubtfully the same as that of Carrière 1855. The present plant in cultivation is very slow-growing, wider than high with mid-green leaves. H,W

- - 'Santis' Draijer 1981 In "Nurs. Cat". A compact upright bush with long, blue leaves. O. Draijer Nurs, Zwanshoek. ('Saentis'). Krüssmann listed this cultivar as *parviflora*. G,K Holland

- - 'Saphir' Hort. Holland   1983 See *PINUS parviflora* 'Saphir'.   W2

- - 'Spingarn' Hort. Amer.   1985 A listed name. No further information.

- - 'Stata' Hort. Amer.   1980 In "Nurs. Cat". Kristick Nurs, Wellsville, PA.

- - 'Stockmann' Hort. Germany
          1988 L. Hachmann Nurs, Barmstedt-in-Holstein.

- - 'Wansdyke' D. van Klaveren
          1980 In "Nurs. Cat". Very dense and slow; spreading habit; short
                needles. **I.** Wansdyke Nurs, Devizes, Wilts, U.K.

- - 'Winton'   See *PINUS koraiensis*.

- - 'Yes-Alpina' Hort. Amer.   1982 In "Nurs. Cat". Iseli Nurs, Boring OR.

PINUS pumilio Haenke   1791 Now known as *PINUS mugo* var. *pumilio*.

PINUS pungens Lambert   1805 Table Mountain Pine. 2n (rarely 3).   20m,Z7   U.S.A.

PINUS pyrenaica Willkommen   Pyrenean Pine. Now known as *PINUS nigra* subsp.
                salzmannii.

PINUS quadrifolia Parlatore ex Sudworth
          1868 Parry Pinion Pine. Known as *PINUS cembroides* var.
                quadrifolia by some authorities. (per Silba, 1984).

PINUS radiata D. Don   1836 Monterey Pine. 3n.   40m,Z7   Mexico

- - **'Aurea'** A Henry   1910 Trees with golden-yellow foliage have several times been
                recorded. Professor Henry records that a form was being
                propagated in New Zealand in 1910, but the clone in
                cultivation is probably a much more recent 'find'. It was
                introduced in 1976 by the Wansdyke Nurs, Devizes.   B,G,K,R   N.Z.

- - var. *binata* (Engelmann) Brewer & Watson
          1880 Named for a tree at the Royal Botanic Garden, Kew in 1875
                that no longer exists.   B,K,R   U.K.

- - **'Cactus'** John Emery   1989 In "Con. Soc. Australia Newsletter 5". A real curiosity dwarf
                plant. Looks more like a cactus than a conifer. Raised by P.C.
                Nitschke, Hahndorf in 1981. **I.** Drue Wholesale Nurs, Berry.

- - var. *cedrosensis* (Howell) Axlerod
          1947   R

- - **'Coleraine'** Hort. Australia
          1981 Dwarf globose bush reported to be reliably dwarf. **O.** Witch's
                broom found by Peter Nitschke, Hahndorf.
- - **'El Dorado'** Reg. Arn. Arb.
          1988 Reg'd. by Int. for Genetics, Placeville, CAL.   W2   U.S.A.

- - **'Fluffy'** Hort. Australia   1993 A new name. A very dense globose plant. A golden seedling
                from 'Gold Nugget'. **O.** Raised by P.C. Nitschke.

- - **'Freeway'** P. Nitschke   1987 In "Con. Soc. Australia Newsletter No.1". A dark green dwarf
                with large winter buds. **O.** A witch's broom found at Stirling.   S. Australia

- - **'Globe'** J. Emery   1989 In "Con. Soc. Australia Newsletter 5". Very compact dwarf.
                O. Peter Nitschke, **I.** Drue Wholesale Plants.

- - **'Gold Nugget'** Hort. Australia
          1989 Raised from a golden witch's broom in a green tree. Compact,
                globe shaped bush. **O.** P.C. Nitschke, **I.** Drue Wholesale
                Nurs.

- - **'Goldie'** Hort. Australia   1993 A golden seedling from 'Gold Nugget'. Very dense, globose
                plant, foliage golden-yellow. **O.** P.C. Nitschke, Hahndorf.

- - **'Isca'** Welch   1979 A large globose form. O. A tree found in the grounds of the
Imperial Hotel, Exeter. I. Wansdyke Nurs, Devizes.   G,W2   U.K.

- - **'Jacob's Gem'** Hort. Australia
          1993 A witch's broom, several seedlings from which were given
names. O. P.C. Nitschke, Hahndorf.

- - **'Majestic Beauty'** Hort. Amer.
          1985 Listed by L.C. Hatch in "Reference Guide".

- - **'Marshwood'** G. Haddow   1990 In "Nurs. Cat". Slow-growing round topped to conical plant
with new foliage creamy-white lasting until autumn. O.
Found in the Tauringature State Forest in New Zealand. I.
Into U.K. by Kenwith Nurs, Bideford, Devon.

- - **'Mortimer Bay'** J. Emery   In "Con. Soc. Australia Newsletter 5". Of normal growth, but
variegated needles, banded yellow and green. Found as a
seedling at S.E. Hobart, Tasmania (1984).   Australia

- - **'Nitschke'** P.Nitschke   1987 In "Con. Soc. Australia Newsletter No.1". Compact flat-
topped plant with no leader. Needles light green in twos,
sometimes threes near terminal bud. O. A witch's broom
found by P. Nitschke near Littlehampton, S. Australia.   Australia

- - **'Ross'** P. Nitschke   1987 In "Con. Soc. Australia Newsletter No.1". A very dwarf
globose plant. O. A witch's broom found by R. Radford and
P. Nitschke at Ross, Tasmania (1983).   Tasmania

- - **'Variegated'** Hort. Australia
          1989 Same as parent but with large patches of yellow foliage,
sometimes whole branches yellow. O. P. C. Nitschke.

- - 'Wee Willie' Hort. Australia
          1993 A listed name. No information yet.

PINUS reflexa Engelmann 1882 Southern Limber Pine. (Often confused with *PINUS flexilis*
or *PINUS strobiformis* (per Rushforth, 1987).   20m,Z6   Mexico

PINUS remorata Mason   1930 Santa Cruz Island Pine. By some authorities regarded as a
sub-species of *PINUS muricata* (per Silba, 1984).

PINUS remota (Little) Bailey & Hawkesworth
          Paperstrill Pinyon Pine. Little known.   7m,Z8   Mexico

PINUS resinosa Aiton   1794   15-20m,Z2   East N.Amer.

- - 'Aurea' Hort. Amer.   1972 A golden form. L. Watnong Nurs, Morris Plains, N.J. O.
Bennett.

- - **'Don Smith'** R.L. Fincham
          1984 In "Amer. Conif. Soc. Bull. 1". A dwarf flat-topped plant
formerly distributed by Watnong Nurs, Morris Plains, N.J. O.
A large witch's broom found by J. Leonard Bailey in
Mendham, N.J. (formerly 'Witch's Broom No. 2$').   U.S.A.

- - **'Globosa'** Rehder   1922 A globose dwarf form to 8ft high which originated as a
seedling in New Hampshire, U.S.A.   B,H,K,R,W2   U.S.A.

- - 'Hansen Globe' Hort. Amer.
          1975 In "Nurs. Cat". Raraflora Nurs, Feasterville, PA.

- - **'Nobska'** Welch   1979 Dwarf as wide as high, brown branches, deep green leaves;
ring of very short leaves around buds. Slower growing than
'Quinobequin'. O. Grown from a witch's broom seed at the
Arnold Arboretum. I. Watnong Nurs, Morris Plains, N.J.   R,W2   U.S.A.

- - **'Quinobequin'** Welch 1979 Dwarf, higher than wide, conspicuous red brown branches,
leaves deep green, a ring of very short leaves around the buds.
O. Arnold Arboretum.   R,W2   U.S.A.

- - 'Ragamuffin' S. Waxman

    1990 In "Int. Pl. Prop. Soc. Bull.". A broad irregular ground-hugging plant raised from a witch's broom. Long bright green leaves. **O.** S. Waxman at the Univ. of Connecticut, Storrs, CT.   U.S.A.

- - 'Sandcastle' S. Waxman

    1981 In "Int. Pl. Prop. Soc. Bull.". An upright dwarf. Foliage dense dark green. **O.** S. Waxman, Univ. of Connecticut, Storrs, CT.   U.S.A.

- - 'Spaan's Fastigiate' Hort. Amer.

    1985 A listed name. L. L.C. Hatch in "Reference Guide."

- - 'Thunderhead' S. Waxman

    1981 In "Int. Pl. Prop. Soc. Bull.". A rather open shrub with long, dark green needles. **O.** S. Waxman, Univ. of Connecticut, Storrs, CT.   U.S.A.

- - 'Watnong' Welch   1979 A very diminutive form raised from a witch's broom in Far Hills, N.J. Smaller and slower than 'Don Smith'. (Formerly distributed as 'Witch's broom No. 1$'). **O.** Don Smith of Watnong Nurs, Morris Plains, N.J. (Note 'Witch's broom No.2$' is named 'Don Smith').   R,W2   U.S.A.

PINUS x *rhaetica* Bruegger   A sporadic hybrid: *PINUS mugo* x *PINUS sylvestris* NIC.   K   Cent. Europe

- - 'Cernolice' Hort. Amer.   1990 A mistake for the following entry.

- - 'Karel Stivin' Welch   1979 Raised at the State Alpine Nurs. at Cerndice.   W2   Czechosl.

PINUS **rigida** Miller   1768 Pitch Pine.

- - 'Aurea' Beissner   1899 Named for a seedling with leaves persistent yellow. **O.** F. von Oheimb Nurs, near Woislowitz.   B   Poland

- - 'Globosa' Allard   1940 In "Rhodora **42**". Named for a tree found in a field. NIC.   B

- - 'Hillside Weeping' Hort. Amer.

    1970 L. E.A. Cope in "Native . . . Conifers . . .". NOM.

- - 'Little Giant' Hort. Amer.   Superfluous synonym for 'Sherman Eddy'.

- - var. *serotina* (Michaux) Loudon

    1898 Pond Pine. Now treated as a separate species.   R

- - 'Sherman Eddy' Welch   1979 An upright dwarf tree with foliage in dense, rich green whorls. **I.** Weston Nurs. Hopkinton, MA. **O.** Found in the Poeono Mts. by Sherman Eddy.   W2   U.S.A.

PINUS **roxburghii** Sargent   1897 Chir Pine. Species closely related to *PINUS canariensis*. 3n.   25m,Z9   Himalayas

PINUS **rudis** Endlicher   1847 Endlicher Pine. 5(4-6)n. Formerly included in *PINUS hartwegii*. (per Rushforth, 1987).   20m,Z7   Mexico

PINUS **rzedowskii** Madrigal & Caballero

    1969 Rzedowskii Pine. 3-4n.   30m,Z8   Mexico

PINUS **sabiniana** Douglas ex D.Don

    1833 Digger Pine. 3n. Named for a Red Indian tribe for whom the large seeds were a source of food. **I.** By Douglas into U.K. (1832).   20m,Z8   West U.S.A.

- - 'Variegata' Carrière   1867 Leaves golden-yellow at the top of the tree. **O.** Found by Carrière in Botanic Garden, Paris.   B   France

PINUS x *saportae*   See *PINUS halepensis*.

PINUS x *schwerinii* Fitschen

    1930 A natural hybrid: *PINUS wallichiana* x *PINUS strobus* that occurred on the Count von Schwerin Estate near Berlin in 1931.   G,K   Germany

PINUS scopulorum (Engelmann) Lemmon

    1897 Rocky Mountain Pine. (But see Rushforth, 1987).   10-30m   West U.S.A.

PINUS serotina Michaux   1803 Pond Pine. By some authorities listed as *PINUS rigida* var. *serotina*. (See Silba, 1984).   20m,Z8   U.S.A.

PINUS sibirica Du Tour   1803 Siberian Stone Pine. 5n. At one time known as *PINUS cembra* var. *sibirica* Loudon.   35m,Z3   Asia

- -'Dwarf Form' Hort. Germany

    1992 L. Horstmann Nurs, Schneverdingen. ('Zwergform').

PINUS x *sondereggeri* Chapman

    1922 A natural hybrid: *PINUS palustris* x *PINUS taeda*.   K   U.S.A.

PINUS sosnowskyi Nakai   1939 Not now recognised by some authorities.

PINUS stankewiczii (Sukaczev) Fomin

    A species close to *PINUS brutia*, of a 3H which some authorities treat it as a variety.   Crimea

PINUS strobiformis Engelmann

    1848 Southwestern White Pine. 5n.   30m,Z6   U. 2HS.A/Mexico

PINUS strobus Linnaeus   1753 Eastern White Pine. Weymouth Pine. 5n.   50m,Z3   East N.Amer.

- - 'Alba' Loudon   1838 Conical tree; young growth pure white. Rare but still in cultivation. See a Hlso 'Argentea' and 'Nivea'.   B,G,K,R   U.K.

- -'Albospicata' P. Lombarts

    1941 In "Nurs. Cat". Not now distinguishable from 'Alba'. Raised in Lombarts Nurs, Zundert.   B   Holland

- - 'Amelia's Dwarf' L.C. Hatch

    1985 In "Reference Guide". A globose, dwarf form; green foliage. Listed Raraflora Nurs. (1979) NOM.('Amerlias Dwarf').   U.S.A.

- - 'Anna Fiele' L.C. Hatch   1988 In "Conifer Database". A globose, congested clone with pale green leaves. Annual growth 40 mm. Becoming popular.   U.S.A.

- - 'Argentea' Sénéclauze   1868 No longer distinguishable from 'Alba'.   U.K.

- - 'Aurea' Elwes & Henry

    1910 Leaves yellowish when young.   U.K.

- - 'Aureovariegata' Sénéclauze

    1868 Part of each leaf yellow. NIC.   G   France

- - 'Bayard' Hort. Amer.   1975 ('Nana' group). A listed name without description. Raraflora Nurs, Feasterville, PA.

- - 'Bennett Broom' Hort. Amer.

    1970 Listed Hillside Nurs, (1970). NOM.

- - 'Bennett Clump Leaf' R.L.Fincham

    1983 In Coenosium "Nurs. Cat". A vigorous tree in which each bundle of leaves grows together as one. More curious than beautiful.   U.S.A.

- - 'Bennett Contorted' Reg'd. Arn. Arb.

    1967 Reg'd. by W. W. Bennett. Christianburg, Virginia. A small tree with foliage contorted.   U.S.A.

- - **'Bennett Dragon's Eye'** L.C.Hatch
        1985 In "Reference Guide". A clone forming a small tree with the *oculus draconis* type of yellow-striped variegation.   U.S.A.

- - 'Bennett Oculus Draconis' Hort. Amer.
        1970 Listed Hillside Nurs. NOM. An illegit. name. Now to be known as 'Bennett Dragon's Eye'.('Bennett O. D').   U.S.A.

- - 'Bennett Wierdo' Hort. Amer.
        1972 Listed Raraflora. NOM. Possibly a superfluous synonym for 'Bennett Contorted'.

- - 'Bergman's Mini' Hort. Amer.   Small mound shaped to globose plant. Dark green leaves. **L.** Kristick Nurs, Wellsville, PA.

- - 'Bergman's Sport of Prostrata' Hort. Amer.
        1980 Dwarf prostrate form which tends to have points along the branches with congested clumps of foliage. Leaves grey-green. **O.** and **I.** Raraflora Nurs, Feasterville, PA.

- - **'Bergman's Variegated'** R. L. Fincham
        1983 In Coenosium "Nurs. Cat". Leaves with yellow bands.   U.S.A.

- - **'Billaw'** Iseli   1990 In "Nurs. Cat". Dense, dwarf, low globe; foliage blue-green.   U.S.A.

- - **'Bloomers Dark Globe'** Vermeulen
        1972 In "Nurs Cat". A medium-sized bush with dark green foliage. (This plant may possibly be found to belong to a species other than *strobus*).   W2   U.S.A.

- - 'Bloomer's Globe' Hort. Amer.   See last item.

- - **'Blue Jay'** Summerhill   1986 In "The Plants we Grow". A dense, low mound, wider than high; foliage has distinct bluish cast. **I.** Summerhill Nurs, Madison, Conn. **O.** S. Waxman, Univ. of Connecticut, Storrs, CT.   U.S.A.

- - **'Blue Mist'** L.C. Hatch   1985 In "Reference Guide". A slow-growing conical form with blue foliage.   U.S.A.

- - **'Blue Shag'** S. Waxman   1978 In "Hort. Science 13". A dense, dwarf form spreading wider than high; foliage blue-green. **O.** S. Waxman, Univ. of Connecticut, Storrs, CT.   G   U.S.A.

- - f. *brevifolia* (Carrière) Rehder
        1949 A botanical category that would embrace all the forms with noticeably short leaves.   B,W2   Europe

- - 'Brevifolia' Carrière   1855 The original clone of f. *brevifolia*, but probably several similar clones are in cultivation.   France

- - 'Brevifolia Elf' Hort. Amer.   An illegit. name. See 'Elf'.

- - var. *chiapensis* Martinez 1940 Now known as *PINUS chiapensis* . (per Rushforth, 1987).   K,R   C. Amer.

- - 'Cockerton' Hort. Amer.   1992 In "Nurs. Cat". Rarafolia Nurs, Kintersville, PA., without description.

- - 'Coffee Run' Hort. Amer.
        1992 In "Nurs. Cat". Rarafolia Nurs, Kintersville, PA., without description.

- - 'Colrain Road' Hort. Australia
        1989 **L.** Yamina Rare Plants, Monbulk. Without description.

- - **'Colson's Nest'** Iseli.   1990 In "Nurs. Cat". A slow, blue-green, mounding dwarf.   U.S.A.

- - 'Compacta' (1) Masters   1896 In "Kew Handlist Conif". No longer identifiable.

- - 'Compacta' (2) Hort. Amer.
    1970 An illegit. name. L. Hillside Nurs, Cat. NOM.

- - 'Compressa' Booth ex Loudon
    1838 The Floetbeck Weymouth Pine. Much shorter in leaf. L.
            Loddiges Cat. (1836). NIC.   Germany

- - **'Coney Island'** S. Waxman
    1989 In "Int. Pl. Prop. Soc. Bull". Originated from a graft found on
            a tree in Woodstock, CT. It forms a dense rounded, shrubby
            plant, with long needles; numerous miniature female cones
            are regularly borne. O. S. Waxman, Univ. of Connecticut,
            Storrs, CT.   U.S.A.

- - **'Contorta'** Slavin   1932 Reported from Seneca Park, Rochester, N.Y.   B,K   U.S.A.

- - 'Contorta Nana' Hort. Amer.
    1972 An illegit. name. Listed Raraflora. NOM. See next item.

- - **'Contorted Dwarf'** Hort. Amer.
    1985 Unacceptable name. Bush with densely twisted leaves. New
            name required.   U.S.A.

- - 'Crazy' L.C. Hatch
    1988 In "Conifer Database". A contorted form, distinct from
            'Contorta'. ('Crazy Form' is unacceptable under the Cultivar
            Code).   U.S.A.

- - **'Curtis Dwarf'** Ed. Mezitt
    1982 In "Nurs. Cat". A diminutive form; compact, dense mound-
            forming, introduced by Weston Nurs, Hopkinton, Mass.   U.S.A.

- - **'David'** S. Waxman   1989 In "Int. Pl. Prop. Soc. Bull.". Raised from seed of a witch's
            broom found in Granby, CT. It makes a small, upright-
            conical tree of interesting outline. O. S. Waxman at Univ. of
            Connecticut, Storrs, CT.   U.S.A.

- - **'Densa'** Masters   1896 In "Kew Handlist Conif". An old form, still planted. Dwarf,
            conical long bluish leaves.   K,W   U.K.

- - **'Donnelly'** L.C. Hatch   1988 In "Conifer Database". Globose, dwarf, foliage medium
            green.   U.S.A.

- - **'Dove's Dwarf'** L.C. Hatch
    1985 In "Reference Guide". Globose to upright semi-dwarf. Listed
            Hillside Nurs, Lehighton, PA, (1970). NOM.   U.S.A.

- - 'Edel' Hort. Hungary   1992 A dwarf form with blue needles. O. M. Barabit's of Sopron,
            Hungary.

- - 'Egon Ecker' Hort. Czechoslovakia
            Globose plant, pale green leaves. originated at Botanic
            Garden, Czechloslovakia. (Could be PINUS *lambertiana*?).

- - **'Elf'** Ed Mezitt   1982 In "Nurs. Cat". Conical habit, to 4 m; short, blue-green
            leaves. Weston Nurs, Hopkinton, Mass. Raised on the
            nursery. ('Brevifolia Elf').   U.S.A.

- - 'Elkins Dwarf' Hort. Australia
    1989 L. Yamina Rare Plants, Monbulk. Without description.

- - **'Fastigiata'** Beissner   1884 An attractive, columnar tree. Said to be 'blister rust' resistant.   B,G,K,R   Germany

- - 'Flat Top' Hort. Amer.   1972 Listed Raraflora, Feasterville, PA. NOM.

- - 'General Pulaski' Hort. Amer.
    1992 In "Nurs. Cat". without description. Rarafolia Nurs,
            Kintersville, PA.

- - **'Glauca'** Beissner 1893 In "Mitt. d. d. d. Ges. **2**". Plants with glaucous foliage turn up from time to time. NIC.   B,K   Germany

- - 'Globosa' Hort. Amer. 1970 An illegit. name. **L.** Hillside Nurs, Lehighton, PA, NOM.

- - **'Golden Candles'** S. Waxman
1985 In "Int. Pl. Prop. Soc. Bull.". Upright shrub with golden candles and leaves. **O.** S. Waxman, Univ. of Connecticut, Storrs, CT.   U.S.A.

- - **'Goldie'** S. Waxman 1990 In "Plant Prop. Soc. Proc.". Dwarfer than 'Golden Candles' and the foliage is a deeper yellow-gold.   U.S.A.

- - 'Gracilis Viridis' Beissner
1891 Leaves graceful, very thin. NIC.   B,K,R   Germany

- - **'Green Shadow'** S. Waxman
1978 In "Hortscience **13**". A multi-trunked rounded shrub with long, thick dark green needles. **O.** S. Waxman, Univ. of Connecticut, Storrs, CT.   U.S.A.

- - **'Greg'** L.C. Hatch 1988 In "Conifer Database". A choice very slow-growing, tight little bun-forming plant with medium-green short leaves. ('Greg's form' and 'Greg's Seedling' are the same).   U.S.A.

- - 'Hazel's Clumpy' Hort. Amer.
1980 Named for Don Smith's wife. **O.** and **I.** Watnong Nurs, Morris Plains, N.J.

- - 'Helen' Hort. Amer. 1975 **O.** Raraflora Nurs, Feasterville, PA. **L.** Kristick Nurs, Wellsville, PA.

- - **'Hershey'** Welch 1979 A plant from a witch's broom found on the Hershey Estate, Penn.   W2   U.S.A.

- - **'Hillside Gem'** Welch 1979 A neat, dwarf, pyramid with upright branching system and attractive blue-grey foliage. Found by L. Zeigenfuss at Whitehaven, Penn. in 1964.   W2   U.S.A.

- - **'Hillside Weeper'** Welch
1979 Found by L. Zeigenfuss at New Ringlod, Penn. in 1966. Listed Hillside (1970).   W2   U.S.A.

- - 'Hillside Winter Gold' Hort. Amer.
See 'Winter Gold'.

- - 'Himmelblau' Hort. Germany
1980 Slow-growing, fine leaves lying closely forward along the branches. Strikingly good dark blue-silver colour.

- - **'Horsford'** Welch 1979 Dense, bun-forming dwarf, with long, thin, mid-green foliage. Found by Horsford in Vermont. ('Horsford Dwarf').   G,W2   U.S.A.

- - **'Horsham'** L.C. Hatch 1985 In "Reference Guide". A dwarf, globose, green form that regularly sets cones even at an early age. **L.** Hillside as 'Horsham Broom' (1970). NOM.   U.S.A.

- - **'Inversa'** Krüssmann 1960 Discovered in a garden in Andover, Mass. See Rushforth, (1987).   B,K,R   U.S.A.

- - **'Jericho'** Welch 1979 An upright dwarf with thin stems and pale yellow-green foliage. Raised by Joe Cesarini from a witch's broom found on Long Is, N.Y.   W2   U.S.A.

- - 'Julian Pott' Hort. Amer. 1992 This is the smallest of the pygmy dwarfs. Rich dark blue-green foliage. The late Mr. Pott developed this from a witch's broom seedling, conical dense. Thirty years 2 ft high.

- - **'Julian's Dwarf'** Hort. Amer.
          1986 A slow-growing, globose selection.   U.S.A.

- - 'Kane' Hort. Amer.   1992 In "Nurs. Cat". Rarafolia Nurs, Kintersville, PA, without description.

- - 'Kelsey' Hort. Amer.   1973 Reported from Gotelli collection. A slow-growing form with multiple stems, recommended for hedging. O. by Kelsey Nurs, ('Nana Kelseyi').   U.S.A.

- - 'Krause's W.B.' Hort. Amer.
          1980 L. J.W. Spingarn, Long Is., N.Y.

- - **'Kruger's Lilliput'** Kruger
          1982 A mutation on a grafted plant of 'Radiata' making a squat, globose plant on the Kruger Nurs, in 1968. Stout, blue-grey leaves about half as long as normal. ('Liliput').   Germany

- - 'Laird's Broom' Hort. Amer.
          1970 Listed Hillside Nurs, Lehighton, PA . A selected form of 'Nana'.

- - 'Lenmore' Hort. Amer.   A mistake for next item.

- - **'Lenore'** Reg'd. Arn. Arb.
          1972 Registered by Highland Park Herb., Rochester, N.Y. A columnar plant of moderate growth rate with fastigiate branch system and mid-green foliage found by H. Vaughan-Eames at Washingon Crossing, N.J.   U.S.A.

- - 'Lilliput' Hort.   See 'Kruger's Lilliput'.

- - 'Lone Pine Broom' Hort. Amer.
          1970 A listed name. No further information.

- - 'Louie' Hort. Amer.   1993 A medium growing plant with very good golden foliage retained all year. According to Greg Williams established plants do not burn in full sun. O. and I. Kate Brook Nurs, Wolcott, Vermont.

- - **'Macopin'** Welch   1979 A dwarf, globose form with blue-grey foliage, raised from a witch's broom found by Wm Gotelli at Macopin, N.J. Free coning. ('Macropin').   G,K,R,W2   U.S.A.

- - 'Martin's Broom' Hort. Amer.
          1968 A listed name. No further information.

- - 'Mary Butler' Hort. Amer.
          1988 A listed name. L. Mitsch Nurs, Aurora. OR.

- - **'Merrimack'** Welch   1979 A dense, compact globose plant with silvery blue leaves raised in the Arnold Arboretum.   G,W2   U.S.A.

- - 'Mill Race' Hort. Amer.   1992 In "Nurs. Cat". Rarafolia Nurs, Kintersville, PA.

- - 'Millstream'   1970 Listed Hillside Nurs, (1970).

- - f. *minima* (Hornibrook) Welch
          1979 A botanical designation covering all the very diminutive cultivars.   B

- - **'Minima'** Hornibrook   1923 An old selection, still in cultivation with short dark-green leaves and conspicuous dark brown branches.   G,H,K,W2 U.K.

- - 'Minuta' Hort. Amer.   1986 An illegit. listed name for a very compact, globose selection with short dark green-blue needles, of unrecorded origin. L. J.W. Spingarn (1980).

- - f. *monophylla* Tubeuf   1897 Leaves in bundles cohering, forming a single leaf.   B,R   Germany

- - f. *monophylla tortuosa* Tubeuf
  1897 Named for a tree with contorted leaves found by Schreiber, in
  Blankenburg, Harz.   B,K   Germany

- - f. *nana* (Hornibrook) Welch
  1979 A botanical designation for slow-growing clones never
  exceeding 3 m.   G,H,W2

- - 'Nana' Hort. ex Knight   1850 A name in loose use for several clones of the last. It should no
  longer be used in a clonal sense.

- - 'Nana Kelseyi'   See 'Kelseyi'.

- - 'Nana Macopin' Hort. Amer.
  1989 An illegit. name. It presumably is descriptive, but an
  acceptable name should be found.

- - 'Nana Secrest' Hort. Amer.
  1980 Small slender pyramidal tree. In "Nurs. Cat". Kristick Nurs,
  Wellsville, PA.

- - 'Nana Variegata' Jaeger in Beissner
  1884 Dwarf, white variegated. NIC.   B   Germany

- - 'Nana Weiss' Hort. Germany
  1966 See 'Reinshaus'.

- - 'Nicolet's Broom' Hort. Amer.
  1967 Reported by J.W. Spingarn. NOM.

- - 'Nivea' Booth ex Knight   1850 Indistinguishable from 'Alba'. NIC.   R   Germany

- - **'Northway Broom'** Welch
  1979 Dwarf globose to flat-topped dwarf plant. A witch's broom
  found by Williams of Hardwick, Vermont.   W2   U.S.A.

- - 'Nova' Loddiges   1836 In "Nurs. Cat". (as a synonym of 'Brevifolia').NIC.   U.K.

- - **'Old Softie'** S. Waxman   1990 In "Int. Plant Prop. Soc. Bull.". A low, very broad bush with
  deep green foliage; raised from a witch's broom seedling. O.
  S. Waxman, Univ. of Connecticut, Storrs, CT.   U.S.A.

- - **'Oliver Dwarf'** Iseli   1990 In "Nurs. Cat". A broad, flattened globe with extremely
  dense, blue-green foliage. Iseli Nurs, Boring, OR.   U.S.A.

- - **'Ontario'** Nordine   1961 In "Plant Prop. Soc. Proc. 11". A very dense dwarf, forming a
  flat-topped globose shaped shrub. It arose in Durand Eastman
  Park, Lake Ontario, Rochester, NY.   W2   U.S.A.

- - **'Ottawa'** Int. Con. Reg. 1984 Named for a pendulous tree with abnormal branching found
  by David Mackenzie at Muskegon, MICH. Listed Hortech,
  Springlake, Michigan. (1985).   U.S.A.

- - 'Palomino's Contorted' Hort. Amer.
  1980 In "Nurs. Cat". Kristick Nurs, Wellsville, PA.

- - 'Parvifolia' Beissner   1916 Named for a tree found by A. Muhle at Temesvár in 1903.
  NIC.   B   Rumania

- - **'Paul Waxman'** S. Waxman
  1986 In "Int. Pl. Prop. Soc. Proc". A dwarf, mounding bush with
  short, curved needles, green and blue-green and sometimes
  cohering. O. S. Waxman, Univ. of Connecticut, Storrs, CT.   U.S.A.

- - 'Pendula' Nelson   1866. A tree with long terminal growths reaching the ground.   B,G,H,K,R   U.K.

- - 'Pendula Wustemeyer'.   See 'Wustemeyer'.

- - 'Pictus' Hort. Holland   1992 A listed name without description.

PINUS STROBUS

- - f. *prostrata* (Beissner) Fernald and Weatherby
1932 In "Rhodora **34**". A local form found on serpentine mountains of Western Newfoundland. — Canada

- - **'Prostrata'** Masters 1896 In "Kew Handlist of Conif.". This, the earliest mention of the name, was raised from a prostrate plant never forming a leader, found in the Arnold Arboretum. B,G,H,K,R,W2 +U.S.A.

- - 'Pumila' (1) Gordon 1875 An early listed clone of 'Nana' that can no longer be identified. NIC. B,H,K U.K.

- - 'Pumila' (2) Hort. Amer. Name in use for a dwarf form of globose habit and twisted, blue-green needles. A new, acceptable name should be found. U.S.A.

- - 'Pygmaea' (1) Den Ouden
1965 This was a case of mistaken identity. It is now known as *PINUS pumila* 'Globe'. B Holland

- - 'Pygmaea' (2) Hort. Europe
1979 An illegit. name listed by by Jeddeloh. Said to originate in Arnold Arboretum. Possibly a *PINUS cembra* form. U.S.A.

- - 'Pygmaea' (3) Hort. Amer. An illegit. name in use for a plant that, after a slow start, reached to 2m.

- - 'Pyramidalis' Silva Tarouca
1913 Listed as a synonym of 'Fastigiata'. Germany

- - **'Radiata'** Hornibrook 1923 A clone distinguished by Hornibrook from 'Nana' in 1923 and still widely planted. It makes a plant wider than high; densely clothed with slender twigs and long bluish leaves. B,H,K,R,W2 U.K.

- - 'Raraflora Glauca Nana' Hort. Amer. An illegit. listed name.

- - 'Redfield' Hort. Amer. 1980 Open form with two different leaves. **O.** and **I.** Kristick Nurs, Wellsville, PA.

- - **'Reinshaus'** D. M. van Klaveren
1982 In "Dendroflora **19**". Dwarf congested globose bush, raised by Albrecht Weiss in his arboretum in Bergstrasse, Heinrichsberg. Germany

- - 'Rowes Multineedle' Hort. Amer.
1980 A listed name. L. J.W. Spingarn, Long Is., N.Y.

- - **'Sayville'** R. L. Fincham 1983 In Coenosium "Nurs Cat". A dwarf globose bush with blue foliage.

- - **'Sea Urchin'** S. Waxman
1978 In "Hort. Science **13**". An extremely dwarf clone; short bluish needles. Needle colour is much more silver in some shade. **O.** S. Waxman, Univ. of Connecticut, Storrs, CT. G U.S.A.

- - **'Soft Touch'** S. Waxman
1985 In " Nurs. Cat". A dense, flattened mound; short, twisted needles. **I.** Summerhill Nurs, Madison, CT. **O.** S. Waxman, Univ. of Connecticut, Storrs, CT. U.S.A.

- - 'Strattonville' Hort. Amer.
1992 In "Nurs. Cat". Rarafolia Nurs, Kintersville, PA.

- - 'Syd's Find' Hort. Amer. 1992 In "Nurs. Cat". Rarafolia Nurs, Kintersville, PA.

- - 'Tabuliformis' R. Smith 1864 In "Plants of the Fir Tribe". NIC. W2 U.K.

- - **'Torulosa'** Hort. Anglia 1978 Probably an illegit. name for a rather strong-growing, open form with twisted branches and leaves. Often confused with 'Contorta'. L. Hillier's Nurs. Winchester. G U.K.

- - 'Twombly's Golden New Growth' Hort. Amer.
                        An illegit. name (4 words not permitted). (Twombly's Golden?).

- - 'UConn' S Waxman   1978 In "Hort. Science **13**". Compact form with bright green needles. Conical, aging to flat-topped shrub. **O**. S. Waxman, Univ. of Connecticut, Storrs, CT.   U.S.A.

- - 'Umbraculifera' Hort. ex Knight
                        1850 Not of Hornibrook 1939, for which see *PINUS wallichiana*.   B,G,K,R,W2   France

- - 'Uncatena' Welch   1979 Similar to 'Merrimack' but much slower. Leaves shorter mid to yellow-green. Raised in Arnold Arboretum.   G,K,R,W2   U.S.A.

- - 'Variegata' Nelson   1866 "Leaves yellow variegated". NIC.   B,R   U.K.

- - 'Verkade' Hort. Amer.   See the following entry.

- - **'Verkade's Broom'** R. L. Fincham
                        1983 In Coenosium "Nurs Cat". A dwarf rounded shrub wider than high leaves light green.   U.S.A.

- - 'Viridis' Carrière   1867 Branches short, thin; foliage all green. NIC.   B   France

- - 'Viridis Pendula' Ordnung ex Beissner.
                        1909 Pendulous tree raised by Ordnung at Eisenburg. NIC   B   Czechosl.

- - 'Weiss' Hort. Germany   1985 A mistake for 'Reinshaus'.

- - **'White Mountain'** Ed. Mezitt
                        1982 In "Nurs. Cat". A clone with intense blue foliage, raised on the Weston Nurs, Hopkinton, MA.   U.S.A.

- - 'Whitstone' Hort. Amer.   1992 In "Nurs. Cat". Rarafolia Nurs, Kintersville, PA.

- - **'Winter Gold'** L.C. Hatch
                        1985 In "Reference Guide". As the name suggests, the golden colour is at its best during the cold months.('Hillside Winter Gold').   U.S.A.

- - 'Witches'-brew'   1989 In "Int. Pl. Prop. Soc. Proc.". A semi-dwarf with an assymetrical habit. Raised from a witch's broom found in Hillsboro, New Hampshire. **O**. Raised by S. Waxman, Univ. of Connecticut, Storrs, CT.

- - **'Wustemeyer'** Wustemeyer ex Reuter
                        1984 In "Amer. Conif. Soc. Bull.". **1** (3): 1982. Raised from a witch's broom by **Wustemeyer** of Schernbeck. At first wrongly distributed as a form of *PINUS monticola*.   Germany

- - **'Wyandanch'** L.C. Hatch
                        1988 In "Conifer Database". A slow-growing columnar form with blue-green foliage.

- - 'Zebrina' Croux ex Bailly
                        1889 Leaves striped yellow. Found by Croux at Sceaux, Paris in 1874. NIC.   B   France

PINUS sylvestris Linnaeus   1753   Scots Pine.   30m,Z2   Europe

The Scots Pine is native almost throughout northern Europe and Asia, reaching as far south as Spain and Turkey. In a species that is inherently variable, and with so great a range, regional variations are to be expected, but these, rather like the dialects often found within a single language, are differences rather than tangible distinctions. In result, many of the large number of varietal names suggested are of uncertain value.

A review of botanical and pseudo-botanical names found "in the literature" (several of which were in fact given to a cultivar or in some cases even to a solitary specimen) was published by A. Carlisle in the U.K. *Journal of Forestry* **31**(2) 1958. The letter - C - in the fourth column below indicates a reference to this paper. In 1964 a Russian botanist, L F Pravdin, put forward a classification which recognised five sub-species *hamata, kulundensis, lapponica, sibirica* and, of course, *sylvestris*. The 'varieties' listed here fall within sub-species *sylvestris* unless otherwise stated.

A very large number of cultivars have been developed of recent years from selected trees, or from witch's brooms or seedlings therefrom.

- - 'Alba' Loudon   1838   Leaves erect; whitish-green. The word has also been used in the timber trade to refer to timber colour and quality.   G,K   U.K.

- - 'Albospicata' Den Ouden   1949   White-tipped foliage; tender. Raised by Pierre Lombarts, Zundert.   B   Holland

- - **'Albyns'** R. Nordine   1968   In "Inter. Plant Prop. Soc. Proc. **18"**. Prostrate seedling found at H.A. Albyn Nurs, Newark, Ohio ('Albyn', 'Albynn's Prostrate').   K,W2   U.S.A.

- - **'Alderly Edge'** Walker   1985   Plant from a witch's broom with glaucous leaves and introduced by Walkers Nurs, Doncaster.   U.K.

- - 'Alhorn' Hort. Germany   1989   A listed name. Hachmann Nurs.

- - var. *alpina* Svoboda   1953

- - var. *altaica* Ledebour   1833   A local variant found on the Altai Mountains.   C   Russia

- - **'Andorra'** Hort. Anglia   1980   Tight bun-shape with green leaves 10-15 mm and conspicuous red-brown winter buds. L. Hillier's Nurs, Winchester.   U.K.

- - *anguina* Schröder   1899   A sporadic variant with snake-like branching.   B,K   Sporadic

- - f. *annulata* Casparin   1882   Rare sporadic variant with foliage peculiarities.   B,K   Germ/Poland

- - var. *aquitana* Schott   1907   Loose-growing form from the Massif Centrale.   C   S. France

- - f. *argentea* (1) Steven   1838   A tall, vigorous tree; leaves and cones silvery-white.   B,C,G,K   Caucasus

- - **'Argentea'** (2) E. Hillier.   1926   A tree with long silvery-blue curved leaves and reddish stems, selected by Edwin Hillier. ('Edwin Hillier' is incorrect).   U.K.

- - 'Argentea' (3) Hort.   Name loosely used for any whitish-glaucous tree.

- - **'Argentea Compacta'** Ordnung   1899   A dwarf form; eventually to 3m, leaves silvery-grey. L. Hesse, (1987).   B,W2   Germany

- - 'Argentea Variegata' Hort. Holl.   1990   Reported from Trompenburg Arboretum. It is possibly = 'Inverleith'.

- - var. *armena* (K. Koch) Fitschen   1930   Now listed under sub-sp. *hamata*.   B,K   Transcaucasica

- - f. *aurea* Ottolander   1876   A questionable botanical category or collective name covering all forms in cultivation whose foliage turns yellow during the winter. This colour-change is characteristic of several of the geographical forms.   B,H,K,W2

- - **'Aurea'** Veitch 1900 A tree-forming clone of the above, with bright, golden-yellow winter foliage. Several clones are in cultivation. G,W2 U.K.

- - 'Aurea Nana' Hort. An illegit. listed name.

- - 'Aurea Nisbet' Hort. Holland
  1986 An illegit. name reported from Trompenburg Arboretum, Rotterdam. L. Jeddeloh Nurs, Oldenburg, Germany. Good gold winter colour, leaves shorter and finer than Aurea.

- - 'Aureopicta' Sénéclauze 1868 A form with most of its leaves golden-yellow. NIC. B,K,W2 France

- - 'Avondene' Hort. Anglia 1992 Dwarf globular, main branches upswept. Dark blue-green leaves to 3cms. Original witch's broom found by Mike Murphy in the New Forest. I. Kenwith Nurs, Bideford, Devon.

- - f. *baenitz* Baenitz A listed form with short leaves. See f. *microphylla*.

- - **'Bakony'** Welch 1979 A strong-growing dwarf with silvery foliage raised from a witch's broom found in the Fenyofo district. K,W2 Hungary

- - var. *balcanica* Svoboda 1950 A variant ocurring in scattered sites. Balkans

- - var. *baltica* Svoboda 1953 See var. *borussica*.

- - 'Barabit's Blue' Hort. Hungary
  1992 A listed name. O. A colour form selected by M. Barabits of Sopron, Hungary.

- - 'Barry Bergman' Hort. Amer.
  1986 Upright tree with white variegation.

- - var. *baschkirica* Svoboda
  1953

- - var. *batava* Schott 1907 A quick-growing form found in the lower reaches of the Rhine. AC Germany

- - **'Beacon Hill'** T.G. Bentham
  1981 In "Dwarf Conifer Notes 2(1)". Raised from a witch's broom found by Wm. Goddard in Beacon Hill Park. Canada

- - 'Beissneriana' Schwerin 1896 Clone with green foliage turning yellow in July. NIC. B,K Germany

- - **'Bennett Compact'** Hort. Amer.
  1986 A dwarf form with stiff, thick, blue needles. O. W.W. Bennett. U.S.A.

- - 'Bennett Mini-leaf' Hort. Amer.
  1979 L. Raraflora, Feasterville, PA. NOM.

- - 'Bennett's Short-Leaf' Hort. Amer.
  1979 L. Raraflora, Feasterville, PA. NOM.

- - **'Bergman'** Welch 1979 Globose dwarf. Eventually quite large. W2 U.S.A.

- - **'Beuvronensis'** Transon ex Beissner
  1891 An old favourite, still popular. (Note the correct spelling). Similar to Bergman but longer in the leaf. B,G,H,K,W2 France

- - **'Black Money'** Hort. Holland
  1986 L. H.J. van de Laar in "Naamlijst . . .". NOM.

- - **'Blue Sky'** Hort. Holland
  1986 L. H.J. van de Laar in "Naamlijst . . .". NOM.

- - **'Boersma'** Int. Con. Reg.
  1982 A decumbent form. Registered by Van Duzen Bot. Gar. **O**. H. Boersma, Richmond, B.C. (1967).   Canada

- - var. *bohemica* Siman   1923 A local form.

- - *bonapartei* Seitz   1926 The Shell Pine. Sporadic form with peculiar bark and cones, found in E. Europe.   K

- - 'Bonna' Hort. Holland   1990 Foliage very blue. Reported from Trompenburg Arboretum, Rotterdam.   G

- - var. *borealis* Svoboda   1953

- - var. **borussica** P.K. Schott
  1907 A variant found in the valleys in N.E. Germany.   B,C   N.Germany

- - var. *bougetii* Flous   1933 Variant found in the northern slopes of the Pyrenees.   Spain

- - var. *brachyphylla* Wittrock   A form with very short leaves. See var. *microphylla*.

- - 'Brevifolia' (1) Heer   1862 Conical crown, short leaves, locally found in Switzerland.

- - **'Brevifolia'** (2)   1975 Dwarf upright slim conical plant. **O**. and **I**. R. Kaye, Waithman Nurs, Silverdale, Lancs.

- - var. *brigantiaca* Gaussen A local form.   D   France

- - 'Buchanan's Gold' G. Haddow
  1985 Short leaved dwarf form, deep gold in winter. Original plant in Royal Edinburgh Botanic Garden. **I**. Kenwith Nurs, Bideford, Devon.

- - 'Bugattii' Jaeger   1865 A mistake.   B,W2

- - 'Bujotii' Sénéclauze   1868 A mistake.   B,W2

- - **'Burghfield'** Hort. Anglia
  1985 Raised from a witch's broom found by C. Franklin of Reading. Conical, short leaves, noticeable red winter buds. **L**. Kenwith Nurs, Bideford, Devon.

- - var. **carpatica** Klika ex Dallimore & Jackson
  1934 A local form found in Central and Eastern Europe.   D   Europe

- - var. **catalaunica** Gaussen ex Dallimore & Jackson
  1923 A local form found in Western and Central Europe.   D   Europe

- - var. **caucasica** Fischer ex Sénéclauze
  1868

- - **'Chantry Blue'** Int. Con. Reg.
  1983 Registered by D.W. Hatch. Slow-growing pyramid to 4m. leaves blue. Originated as a witch's broom found by B. Reynolds on Horsell Common, Woking, Surrey, (1972).   U.K.

- - 'Clumber Blue' Hort. Anglia
  1990 Dwarf globose plant with dark blue-green needles. **O**. and **I**. Walker Nurs, Blaxton, Doncaster.

- - 'Columnaris' Croux   1889 A superfluous synonym for var. *fastigiata*.

- - 'Columnaris Compacta' Croux
  1889 A dense, columnar form raised at Sceaux, Paris. NIC.   B,D,K   France

- - 'Compact' Hort. Amer.   1986 An unacceptable listed name.

- - 'Compressa' Carrière   1867 A dwarf, fastigiate cultivar no longer identifiable in cultivation. NIC.   B,H,K,W2   France

- - *condensata* Fries   1890 A sporadic, spreading, bush form.

- - 'Corley' Hort. Anglia   1985 A listed name. Possibly a superfluous name for 'Frensham'

- - var. *cretacea* Kalenicz   1934 A depauperate form occurring in Russia on calcareous sites.   C   Russia

- - 'Dereham' Hort. Anglia.   1979 Small globose plant with short mid-green leaves. One of a group of dwarfs raised from seed of a witch's broom by D. Hoste about 1970.I. Wansdyke Nurs. Devizes, Wilts. (See also 'Northam', 'Pulham', 'Reedham' and 'Sandringham').   W2

- - f. *diabolica* Schwerin   1932 Named for a sprawling tree found on the Kackrow Estate. NIC.   B   Germany

- - f. *divaricata* Fitschen in Beissner
    1930 Name loosely in use for any tree with large leaves.   K   Germany

- - 'Doone Valley' H.G. Hillier
    1971 In "Hillier's Manual". A dwarf, irregularly conical bush with glaucous foliage. Raised from a witch's broom found by W.B. Archer and named after his residence near Farnham.   R,W2   U.K.

- - 'Drath' Hort. Germany   1987 An upright-growing form with good blue foliage.   G

- - 'Edwin Hillier'   See 'Argentea' (2).

- - var. *engadinensis* Heer   1862 A local form occurring in the Engadine Alps, parts of Switzerland and the Tyrol.   B,C,K   C. Europe

- - *erecta* Mouillefert ex Loudon
    1838 Clone now unidentifiable in cultivation.

- - *erythranthera* Sanio   1871 A form with brightly-coloured staminate flowers.   B,K   Sporadic

- - f. *fastigiata* Carrière   1867 A fastigiate form that turns up from time to time.   Sporadic

- - 'Fastigiata' Carrière   1856 A narrowly fastigiate clone of the last with blue-green foliage. Name now loosely used for any similar tree.   B,C,G,K,R   U.K.

- - 'Fastigiata Drath'   See 'Drath'.   G

- - 'Fastigiata Glauca' Schelle
    1920 A listed name. NIC. See note under 'Fastigiata' above.   AC   Germany

- - var. *fennica* Svoboda   1953 ?

- - f. *fominii* Kondratjuk   1950 A name of uncertain application.

- - 'French Blue' Monrovia   1986 In "Nurs. Cat". Compact form with a persistent, blue foliage.   U.S.A.

- - 'Frensham' Wansdyke   1979 In "Nurs. Cat". A slow-growing form, congested growth; blue-green. Raised from a witch's broom found by R.S. Corley, on Frensham Common, Surrey.   W2   U.K.

- - f. *funebris* Svoboda   1953 A listed name.

- - 'Genèvensis' Beissner   1898 Dwarf bush with low spreading habit. Originated probably on the Simon-Louis Nurs, Metz. NIC.   B,H,K,W2   France

- - f. *gibba* Christ   1864 A variant with abnormal cones.

- - f. *gibberosa* Kihlmann   1904 Named for a tree with knobbly trunk in the Wirthy Arboretum. NIC.   B,K

- - 'Glauca' Hort. Germany   1990 An illegit. listed name.

- - 'Glauca Compacta' Krüssmann
    1979 Narrowly conical form with dark blue foliage. Selected by Hesse.   K   Germany

- - **'Glauca Draht'** Krüssmann
  1979 A vigorous conical tree; foliage colour deep blue. Selected by Draht.   K   Germany

- - 'Glauca Globosa' Hort. Amer.
  1986 An illegit. listed name.

- - 'Glauca Nana' Hort. Amer.
  1986 An illegit. listed name.

- - **'Globosa'** Hort. ex Lawson
  1852 A small, compact rounded tree. Still in cultivation.   B   U.K.

- - 'Globosa Nana' Hort. Amer.
  1989 Low-growing, compact, with stiff branches and cylindrical buds.

- - 'Globosa Viridis' Beissner
  1900 A mistake. Now listed as *PINUS nigra* 'Globosa Viridis'.   Not as B,G,K,W2

- - **'Gold Coin'** Welch
  1979 Slow-growing form with good yellow winter foliage. **O.** R.S. Corley. **I.** Don Hatch, Chantry Nurs, Honiton.   G,R,W2   U.K.

- - **'Gold Medal'** Welch
  1979 Faster in growth than 'Gold Coin' and the best winter gold clone in cultivation. **I.** Wansdyke Nurs, Devizes, Wilts.   G,R,W2   U.K.

- - **'Grand Rapids'** Nordine
  1961 In "Proc. Int. Plant Prop. Soc. **11**". Prostrate form with deep green foliage, found by C.E. Morris in a planting at Grand Rapids, Mich.   W2   U.S.A.

- - 'Greg's Gold' Hort. Amer.
  1992 Plant in Arboretum Trompenburg, Rotterdam, Holland.

- - **'Greg's Variegated'** Hort. Amer.
  1986 A listed name for a tree with creamy-yellow variegation. **L.** E.A. Cope. In "Native . . . Conifers . . . ".

- - 'Guadarama' Hort. Amer.
  1975 In "Nurs. Cat". Raraflora Nurs, Feasterville, PA. **L.** Kristick Nurs, Wellsville, PA. (1980).

- - var. *haguenensis* Loudon
  1838 A form found in the forests of the Rhine. Possibly not distinct from var. *superrhenana*.   B,C   Germany

- - 'Hale's Prostrate' Hort. Amer.
  1986 A listed name.

- - var. *hamata* Steven
  1838 Caucasian Scots Pine. Now accepted as a sub-species. (per Pravdin, 1964).   B,K,R   Crimea,Caucasus

- - **'Heit's Pygmy'** L.C. Hatch
  1988 In "Conifer Database". A diminutive green bush, wider than high.   U.S.A.

- - 'Helene Bergman' Hort. Amer.
  1986 A listed name.

- - 'Helga' Hort. Germany   1989 An illegit. name. **L.** Hachmann Nurs.

- - var. *hercynica* Munch
  1924 A tall, straight-stemmed form found in the mountains of Central Germany and Switzerland.   C   C. Europe

- - 'Hersley Dwarf' L. Walker
  1984 Dwarf plant, globose later conical, shortish blue-green leaves.

- - 'Hexenbesen Diesteldorf' Hort. Germany
  1992 A listed name. Horstmann Nurs, Schneverdingen.

- - **'Hibernia'** Jeddeloh   1975   Rounded bush; foliage grey. Found by J. zu Jeddeloh as a witch's broom in Ireland in 1962. It was at first distributed as 'Hibernica'. **O.** and **I.** J. zu Jeddeloh, Oldenburg.   K,W2   Germany

- - **'Hillside Creeper'** Welch   1979   Strong-growing, prostrate, dark green leaves. A seedling selected by Layne Ziegenfuss in 1970.   G,W2   U.S.A.

- - 'Hillside Weeping' Hort. Amer.   1985   A listed name.

- - f. *horizontalis* D Don   1814   Not now distinguished within var. *scotica*.

- - 'Horndal' Hort. Sweden   1984   Dwarf slightly monstrous thick branches. **O.** and **I.** Tage Lundell, Helsingborg.

- - 'Hoste Dwarf' Hort. Anglia   1988   Dwarf upright growing short dark green leaves rather stiff branches. Grown from a witch's broom seedling collected by Dixon Hoste. **I.** Kenwith Nurs, Bideford, Devon.

- - var. *iberica* Svoboda   1953   A local variant with horizontal branching.   D   W. Europe

- - **'Iceni'** Mercer & Hay   1953   In "Gardens and Gardening IV".A semi-dwarf bush with bluish-green foliage This spelling is correct; it is an old tribal name.   K,W2   U.K.

- - var. *illyrica* Svoboda   1953   A local variant, often with twisted trunk.   D   S.E. Europe

- - var. *imeritana* Regel ex Sénéclauze   1868   A local variant, no longer distinguished within the species.

- - 'Inops' Hort. Germany   1980   In "Nurs. Cat". J. zu Jeddeloh, Oldenburg.

- - f. *intermedia* Loudon   1838   A sporadic form no longer distinguished within the species.

- - **'Inverleith'** Welch   1979   Named for an old tree with creamy-white variegation in the Royal Botanic Garden, Edinburgh.   R,W2   Scotland

- - 'Irchester Park' Hort. Anglia   1988   A listed name. **O.** Hilliers Nurs, Winchester.

- - 'Istvandi' Hort. Hungary   1992   A listed dwarf form. **O.** M. Barabits of Sopron, Hungary.

- - var. *jacutensis* Svoboda   1953

- - **'Jade'** Hort. Anglia   1980   A small flat topped plant with down-curved side branches, leaves jade green. **O.** Raised from a mutation on 'Iceni'.   R

- - 'Janssen Witch' Hort. Amer.   1992   L. Foxborough Nurs, Maryland, without description.

- - **'Jeremy'** Int. Con. Reg.   1982   A diminutive low-spreading plant with short dark-green leaves and prominent bright brown buds. Propagated from a witch's broom found at Wellingborough, Northants by B. Reynolds in 1973. Registered and **I.** by Don Hatch in 1982.   U.K.

- - 'John Boy' D.W. Hatch   1987   Dwarf, low growing, all branches upright, short mid-green leaves, turning yellow on strong shoots in winter. **O.** and **I.** Don Hatch, the last dwarf he worked on, Chantry Nurs, Honiton.

- - **'Kámon Blue'** Krüssmann   1983   Foliage intensely blue, otherwise normal. Selected by E. Barabits of Sopron, about 1965.   K   Hungary

- - var. *kasatchstanica* Svoboda   1953   A listed name.

- - f. *katakeimos* Graebner	1899	Stunted form resulting from coastal climate.	B,C,K	Baltics
- - 'Kelpie' Hort. Anglia	1990	Globe shaped plant with all branches upright, short leaves. **O.** and **I.** Almondell Nurs, Methven, Scotland.		
- - 'Kenwith' G. Haddow	1986	A blue-green bush with congested foliage. **O.** and **I.** Kenwith Nurs, Bideford, Devon.		
- - f. *kienitzii* Sietz	1926	The Flakebark Pine. A form with peculiar bark.	B,C,D,K	Sporadic
- - var. *kochiana* (Klotsch) Pravdin	1964	A variant of the sub-species *hamata*.		
- - 'Kluis Pyramid' Hort. Amer.	1985	A listed named for a dense, conical tree. Coenosium Gardens, then of Lehighton, PA.		
- - var. **kulundensis** Sucakzew		The Scots Pine of the steppelands of U.S.S.R. Now accepted as a sub-species (per Pravdin, 1964).		Russia
- - 'Kurznadelig' Hort. Germany	1992	An unacceptable listed name. Horstmann Nurs, Schneverdingen.		
- - f. *laevigata* Schwerin	1911	Shingle Pine. A form with curious overlapping scaly bark.		Sporadic
- - 'Lakeside Dwarf' Hort. Anglia	1990	Upright quite strong growing tiered branches, dark blue leaves to 4cms. **O.** and **I.** Walker Nurs, Blaxton, Doncaster.		
- - var. **lapponica** Fries	1888	The Scots Pine of northern Scandinavia and Asia. Now recognised as a sub-sp.. (per Pravdin, 1964).	B,K	N Euro/Asia
- - 'Larchwood' Hort. Anglia	1992	Plant in Windsor Great Park, Berks, without description.		
- - f. *latifolia* Gordon	1858	Variety with unusually large leaves.	B,C,D,K	Caucasus
- - 'Little Ann' Hort. Anglia	1988	A plant in Rosemoor Gardens, Torrington, Devon. Low-spreading wiry looking. Witch's broom seedling.**O.** and **I.** D. Hoste, Manchester.		U.K.
- - 'Little Brolly' Hort. Anglia	1989	Flat topped spreading plant, branches curved and wiry. Seedling from a witch's broom. **O.** and **I.** Almondell Nurs, Methven, Scotland.		
- - **'Little Orphan'** Reg. C.O.P.F.	1972	A sport making a slow-growing conical tree. Selected by E.F. Johnston.		Canada
- - **'Lodge Hill'** Don Hatch	1981	In "Nurs. Cat". More dense than 'Beuvronensis'; blue-grey foliage and dark buds. I. Chantry Nurs, Honiton, Devon.**O.** A witch's broom on a tree at Roundstone, Surrey.	G	U.K.
- - 'Longmoor' Don Hatch	1982	Globose to conical, long dark green leaves, dark red cylindrical winter buds.		
- - f. *lubbonii* Staszkievicz	1958	A local form with short leaves.	K	Carpathian Mts.
- - f. *macrocarpa* Schröder	1894	Sporadic form with very large cones.	B,C,D,K	Moscow
- - **'Martham'** Welch	1977	A flat-topped little plant, with tightly packed, short, dark-green needles. One of J. D. Hoste's seedlings, introduced by Wansdyke Nurs, Devizes in 1977.		U.K.

- - var. *microphylla* Beissner
  1891 A now-unidentifiable variant with short leaves found by Count Schwerin. It serves as a group name, but should not be used as a cultivar name. K

- - **'Mitsch Weeping'** L.C. Hatch
  1985 In "Reference Guide". Prostrate unless stem-trained, longish glaucous-green leaves; quite large pale brown winter buds. U.S.A.

- - 'Mölln' Hort. Germany 1969 A listed name.

- - var. *mongolica* Litvinov 1905 Mongolian Scots Pine. C,R Mongolia

- - 'Monophylla' Hodgins ex Loudon
  1838 A curiosity raised in the Hodgins Nurs. in 1830. NIC. B,D,K Ireland

- - f. *monticola* Schröder 1895 A curiosity with twisted growth and numerous, persistent cones. NIC. B,C,D,K Sporadic

- - 'Moseri' Moser 1890 Now again listed under *PINUS nigra*. G,K,W2 France

- - 'Mount Vernon Blue' Hort. Amer.
  1986 A listed name for a selected colour form.

- - f. *nana* (1) Pallas 1784 The Bog Pine. Stunted plants growing in waterlogged soil.

- - 'Nana' (2) Carrière 1855 Now only of value as a collective name covering all dwarf forms of the species. B,H

- - **'Nana'** (3) Knight 1851 Often confused with 'Watereri'. But see Welch (p. 330, 1979) and illustration in the book *Conifers*. G,W2 Europe

- - 'Nana Glauca' Hort. Canada
  1987 An illegit. listed name. L. T.J. Cole. NOM.

- - var. *nevadensis* Christ 1863 A variant found in the Sierra Nevada. Possibly not distinct from var. *hispanica*. B,D,K Spain

- - 'Nigrescens' Hort. Ireland
  1989 Reported from the National Botanic Gardens, Dublin.

- - **'Nisbet's Gem'** Welch 1979 At one time distributed in U.K. as 'Beuvronensis (Nisbet's form)'. Slower growing than 'Beuvronensis' with shorter leaves and rather more upright. K,W2

- - var. *norvegica* Svoboda 1953

- - 'Nymans' Hort. Anglia 1985 Reported from Windsor Great Park, Berks. NOM.

- - var. *obensis* Svoboda 1953

- - 'Oberbozen' Hort. Germany
  1992 A listed name. Horstmann Nurs, Schneverdingen.

- - 'Oppdal' Hort. Germany 1986 Derived from a witch's broom. G

- - var. *pannonica* Schott 1907 A free-flowering local variant found in western Hungary. B,C,D Hungary

- - f. *parvifolia* Heer 1862 A sporadic variant with sparce foliage. B,C,D,K Sporadic

- - 'Pasfield' Hort. Anglia 1985 Dwarf conical, grey-green leaves. Reported from Windsor Great Park, Berks, NOM. U.K.

- - 'Pendula' Lawson 1852 A clone no longer clearly identifiable, so the name should not be re-used for other clones. B,D U.K.

- - **'Perkeo'** J Carl 1973 A dwarf form raised from a witch's broom and introduced by Pfortzeimer Alpengarten. Long glaucous leaves. Austria

- - 'Pierson's Ridge' Hort. Amer.
  1986 A listed name.

- -'**Pixie**' G. Haddow 1983 Small globular plant with light-green leaves. **O.** and **I.** Don Hatch, Chantry Nurs, Honiton. **L.** Kenwith Nurs, Bideford, Devon. G U.K.

- - f. *plicata* Schenk 1925 Dwarf, rounded bush to 2m.

- - var. *polonica* Svoboda 1953

- - var. *pontica* Svoboda 1953

- - 'Prostrata' Hort. Amer. 1967 An illegit. name. **L.** Raraflora, Feasterville, PA.

- - '**Pulham**' Welch 1977 A broadly conical dwarf with tiered branch system; leaves grey to 20mm. **O.** J. Dixon Hoste seedling from a witch's broom. **I.** Wansdyke Nurs. in 1977. U.K.

- - 'Pumila' Beissner 1891 A superfluous synonym for 'Watereri'. H

- - 'Pygmaea' Beissner 1909 Dense rounded bush. Probably no longer identifiable. H,W2

- - 'Pygmaea Microphylla' Sénéclauze 1868 A very diminutive plant with tiny leaves found in a wood by Sénéclauze. NIC. France

- - f. *pyramidalis* Elwes & Henry 1908 A superfluous synonym for f. *fastigiata*. C,D Sporadic

- - '**Pyramidalis Compacta**' Hornibrook 1923 A narrowly conical dwarf with a thick trunk, leaves blue and slightly incurved. **O.** The Simon-Louis Nurs. at Metz. B,H,K,W2 France

- - 'Pyramidalis Glauca' Beissner 1891 A compact conical dwarf. NIC. B,D,K Holland

- - var. *pyrenaica* Svoboda 1953 A sporadic form. D C. Europe

- - 'Raraflora Seedling' Hort. Amer.
  An unacceptable name listed by Raraflora in 1967.

- - 'Raraflora Brevifolia' Hort. Amer.
  An illegit. name listed by Raraflora in 1967.

- - '**Reedham**' Welch 1977 A diminutive plant with small, dark-green leaves tightly packed on sturdy, stiff, symmetrically set branches; buds small, resinous. Another of the J. Dixon Hoste witch's broom seedlings. **I.** Wansdyke Nurs. U.K.

- - 'Reflexa' Heer 1862 A sporadic variant, differing only in the cone shape. C Switzerl.

- - 'Rependa' Krüssmann 1983 Possibly a superfluous name for the following. K

- - '**Repens**' (1) Welch 1979 A dwarf spreading plant with long, thick, grey-blue leaves. Groups of winter buds, coalesced into one and very resinous. Found on the Skylands Farm. A most distinctive plant. **L.** J.W. Spingarn, L. Is., N.Y. (1980). G,W2 U.S.A.

- - 'Repens' (2) Hort. Germany 19?9 Listed J. zu Jeddeloh. NOM. Possibly the same as last. The name is loosely used for any spreading form. K

- - var. *rhodopaea* Svoboda 1966 A sporadic variety, often with a crooked trunk. D E. Europe

- - var. *rigensis* Loudon 1838 A vigorous local variant from the Gulf of Riga. B,C,K Scandinavia

- - **'Riverside Gem'** Krüssmann
  1972 Upright and large in time; a bush propagated from a witch's broom found by B. Harkness in Riverside Cemetery, Rochester, N.Y. — K,W2 — U.S.A.

- - **var.** *romanica* Svoboda — 1950 A local form found in the Carpathians. (Spelling varies.) — D — E. Europe

- - **var.** *rossica* Svoboda — 1950

- - 'Rowe's Broom' Hort. Amer.
  1988 In "Nurs. Cat". Mitsch Nurs, Aurora, OR.

- - **var.** *rubra* (Miller) Reichard
  1780 The Highland Pine. Not now distinguished within the species. — B,C — Scotland

- - **f.** *rubra* — Term formerly used for the colour of the wood.

- - **'Rustic'** G. Bentham — 1985 In "Dwarf Conifer Notes 2(1)". A curious form raised from seed by Wm Goddard. The dark green leaves and the branches are thick and twisted. — U.S.A.

- - **'Sandringham'** Welch — 1977 A flat-topped bush with very congested growth; Leaves varying in length; buds often in clusters. Raised by J. Dixon Hoste. — U.K.

- - **var.** *sarmatica* Zapal in Dallimore & Jackson
  1966 A sporadic form. — D — E. Europe

- - **'Saxatilis'** Carrière — 1867 A very slow-growing, flat-topped, thin-branched dwarf. L. Hillside Nurs, Lehighton, PA. (1970), but doubtfully the same clone as Carrière's plant. — B,H,G,K,W2 — U.S.A.

- - 'Sayville' Hort. Amer. — 1974 A conical dwarf with ascending branches and short, stiff, bluish-green leaves. I. Johnson Ave Nurs, Sayville, N.Y. — U.S.A.

- - **f.** *scariosa* Loudon — 1838 An early noticed local variant with unusual cones. NIC. — C — The Alps

- - **var.** *scotica* Schott — 1907 The indigenous Scots Pine of Scotland. — C,K — Scotland

- - 'Scott's Dwarf' Hort. Anglia — A superfluous synonym for 'Nisbet's Gem'.

- - 'Scrubby' L. Walker — 1985 Very slow-growing in early years, but putting up a leader later to 15cms annually with clusters of short branches/branchlets at the base of each year's growth. Leaves short, dark green recurving. O. and I. Walkers Nurs, Blaxton, Doncaster.

- - 'Sei' Hort. Hungary — 1992 A blue selection. O. Kámon Arboretum, Szombathely, Hungary.

- - **f.** *seitzii* Schwerin — 1926 — B,K — Germany

- - **'Sentinel'** G. Bentham — 1981 In "Dwarf Conifer Notes 2(1)". A seedling by Wm Goddard from 'Fastigiata', but with slower, denser growth. Good blue colour, straight leaves at 45o. — K — U.S.A.

- - **var.** *septentrionalis* Schott
  1907 The Scots Pine of Central and Southern Scandinavia. — E. Europe

- - **'Sherwood'** — 1985 A dwarf with dense, rather upright habit. ('Sherwoodii' is illegitimate).

- - **var.** *sibirica* Ledebour — 1833 Not now distinguished within the species. (per Silba, 1984).

- - 'Skiabloba' Hort. Scandinavia
1986 Original plant in Windsor Great Park, Berks. Dwarf upright
with multiple leading shoots which give the plant a look of
character. Origin unknown but the new candles and leaves
come out very early in the year and it's origin is probably
Swedish.

- - 'Skjak I' G. Haddow   1984 Low growing, globose shape, haphazard branch system,
annual growth 4cms; short dark green leaves widely spaced.
Free flowering, new growth starts early. **O.** Tage Lundell,
Helsingborg. **I.** Kenwith Nurs, Bideford, Devon.

- - 'Skjak II' G. Haddow   1984 A mound-forming dwarf with short mid-green leaves and an
annual growth of up to 2 cms. raised from a witch's broom
found by Tage Lundell of Helsingborg, Sweden. About the
smallest dwarf Scots in commercial cultivation. New growth
starts early. **I.** Kenwith Nurs, Bideford, Devon.

- - **'Skogbygdi'** G Horstmann
1986 In "Nurs. Cat". A diminutive plant propagated from a witch's
broom. With weak growth to 1cm annually and a curious
flattened habit of growth. Mid green leaves, new growth starts
early.   Germany

- - 'Sosnowski' Hort. Germany
1973 In "Nurs. Cat". J.zu Jeddeloh, Oldenburg.

- - **'Spaans Slow Column'** R.L. Fincham
1984 In "Amer. Conif. Soc. Bull. 1(4)". A slow-growing seedling
from 'Fastigiata' raised by the late Jon Spaan of Oregon.   G   U.S.A.

- - 'Spanish' Hort. Amer.   1986 A listed name for a widespreading clone.

- - f. *spiralis* Carrière   1859 A sporadic form with long, twisted needles.   K

- - 'Spiralis' Carrière   1859 A clone of the previous item found by Sénéclauze. NIC.   B   France

- - 'St. George' Hort. Anglia   1993 Tight globular dwarf plant, glaucous leaves, bright rich red
winter buds. **O.** M. McGregor, Wales. **I.** Kenwith Nurs,
Bideford, Devon.

- - 'Straver' Hort. Holland   1992 L. Wiel Linssen, Baexem, without description.

- - var. *subillyricum* Corona
1955 Name used for a local form in Trentino Provence.   C   Italy

- - 'Supergold' Hort. Germany
1992 A listed name. Horstmann Nurs, Schneverdingen.

- - var. *superrhenana* Schott
1907 A local form in the Upper Rhine district.   C

- - var. *sylvestriformis* (Takenouchi) Cheng et C D Chu
1978 A 'nov. comb' from the "Chinese Flora".   China

- - **'Tabuliformis'** Barron   1875 A descriptively named form with dark green short leaves.
Young plants conical, later flat-topped.   H,R,W2   U.S.A.

- - 'Tage' G. Haddow   1988 Dwarf, low-growing spreading dark green twisting leaves. **O.**
an unnamed plant sent by Tage Lundell, to G. Haddow. **I.**
Kenwith Nurs, Bideford, Devon.

- - 'Tilhead' R. Watson   1988 Dwarf upright tiered branches, blue leaves to 4cms. **O.**
Witch's broom found by R. Watson. **I.** Treborth Nurs,
Bangor, N. Wales.

- - 'Tortuosa' (1) Don of Forfar ex Lawson
1852 Named for an old tree in a forest in Saxony. NIC.   B,K   Germany

- - 'Tortuosa' (2) Hort. Canada
  1980 The name is also, illegally, in use for a vigorous form with contorted growth. I. Floravista Gardens, Vancouver Island, B.C.

- - 'Treasure' Hort. Anglia 1990 Dwarf globular, glaucous green curved leaves to 3cms. From a witch's broom. I. Wansdyke Nurs, Devizes.

- - **'Trenton Weeper'** Vermeulen
  1971 In "Nurs. Cat".

- - 'Tulsfelder Zwerg' Hort. Holland
  1992 L. Wiel Linssen, Baexam, without description.

- - f. *turfosa* Woerlitz 1893 A small tree found in heathy, coastal areas. B,K Baltics

- - 'Twiggy' Hort. Amer. 1986 A listed name for a many-branched globose, rather open form with very good blue colour. L. Coenosium, Lehighton, PA.

- - 'Umbraculifera' Carrière 1855 A low, domed shrub. NIC. B,H,K France

- - 'Umbrella' Hort. Anglia 1992 Plant in Windsor Great Park, Berks, without description.

- - var. *uralensis* Fischer A local variant found on the Ural Mountains. U.S.S.R.

- - 'Variegata' Carrière 1855 A rather tender variegated form. NIC. B,D,K,W2 France

- - 'Vera Hayward' Hort. Anglia
  1985 Pyramidal, quite strong growing, mid green leaves to 4cms. O. and I. Wansdyke Nurs, Devizes, Wilts.

- - var. *vindelica* Schott 1907 A local variant found in Switzerland and Austria. C C. Europe

- - **'Virgata'** Caspary 1882 Trees with snakelike foliage occasionally turn up. B,K Sporadic

- - **'Viridis Compacta'** Hornibrook
  1923 A dwarf form with dark green, much twisted leaves. Possibly no longer distinguishable. B,H,K,W2 U.K.

- - 'Vlkancice' Hort. Holland
  1992` L. Wiel Linssen, Baexam, without description.

- - var. *vocontiana* Guinier & Gaussen ex Dallimore & Jackson
  1966 A listed name. D

- - **'Watereri'** Beissner 1891 A very popular 'dwarf' form, but it becomes a small tree in time. The mother tree is on the Knap Hill Nurs, Woking, Surrey. ('Pumila', 'Watereriana', 'Nana'). B,G,K,R,W2 U.K.

- - **'Westonbirt'** Hort. Anglia
  1985 Raised from a witch's broom found by H.J. Welch in the Westonbirt Arboretum, Gloucestershire. I. Wansdyke Nurs, Devizes. U.K.

- - 'Windsor' Hillier 1971 Name for a witch's broom that reverted. NIC. K,W2

- - 'Wintergold' H.J. Grootendorst
  1977 In "Dendroflora 13-14". A compact form, bright yellow in winter. Holland

PINUS szemaoensis Liang 1982 Not now distinguished within *PINUS insularis*. (per Silba, 1984).

PINUS tabulaeformis Carrière
  1867 Chinese Red Pine (tabuliformis). 30m,Z5 China

- - var. *densata* (Masters) Rehder
  1923 Southern Chinese Pine. By some authorities now recognised as a distinct species. (per Rushforth, 1987). B,K,R S. China

- - var. *mukdensis* Uyeki	A local variant with minor foliage differences.	Z5	N.E. China
- - var. *yunnanensis* (Franchet) Shaw	1914 Now regarded as a distinct species. (per Rushforth, 1987).		
PINUS taeda Linnaeus	1753 Loblolly Pine.	30m,Z7	U.S.A.
- - 'Cochran' L.C. Hatch	1988 In "Conifer Database". A genetic dwarf-form. O. N. Carolina State University.		U.S.A.
- - 'Compacta' Hort. Amer.	1985 This, and 'Nana' are invalid names for slow-growing clones.		
- - 'Dixie' L.C. Hatch	1988 In "Conifer Database". O. Similar to 'Cochran', but makes a smaller plant.		U.S.A.
- - var. *echinata* (Miller) Castigl.	No data.		
- - 'Pendula' Hort. Amer.	1985 An illegit. name.		
PINUS taiwanensis Hayata	1911 Taiwan Black Pine. Rare in cultivation.	15m,Z8	Taiwan
PINUS takahasi Nakai	Xinghai Pine. A little-known species close to *PINUS tabulaeformis*.	20m,Z6	N. Korea
PINUS tecumumanii Schwerdtf.	1953 A rare form close to *PINUS patula*.		N. Guatemala
PINUS tenuifolia Bentham	1842 Now known as *PINUS maximinoi* Moore.		
PINUS teocote Schlechtendal & Chammiso	1830 Teocote Pine.	30m,Z7	S. Mexico
- - var. *macrocarpa* Shaw	1914 A variant with larger cones.		S. Mexico
PINUS thunbergiana Franco	1949 Now generally known as *PINUS thunbergii*, but some authors still use this name. (See Silba, 1984).		
PINUS thunbergii Parlatore	1868 Japanese Black Pine. (Note. This is the accepted spelling).	25m,Z6	Japan

This species is used in the Bonsai industry in Japan, where many selections have been named that are not cultivars in the normal sense. A number of 'vars.' were listed in 1890 that in some cases were cultivars or groups of cultivars rather than botanical entities, but they are retained here since they serve as useful Group names. The words *kuromatsu* or *matsu* being the specific name in Japan should not be used in cultivar names published since Jan 1959.

- - 'Akame'	1976 A clone of var. *corticosa*. Received in U.K. by Wansdyke Nurs, in 1976. Upright tiered branches, slightly incurved leaves, bark ages quickly.		Hort. Japan
- - 'Albovariegata'	See 'Variegata'.		
- - 'Aocha-matsu' L.C. Hatch	1985 In "Reference Guide". An upright form with many leaves yellow.		Hort. Japan
- - 'Arakawa-sho' Welch	1979 Rough-bark Pine. A clone of var. *corticosa*.	W2	Hort. Japan
- - 'Aurea' Fitschen in Beissner	1930 Clumps of golden-yellow leaves among the green.		Hort. Japan
- - 'Banshosho' Wm. N. Valavanis	1975 In the book "Japanese Five-needle Pine". A dense, globose plant with dark green foliage and multiple buds. Foliage much lighter green when grafted on *sylvestris.*.		Hort. Japan
- - 'Benijanome' Welch	1979 A clone of var. *oculus-draconis* in which the variegation turns pink in winter.	W2	Hort. Japan

- - 'Beni-kujaku' R.L. Fincham

1989 In Coenosium "Nurs. Cat". Tree with pale yellow patches on some leaves, sometimes pink during the winter. U.S.A.

- -'Chase's Yellow' Hort. Amer.

1991 A listed name. L. Rarafolia Nurs, Kintersville, PA.

- - 'Compacta' Hort. Anglia   1980 Slow-growing upright plant with very nearly black-green leaves. L. Hillier'S Nurs, Winchester.

- - var. *corticosa* T. Makino

1940 In "Illus. Flora of Japan". *A botanical designation covering all forms with abnormally thick, corky bark.* Many selections within this variety have been made because of its value in the art of Bonsai. Japan

- - "Corticosa" Hort.

See the previous item. The word should not be used as, or be included in, a cultivar name.

- - 'Dai-nagon' Hort. Anglia

In "Nurs. Cat". A dwarf globose plant, upright branch system, short stiff very dark-green leaves. O. Japan. I. Wansdyke Nurs, Devizes. Kenwith Nurs, Bideford, Devon, (1992).

- - 'Eechee' Hort. Amer.   1975 Clone with rapidly ageing bark. O. Japan. I. Raraflora Nurs, Feasterville, PA.

- - 'Elmwood' Hort. Amer.   1992 A listed name. From a witch's broom. L. Foxborough Nurs, Maryland, PA.

- - 'Fuji' Welch   1979 A clone of var. *corticosa*.   W2   Hort. Japan

- - 'Ganseki-matsu' Welch   1979 Rockstone Pine. A clone of var. *corticosa*.   Hort. Japan

- - 'Gan seki sho' Hort. Amer.

1988 L. Mitsch Nurs, Aurora, PA.

- - 'Girard Dwarf' L.C. Hatch

1985 In "Reference Guide". A dense dwarf form with very short leaves.('Girardii Nana' is illegit).   U.S.A.

- - var. *globosa* Mayr   1890 A commercial equivalent of 'Kuro-bandaisho'.   B,H   Hort. Japan

- - 'Hayabusa' Hort. Anglia   1977 Received in U.K. by Wansdyke Nurs.   Hort. Japan

- - *'HitoBánó-matzu'* Mayr   1890 A clone of var. *monophylla*. NIC?   Hort. Japan

- - 'Ichiyo' Hort. Amer.   1988 L. Mitsch Nurs, Aurora, PA.

- - 'Iihara'   1976 A clone of var. *corticosa*. Upright growing, main branches upright, very dark spiky green leaves. L. Wansdyke Nurs.   Hort. Japan

- - 'Ippon-matzu' Mayr   1890 A clone of var. *monophylla*. NIC.   Hort. Japan

- - 'Iseli Golden' Iseli   1990 In "Nurs. Cat". Upright growing, foliage variegated pale-yellow.   U.S.A.

- - 'Iwai' Welch   1979   W2   Hort. Japan

- - 'Janome-matsu' Mayr   1890 A commercial equivalent of var. *oculus-draconis*.

- - "Kashima-matsu" Welch   1979 A name in use in the Bonsai industry only. Not a true cultivar name.   W2

- - 'Katasogematzu' Mayr   1890 A commercial synonym of var. *pectinata*.(='Katsuga' ?).   Hort. Japan

- - 'Katsuga' Hort Amer.   1975 Imported from Japan. I. Raraflora Nurs, Feasterville, PA. ('Katasogematzu'?).

- - **'Kikko-sho'** Welch   1979   Tortoise-shell Pine. A clone of var. *corticosa*. Bark marked in tortoise-shell pattern.   Hort. Japan

- - 'Kokuho' Hort. ?   Upright growing rather fast and open.

- - **'Kotobuki'**   1976   In "Conifer Database". A narrowly upright tree with dense, dark green, bushy foliage. Much slower-growing and tighter grafted on thunbergii. L. Wansdyke Nurs, Devizes.   G   Hort. Japan

- - **'Koyosho'** R.L. Fincham
    1989   In Coenosium "Nurs. Cat". Slow-growing globose form with mid green needles.   Hort. Japan

- - **'Kujaku'** L.C. Hatch   1988   In "Conifer Database". New needles mottled, pink to cream.   U.S.A.

- - **'Kuro-bandaisho'** Mayr   1890   A commercial equivalent of var. *globosa*.   W2   Hort. Japan

- - **'Kuro-fuiri-matzu'** Mayr
    1890   A clone of var. *oculus-draconis*. NOM. NIC?   Hort. Japan

- - **'Kuro-semmosho'** Mayr   1890   A clone of var. *tortuosa*. NIC.   Hort. Japan

- - 'Kyokko' Hort. ?   A listed name. Possibly same as 'Kikko-sho'. ('Koko').

- - 'Maijima' Hort. Holland   1990   Plant in Arboretum Trompenburg. Dwarf form with tiered branches and dark-green leaves.

- - **'Majestic Beauty'** Monrovia
    1986   In "Nurs. Cat". A selected form with dark green needles.   U.S.A.

- - "Mikawa-matzu" Welch   1979   A name in use in the Bonsai industry only. Not a true cultivar name.   W2

- - 'Mini Mounds' Hort. Amer.
    1991   A listed name. L. Rarafolia Nurs, Kintersville, PA.

- - 'Monina' Hort. Amer.   See 'Majestic Beauty'.

- - var. ***monophylla*** Mayr   1890   Leaves fused together so as to appear single.   B   Hort. Japan

- - **'Mount Hood Prostrate'** Iseli
    1990   In "Nurs. Cat". Low, with long, sweeping branches; dark-green needles.   U.S.A.

- - 'Nagata' Hort. Amer.   1975   Imported from Japan. I. Raraflora Nurs, Feasterville, PA.

- - 'Nana' Hort.   See 'Compacta'.

- - 'Nee' Hort. Amer.   1975   Slow-growing with bark ageing quickly and splitting longitudinally. O. Japan. I. Raraflora Nurs, Feasterville, PA.

- - *"nishiki"*   A Japanese adjective meaning *"having coarse bark"*. It should not form part of a cultivar name.   W2

- - var. ***oculus-draconis*** Mayr
    1890   "Dragon's Eye". Leaves variegated and green in bands along each leaf. The commercial equivalent of 'Janome'.   B,R   Hort. Japan

- - **'Oculus-draconis Tortuosa'** Mayr
    1890   A clone of the last with contorted foliage. NIC.   B   Hort. Japan

- - 'Ogi-matsu' Hort. Amer.   1988   L. Mitsch Nurs, Aurora, PA.

- - **'Ogon'** Hort. Amer.   1986   Foliage bright golden-yellow if in full sun, during the summer. (Not the same as 'Aurea').

- - 'Okinakabu' Hort. Amer.   1975   Imported from Japan. Seems to be in part a pendulous plant with long dark green leaves.

- - var. *pectinata* Mayr   1890   B   Hort. Japan

- - var. *pendula* Mayr   1890   Branches and leader pendulous, making an unattractive tree.   B,H   Hort. Japan

- - **'Porky'** Hort. Amer.   1985   A listed name for a clone of var. *monophylla*. Slow-growing quite long dark green needles.

- - 'Prostrata' Hort. Amer.   1985   An illegit. listed name.

- - 'Pygmaea' Hort. Amer.   1990   An illegit. name for a clone that is very slow-growing but has leaves of normal size.

- - **'Sayonara'** H.J. van de Laar
         1976   In "Dendroflora 20". Name suggested in place of 'Yatsubusa'. See also 'Yatsubusa'.   Hort. Europe

- - 'Senryu' Hort. Anglia   1985   A listed name.

- - **'Shidarematsu'** Welch   1979   A clone of var. *pendula*.   W2   Hort. Japan

- - *'Shimo-fuiri-matsu'* Mayr
         1890   A clone of var. *variegata*.   Hort. Japan

- - **'Shioguro'** G. Haddow   1990   Dwarf bush densely clothed with very dark green foliage.   G   Hort. Japan

- - **'Shiragamatzu'** Mayr   1890   A clone of var, *variegata*.   Hort. Japan

- - **'Shirofume-matzu'** Mayr
         1890   A clone of var. *variegata* with a snowlike variegation.   Hort. Japan

- - **'Shirome Janome'** R.L. Fincham
         1989   In Coenosium 'Nurs. Cat". A form with two bright yellow bands on each leaf.   Hort. Japan

- -**'Suiken'** R.L. Fincham   1989   In Coenosium "Nurs. Cat". Strongly twisted needles.   Hort. Japan

- - 'Sunsho' Hort. Japan   1973   Received at Wansdyke Nurs, Devizes. Wilts, U.K. from Dr Rokujo. Upright growing, short thick leaves. Grafted on *thunbergii* the plant has branchlets on which all the needles are gold. The plant is all green on *sylvestris*.   Hort. Japan

- - 'Taihei' Hort. Japan   1976   Received at Wansdyke from Aritaki. Upright clone with rough bark.

- - **'Thunderhead'** J Vermeulen
         1987   In "Nurs. Cat". A compact form with dark green foliage and large white buds. An illegit. name. See Art. 50 of the Cultivated Code but it is now in general use and becoming popular.   U.S.A.

- - var. *tigrina* Mayr   1890   Golden-yellow flecks, irregularly scattered, not in a pattern as in vars. *oculus-draconis* and *variegata*.   B   Hort. Japan

- - **'Torafumatsu'** Mayr   1890   A commercial equivalant of var. *tigrina*.   W2   Hort. Japan

- - var. *tortuosa* Mayr   1890   Growth contorted, needles twisted like a corkscrew.   B,H   Hort. Japan

- - 'Trifoliata' Mayr   1890   Mayr lists several names then in use, possibly for seedlings retaining juvenile foliage. NIC.   Hort. Japan

- - **'Tsukasa'** Wm. N.Valvanis
         1975   A clone of var. *corticosa* that soon develops a corky bark which splits vertically up the trunk.

- - 'Tura-ku-Kuromatsu' Hort. Amer.
         1985   See 'Tora-fu-matsu'.

- - var. *variegata* Mayr   1890   Forms with variegations in different patterns. ('Albovariegata').   B   Hort. Japan

- - 'Yamato' Hort. Japan 1976 A clone of var. *corticosa*.

- - 'Yatsubusa' Wansdyke 1976 An unsatisfactory name, not recommended. The clone cultivated in Europe has been re-named 'Sayonara'. More than one clone in cultivation in Europe. The1976 Wansdyke clone is more dwarf than the Dutch clone renamed 'Sayonara'.

- - 'Ye-i-kan' Hort. Sweden 1980 O. Unknown. Tight globular form, short mid-green needles, originated from a witch's broom. I. Tage Lundell, Helsingborg.

- - 'Yoshimura' Hort. 1992 A listed name.

- - 'Yumaki' Hort. Amer. 1989 Dwarf upright plant possibly semi-fastigiate to fastigiate with medium length, dark green leaves. L. Coenosium Gardens, Lehighton, PA. ('Yamato' may possibly be the same clone).

PINUS torreyana Parrey ex Carrière
 1855 Torrey Pine, Soledad Pine.   15m,Z9 California

PINUS tropicalis Morelot 1851 Tropical Pine. A rare species. 2/3n. Z10   Cuba

PINUS tuberculata Gordon 1849 Now known as *PINUS attenuata*.

PINUS uncinata Miller ex Mirbel
 1806 Mountain Pine.   25m,Z6 Alps, Spain

- - **'Aureovariegata'** Schelle
 1909

- - 'Drussetcha' Hort. Holland
 1992`Plant in Arboretum Trompenburg, without description.

- - 'Erzgebirge' Hort. Germany
 1983 In "Nurs. Cat". A listed name without description. Horstmann Nurs, Schneverdingen.

- - 'Etschtal' G. Horstmann 1983 In "Nurs. Cat". O. Witch's broom found high on the Etschtal, formerly listed as "No.19".   Germany

- - 'Fritsche' Hort. Germany 1992 A listed name without description. Horstmann Nurs, Schneverdingen.

- - 'Fussball' Hort. Germany
 1992 A listed name without description. Horstmann Nurs, Schneverdingen.

- - 'Goldesel' Hort. Germany
 1992 A listed name without description. Horstmann Nurs, Schneverdingen.

- - **'Grüne Welle'** G Horstmann
 1983 In "Nurs. Cat". A dwarf, irregular plant. Formerly listed as "No.9".   G   Germany

- - 'Inntal' Hort. Germany 1992 A listed name without description. Horstmann Nurs, Schneverdingen.

- - 'Ladisco' Hort. Germany 1983 A listed name without description. Horstmann Nurs, Schneverdingen.

- - **'Leuco-like'** G. Horstmann
 1983 In "Nurs. Cat". A vigorous, upright grower, with congested, dark green leaves. Formerly listed as "No.2".   G,K   Germany

- - 'Matte' J. zu Jeddeloh 1990 Dwarf tight congested low-growing plant.

- - 'No. 65' Hort. Germany   1988 Selection made at the Horstmann Nurs, and now distributed under this name. Dwarf globose plant with thick stumpy orange candles, dark-green leaves. An acceptable name should be found.

- - 'Offenpass' G. Horstmann

   1983 In "Nurs. Cat". A conical dwarf with dark green foliage. **O.** A witch's broom found south of the Offen Pass, formerly listed as "No.17".   Austria

- - **'Paradekissen'** G. Horstmann

   1983 In "Nurs. Cat". A dwarf growing cushion form. **O.** From a witch's broom found by Horstmann near Graubunden.   G,K   Switzerl.

- - var. *rostrata* (Antoine) Gordon

   1858 Makes a small tree. Possibly a hybrid with *PINUS mugo*.   G,R   Europe

- - var. *rotundata* (Link) Antoine   Possibly a hybrid with *PINUS mugo*.   K

- - **'Rumanien'** Hort. Germany

   1992 A listed name without description. Horstmann Nurs, Schneverdingen., Germany

- - **'Sonderherkunfte'** G. Horstmann

   1983 In "Nurs. Cat". A narrowly conical tree with dark green foliage. Probably a hybrid with *nigra*.   Germany

PINUS virginiana Miller   1768 Virginia Pine, Scrub Pine.   20m,Z5   U.S.A.

- - 'Creeping' Hort. Germany

   1992 A listed name. An acceptable name should be found.

- - 'Hexenbesen' Hort. Germany

   1992 A listed name. An acceptable cultivar name is required.

- - **'Nashawena'** Welch   1979 A spreading plant with congested branching system. **O.** Raised by A.J. Fordham at Arnold Arboretum from seed from a witch's broom.   W2   U.S.A.

- - **'Pocono'** Welch   1979 Similar to previous entry but densely clothed with green lvs.   W2   U.S.A.

- - **'Wate's Golden'** M.Kristick   Eventually small tree. Foliage rich golden-yellow in winter.   U.S.A.

PINUS wallichiana A.B. Jackson

   1938 Western Himalayan Pine; Blue Pine. (Formerly known as *PINUS excelsa* and as *PINUS griffithii*.   35m,Z6   E. Asia

- - 'Compacta' Hort. Anglia   1985 An illegit. listed name.

- - var. **dalatensis** (Ferre) Silba

   1984 Here listed as a separate species, *PINUS dalatensis*. (per Rushforth, 1987).   Z10   Asia

- - 'Densa' Krüssmann   1983 Close-growing conical form. L. J. zu Jeddeloh Nurs, Oldenburg (1969). Having come to him from America.   K   U.S.A.

- - 'Densa Hill' Hort. Germany

   1990 This name, in a later catalogue, is probably the same as the last item.

- - **'Frosty'** Hort. Amer.   1986 Growth rapid; foliage appears frosted in autumn and winter. (Note. This may be so grafted on *PINUS strobus* but no frost occurs when on *PINUS wallichiana* in the U.K).

- - **'Glauca'** Krüssmann   1983 Foliage glaucous blue. Similar forms turn up occasionally.   K   Sporadic

- - 'Glauca Compacta' Hort. Germany

   1979 An illegit. listed name.

- - **'Globosa'** Mayr   1890 Habit semi-globular, dense.   Hort. Japan

- - **'Monophylla'** Carrière   1867 Leaves fused together.   H   France

- - 'Morton' Hort. Amer.   1992 **O.** a selection by the Morton Arboretum, Illinois. **L.** Buchholz Nurs, Oregon.

- - **'Nana'** R. Smith   1872 A dense, dwarf bush, with leaves shorter and more silvery than normal.   G,H,K,W2   U.K.

- - 'Paktia' Horstmann   1992 In "Nurs. Cat". J. zu Jeddeloh Nurs, Oldenburg. Hardy mountainous strain; emerald-green colour.

- - **'Silver Star'** Krüssmann

    1983 A seedling with stiffer, shorter and more silvery needles. **O.** Raised by A. Plattner.   K,R   Germany

- - **'Umbraculifera'** Carrière

    1867 Large bush; long needles, often kinked.   K,R,W2   France

- - **'Vernisson'** Krüssmann   1983 Hardy tree with fastigiate branches. Discovered in the Arboretum Les Barres.   K,R   France

- - **'Zebrina'** Croux   1889 Each leaf with a gold band. Raised on the Croux Nurs. at Sceaux. Needs full sun to develop colour.   G,H,K,R   France

PINUS wangii Hu & Cheng

    1948 Wang Pine. A rare species, not yet in cultivation.   20m,Z9   China

PINUS washoensis Mason & Stockwell

    1945 Washoe Pine. A rare species near to *PINUS jeffreyi*.   U.S.A.

PINUS x *wettsteinii* Fritsch

    1889 *PINUS mugo* x *PINUS nigra*. The original cross was found in the Botanical Garden in Vienna, Austria. It differs from *nigra* in having longer branches and shorter leaves.

PINUS wincesteriana Gordon

    1858 Winchester Pine (formerly known as *PINUS michoacana* var. *cornata* (per. Rushforth, 1987).   Z9   Mexico

PINUS yunnanensis Franchet

    1899 A little-known species allied to *PINUS tabuliformis*.   30m,Z9   China

PLATYCLADUS Spach (1842)

Cupressaceae

This monotypic Genus has had difficulty in finding a settled home in the nomenclature. It was included by Linnaeus in 1753 within the Genus *THUJA* as *THUJA orientalis* and as such it has long been known in gardens. But later botanists (and, indeed, horticulturists) have questioned its affinity with that species and in 1847 Endlicher proposed a new generic name *BIOTA*, and as *BIOTA orientalis* it was listed by some authorities, although the name THUJA remained in general horticultural use. Botanical opinion, however, has remained firm that it is not a THUJA. Actually, unknown to Endlicher in 1847, the botanist Spach had, in 1842, published the name *PLATYCLADUS stricta* and the application of the *International Rules of Nomenclature* requires the use of the combination *PLATYCLADUS orientalis* to be used if the species is not considered to be a *THUYA*.

But since *THUJA orientalis* has been the name in use almost without interruption ever since the days of Linnaeus this academic change will be accepted slowly, if ever, in horticultural circles, so the variants and cultivars will here be found listed under that name for the greater convenience of present-day horticulturists.

PLATYCLADUS orientalis (L.) Franco
> 1949 Biota, Oriental Arborvitae. Formerly known as *BIOTA orientalis* (L.) Endlicher (1847); *PLATYCLADUS stricta* Spach (1842). It is here listed under *THUYA orientalis* with it's numerous cultivars.

E. Asia

PODOCARPUS L'Heritier ex Persoon (1807)

Podocarpaceae

The Podocarps are a large genus, second in number of species only to the pines. At one time they would have topped the chart, but a number of species once included in *PODOCARPUS* are now settled in their own Genus *PRUMNOPITYS*. The Genus now comprises about 90 species of evergreen trees and low shrubs (the former producing valuable timber) largely confined to the mountain forests of the warm temperate to tropical lands in the southern hemisphere, and therefore not hardy in cool temperate areas. The genus has been studied afresh of recent years, as a result of which numerous name changes have been made and the listings in earlier books such as Dallimore and Jackson (1960) and Krüssmann (1983) need to be treated with caution. The nomenclature here mainly follows Silba, (1984), whose classification was based on the revision of the genus by Prof. D. J. de Laubenfels. The following are hardy in U.K. but all are slow-growing.

PODOCARPUS acutifolius Kirk
> 1873 Acute-leaved Totara. Erect tree. Lvs thin and leathery, brownish, esp. in winter, very sharply long-pointed.   9m,Z8   N.Z.

- - 'Golden Dwarf' Hort. Anglia
> 1985 A listed name.

PODOCARPUS alpinus R. Brown ex Mirbel
> 1825 This name was never validly published, and so the accepted valid name is *PODOCARPUS lawrencei*.   3m   Australia

PODOCARPUS andinus   1847 Now known as *PRUMNOPITYS andina*.

PODOCARPUS chilinus Richard
> 1810 Now known as *PODOCARPUS salignus*.

PODOCARPUS cunninghamii Colenso
> 1844 Now generally listed as *PODOCARPUS hallii*.   N.Z.

- - 'Aureus' Hort. Anglia   1974 See *PODOCARPUS totara* 'Aureus'

PODOCARPUS DACRYDIOIDES

PODOCARPUS dacrydioides Richard
1862 Now known as *DACRYCARPUS dacrydioides*.

PODOCARPUS distichus Buchholz and Gray
1951 Now known as *PRUMNOPITYS ferruginioides*.

PODOCARPUS ferrugineus Don ex Lambert
1832 Now known as *PRUMNOPITYS ferruginea*.

PODOCARPUS ferruginioides Compton
1922 Now known as *PRUMNOPITYS ferruginioides*.

PODOCARPUS hallii Kirk 1889 A species similar to *PODOCARPUS totara* but it is smaller and has thin, papery bark. Rarely seen in cultivation.   8-20m   N.Z.

- - **'Roro'** G. Hutchins 1993 Collected by Graham Hutchins of County Park Nurs, Hornchurch, Essex, from an unrecorded area of N.Z. It is a male clone with sharply pointed green leaves, at first creamy with a pink tinge.

PODOCARPUS ladei Bailey
1905 Now known as *PRUMNOPITYS ladei*.

PODOCARPUS lawrencei Hooker f. ex Hooker
1845 A variable sprawling shrub with round-ended, blue-green lvs. Formerly known as *PODOCARPUS alpinus*. (Not = *PODOCARPUS acutifolius*).   Australia

- - **'Alpine Lass'** Hutchins 1991 A slow-growing selection with small green leaves 6-8 mm long x 2 mm wide. A female clone. Formerly cultivated in U.K., as *PODOCARPUS alpinus*.   U.K.

- - **'Blue Gem'** Van Klaveren
1983 In "Dendroflora **20**". A spreading plant with cream young foliage tinged purple; turning bluish-green. A female clone.   Tasmania

- - **'Purple King'** Hort. N.Z.
1990 A listed name for a vigorous, rather open clone; foliage shiny purple in winter.

PODOCARPUS lawrencei x **PODOCARPUS acutifolius**

- - **'Autumn Shades'** Hutchins
1993 A strong-growing, wide-spreading plant with green foliage bronze in winter.   U.K.

PODOCARPUS lawrencei x **PODOCARPUS nivalis**. Hybrids raised by G. Hutchins.

- - **'Blaze'** Hutchins 1993 A neat, slow-growing hybrid (1986) with changing coloured foliage in both spring and autumn.   U.K.

- - **'Country Park Fire'** Hutchins
1993 A low spreading shrub with new spring foliage cream soon turning to salmon pink and later green, bronze in winter, and bright-red berries in autumn and winter.   U.K.

- - **'Spring Sunshine'** Hutchins
1993 A selection similar to 'Country Park Fire', but new spring foliage turns from cream to yellow.   U.K.

- - **'Young Rusty'** Hutchins
1993 A very free-fruiting clone with rust-coloured foliage.   U.K.

PODOCARPUS macrophyllus (Thunb.) Don in Lambert
1824 Kusamaki. A tree with spectacular, large leaves.   8-25m,Z7   Japan, China

- -**'Angustifolius'** Dallimore & Jackson
1923 A form with leaves abnormally narrow.   B,K,R   Hort. Japan

- - var. *appressus* (Maxim.) Matsumara			
	1905 A minor variant, NIC.	B,H	Japan
- - 'Argenteus' Gordon	1862 This, 'Argenteovariegata' Kent and 'Albo-variegatus' Hort.ex Dallimore and Jackson were whitish-variegated forms, possibly identical.	B,K	Hort. Japan
- - 'Aureus' Gordon	1862 This and 'Luteo-variegatus' Hort. ex Dallimore and Jackson were yellow-variegated forms, possibly identical.	B,K,R	Hort. Japan
- - var. *chingii* Gray	1958 Now listed as *PODOCARPUS chingianus*..	B,K	China
- - 'Hillier's Compact' Den Ouden/Boom			
	1965 Named for a plant in Sir Harold Hillier's garden.	B	U.K.
- - var. *maki* Siebold ex Endlicher			
	1847 (Nageia). Now known as *PODOCARPUS chinensis*. The Shrubby Podocarp.	B,K,H	China, etc.
- - var. *nakaii* (Hayata) Li and Keng.			
	1954 Now treated as a distinct species. (See Silba, 1984).	K	Formosa
- - 'Variegatus' Dallimore & Jackson			
	1923 Several variegated forms are in cultivation.		Hort. Japan
***PODOCARPUS nagi* (Thunberg) Makino. *(PODOCARPUS nageia)*..**			
	The spelling in the next item is preferred.		
***PODOCARPUS nakaii* Hayata**			
	1916 Nageia.		N. Taiwan
***PODOCARPUS nivalis* Hooker f.**			
	1843 A spreading shrub near to *PODOCARPUS lawrencei*.	Z7	
- - 'Aureus' Hort. Anglia	1971 An illegit. name. See next item.		
- - 'Bronze' Welch	1966 Named for the metallic colouring of the foliage.	W2	Hort. N.Z.
- - 'Clarence' Hutchins	1993 A semi-erect clone collected by G. Hutchins of County Park Nurs, Hornchurch, Essex on the upper reaches of the Clarence River (1981).		U.K.
- - var. *erectus* Cockayne	1916 A variant with an erect habit. Intermediate forms occur.	K	
- - 'Green Queen' Hutchins			
	1993 A strong-growing female clone with bright green leaves. Collected from near Lake Tennyson (1977).		U.K.
- - 'Jack's Pass' Welch	1979 An erect-growing form collected near Jack's Pass in 1977 and put into circulation by Campana Nurs, Christchurch. Probably a hybrid *PODOCARPUS nivalis* x *PODOCARPUS hallii*.	W2	U.K.
- - 'Little Lady' Hutchins	1991 A female plant that fruits freely even when young, collected on Mt. Princess by Graham Hutchins of County Park Nurs, Hornchurch, Essex, U.K.		U.K.
- - 'Livingstone' Hutchins	1993 A bright green bushy female clone. O. Seed collected in the Livingstone range of Mountains (1985).		U.K.
- - 'Lodestone' Hutchins	1993 A yellow-green male plant collected from near Mt. Arthur (1990).		U.K.
- - 'Moffatt' Hutchins	1993 A compact, bushy, female clone: dark-green slightly bronzed in winter.		U.K.
- - 'Otari' Harrison	1975 Raised from a plant at the Otari Native Plant Museum at Wellington. It is said to be a hybrid with *PODOCARPUS cunninghamia*. Many of the species will hybridise freely.		N.Z.

- - 'Park Cover' Hutchins   1993   A strong-growing, prostrate form. **O**. Seed collected on Mt. Southey (1981).   U.K.

- - **'Princess'** Hutchins   1993   A strong-growing female clone. **O**. Seed collected on Mt. Princess (1981). Foliage green, with bronze growing tips.   U.K.

- - 'Prostrate' Hort. N.Z.   An unacceptable name for a wide-growing plant. **O**. Raised from seed collected at Mount Southey (1981).

- - 'Ruapehu' Hutchins   1993   A clone with brown foliage. **O**. Seed collected on Mt. Ruapehu (1990).   U.K.

PODOCARPUS nubigenus Lindley ex Paxton
   1851   Chilean Podocarpus. Similar to but less hardy than *PODOCARPUS totara*.   S. America

PODOCARPUS salignus D. Don ex Lambert
   1824   The Willow-leaf Podocarp.   20m,Z7   Chile

PODOCARPUS standleyi (Buchholz and Gray)
   1848   Now known as *PRUMNOPITYS standleyi*.

PODOCARPUS taxifolia Kunth
   1817   Now known as *PRUMNOPITYS montana*.

PODOCARPUS totara D. Don ex Lambert
   1832   Totara.   30m,Z8   N.Z.

- - **'Aureus'** Harrison   1975   As 'Aurea', but it has been known for 20 years, so the form 'Aureus' is presumably valid.   G,R,W2   N.Z.

- - var. *hallii* (Kirk) Pilger   1889   Now known as *PODOCARPUS cunninghamii*.

- - **'Pendula'** Hort. N.Z.   A pendulous form that originated with a tree at Sundrum, near Geraldine in South Island.

A large number of other species are not hardy in U.K., but several are used for ornamental planting in warmer zones. No cultivars have so far been recorded.

PRUMNOPITYS Philippi (1860) Plum Yew.

Podocarpaceae

A genus closely related to *Podocarpus* (and still included therein by some authorities), differing mainly in the fruiting parts. The plum-like fruit is quite a tasty delicacy.

PRUMNOPITYS andina (Poeppell ex Endlicher) De Laubenfels
   1978   The Plum Yew. Formerly known as *PODOCARPUS andina*.   Z7   S. America

- - **'Golden Dwarf'** Hort. Anglia
   1990   A listed name. No other information.

PRUMNOPITYS elegans Philippi
   1860   Now known as *PODOCARPUS andinus.*.

The following species also are recognised, but none is hardy in cool, temperate climates.

PRUMNOPITYS amara (Blume) De Laubenfels
   1978   Formerly listed under *PODOCARPUS*.   Australasia

PRUMNOPITYS exigua De Laubenfels in Silba
             1984 A new species near to *PRUMNOPITYS montana.*   N. Bolivia

PRUMNOPITYS ferruginea (D Don) De Laubenfels
             1978 Formerly known as *PODOCARPUS ferruginea.*   25m,Z5   N.Z.

PRUMNOPITYS ferruginioides (Compt.) De Laubenfels
             1978 Formerly known as *PODOCARPUS ferruginioides* and as
                     PODOCARPUS distichous.   New Caledonia

PRUMNOPITYS harmsiana (Pilger) De Laubenfels
             1978 Formerly known as *PODOCARPUS harmsiana* and as *P.*
                     utilion.   S. America

PRUMNOPITYS ladei (Bailey) De Laubenfels
             1978 Formerly known as *PODOCARPUS ladei.*   Australia

PRUMNOPITYS montana (H. B. and W.) De Laubenfels.
             1978 Formerly known as *TAXUS montana* H. B. and W.(1805) and
                     as *PODOCARPUS taxifolia* Kunth.   S. America

PRUMNOPITYS spicata (Mirbel) Masters
             1825 Matai. A rare species, near *P andina* but less hardy.   25m,Z9   N.Z.

PRUMNOPITYS standleyi (Buchholz and Gray) De Laubenfels
             1978 Formerly known as *PODOCARPUS standleyi.*   Costa Rica

PRUMNOPITYS taxifolia (Sol. ex D Don) De Laubenfels
             1978 Formerly known as *PODOCARPUS spicata.*   N.Z.

PSEUDOLARIX Gordon (1858)

P i n a c e a e

A monotypic genus having deciduous foliage as *LARIX*, but the cones disintegrate when ripe.

PSEUDOLARIX amabilis (Nelson) Rehder
             1919 The Golden Larch.   20m,Z4   China

- - 'Annesleyana' Hornibrook
             1923 Named for a plant at Castlewellan, Co. Down. NIC.   B,H,K   Ireland

- - **'Dawsonii'** Hornibrook   1923 Named for the raiser of a seedling. NIC.   B,H,K   U.S.A.

- - *nana* Beissner   1891 A botanical designation for all dwarf forms. Any such turning
                     up, should receive new cultivar names.   B,H,K

PSEUDOLARIX kaempferi (Lindley) Gordon
             1858 Now known as *PSEUDOLARIX amabilis.*.

PSEUDOTAXUS Cheng (1947)

A rare, monotypic Genus allied to *TAXUS*.

PSEUDOTAXUS chienii (Cheng) Cheng		
1947 White-berry Yew.	4m,Z7	China

PSEUDOTSUGA Carrière (1867). Douglas fir.

Pinaceae

The Douglas firs are a Genus of forest trees with similarities to *ABIES, PICEA* and *TSUGA*, but with distinctive, long, narrow buds. There still seems to be uncertainty about the best classification. The nomenclature here follows Rushforth, 1987.

PSEUDOTSUGA brevifolia Cheng & Fu		
1978 Short-leaf Douglas Fir. A new species probably not in western cultivation.	Z9	China
PSEUDOTSUGA douglasii Now known as *PSEUDOTSUGA menziesii*.		
PSEUDOTSUGA flahaultii Flous		
1962 A species doubtfully distinct from *PSEUDOTSUGA menziesii* var. *glauca*. Rare in cultivation.		Mexico
PSEUDOTSUGA forrestii Craib		
1919 Forrest Douglas Fir.	16m,Z8	Yun
PSEUDOTSUGA gaussenii Flous		
1936 Gaussen Douglas Fir. Similar to *PSEUDOTSUGA flahaultii*.		Mexico
PSEUDOTSUGA glauca Doubtfully distinct from *PSEUDOTSUGA menziesii* var. *glauca*.		
PSEUDOTSUGA guinieri Flous		
1936 Similar to *PSEUDOTSUGA flahaultii*.		Mexico
PSEUDOTSUGA japonica (Shirawasa) Beissner		
1896 Japanese Douglas Fir.	30m,Z6	Japan
PSEUDOTSUGA macrocarpa (Vasey) Mayr		
1840 Big-cone Douglas Fir.	15,25m,Z7	S California
PSEUDOTSUGA macrolepis Flous		
1936 Now merged in *PSEUDOTSUGA menziesii* by some authorities, (See Rushforth, 1987).		Mexico
PSEUDOTSUGA menziesii (Mirbel) Franco		
1950 Douglas Fir. At one time included in *ABIES* and long known as *PSEUDOTSUGA taxifolia* and also as *PSEUDOTSUGA douglasii*.	60m,Z5	N America
- - 'Albospica' Fitschen 1930 Young lvs white. Raised by Van Geert of Antwerp. NIC.	B,K,R	Belgium
- - 'Anguina' Dallimore & Jackson		
1923 Named for a curious tree at Endsleigh, Devon. NIC.	B,K,R	U.K.
- - 'Appressa' Fitschen 1930 Named for a peculiar tree found by Von Schwerin in 1901. NIC.	B,K	Germany

- - 'Argentea' Beissner   1891 Named for a tree with white foliage, raised by Kosters Nurs, at Boskoop. NIC.   B,K   Holland

- - 'Argentea Compacta' Beissner
     1891 Named for a dwarf plant raised by Hans of Hernhut. NIC.   B,K   Germany

- - 'Argentea Pendula' Beissner
     1893 Named for a pendulous tree raised by Weisse in Kamenz. NIC.   B,K   Germany

- - 'Astley' Hornibrook   1929 Named for a plant raised from a witch's broom found in a garden at Ockley, Surrey.   B,H,W2   U.K.

- - **'Astro Blue'** Vermeulen   1978 In "Nurs. Cat". Dense, broadly conical; foliage blue. **I.** Vermeulen Nurs, Neshanic Station, N.J.   U.S.A.

- - 'Aurea' Sénéclauze   1868 Named for a seedling on the Sénéclauze Nurs, Bourg Argental, Loires.   B,K   France

- - 'Aureovariegata' Hort. Amer.
     1990 An illegit. listed name. No other information.

- - **'Big Flats'** Hort. Amer.   1957 Vigorous tree with pendent branches and long, glaucous leaves. **O.** Selected by Dick Fennechie at N.Y. State Nurs, at Big Flats, near Elmira, in 1955.   U.S.A.

- - **'Blue Wonder'** Lombarts
     1957 Conical tree with very blue foliage, raised on the Lombarts Nurs, Zundert, in 1910.   B,G,K,R   Holland

- - 'Bonitzi' Hort. Germany   1983 In "Nurs. Cat". Horstmann Nurs, Schneverdingen.

- - f. *brevibracteata* (Antoine) Ascherson and Graebner
     1840 Low-growing form with stout branches and large leaves.   B,G,K   Sporadic

- - **'Brevifolia'** (Masters) Fitschen
     1930 Dwarf or small tree with short pale green foliage and red buds.   B,H,K,R,W2   U.K.

- - f. *caesia* (Schwerin) Fitschen
     1950 Fraser River Douglas Fir. An intermediate category accepted by some writers to cover trees with glaucous foliage. Between the typical form and var. *glauca*.   B,K,R   Sporadic

- - 'Caesia Erecta' Schwerin   1922 A clone of the last with branches held erect. NIC.   B,K   Germany

- - 'Candida' Dallimore and Jackson
     1948 Name raised for a tree found at Waterford. NIC.   B   Ireland

- - 'Carnefix Weeping' Hort. Amer.
     1990 See 'Idaho Weeper'.

- - 'Cedroides' Schwerin   1917 Name given to a certain stunted tree found by Count von Schwerin. NIC.   B   Germany

- - 'Cheesemanii' Hornibrook
     1939 Name given to a dwarf plant by the foreman on the Lock King Nurs, Weybridge, Surrey. **O.** As 'Fletcheri' and 'Nana'. NIC.   B,H,R   U.K.

- - 'Compacta' Beissner   1891 Now probably in use for several compact clones.   B,H,W2   Germany

- - **'Compacta Glauca'** (1) Ansorge ex Beissner
     1902 Descriptive name for a seedling raised on the Ansorge Nurs, Hamburg-Flottbeck. Probably NIC.   B,H,K   Germany

- - 'Compacta Glauca' (2) Hort. Amer.
     1968 Now known as 'Astro Blue'.

- - 'Compacta Holmstrupii' Hort. Germany
  A mistake for 'Holmstrupii'.

- - **'Compacta Viridis'** Beissner
  1902 Compact, conical; light green foliage, red buds. Raised by
  Hellemänn at Moorende, nr Bremen. NIC.   B,H   Germany

- - 'Crispa' Schwerin   1930 Name raised for a tree with twisted leaves. NIC.   B,K   Germany

- - 'DeGroot's Compact' Hort. Amer.
  1985 A listed name. No further information.

- - 'Delbert's Weeping' Hort. Amer.
  1985 A listed name. No further information.

- - **'Densa'** Slavin
  1932 Dense, flat-topped shrub, leaves light-green to yellow-green.
  Originated from an old plant in Highland Park, Rochester,
  N.Y.   B,H,K,R,W2   U.S.A.

- - 'Denudata' Carrière   1967 Named for a 'Snake-branch' tree. NIC.   B,K   Germany

- - **'Dumosa'** Carrière   1867 Spreading bush with monstrous branches and foliage. Raised
  on André Leroy Nurs, Angers.   B,H,K   France

- - 'Ed's Dwarf' Hort. Amer.   1975 A listed name. Raraflora Nurs, Feasterville, PA.

- - 'Elegans' Fitschen in Beissner
  1930 An ascending form with pendulous, blue-green foliage.   B,G,K   Germany

- - 'Elongata' Schwerin   1927 Named for a spreading tree in Count von Schwerin's garden.
  NIC.   B,K   Germany

- - 'Emerald Falls' Hort. Amer.
  1975 A listed name. Raraflora Nurs, Feasterville, PA.

- - 'Faberi' Schwerin   1917 Leaves turning golden-yellow. O. H H Faber Nurs, Dundee,
  Ill.   B,K   U.S.A.

- - 'Fastigiata' Knight ex Gordon
  1858 Probably other clones are now in cultivation.   B,G,K   U.K.

- - **'Fletcheri'** Hort.   1923 Popular broad, spreading dwarf form with mid green foliage,
  older leaves dark green. Raised on the Lock King Nurs,
  Weybridge.   B,G,H,K,R,W2   U.K.

- - **'Fretsii'** Beissner   1905 Dense shrub or small tree with thick, short shoots; dark grey-
  green leaves. Raised by C. Frets and Son, Boskoop.   B,G,H,K,R,W2   Holland

- - **'Garibaldi'** Hort. Germany
  1983 Dwarf globose plant with grey-green leaves. O. and I.
  Horstmann Nurs, Schneverdingen.

- - var. *glauca* (Beissner) Franco
  1950 Rocky Mountains Douglas Fir. A regional variant making a
  smaller tree; foliage glaucous above. Several cultivars would
  belong here.   B,K,R   U.S.A.

- - 'Glauca Fastigiata' Hort. Amer.
  1913 Raised in the Parks Dept., Rochester, N.Y. NIC.

- - 'Glauca Lombarts' Den Ouden
  1940 Now renamed 'Blue Wonder'.   B   Holland

- - 'Glauca Pendula' P. Smith ex Beissner
  1891 Raised from seed by Simon-Louis Bros, Metz.   B,K   France

- - 'Glauca Pyramidalis' Hort. Amer.
  A listed name.

- - 'Globosa' Beissner   1905 Named for a seedling (1910) that was never propagated. NIC.   B,H,K,W2   Germany

- - 'Gotelli's Pendula' Hort. Amer.   An illegit. name for a grey-green prostrate plant of
unrecorded origin. L. J.W. Spingarn, Long Island (1980).

- - **'Graceful Grace'** Reg'd. Arn. Arb.
     1968 Narrow, compact, pendulous; long, glaucous needles.   U.S.A.

- - **'Hess Select Blue'** Cope   1986 In "Native . . . Conifers . . . ". Conical tree with blue foliage.
(Probably ='Glauca Pyramidalis'). (Names also used 'Hess
Select' and 'Hess Blue' and 'Select Blue').   U.S.A.

- - 'Hillside Gold' Hort. Amer.   See 'Hillside Yellow'.

- - **'Hillside Pride'** Welch   1979 A diminutive conical plant with dense, dark green foliage. **O.**
Found by Layne Zeigenfuss as a seedling. (1951)   G,R,W2   U.S.A.

- - **'Hillside Yellow'** Hort. Amer.
     1970 **L.** Hillside Gardens, Lehighton, PA.   U.S.A.

- - 'Hofman' Hort. Germany
     1983 A listed name. No further information.

- - **'Holmstrup'** H.J. Grootendorst
     1965 In "Dendroflora 2". Dense, conical habit, ascending brs. **O.**
Asger. M. Jensen Nurs, Holmstrup.   K,W2   Denmark

- - 'Hoyt Dwarf' Hort. Amer.
     1985 A listed name. No further information.

- - **'Idaho Gem'** Iseli   1986 In "Nurs Cat". Diminutive form with short leaves and
noticeable red buds, from a witch's broom found by W.
Carnefix, Idaho.   U.S.A.

- - **'Idaho Weeper'** R.L. Fincham
     1989 In Coenosium Gars. "Nurs. Cat". With irregular, pendulous
habit. **O.** Found by Warren Carnefix in Idaho.   U.S.A.

- - 'Iseli Weeping' Hort. Amer.
     1988 Now known as 'Idaho Weeper'.

- - **'Julie'** G. Haddow   Dwarf upright plant leader growing to one side, with short
glaucous green leaves, new foliage in rosettes. From a
mutation. **O.** and **I.** Kenwith Nurs, Bideford, Devon.   U.K.

- - 'Julie's Jewel' Hort. Amer.
     1985 A listed name. No further information.

- - **'Knaphill'** H. Corder   1975 In Weasdale "Nurs. Cat". Slow-growing bush with pale blue
foliage. **O.** Seedling on the Knaphill Nurs, Woking, Surrey.   U.K.

- - 'Knap Hill Seedling' Hort. Anglia
     1989 See previous entry.

- - 'Kooteney-Lake' Hort. Germany
     1983 A listed name.

- - f. *laeta* Schwerin   1909 Branches erect; foliage green. NIC.   B,K   Germany

- - 'Leptophylla' Hornibrook
     1923 Named for a small bush in the garden at Blandsfort,
Abbeyleix. NIC.   B,H,K   Ireland

- - **'Les Barres'** (Esch.) Hort. Holland
     1991 Dwarf plant with dark-green wide radial leaves. **L.** Libo
Nurs, Baexam.

- - 'Little Jamie' Hort. Amer.
     1992 A listed name. No information.

- - **'Little Jon'** Regd. Arn. Arb.

1969   A dwarf form discovered by Albert Ziegler amongst normal trees near Wrightsville, PA, in 1967. ('Little John' is incorrect).   R.W2   U.S.A.

- - **'Lohbrunner'** Hort. Canada

1981   Dwarf globose plant eventually wider than high. New leaves pale green and incurved, later much darker. L. G. Bentham, Victoria, BC.

- - 'Lombarts' Hort. Holl.   1936   See 'Blue Wonder'.   B

- - **'Lombartsii Pendula'** Lombarts

1936   In "Nurs. Cat". Lombarts Nurs. Zundert. **O.** Raised from seed by Pierre Lombarts (1910).   B   Holland

- - 'Lythgoe' Hort. Amer.   1975   A listed name. Raraflora Nurs, Feasterville, PA.

- - **'Marshall'** Reg'd. Arn. Arb.

1963   Dense, conical tree. **O.** Marshall Nurs, Arlington, Nebraska.   K   U.S.A.

- - **'McKenzie'** Hort. Germany

1983   Slow-growing pyramid with yellow-green foliage. **O.** and **I.** Horstmann Nurs, Schneverdingen.

- - 'McKenzie Pass' Hort. Germany

1983   In "Nurs. Cat". Horstmann Nurs, Schneverdingen.

- - 'Mihalic's Dwarf' Hort. Amer.

1970   L. J.W. Spingarn, then of Baldwin, N.Y. Growth dwarf, irregular. **O.** Anthony J. Mihalic Nurs, Cherdon, Ohio.

- - **'Moerheimii'** (Ruys) Fitschen

1930   Dense, upright. **O.** B Ruys, Royal Nurs, Moerheim, Dedemsvart,   B,K,R   Holland

- - 'Mt. Vernon Dwarf' Hort. Amer.

1975   A listed name. Raraflora Nurs, Feasterville, PA.

- - **'Mucronata Compacta'** Hort. Amer.

1967   Possibly an illegit. name. **O.** Shelton College, now Ringwood State Park, N.Y.

- - 'Mucronata Nana Compacta' Hort. Amer.

1985   A listed name. Probably same as last entry.

- - 'Nana' Hornibrook   1923   Similar in habit to 'Fletcheri' but foliage green, the names having been switched in the trade.   B,H,K,R

- - 'Nana Compacta' Hort. Amer.   Similar to or the same as previous item.

- - 'Nettleton' Hort. Amer.   Now known as 'Idaho Gem'.

- - 'Nidiformis' Hahn   1940   Low, spreading bush. **O.** Eisenburg Nurs, Eisenburg.   B,K   Czechosl.

- - **'Oudemansii'** Hornibrook

1939   Slow-growing. **O.** Found on the Schovenhorst Estate, Putten.   B,G,H,K,W2   Holland

- - **'Pamonia'** Hort. Holland

1991   Dwarf plant with grey-blue foliage. L. Libo Nurs, Baexam.

- - 'Parkland Dwarf' Hort. Amer.

1986   A listed name for a low bush. More vigorous than 'Fletcheri'.

- - *pendula* Neumänn   1853   Weeping forms were early noted, and turn up from time to time, so the name is merely descriptive.   B   Sporadic

- - 'Pendula Glauca' Hort. Amer.

1986   Probably an illegit. name for a new pendulous selection.

- - **'Pila loda'** Hort. Germany
  1991 Dwarf plant, globose, very slow-growing, leaves pale blue. **I.** Horstmann Nurs, Schneverdingen.

- - 'Praq' Hort. Germany   1991 A listed name.

- - 'Prostrata' Hort. Amer.   1986 An illegit. but presumably descriptive name.

- - **'Pumila'** Paul   1899 In "Nurs. Cat". A shrubby form. **O.** Anthony Waterer, Knaphill Nurs, Surrey. Possibly NIC.   B,K,W2   U.K.

- - **'Pygmaea'** Hornibrook   1923 An extremely slow-growing variety found in the Arnold Arboretum.   B,H,K   U.S.A.

- - 'Pyramidalis' Hort. Germany
  1913 **O.** H.A. Hesse Nurs, Weener-on-Ems. NIC.   B   Germany

- - **'Pyramidata'** Bailey   1933 Conical, slow-growing. NIC.   B,K   U.S.A.

- - **'Radium'** Hort. Germany
  1983 Dwarf plant, conical and open. Leaves light blue, later grey-green. **O.** and **I.** Horstmann Nurs, Schneverdingen.

- - f. *revoluta* Sudworth   1897 Leaves curled. NIC.   B   Sporadic

- - 'Rissen' Hort. Holland   1992 A listed name.

- - **'Skyline'** Hort. Amer.   1992 Strong growing with bizarre snake-like branches. Light blue needles. **O.** Otto Solburger as a mutation on a normal tree. **I.** Buccholz & Buccholz Nurs, Gaston, Oregon. ('Skylands' is incorrect).

- - 'Slavinii' Slavin   1937 Named for a concal tree found at Cobb's Hill Reservoir, Rochester, N.Y. NIC.   B,K,W2   U.S.A.

- - 'Spaan's Weeper' Hort. Amer.
  1980 A listed name. J.W. Spingarn, Long Is., N.Y.

- - 'Stairii' Gordon   1871 New spring foliage cream changing to light green in autumn. Named for a tree found at Castle Kennedy, the seat of the Earl of Stair. L. Kenwith Nurs, Bideford, Devon. (1992).   B,K,R   Scotland

- - 'Standishiana' Gordon   1862 Named for a tree found on the Standish Nurs, Bagshot. NIC.   B   U.K.

- - 'Stricta' Carrière   1867 Named for a tree raised on the Sénéclauze Nurs, Bourg Argental, Loires.   B,K   France.

- - f. *suberosa* Lemmon   1893 A local variant, with corky bark.   B   N.Arizona,U.S.A

- - **'Suringarii'** Schwerin   1927 Named for a peculiar tree found at Renkum.   B,K   Holland

- - 'Taranto' Krüssmann   1972 Named for a tall, graceful tree at the Villa Taranto, Pallanza. NIC.   K   Italy

- - **'Tempelhof Compact'** Den Ouden/Boom
  1965 A very compact, bushy form. Found by G. van Asselt, of Putten. **I.** L Konijn and Son, Reeuwijk.   B,G,K,R,W2   Holland

- - **'Valdenzia'** Hort Holland
  1991 Dwarf plant, new foliage rosette-like and light green, older foliage dark-green. L. Libo Nurs, Baexam.

- - 'Variegata' McDonald   1871 Named for a tree with dull-yellow leaves. NIC.   B,G,.K   U.K.

- - 'Vertrees' Hort. Amer.   1986 A witch's broom. L. J.W. Spingarn, L.I., N.Y.

- - 'Viminalis' Schwerin   1920 Named for a snake-branched, pendulous tree found in the forest at Charlottelund near Copenhagen. NIC.   B,K   Denmark

- - f. *viridis* Schneider in Silva Tarouca.
  1913 A form with green foliage.   Sporadic

- - 'White Mountain Weeping' Hort Amer.
  1982 Blue pendulous form. L. Coenosium Nurs, Lehighton, PA.

- - 'Woking' Hort. Anglia   1985 A listed name. Dwarf propagated from a witch's broom - short
                                    yellow-green leaves. I. Wansdyke Nurs, Devizes.

- - 'Young's Broom' Hort. Amer.
  1980 A listed name without description. L. M. Kristick, Wellsville,
        PA.

- - 'Yzeuriana' Hickel   1920 Conical tree, foliage peculiar. NIC.   B   Germany

- - **'Zioga's Dwarf'** G. Williams
  1990 Dwarf upright plant, short mid-green curved leaves. L. Kate
        Brook Nurs, Wolcott, Vermont.   U.S.A.

PSEUDOTSUGA rehderi Flous
  1936 Species close to *PSEUDOTSUGA menziesii*. (See Rushforth,
        1987).   50m,Z5   Mexico

PSEUDOTSUGA sinensis Dode
  1912 Chinese Douglas Fir.   30-50m,Z5 China

PSEUDOTSUGA taxifolia   Now known as *PSEUDOTSUGA menziesii*.

PSEUDOTSUGA wilsoniana Hayata
  Taiwan Douglas Fir.   30-50m,Z8 Taiwan

PSEUDOTSUGA xichangensis Kuan & Zhou
  A recently described species allied to *PSEUDOTSUGA*
  wilsoniana.   Sichuan

RETINOSPORA Siebold and Zuccarini.(1842).

An abandoned Genus once held to contain a number of plants in cultivation whose true identity was not at the time known. They have now found homes in one or other species of *Chamaecyparis* or *Thuja* (now *Platycladus) orientalis*. Regrettably the name survives in some quarters. The following names were not consistently used and anomalies can be found in the older conifer books. None should nowadays be used.

RETINOSPORA dubia Carrière
  1867 Now known as *THUJA occidentalis* 'Ericoides'.
RETINOSPORA Ellwangeriana   Now known as *THUJA occidentalis* 'Ellwangeriana'.(='Tom
                                Thumb')

RETINOSPORA ericoides (1) Zuccarini
  Now known as *CHAMAECYPARIS thyoides* 'Ericoides.

RETINOSPORA ericoides (2) Hort.
  Now known as *THUJA occidentalis* 'Ericoides'.

RETINOSPORA ericoides (3) Barry
  1875 In Gordon, "Pinetum", ed. 2. (In synonymy -
        "Ellwangeriana".)

RETINOSPORA ericoides leptoclada (4) Masters
>1896 In "Journ. Linn. Soc." Now known as *CHAMAECYPARIS thyoides* 'Andelyensis'.

RETINOSPORA filicoides Veitch   Now known as *CHAMAECYPARIS obtusa* 'Filicoides.

RETINOSPORA filifera Standish   Now known as *CHAMAECYPARIS pisifera* 'Filifera'.

RETINOSPORA juniperoides (1) Carrière
>1867 Now known as *THUJA orientalis* 'Decussata'.

RETINOSPORA juniperoides (2)   Now known as *THUJA occidentalis* 'Ericoides'

RETINOSPORA leptoclada (1)
>1867 Now known as *CHAMAECYPARIS thyoides* 'Ericoides'

RETINOSPORA leptoclada (2) Siebold
>1861 Now known as *CHAMAECYPARIS pisifera* 'Squarrosa Intermedia'

RETINOSPORA lycopodioides Standish
>1861 Now known as *CHAMAECYPARIS obtusa* 'Lycopodioides'.

RETINOSPORA obtusa Sieb. and Zucc.
>Including its cultivars , Now known as *CHAMAECYPARIS obtusa.*

RETINOSPORA pisifera Sieb. and Zucc.
>Including its cultivars , now known as *CHAMAECYPARIS pisifera*

RETINOSPORA sanderi   Now know as *THUJA (PLATYCLADUS) orientalis* 'Sanderi',

RETINOSPORA squarrosa Sieb. and Zucc.
>Now known as *CHAMAECYPARIS pisifera* 'Squarrosa'.

RETINOSPORA squarrosa leptoclada (Sieb) Gordon
>1858 Now knowns as *CHAMAECYPARIS pisifera* 'Squarrosa Intermedia'.

SAXEGOTHAEA Lindley (1851)

P o d o c a r p a c e a e

This is a monotypic genus from Chile with foliage similar in general appearance to *Taxus* (but less regularly arranged), and differing from that Genus in the cones.

SAXEGOTHAEA conspicua Lindley
>1951 Prince Albert's Yew.   17m   Chile

SCIADOPITYS Siebold and Zuccarini (1842)

Pinaceae

A monotypic genus with cones similar to *Sequoia* but with distinctive foliage consisting of terminal whorls of long, leaf-like cladodes suggestive of the ribs of an umbrella, and tiny true leaves along the shoot.

SCIADOPITYS verticillata (Thunberg) Siebold and Zuccarini

	1842 Japanese Umbrella Pine.		40m,Z6	Japan
- - 'Anne Haddow' Hort. Anglia	A listed name for a form golden in Spring and Summer. The original plant is in the Trompenburg Arboretum, Rotterdam.			
- - 'Aurea' Beck	1889 Leaves yellow.		B,G,K	Japan
- - 'Columnaris' Hort.	An illegit. listed name.			
- - 'Compacta' Hort. Germany	An illegit. name for a squat bush with dark green leaves.			
- - 'Cream Star' Hort. Germany	L. K. Wittboldt-Muller.			
- - 'Cross Compact' Hort. U.S.A.	A listed name. O. Cross Nurs?			
- - **'Firework'** Hort. Germany	1992 Small plant with green leaves with outer ends variegated with pinky-yellow. O. and I. K. Wittboldt-Muller, Verden-Eitze. ('Feuerwerk').			
- - **'Gold Star'** Hort. Germany	1992 Slow-growing plant with bright golden foliage. O. and I. K. Wittboldt-Muller, Verden-Eitze.			
- - 'Golden Rush'	O. K. Wittboldt-Muller. Foliage light-gold.			
- - 'Goldie' Hort. N.Z.	1984 L. Duncan and Davies, New Plymouth			
- - 'Green Cushion' Hort. Canada	A listed name. O. Gordon Bentham, Floravista Gardens.			Canada
- - 'Green Parasol' Hort. Canada	A listed name. O. Gordon Bentham, Floravista Gardens.			Canada
- - **'Green Star'** Wittboldt-Muller	1987 Slow-growing; leaves slightly recurved.		G	Germany
- - 'Grüne Kugel'	O. K. Wittboldt-Muller. Dwarf, very multi-branched little plant.			
- - 'Helene' Hort. U.S.A.	See 'Helene Bergman'.			
- - 'Helene Bergman' Hort. U.S.A.	1981 A listed name for a variegated form, not shewing on young plants. O. Raraflora, Feasterville, PA. (1970).			
- - **'Jeddeloh Compact'** Jeddeloh	1990 Upright slow-growing compact plant. O. and I. J.zu Jeddeloh, Oldenburg.			
- - **'Joe Kozey'** S. Waxman	1986 In "Int. Pl. Prop. Soc. Bull". Tall, narrow tree. O. Raised from seed at University of Connecticut, Storrs, CT. ('Joe Cozey').			U.S.A.
- - **'Knirps'** Krüssmann	1985 A globose dwarf maybe conical later, with very dense growth, yellow-gold foliage. O. Raised from seed on Hachmann Nurs, Barmstedt. 1966. I. 1983.		K	Germany
- - **'Longneedle'** Hort. Germany	1992 A plant with longer than normal leaves. O. and I. K. Wittboldt-Muller, Verden Eitze.			
- - **'Mecki'** Hort. Germany	1990 Dwarf plant with short, dark-green leaves. O. Wittboldt-Muller. L. J.zu Jeddeloh Nurs, Oldenburg.			

- - **'Ossorio Gold'** Hort. Amer.
 1990 Slow-growing plant with long golden needles. **O.** Ossorio. **L.**
 Coenosium Gardens, Lehighton, PA.

- - **'Pendula'** Bean 1914 Branches pendulous. B,K U.K.

- - **'Picola'** Hort. Germany 1986 Dwarf, globose to conical, shiny, dark green leaves. **O.** and **I.**
 K. Dierks Nurs, Bad Zwischenahn.

- - **'Pygmy'** Iseli **O.** G. Bentham, Floravista Gardens. Canada

- - 'Pyramidalis Compacta' Hort. Germany
 Listed Jeddeloh Nurs, Oldenburg. K

- - **'Short Needle'** Hort. Germany
 1992 Slow-growing form with short needles. ('Shorty'). **O.** and **I.** K.
 Wittboldt-Muller, Verden-Eitze.

- - **'Stenschnuffe'** Hort. Germany
 1992 A globose plant with all strong growing shoots producing
 three buds coalesced together. **O.** and **I.** K. Wittboldt-Muller,
 Verden-Eitze.

- - **'Strachan'** Hort. Anglia 1992 Dwarf form with short ascending branches and short very
 dark-green leaves. **O.** J. Strachan, Perthshire. **L.** Kenwith
 Nurs, Bideford, Devon. U.K.

- - **'Turned Needle'** Hort. Germany
 1992 A slow-growing plant with curly or recurved needles. **O.** and
 I. K. Wittboldt-Muller, Verden-Eitze.

- - **'Variegata'** Fortune ex Gordon
 1862 Some leaves pale yellow. **I.** von Siebold (1859). B,K Hort. Japan

- - **'Wintergreen'** S. Waxman
 1985 In "Int. Pl. Prop. Soc. Bull". A vigorous tree with foliage dark
 green that does not bronze in winter. **O.** Raised at the
 University of Connecticut Nurs, Storrs, CT. U.S.A.

SEQUOIA Endlicher (1847)

Taxodiaceae

A monotypic genus with a claim to have produced the tallest tree in the world. It is readily distinguishable from the
Wellingtonia (*SEQUOIADENDRON*) by the thick, corky bark.

SEQUOIA gigantea See *SEQUOIADENDRON giganteum*.

SEQUOIA sempervirens (D. Don) Endlicher
 1847 Coastal Redwood. 45m,Z7 Western U.S.A.

- - **'Adpressa'** Carrière 1867 Slow-growing; young tips creamy-white. Probably a
 cultivariant of 'Albo-spica'.L. Rovelli Bros. Nurs, Pallanza,
 (1903). B,G,K,R,W2 Italy

- - 'Albospica' Veitch 1881 Tree with young growth creamy-white. See also 'Adpressa'. U.K.

- - 'Aptos Blue' Hort. N.Z. 1984 May be same as 'Soquel'. **L.** Duncan and Davies, New
 Plymouth.

- - 'Argentea' E.A. Cope   1986   In "Native . . . Conifers . . . ". An illegit. name for clone with patches of white on young foliage.   U.S.A.

- - 'Balaton' Hort. Germany   1983   A listed name. **L.** Horstmann Nurs, Schneverdingen. (1992).

- - **'Cantab'** Hort. Anglia   1977   Tree with leaves short and very wide. **O.** A mutation on a tree in Cambridge University Botanic Garden. See also 'Prostrata'.   R   U.K.

- - 'Compacta' Nelson   1866   Compact branched. NIC.   B

- - 'Filifera Elegans' Rovelli   1904   Growth cordlike. **O.** Raised on Rovelli Bros Nurs, Pallanza.   B,K   Italy

- - 'Filoli' Saratoga   A synmetrical selection with glaucous blue foliage.   U.S.A.

- - **'Glauca'** R. Smith   1867   Leaves conspicuously glaucous. Doubtless other clones now in cultivation.   B,K   U.K.

- - 'Glauca Pendula'   1985   A listed name.

- - **'Goldie'**   L. Duncan and Davies Nurs, New Plymouth.   N.Z.

- - 'Gracilis' Carrière   1867   Branches slender. NIC.   B   France

- - 'Herk' Dr. Martin   1992   L. Horstmann Nurs, Schneverdingen.

- - 'Lawsoniana' R. Smith   1867   A clone no longer identifiable.   B   U.K.

- - **'Los Altos'** L.C. Hatch   1988   In "Conifer Database". A strong-grower. Foliage light green, becoming darker.   U.S.A.

- - **'Majestic Beauty'** Monrovia
   1981   Dense, branching; soft, bluish-green foliage. **O.** Monrovia Nurs, Azusa, CAL.   U.S.A.

- - 'Nana Pendula' Hornibrook
   1923   A prostrate dwarf plant found at Curragh Grange, Co. Kildare. NIC.   B,K,W2   Ireland

- - 'Pendula' Rovelli   1899   A pendulous tree. **O.** Rovelli Nurs, Pallanza. NIC.   B,K,R   Italy

- - **'Prostrata'** R.S. Gilmour
   1949   In "Roy. Hort. Soc. Journ, 74". A prostrate plant with broad leaves. It is in fact a cultivariant of 'Cantab', to which it usually reverts. Easily damaged by frost.   B,G,K,R,W2   U.K.

- - 'Repens' Hort. Amer.   1966   A listed name. Probably same as previous item.

- - **'Santa Cruz'** Monrovia   1981   In "Nurs. Cat". A large conical tree with pendent terminal growths, **O.** Monrovia Nurs, Azusa, CAL.   U.S.A.

- - **'Soquel'** Monrovia   1981   Large conical tree with upswept branches; foliage dark green. **O.** Monrovia Nurs, Azusa, CAL.   U.S.A.

- - 'Taxifolia' Carrière   1867   A clone no longer identifiable.   B   France

- - 'Variegata' Carrière   1890   A strong-growing tree with monstrous foliage; foliage often variegated. NIC.   B,K   France

- - 'Woodside Blue' Hort. Amer.   A listed name. No further information.

SEQUOIADENDRON Buchholz (1939)

Taxodiaceae

A monotypic genus formerly included in *SEQUOIA*, differing therefrom in only bearing scale-like leaves, having naked buds and larger cones. The popular name Wellingtonia is no longer recognised botanically.

SEQUOIADENDRON giganteum (Lindley) Buchholz

	1939	Wellingtonia, Big tree.	50m,Z6	California
- - 'Argenteum' Beissner	1891	('Argentea'). Shoots and leaves silver-variegated.	B,K	Hort. U.S.A.
- - 'Aurea' Nicholson	1886	Now known as 'Aureovariegata' (Aureum').	R	
- - 'Aureocompactum' Carrière	1867	Compact; young leaves golden-yellow. **O.** Guibert, nurseryman at Passy, near Paris. NIC.	B	France
- - **'Aureovariegatum'** May	1856	Some smaller twigs golden-yellow. **O.** Lough Nurs, Cork. NIC.	B,K	Ireland
- - 'Columnaris' Schelle	1909	A form with columnar habit. NIC.	B	Germany
- - 'Compactum' Beissner	1891	A conical form of compact habit. NIC.	B,K	Germany
- - 'Cylindricum' Koch	1873	Named for a tree with peculiar branch system and foliage in a nursery at Ghent. NIC.	B	Belgium
- - 'Elongatum' Hort. Germany.	1964	An illegit. name for a clone insufficiently distinctive to be worth retaining.		
- - 'Flavescens' Beissner	1884	Leaves yellowish. No other information. NIC.	B	Germany?
- - 'Glaucum' Otto	1860	Leaves conspicuously glaucous. NIC.	B,G,K,R	Germany
- - 'Greenpeace' Hort. Holland		A listed name.		
- - 'Hazel Smith' Hort. Amer.	1988	A listed name for a hardy selection with bluish leaves. **L.** Mitsch Nurs, Aurora, OR.		
- - 'Hexenbesen Eschrich' Hort. Germany	1983	An unsatisfactory name that should be replaced.		
- - 'Holmesii' Beissner	1891	Habit compact and columnar. **O.** Holmes Nurs. NIC.	B	U.K.
- - 'Moonie Mini' Hort. Amer.	1992	A witch's broom, main trunk twisted like a pretzel, also the foliage. **L.** Buchholz & Buchholz Nurs, Gaston, PA.		
- - 'Pendulum' Carrière	1871	A columnar tree with strongly pendulous branches. **O.** Lalande Nurs, Nantes (1863).	B,G,K,R	France
- - 'Pygmaeum' Beissner	1891	A dwarf bush with light green foliage.	B,G,K,R,W2	France
- - 'Pyramidale Glaucum' Hesse ex Schelle	1900	A conical form with glaucous foliage. NIC.	B	Germany
- - 'Requiem' Hort. Hungary		A dwarf form. **O.** Elemér Barabits, Sopron Arboretum.		Hungary
- - 'Strictum' Sénéclauze	1868	A columnar tree with very short, crowded branches. **O.** Raised on Sénéclauze Nurs, Bourg Argental, Loires.	B	France
- - 'Variegatum' Carrière	1867	A form with white variegation.	B	France

TAIWANIA Hayata (1906)

Taxodiaceae

A genus usually accepted as consisting of two, very similar species. In the wild it makes a very large tree bearing scale-like leaves, but in cultivation only juvenile foliage similar to *CRYPTOMERIA* is produced.

TAIWANIA cryptomerioides Hayata
           1906 Taiwania, Formosan Cryptomeria.   60m,Z8   Taiwan

- - var. *flousiana* (Gaussen) Silba
           1984 See *TAIWANIA flousiana* . (per Rushforth, 1987).

TAIWANIA flousiana Gaussen
           1939 Chinese Taiwania, Coffin tree.   75m,Z8   China

TAIWANIA yunnanensis Koidzu
           1942 Now known as *TAIWANIA flousiana*.

TAXODIUM Richard (1810) Bald Cypress

Taxodiaceae

The Bald cypresses are now regarded as consisting of three species of deciduous tree, all much alike. It differs from *METASEQUOIA* in bearing buds and leaves alternately along the shoot, and *GLYPTOSTROBUS* in the cones. The nomenclature has been much confused in the past. Taxonomy here follows Rushforth (1987). Several trees with minor variations were given names during the past century, but they were probably never propagated, and have long lost sight of. Any similar variants worth perpetuating that turn up should be given new clonal names.

TAXODIUM ascendens Brongniart
           1827 Pond Cypress. A small tree, seldom forming aerial roots, known as 'knees'.   20m,Z7   U.S.A.

- - 'Elegans' Beissner   1891 Branches drooping, branchlets very thin. NIC.   B   Germany

- - 'Intermedium' Carrière   1859 A strong-growing tree, leaves mainly scale-like. NIC.   B   France

- - **'Nutans'** (Aiton) Rehder   1926 The commonest clone in cultivation in U.K. A slow-growing columnar tree with the young leaves held erect on the branchlets.   B,K,R   U.S.A.

- - **'Prairie Sentinel'** Reg'd. Arn. Arb.
           1971 A vigorous, upright tree. **O.** and **I.** E. Cully, Cully Nurs, Jacksonville, ILL. NIC.   U.S.A.

- - 'Tuberculatum' Carrière   1959 Named for a tree found by Carrière in a park at Peyrouse, NIC.   B   France

- - 'Virgatum' Sénéclauze   1868 A columnar tree raised by Sénéclauze. NIC.   B   France

- - 'Xianyechisha' W.C. Cheng & L.K. Fu
           1978 In "Flora Reipublicae Popularis Sinicae" ("Flora of China") 7. Description in Chinese.

- - 'Yuyechisha' W.C. Cheng & L.K. Fu
           1978 As above.

- - 'Zhuiyechisha' W.C. Cheng & L.K. Fu
           1978 As above.

TAXODIUM distichum (Linnaeus) Richard
1810 Swamp cypress. Grows naturally in swampy areas in which it develops aerial roots, known as 'knees'.   30m,Z5   U.S.A

- - var. *ascendens* Carrière ex Masters
1892 Now recognised as a species, *TAXODIUM ascendens* (per Rushforth, 1987).   U.S.A.

- - 'Attenuatum' Carrière   1859 A selection with peculiar cones. NIC.   B   France

- - **'Aureum'** A.C. Mitchell   1972 In "Conifers in the British Isles".   U.K.

- - 'Compactum' Carrière   1859 Named for a tree with dense foliage found by Carrière on a local farm. NIC.   B   France

- - 'Conicum' Carrière   1859 Named for a now-unidentifiable tree. NIC.   B   France

- - 'Dacrydioides' Sénéclauze
1868 Named for a seedling raised on the Sénéclauze Nurs. NIC.   B   France

- - 'Denudatum' Carrière   1855 Named for a tree raised on the A. Leroy Nurs, Angers. NIC.   B   France

- - 'Fasciatum' Carrière   1867 Named for a stunted, monstrous plant. NIC.   B   France

- - 'Fastigiatum' de Vos   1867 A fastigiate form no longer identifiable. Perhaps a superfluous name for *TAXODIUM ascendens* .   B   Holland

- - 'Gracile' Carrière   1859 Named for a spreading tree, no longer identifiable.   B   France

- - 'Hursley Park' H.G. Hillier
1971 In "Hilliers Manual". A dwarf form raised from a witch's broom found on an 8m tree at Hursley Park near Winchester in 1966. In cultivation but rare.   G

- - var. *imbricarium* (Nuttall) Croom
1837 Now listed under *TAXODIUM ascendens*. NIC.   U.K.

- - 'Intermedium' Carrière   1859 Named for a tree found by Carrière in a castle park. NIC.   B   France

- - 'Knightii' Carrière   1859 Named for a tree found by Carrière in a garden. NIC.   B   France

- - f. macrocarpum Carrière   1859 A variant with large, smooth cones. Not now identifiable.   B   France

- - 'Microphyllum' (Brongniart) Henkel & Hochstetter
1833 A shrubby plant, no longer identifiable.   B   Germany

- - 'Monarch of Illinois' Reg'd. Arn. Arb.
1969 A conical tree with horizontal branches. O. and I. E. Cully of Cully Nurs, Jacksonville, ILL.   U.S.A.

- - 'Nanum' Carrière   1855 A compact dwarf bush. O. Chateney Nurs, Tours. NIC.   B   France

- - 'Nigrum' Carrière   1867 Named for an unidentifiable bush. NIC.   B   France

- - 'Nutans' (1) Carrière   1867 Now known as *TAXODIUM distichum* 'Pendens'.

- - 'Nutans' (2) Sweet   1827 See *TAXODIUM ascendens* 'Nutans'.

- - 'Patens' Aiton   1813 An open, straggling tree. No longer identifiable. NIC.   B   U.K.

- - 'Pendens' Carrière   1855 Now known as *TAXODIUM distichum* 'Pendens'.   B,K,G   France

- - var. *pendulum* Horsey   1925 See *TAXODIUM ascendens* 'Nutans'.

- - 'Pendulum Novum' P. Smith ex Beissner
1891 Long, pendulous branches. NIC.   B   Germany

- - f. *protuberans* Carrière   1859 Another variant no longer identifiable.   B   France

- - 'Pyramidatum' Carrière   1859 Named for a narrowly conical tree found by Carrière. NIC.   B   France

- - 'Recurvum' Van Geert	1862	Named for a tree with an umbrella-like crown. NIC.	B	Belgium
- - 'Secrest' Hort. Amer.	1992	Flat topped dwarf. O. Witch's broom at Secrest Arboretum, Ohio. L. Coenosium Gardens, Aurora, OR.		

TAXODIUM mucronatum Tenore

	1853	Montezuma Bald Cypress. A very long-lived tree, with semi-evergreen or persistent foliage, it flowers in the autumn.	20m,Z8	Mexico

TAXUS Linnaeus (1753)

Taxaceae

The Yews form a group of ten to a dozen species widely dispersed around the world, usually given separate specific status in each part of the world where they are found, although the differences hardly justify so doing. Being very hardy, they are useful garden plants in the colder areas, and within several of the species very many selections have been named and introduced into cultivation - some almost identical. A feature of the genus is an almost total inability to develop fresh leader growth following damage. Because of this peculiarity discrepant descriptions of "habit" are quite usual. The taxonomy here follows Rushforth, (1987).

TAXUS adpressa Knight   1851 Now known as *TAXUS baccata* 'Adpressa'.

TAXUS baccata Linnaeus   1753 English Yew, Common Yew.   12-25m,Z6   Europe

- - f. *adpressa* (Carrière) Beissner
  1887 This quite distinctive group of short-leaved forms are usually listed as cultivars, although such forms turn up in seed-beds.   W   Sporadic

- - 'Adpressa' Hort. ex Lindley & Gordon
  1850 A female clone with short leaves. First reported at the Dickson Nurs, Chester. (1828).   B,D,G,H,K,R,W   U.K.

- - 'Adpressa Aurea' Beissner
  1897 Young shoots golden-yellow. O. Fisher, Son and Sibray, Handsworth Nurs, Sheffield. (1885). I. Standish Nurs, Ascot, Surrey.   B,G,K,W2   U.K.

- - 'Adpressa Aureovariegata' Beissner
  1897 As last, but each leaf carries a central green stripe.   Germany

- - 'Adpressa Erecta' Nelson
  1866 An upright-growing female clone. O. The Standish Nurs, Ascot.   B,D,K,W   U.K.

- - 'Adpressa Fowle' Reg'd. Arn. Arb.
  1965 Name changed to 'Fowle'.   U.S.A.

- - 'Adpressa Pendula' Gibbs
  1926 O. Received from 'a Quaker gentleman named Morris living in Philadelphia'. Not now listed at the Morris Arboretum!   B   U.S.A.

- - 'Adpressa Pyramidalis' Den Ouden
  1949 More upright in habit than 'Erecta'. O. C. Frets and Sons, Boskoop.   B,D,K,W   Holland

- - 'Adpressa Stricta' Carrière
  1867 Indistinguishable from 'Adpressa Erecta'. A male clone.   B,R   France

- - 'Adpressa Variegata' Nelson
  1866 A slender bush, partly variegated yellowish or creamy-white. Several clones now in cultivation differ slightly in colour.   B,D,K,R,W2   U.K.

- - 'Albovariegata' Späth   1883 In "Nurs. Cat". Regular white variegation.   B,D,K,W   Germany

- - 'Aldenham Gold' Hort. Anglia
  1988 Dwarf cushion shaped, new foliage gold, fading to variegated in autumn. O. J.W. Archer. I. Kenwith Nurs, Bideford, Devon.

- - 'Aldenhamensis' Gibbs   1926 Named for a tree at Aldenham, residence of the Hon. Vicary Gibbs.   B   U.K.

- - 'Amberg' Hort. Amer.   1985 A listed name. No further information.

- - 'Amersfoort' Meyer   1961 Dense, upright bush with very distinctive oval leaves. O. Unrecorded.   B,G,K,R,W   France

- - 'Argentea' Loudon ex Gordon
  1858 Silvery-white striped leaves.   U.K.

- - 'Argentea Minor' Hort. Anglia   Now known as 'Dwarf White'.   B,G,K,W   U.K.

- - f. *aurea* Pilger   1903 A botanical designation for the golden-yellow coloured clones.   R   Sporadic

- - 'Aurea' Nelson   1866 "The Golden Yew". Now only useful as a collective name for several selections with yellow foliage.   B,D,G,K,W

- - 'Aurea Pendula' Hort. Anglia
1988 An illegit. listed name.

- - 'Aureomarginata' Hort. Anglia
1985 An illegit. listed name.

- - **'Aureovariegata'** Henkel & Hochstetter
1865 Foliage green, later tinged yellow.   B,D,K   U.K.

- - 'Aurescens' Hort. Amer.   1986 An illegit. listed name.

- - 'Backhousii' Backhouse   1895 In "Nurs. Cat". Backhouse and Sons, York. NIC.   B,K   U.K.

- - **'Barronii'** Barron   1868 A copper-yellow female selection. O. Raised from seed of the original 'Aurea' by Wm Barron of Elvaston Castle Nurs, Derby.   B,D,K,W   U.K.

- - **'Beteramsii'** Schwerin   1927 A vigorous columnar form. O. Raised from seed on Jac Beterhams Nurs, Geldern.   B,K   Germany

- - 'Blue John' Beissner   Commercial equivalent of 'Glauca'. ('Blue Jack').   B   Germany

- - 'Brevifolia' Nelson   1866 Probably a mistake for 'Adpressa'. NIC.

- - 'Brocklebank' Gibbs   1926 Named for a plant of unknown origin, less than 30cm high. NIC.   U.K.

- - 'Brzeg' Hort. Holland   1992 Reported from the Botanic Garden, at Wroclaw.   Poland

- - 'Buxifolia' Hort. Amer.   1986 An illegit. listed name.

- - 'Buxtonensis' Gibbs   1926 Named for a tree at Aldenham, Herts. NIC.   B,D,K   U.K.

- - **'Cappenberg'** Den Ouden/Boom
1965 A slow, narrowly fastigiate form found in a private garden by G. Bootsman, Blijdenstein Pinetum.   B,G,K   Holland

- - 'Carona'   See 'Nissen's Corona'.   B

- - **'Cavendishii'** Hornibrook
1932 Spreading form of unrecorded origin. Still listed in U.K.   B,D,G,H,K,W   U.K.

- - **'Cheshuntensis'** (1) Paul
1861 An erect, female clone. O. Raised from seed at the Wm Paul Nurs, at Cheshunt. Still listed in U.K.   B,D,K   U.K.

- - 'Cheshuntensis' (2) Hornibrook
1923 A mistake: name now changed to 'Paulina'.   H,W   U.K.

- - 'Columnaris' Carrière   1867 An extremely fastigiate seedling; foliage green with edging yellow.   B,H,K,W   France

- - 'Compacta' Beissner   1910 Dwarf, globose, later becoming broadly oval or conical. I. Den Ouden Nurs, Boskoop. O. Dervaes' Nurs, Wetteren. NIC.   B,D,H,K,R,W   Belgium

- - 'Compressa' Carrière   1867 Narrowly conical dwarf form. NIC.   B,H,K   France

- - 'Conica' Schelle   1909 As previous entry. NIC.   B   Germany

- - 'Contorta' Gibbs   1926 Branches contorted, foliage bizarre. O. Arnold Arboretum?   B,H,K   U.S.A.

- - 'Contortifolia' Gibbs   1926 Named for a plant with distorted leaves found at Aldenham. NIC.   B   U.K.

- - **'Corleys Coppertip'** Int.Con. Reg.
1983 **I.** Chantry Nurs, Honiton, Devon. **O.** A dwarf seedling from 'Dovastonii Aurea', raised by R.S. Corley of High Wycombe, Bucks.   G   U.K.

- - 'Corona' Hort.   See 'Nissen's Corona'.   W

- - 'Cristata' H.J. van de Laar
1986 In "Naamlijst . . . ". No information.   Holland

- - 'Crowderi' Moore   1860 No longer identifiable.   B

- - **'David'** H.J.van de Laar   1990 In "Dendroflora 27". A hardy fastigiate selection with yellowish lvs. **O.** Raised from seed by M.M Bömer, Zundert (1967).   Holland

- - 'Davidiana' Gibbs   1926 Named for a fastigiate golden plant at Aldenham, probably never propagated. NIC.   B,D   U.K.

- - 'Davie' Reg'd. Arn. Arb.   1970 Named for a seedling found by Mrs D.M. Metheny of Seattle, WA. NIC?   U.S.A.

- - 'Davisii' Hesse ex Schneider
1913 A columnar form. **O.** Hesse Nurs, Weener-on-Ems. NIC.   B,K   Germany

- - 'Decora' (1) Hornibrook   1939 "The tiniest of all Yews". Habit low and spreading. **O.** Oestoek Nurs, Boskoop. NIC.   B,D,G,H,K   Holland

- - **'Decora'** (2) Hillier   1964 In "Dwarf Conifers". Bush with large, sickle-shape leaves.   W   U.K.

- - 'Dovastoniana' Leighton
1841 In "Flora of Shropshire". 'The Westfelton Yew'. A tree-form with widespreading branches and pendulous branchlets. **O.** A seedling raised by John Dovaston at Westfelton near Shrewsbury, in 1777.   B,D,G,K,R,W   U.K.

- - 'Dovastonii' Hort.   A mistake for previous entry.

- - **'Dovastonii Aurea'** Sénéclauze
1868 A tree similar to the previous item, but with golden-yellow foliage. **O.** Raised on the Sénéclauze Nurs, Bourg Argental, Loires.   B,D,G,K,R,W   France

- - 'Dovastonii Aurea Pendula', 'Dovastonii Aureovariegata' and 'Dovastonii Variegata' are listed names, probably superfluous for the same plant.

- - 'Drinkstone Gold' Hort. Anglia
1990 Deep orange-gold upright strongly growing form. **O.** Mr. Barcock, Drinkstone Nurs. **I.** P.W. Plants, Norfolk.   U.K.

- - 'Dwarf Grayswood' Hort. Anglia
1992 Plant in Windsor Great Park, Berks, without description.

- - **'Dwarf White'** Den Ouden/Boom
1965 A slow-growing spreading form with foliage whitish in late Spring. The name replaces the illegit. name 'Argentea Minor' used by H. G. Hillier in "Dwarf Conifers" (1964). Seems very prone to phytophera.   B,W2   U.K.

- - 'Elegantissima' Lawson
1852 Dense, large, spreading bush with ascending branches; young foliage deep golden-yellow, turning later to straw-colour. A female clone that berries freely, but a male clone is also reported. **O.** Fisher, Son and Sibray, Handsworth Nurs, Sheffield.   B,D,K   U.K.

- - **'Elvastonensis'** Barron   1868   A slow-growing shrub with orange-coloured young shoots and winter foliage. **O.** It originated as a coloured mutation on a normal (male) tree at Elvaston Castle, Derbyshire.   B,K   U.K.

- - **'Epacrioides'** Nelson   1866   A dense, dwarf form, similar to 'Ericoides' but some larger leaves inter-mingled up the stems.   B,D,K,W   U.K.

- - **'Erecta'** Loudon   1838   The Fulham Yew. Branches horizontal, soon turning upwards forming a broad and apparently fastigiate tree. Dark glossy green lvs, 16 mm long. A male clone.   B,D,K   U.K.

- - 'Erecta Aurea' Barron   1880   In "Nurs. Cat". Similar to last, but leaves entirely gold in colour.   B,K   U.K.

- - 'Erecta Aureovariegata' Smith   1874   Gold-striped Yew. An upright, variegated form of 'Erecta'. NIC.   B,D,G,K   U.K.

- - **'Erecta Semperaurea'** Beissner   1910   Now known in the trade as 'Semperaurea'.   Germany

- - **'Ericoides'** Carrière   1855   Erect, slow-growing bush; leaves narrow short and spreading horizontally from the stems; buds large.   B,D,H,K,W   France

- - 'Expansa' Carrière   1867   Wide-spreading bush; dark green lvs often sickle-shaped.   B,D,H,K,W   France

- - **'Fastigiata'** Loudon   1838   Irish Yew, Florence Court Yew. A fastigiate tree (at first narrowly so, becoming broader with age) with dark green leaves, radially set. A female clone, probably mother to all the columnar Yews, but a male form is known. **I.** Lee and Kennedy Nurs, Hammersmith. **O.** Found on a farm in County Fermanagh in 1780.   B,D,G,K,R,W   Ireland

- - 'Fastigiata Aurea' (1) Sénéclauze   1868   A fastigiate plant with lvs especially yellow beneath. NIC.   B,D,G,K,R   France

- - 'Fastigiata Aurea' (2) Barron   1875   In "Nurs Cat". Now known as 'Standishii'.   U.K.

- - **'Fastigiata Aureomarginata'** Fisher ex Veitch   1881   Lvs edged golden-yellow during first season. **O.** Fisher, Son and Sibray, Handsworth Nurs, Sheffield.   B,D,K,R,W   U.K.

- - 'Fastigiata Aureovariegata' Fisher & Holmes   1860   Leaves golden variegated.   B,K,W2   U.K.

- - 'Fastigiata Melfard' Hort. Germany   A mistake. See 'Melfard'.

- - 'Fastigiata Nana' Hort. Amer.   1986   An illegit. listed name.

- - **'Fastigiata Nova'** Vollert ex Beissner   1903   Fast-growing, narrowly fastigiate clone. **O.** Raised on the Vollert Nurs, Forsteck, Kiel.   B,K   Germany

- - **'Fastigiata Robusta'** Zulauf ex Hahn   1950   A hardy, robust form. **O.** Found in the wild by Herman Zulauf at Schinznach-Dorf.   B,G,K   Germany

- - 'Fastigiata Variegata' Lawson   1882   Young leaves white-variegated; turning green later. NIC.   B,K   U.K.

- - 'Fastigiata Viridis' Den Ouden   1949   Strongly fastigiate form with dense, pale green foliage. **O.** and **I.** Wezelenberg Nurs, Hazerwoude, Boskoop.   B,K   Holland

- - 'Fisheri' R. Smith   1865   Widespreading form with branches - some green, some yellow. **O.** Probably Fisher and Holmes, Sheffield, NIC.   B,D,K   U.K.

- - 'Flushing' Hort. Europe   1986 A mistake for *TAXUS* x *media* 'Flushing'.   G,K   U.S.A.

- - **'Fowle'** Int. Con.. Reg.   1979 The accepted name in place of 'Adpressa Fowle'. Low
spreading plant, dark-green oval leaves. New growth pale
cinnamon.   W2   U.S.A.

- - *"foliis variegatis"* Loddiges
   1820 In "Nurs. Cat". (*"fol. var."*). Now known as 'Variegata'.   U.K.

- - 'Foxii' Carrière   1855 See 'Nana' (1).   H   U.K.

- - 'Fructoluteo' Loudon   1838 Now known as 'Lutea'. Berries are yellow.   R   U.K.

- - 'Giraldii' Hort. Holland   A bushy form of uncertain identity. Possibly the same as
known in U.S.A. as *TAXUS cuspidata* 'Giraldii'.'   G

- - **'Glauca'** Carrière   1855 A vigorous, open-growing, male clone with dark bluish green
foliage most noticeable in spring. ('Blue John' and 'Blue
Jack').   B,D,K   U.K.

- - **'Glenroy New Penny'** C and M Dadd
   1982 In "Nurs. Cat". Shrub with young foliage a bright copper
colour, paler during Winter. **O.** and **I.** Ballalheannagh Gdns,
Glen Roy, Lonan, I. of Man.   U.K.

- - **'Gold Haze'** L. Konijn   1980 Upright bush with golden-yellow foliage. **O.** and **I.** L. Konijn
Nurs, Lunteren, Ederveen.   Holland

- - **'Goud Elsje'** L.Konijn   1968 In "Sortimentslijst". Upright-growing bush; foliage slightly
more yellow than 'Elegantissima'. ('Goudelsje' is incorrect).   G   Holland

- - 'Gracilis' Nelson   1866 "The slender-branched variety". NIC.   U.K.

- - **'Gracilis Pendula'** Lauche
   1880 Vigorous erect-growing form with pendulous branches.   B,K,W   Germany

- - 'Graciosa' Hort. Holland   1986 A name of doubtful validity.   G

- - 'Grandis' Hort. Ireland   1989 Reported from National Botanic Gardens. Dublin.

- - 'Green Column' Hort. Germany   A very slow-growing, dark green fastigiate form with oval
leaves, suitable for alpine gardens. L. J zu Jeddeloh Nurs,
Oldenburg.   Germany

- - **'Green Diamond'** H.J. van de Laar
   1990 In "Dendroflora 27". A very dark green slow-growing flat-
globose plant said to have been raised from seed in 1970. **O.**
J. Philipsen. Helenaveen. **L.** Libo Nurs. Baexam, Holland.

- - 'Green Silver' Hort. Amer.
   1986 A mistake for 'Silver Green'.

- - 'Handsworthiana' Fisher   1896 A fastigiate form with dark green foliage. NIC.   B,K   U.K.

- - **'Hessei'** Hesse   1932 In "Nurs. Cat". A fastigiate form with large green leaves.
sometimes sickle-shape. **O.** and **I.** H.A. Hesse Nurs. Weener-
on-Ems.   B,K   Germany

- - 'Hibernica' Loddiges   1820 In "Nurs. Cat". NOM only. Although the first name to be
used, 'Fastigiata' is now accepted as the valid name.   Ireland

- - 'Hodgtonii' Barron   1875 In "Nurs. Cat". NOM. NIC.   U.K.

- - 'Hoersholm' Hort. Anglia
   1970 L. "Hilliers Conif. Conf. List".   Denmark ?

- - **'Hopkins'** Int. Con. Reg.
  1986 Named for a prostrate plant with deeply gold colour, of
  unrecorded origin, found by S.J. Hopkins of Sanderstead,
  Surrey, in 1964.   U.K.

- - 'Horizontalis' Pépin   1850 Named for a tall tree with strikingly horizontal branches. **O.**
  Bertin Nurs, Versailles.   B,D,H,K,W   France

- - 'Horizontalis Elegantissima' W.J. Bean
  1914 As previous entry, but young leaves golden. NIC.   B,D,K

- - **'Imperialis'** Carrière   1855 Branches ascending, foliage sparce. NIC.   B,D,K   France

- - **'Ingeborg Nelleman'** H.J. Grootendorst
  1979 In "Nurs. Cat". A broad, spreading, rounded bush. Young
  growth bronze, becoming yellow.   G,K

- - 'Intermedia' Carrière   1867 Similar to 'Fastigiata' but more open habit. **O.** Raised by
  Briot, Trion Gardens, Versailles. NIC.   B,K   France

- - 'Jacksonii' W.M. Paul   1861 A pendulous form similar to 'Dovastoniana'. **O.** Wm Paul
  Nurs, Cheshunt. NIC.   B,D,G,K,W   U.K.

- - 'Judish' Hort. Anglia   1992 Plant in Windsor Great Park, Berks, without description.

- - 'Kadett' Hort. Holland   See 'Nissen's Kadett'.

- - **'Knirps'** Möll ex Krüssmann.
  1955 Very slow-growing, irregular shrub. **O.** Peter Möll, Heister-
  Bacherott.   B,D,K,R,W   Germany

- - 'Laevigata' Gibbs   1926 Named for a golden-variegated tree at Aldenham, Herts. NIC. B   U.K.

- - 'Libo' Hort. Holland   1992 A listed name.

- - 'Lieta' Hort. Amer.   1985 A listed name. No further information.

- - 'Linearis' Carrière   1855 A selection from the wild by Rosenthal that makes a wide-
  spreading tree.   B,K   Czechosl.

- - 'Litfass' Hort. Holland   1992 A listed name. **L.** Libo Nurs, Baexam.

- - 'Longifolia' Jensen   A broadly arching form of unrecorded origin. **I.** A.M. Jensen
  Nurs, Holmstrup.   B   Denmark

- - 'Lutea' Endlicher   1847 A form with yellow-coloured fruit. (Possibly the same as
  'Xanthocarpa').   B,D,G,K   Germany

- - 'Macnabiana' Beissner   1909 No longer identifiable.   B   Germany

- - 'Macrocarpa' Hort. Europe
  1890 Named for a tree in the Botanic Garden at Innsbruck. NIC.   B   Austria

- - **'Melfard'** Krüssmann   1972 Compact, fastigiate tree with small, dark green leaves.
  ('Melford' and 'Melfordii' are incorrect).   G,K   Germany

- - 'Michelii' Barbier ex Slavin
  1932 Wide-spreading shrub. Fem. **O.** Barbier Nurs, Orleans.   B   France

- - 'Miniata' Carrière   1867 An open-growing dwarf. **O.** Jardin des Plantes, Paris (1862).
  NIC.   B,H,W   France

- - 'Mitchelliana' Barron   1875 In "Nurs. Cat". NOM. NIC.   U.K.

- - **'Möll'** Krüssmann   1955 A slow-growing dwarf with small leaves. **O.** Peter Möll Nurs,
  Heisterbacherott (1935).   B   Germany

- - 'Monstrosa' Carrière   1855 An open form not now identifiable.   B,H,W   France

- - **'Morris Golden Spreader'** Hort. Amer.
  1985 A listed name for a spreading form with the young leaves
  golden-yellow.

- - **'Nana'** (1) Knight   1950 A very slow-growing shrub, rare but still in cultivation.
  (=*TAXUS baccata foxii* in "Kew Handlist of Conifers" 1903).   B,D,H,K,R,W   U.K.

- - 'Nana' (2) Wm.Paul in Gordon
  1875 Now renamed 'Paulina'.   H   U.K.

- - 'Nana' (3) W.J. Bean   1914 Dwarf and spreading in habit.   U.K.

- - 'Nana' (4) W.J. Bean   1908 In "Holly Box and Yew". Now known as 'Parvula'.   H   U.K.

- - 'Nana Parvula' Hort. Anglia
  1984 A mistake for 'Parvula'.

- - **'Neidpathensis'** Wm. Paul
  1861 Named for a male tree resembling 'Cheshuntensis', found at
  Neidpath Castle, Tweedale. ('Nidpathensis').   B,D,K   Scotland

- - **'Newport'** Hort. Europe   1986 A dense, columnar selection.   G

- - 'Nidpathensis'   See 'Neidpathensis'.

- - **'Nigra'** Paul   1861 A striking plant of bold and rather upright growth; lvs
  blackish-green. Plants in cultivation in America under this
  name are listed under *TAXUS cuspidata*.   B   U.K.

- - **'Nissen's Corona'** Nissen
  1957 In "Nurs. Cat". A broad, spreading bush, leaves fresh green.
  O. J. Nissen Nurs, Aprath. near Wuppental (1934).   B,K   Germany

- - **'Nissen's Kadett'** Nissen
  1957 In "Nurs. Cat". Loose, conical clone with foliage sparse, dark
  green. **O.** As last entry.   B,K,W2   Germany

- - **'Nissen's Page'** Nissen   1957 In "Nurs. Cat". A dense, bushy form; leaves light green. **O.**
  As last entry.   B,K,W2   Germany

- - **'Nissen's Praesident'** Nissen
  1957 In "Nurs. Cat". A Vigorous, spreading clone; foliage deep
  green. **O.** As last entry.   B,K,W2   Germany

- - **'Nissen's Regent'** Nissen
  1957 In "Nurs. Cat". Similar to 'Nissen's Corona', irregular growth
  but finer needles, deep green. **O.** As last entry.   B,K   Germany

- - **'Nutans'** Beissner   1910 Dwarf, rounded bush; leaves dark green, sickle-shaped. **I.**
  Den Ouden Nurs, Boskoop, (1910). **O.** Raised on Dervaes'
  Nurs, Wetteren.   B,D,G,H,K,R,W Belgium

- - 'Ommberg' Reg'd, Arn. Arb.   In "Arnoldia 38". ('Ornberg').   U.S.A.

- - **'Ostenberg'** Hort. Holland
  1986 L. H J van de Laar in "Naamlijst . . .". NOM.   Holland

- - **'Overeynderi'** Schneider
  1923 A densely fastigiate or conical form, widely planted. **O.** C. G.
  Overeynder Nurs, Boskoop.   B,K   Holland

- - 'Page' Hort.   See 'Nissen's Page'.   B,W

- - 'Parade' Hort. Europe   See *TAXUS x media* 'Flushing'.   U.S.A.

- - 'Parvula' V.Gibbs   1926 A low-growing, spreading shrub. (= 'Nana' (3), above) NIC.   B,D,G,H,W   U.K.

- - **'Paulina'** V. Gibbs 1926 A dense, compact bush with irregular glossy, dark green leaves. **O.** Geo. Paul Nurs, Cheshunt, Herts, (= 'Nana' (2), above). B,D,H,K,W U.K.

- - 'Pendula' Rinz 1857 An early pendulous selection of loose habit: leaves glaucous green. B,W Germany

- - 'Pendula Graciosa' Overeynder 1880 In "Sieboldia 6". A strongly pendulous form. **O.** Raised on C.G. Overeynder Nurs, Boskoop. B,K Holland

- - 'Pendula Variegata' Nelson 1866 "The pendulous variegated form". NIC. B U.K.

- - 'Pirat' (Buchtmann) 1992 A listed name.**L.** Horstmann Nurs, Schneverdingen.

- - 'Praesident' Hort. Europe See 'Nissen's Praesident'. B,W

- - **'Procumbens'** Loddiges 1820 In "Nurs. Cat". NOM. The name is in use for a procumbent form with pale green leaves. B,G,H,K,W U.K.

- - 'Prostrata' W.J. Bean 1916 A low, trailing form. NIC. B,H,K,W U.K.

- - 'Pseudoprocumbens' Hornibrook 1923 Named for a low shrub with pendulous tips at one time in the National Botanic Garden, Dublin. NIC. B,H,K,W Ireland

- - 'Pumila Aurea' V. Gibbs 1926 A listed name for a cushion-forming plant with golden lvs. According to Hornibrook, the smallest known cultivar. B,D,H,K,W Ireland

- - **'Pygmaea'** Beissner 1910 A dwarf form with upright branching system. **I.** Den Ouden Nurs, Boskoop. **O.** Dervaes Nurs, Wetteren. B,D,K,R,W Belgium

- - 'Pyramidalis' Lawson 1852 An early conical selection. NIC. B,D U.K.

- - 'Pyramidalis Aureomarginata' Beissner 1909 Similar to last, but leaves yellow-margined. NIC. B Germany

- - 'Pyramidalis Variegata' Nelson 1866 No longer identifiable. NIC. B,D U.K.

- - 'Racket' Hort. Amer. 1986 See following entry.

- - **'Raket'** P. de Vogel 1968 In "Dendroflora 5". A dense form selected before 1967 by Haalboom. K Holland

- - 'Recurvata' Carrière 1855 A handsome form with recurved branches and leaves directed upwards. NIC. B,W France

- - 'Regent' Hort. Europe See 'Nissen's Regent'. B

- - **'Repandens'** Parsons 1887 In "Nurs. Cat". Widespreading, low bush with large, glossy, dark green leaves. A female clone. Several U.S.A.

- - 'Repandens Aurea' Hort. This illegit. name is widely used for low-growing cultivariants of 'Dovastonii Aurea'. G,K,W2

- - 'Repens' Hort. Amer. An illegit. listed name. Possibly a mistake for 'Repandens', or a similar selection.

- - 'Repens Aurea' Hort. See 'Repandens Aurea'.

- - 'Robusta' Hort. A mistake for *TAXUS cuspidata* 'Robusta'.

- - **'Rushmore'** Robinson 1978 In "Nurs. Cat". A dwarf form with an upright, spreading habit and thick, dark green ovate leaves. **O.** and **I.** Robinson Nurs, Knockholt, Kent ('Rushmoor') U.K.

- - **'Schwarzgrun'** Krüssmann
  1979 'A good, dark green hedging plant'. **O.** Heinrich Kordes Nurs, Bilsen, Holstein. — G,K — Germany

- - **'Semperaurea'** Dallimore
  1908 In "Holly, Yew and Box". A popular, wide-spreading male clone with golden-yellow foliage throughout the year. — B,D,G,K,R,W — U.K.

- - 'Severin' Severin
  1911 Conical; leaves dark green. NIC. **O.** H. Severin Nurs, Kremmen. — B — Germany

- - 'Sieboldii' Beissner
  1909 A flat-topped plant, female clone. **O.** Raised in the Muscau Nurs, Muscau. NIC. — B,H — Germany

- - **'Silver Green'** Clarke
  1947 In "Garden Aristocrats 14". A compact bush with deep green leaves having a silvery sheen. **O.** and **I.** The W.B. Clarke Nurs, San José, Cal. — B — U.S.A.

- - 'Silver Spire' Hort. Anglia
  1989 A listed name for a slow-growing upright, silver-variegated clone, at its best during the winter. **O.** and **I.** Treseders Nurs, Truro, Cornwall.

- - 'Silver Van' Hort. Australia — A listed name.

- - 'Smaragd' Hort. Anglia — A listed name.

- - 'Sparcifolia' Hort. ex Loudon
  1842 In "Encyclopedia of Trees and Shrubs". Leaves scattered. NIC. — U.K.

- - 'Spieckermann' Krüssmann
  1979 A wide-spreading bush, lacking a leader. **O.** A selection on the Holsteiner Nurs. — K — Germany

- - **'Standishii'** Dallimore
  1908 In "Holly, Yew and Box". Slow-growing, fastigiate; foliage bright golden-yellow. ('Fastigiata Standishii'). — B,G,K,R,W — U.K.

- - 'Straight Hedge' Hort. Amer.
  1988 A listed name for a compact, dark green form, selected for hedging. Here listed under *TAXUS cuspidata*.

- - f. *stricta* (Lawson) Rehder
  1949 A botanical name for all the fastigiate forms found in the species. — U.K.

- - 'Stricta' Lawson
  1836 Probably the prior name, but 'Fastigiata' is now in universal use. ('Hibernica'). — B,K — U.K.'

- - 'Stricta Viridis' Hort. Europe
  1986 Now known as *TAXUS* x *media* 'Viridis'. — G

- - **'Summergold'** H.J. Grootendorst
  1968 In "Dendroflora 5". A large, widespreading bush. **O.** J. van Ravensberg Nurs, Hazerwoude. — G,K — Holland

- - 'Tardiva' Wells — 1863 Now known as 'Adpressa'.

- - 'Thomlene' Hort. Anglia — 1992 Plant in Windsor Great Park without description. We are not sure that it is different to 'Thomsen'.

- - 'Thomsen' Thomsen
  1964 In "Nurs. Cat".A very slow-growing conical bush with dark green leaves. **O.** A seedling found on the Thomsen Nurs, Skalborg, (1952). — B,G — Denmark

- - 'Thomsens Dwarf' Hort. — A mistake for 'Thomsen'. — K

- - 'Tiny' Hort. Amer. — 1980 A listed name. L. J.W. Spingarn, L.Is., N.Y.

- - 'Tortuosa' Knight & Perry
          1850 NOM. NIC.

- - 'Variegata' Loudon x Gordon

1770 An early female selection with leaves margined white. NIC. See 'Argentea'.	B,D	U.K.

- - **'Washingtonii'** R. Smith

1864 An open, loose shrub with upturned, yellowish-green leaves.	B,D,G,K,R,W	U.K.

- - 'Watnong Gold' Hort. Amer.
          1992 Grows like 'Repens Aurea' but a brighter gold colour. In "Nurs. Cat". Mitsch Nurs, Aurora, OR.

- - **'Weeping Curl'** L. Konijn

1968 In "Sortimentslijst". NOM.	G	Holland

- - **'Westerstede'** H.J. van de Laar

1978 In "Dendroflora **20**". An upright form with rather dense, dark green foliage. **O.** W. Helmers.		Germany

- - **'Wiesmoor Gold'** Krüssmann

1983 An irregularly columnar, golden selection. **O.** Martin Zimmer Nurs, Wiesmoor.	K	Holland

- - 'William Barron' V. Gibbs

1926 Not now identifiable. Probably the same as 'Barronii'.	B	U.K.

- - 'Wintonensis' Hillier

1926 In "Nurs. Cat". **O.** Raised on the Hillier Nurs, Winchester (1918) but no longer listed by them. Probably NIC.	B	U.K.

- - 'Wrightii' Hort. Ireland 1989 Reported from the National Botanic Garden, Dublin.

- - 'Xanthocarpa' Kunze

1864 A tree with yellow fruit. Not distinguishable from 'Lutea'.		Germany

- - 'Zaunkonig' Hort. Germany
          1992 A listed name.

TAXUS brevifolia Nuttall

1849 Californian Yew; Oregon, Pacific or Western Yew.	10-25m,Z4	West U.S.A.

- - 'Erecta' Hort. Amer.   1986 An illegit. listed name, presumably descriptive. This name and the following three names should be replaced if selections are justified.

- - 'Nana' Hort. Amer.   1986 An illegit. listed name. See the above note.

- - 'Nutallii' Hort. Amer.   1986 An illegit. listed name.

- - 'Pyamidalis' Hort. Amer.   1986 An illegit. listed name. See note under 'Erecta'.

TAXUS canadensis Marshall

1785 Canadian Yew. A hardy species of little ornamental value.	2m,Z2	Canada

- - 'Aurea' (1) Sénéclauze

1868 A hybrid with *TAXUS baccata* 'Aurea'. A very dwarf form with leaves edged golden yellow, Raised on the Sénéclauze Nurs, Bourg Argental, Loires. NIC.	B,D,K	France

- - 'Aurea' (2) Bailey

1933 Slightly variegated with yellow.		U.S.A.

- - 'Carnea' Hort. ex Sénéclauze

1868 Fruit with pink aril. NIC.	B	France

- - 'Chabot' Hort. Amer.   1962 Reported from the Gotelli Collection as having been received from the Montreal Botanic Garden.

- - 'Compacta' Hort. Amer.   1986 Now known as *TAXUS* x *hunnewelliana.*

- - 'Densa' Hort. Amer.   1976 Probably same as next item.

- - 'Dwarf Hedge' L.C. Chadwick
>
> 1976 A compact, somewhat erect clone **O**. Wymans Nurs,
> Framingham, Mass. (1915). NIC. See also 'Stricta'.   U.S.A.

- - 'Fastigiata' Hort. Amer.   1986 An illegit. listed name.

- - 'Fastigiata Hammondii' Hort. Ireland
>
> Reported from the National Botanic Garden, Dublin.   Ireland

- - var. *floridana* (Nuttall et Chapman) Silba 1984
>
> The Florida Yew. Regarded by some authorities as a distinct
> species. (per Rushforth, 1987).   Florida

- - 'Hillside' Hort. Amer.   1985 A listed name. NOM. No further information.

- - **'Pyramidalis'** Rinz   1857 An erect-growing dwarf. (See 'Dwarf Hedge').   B,D,K   East N. Amer.

- - 'Stricta' Bailey   1933 Indistinguishable from 'Dwarf Hedge'.   U.S.A.

- - 'Thompsonii' Hort. Amer.
>
> 1962 An illegit. name.

- - 'Variegata' Carrière   1867 Leaves at first white, becoming green. NIC.   B   France

TAXUS celebica (Warburg) Li
>
> 1963 A little-known species merged with *TAXUS mairei* by some
> authorities. (per Rushforth, 1987).   K

TAXUS chinensis (Pilger) Rehder
>
> 1919 Chinese Yew.   6-15m,Z5   China

This species, together with *celebica, mairei, speciosa, sumatrana, wallichiana* and *yunnanensis*, form a group on the taxonomy of which botanists are not agreed. Here we follow Rushforth, (1987).

TAXUS cuspidata Siebold & Zuccarini
>
> 1846 Japanese Yew.   20m,Z4   Japan

This species hybridises freely with *TAXUS baccata* and the selected crosses are now listed under the hybrid species name *TAXUS* x *media*. A cross may incline towards one or other parent, making the correct assignment in some cases difficult. If a name is not listed under this species, check under *TAXIS baccata* and *TAXIS* x *media*. Here we follow Krüssmann (1983).

- - **'Adams'** Chadwick & Keen
>
> 1972 Columnar, foliage peculiar; variable. **O**. Adams Nurs,
> Springfield, Ohio. Other names are found. See under *TAXUS* x
> *media*.   U.S.A.

- - 'Andersonii' D. Hill   1936 In "Hill's Book of Evergreens". Now known as *TAXUS* x
> *media* 'Thayeri'.   U.S.A.

- - 'Aristocrat' Chadwick & Keen
>
> 1976 Here listed under *TAXUS* x *media*.   U.S.A.

- - 'Aurea' Hort. Amer.   1986 An illegit. listed name. **L**. E.A. Cope. In "Native . . . Conifers
> . . .". NOM.

- - **'Aurescens'** Rehder   1920 Low bush, leaves at first orange-yellow, fading to pale
> yellow. **O**. Hall Estate, Bristol, R.I.   B,D,K,W   U.S.A.

- - 'Barnes' Hort. Amer.   1986 A listed name. **L**. E.A. Cope. In "Native . . . Conifers . . ."..
> NOM.

- - **'Bobbink'** L.C. Chadwick
>
> 1951 A dense, conical dwarf. **O**. Bobbink & Chapman Nurs, East
> Rutherford, N.J. ('Midget'). A popular clone.   W2   U.S.A.

- - 'Brand' Hort. Holland   1986 **L**. H. J. van de Laar in "Naamlijst . . ." NOM.

- - 'Bright Gold' Hort. Amer.
      1986 An unacceptable listed name for a low-growing golden-yellow form. A brighter colour than 'Aurescens'.

- - 'Browni' Hort.
      1986 See under *TAXUS* x *media*. **L.** E.A. Cope. In "Native . . . Conifers . . .".

- - 'Buffumi' Hort. Amer.
      1985 An illegit. listed name for a male clone.

- - 'Bulkii' Hort. Amer.
      1985 A trade name for upright plants of 'Capitata' raised from cuttings. (See also 'Expansa').

- - **'Capitata'** Kammerer
      1936 Name limited in the trade to plants of fastigiate growth. Usually raised from seed. (See also 'Expansa').   B,K   U.S.A.

- - 'Capitata Aurea' Hort.
      1986 Name illegit. Possibly a superfluous name for 'Aurea'.   G

- - 'Cherry Hill' Hort. Amer.
      1985 A listed name. **L.** L.C. Hatch in "Reference Guide". NOM.   U.S.A

- - 'Cole's Globe' Hort. Amer.
      1985 A listed name. No further information.   U.S.A.

- - **'Columnaris'** L.C. Chadwick
      1940 A broadly upright selection. Probably NIC.   B,K   U.S.A.

- - 'Columnaris Compacta' Hort. Amer.
      1986 Narrower and faster growing than 'Capitata'. Leaves dark green, berries red.

- - 'Compacta' W.J. Bean
      1914 No longer distinguishable from 'Nana'.   H   U.K.

- - 'Contorta' Fitschen
      1930 A dwarf shrub with branches and branchlets twisted. NIC.   B,D,H   Germany

- - 'Corliss Special' Hort. Amer.
      1986 A listed name. **L.** E.A. Cope. In "Native . . . Conifers . . ". NOM.

- - 'Cross Hardy Spreader' Hort. Amer.
      An unsatisfactory name that should be replaced. NOM..

- - **'Densa'** Rehder in Bailey
      1917 Similar to but lower-growing than 'Nana'. **I.** Parsons Nurs, Flushing, N.Y.   B,D,H,K,R,W   Hort. Japan

- - 'Densiformis' Hort.
      See *TAXUS* x *media* 'Densiformis'.

- - 'Densiformis Hartline' Hort. Amer.
      An illegit. listed name. **L.** L.C. Hatch in "Reference Guide". NOM.

- - 'Depressa' Hort. Amer.
      1986 An illegit. listed name for a widespread, decumbent form. **L.** E.A. Cope. "In "Native . . . Conifers . . . ".

- - **'Erecta'** L.C. Chadwick   1951 An erect form; lvs dense and compact. **O.** Probably at Cole Nurs, Painsville, Ohio, but no longer propagated by them.   B   U.S.A.

- - **'Expansa'** Hort. Amer.   1951 Name used in the trade for specimens of 'Capitata' which develop a spreading habit.   B,K   U.S.A.

- - 'Farmen' Hort. Europe   1986 A broad, compact bush; branches upright; foliage fresh green. **L.** Poul Frederiksen, 4900 Nakskov, (as a *TAXUS* x *media* form).   Denmark

- - 'Farmington' Hort. Amer.
      1985 A listed name. **L.** L.C. Hatch in "Reference Guide". No further information.

- - 'Fastigiata' Hort. Amer.   1986 An illegit. listed name. **L.** E.A. Cope. In "Native . . . Conifers

- - 'Fructo-lutea' Hort.   Now known as 'Luteobaccata'.

- - 'General Greene' Hort. Amer.
  1985 A listed name. L. L.C. Hatch in "Reference Guide". NOM.

- - 'Giraldii' Hort. Holland   1986 A listed name for an undocumented clone. NOM.

- - "Globe Shape" Hort. Amer.   Plants at one time sold under this name were propagans from spreading shoots of 'Robusta', sheared into shape.

- - 'Gold Queen' Hort. Amer.
  1992 In "Nurs. Cat". Rich's Foxwillow Pines, Woodstock, ILL.

- - 'Golden Jubilee' Hort. Holland
  1986 L. H. J. van de Laar in "Naamlijst . . .". NOM.

- - 'Green Valley' H.J. van de Laar
  1986 In "Dendroflora 23". Claimed to be an improved form of 'Nana'.   Holland

- - 'Green Wave' Wyman   1960 Low mound with graceful brs arching over. Lvs dark green. Selected and patented by Richard M Wyman. (c. 1960).   U.S.A.

- - 'Heasleyi' Hort. Amer.   1985 An illegit. listed name. NOM.

- - 'Hill' Hort. Amer.   1985 Here listed under *TAXUS* x *media*. ('Hillii').

- - 'Hiti' (1) Chadwick & Keen
  1976 A columnar clone that becomes a dense vasiform. A whorl of strong semi-apical buds is characteristic. O. Seedling at the Hiti Nurs, Pomfret, Conn.   U.S.A.

- - 'Hiti' (2) Krüssmann   1972 Said to be indistinguishable from, and here listed as *TAXUS* x *media* 'Stovekenii'.   K   Hort. Europe

- - 'Hoytii' Hort. Amer.   1986 Possibly a mistake for 'Hiti'?

- - 'Intermedia' L.L. Kumlein
  1936 In "Hill's Book of Evergreens".A slow-growing shrub. Similar to 'Nana', but faster-growing. O. Richard Brown. Cottage Gardens, Queens, N.Y.   B,D,K   U.S.A.

- - 'Jeffreyi' Kelsey   1960 A narrowly columnar heavily fruiting clone with dark green leaves. L. Kelsey Nurs, Highlands, N.J. ('Jeffrey's Pyramid').   U.S.A.

- - 'Kelsey' L.L. Kumlein   1946 In "Friendly Evergreens". The 'Kelsey Yew'. A bush form, setting twists freely.   U.S.A.

- - 'Kelsey Straight' Hort. Amer.
  1985 "Upright". Probably the same as previous item.

- - f. *latifolia* (Pilger) Fitschen
  1903 A local form, not now distinguished within the species.   B,K   Japan

- - 'Low Boy' Hort. Amer.   1985 A listed name. NOM.

- - 'Luteobaccata' Miyabe & Tatewaki
  1934 A clone with the aril of the seed yellow. ('Fructolutea').   B,G,K,R   Hort. Japan

- - 'Meadowlark' Hort. Amer.
  1985 A listed name. NOM.

- - 'Midget' Chadwick & Keen
  1976 A superfluous name for 'Bobbink'.

- - 'Minima' Slavin   1932 The Pygmy Japanese Yew. An extremely diminutive form. O. Selected by B. H. Slavin, Director of Parks, Rochester, N.Y.   B,D,H,K,W   U.S.A.

- - **'Moraine'** Reg'd. A. A. N.
  1951 Globose; dark green. **I.** Siebenthaler Nurs, Dayton, Ohio. U.S.A.

- - f. *nana* Rehder 1902 A bushy form occurring sporadically in the wild. Many selections have been made in this group. B Japan

- - **'Nana'** (Rehder) Wilson 1916 A dense, dark green, spreading bush: a male clone (probably a group of clones in cultivation) of f. *nana*. D,H,K,W U.S.A.

- - 'Nana Compacta' Hort. Amer.
  1986 An illegit. listed name. NOM.

- - 'Nana Erecta' Hort. Amer.
  1985 An illegit. listed name. NOM.

- - 'Nana Femina' Hort. Amer.
  1985 An illegit. listed name. NOM.

- - 'Nana Grandifolia' Hort. Amer.
  1986 An illegit. listed name. NOM.

- - 'Nana Pyramidalis' Hort. Amer.
  1982 An illegit. listed name for a heavy, broad conical form with dark green foliage. A female clone. **L.** Weston Nurs, Hopkinton, MA.

- - 'Nidiformis' Hachmann 1984 An illegit. name. G

- - **'Nigra'** (1) Mitchell 1972 In "Conifers in the British Isles". A male clone with peculiar foliage. Named for a tree in the National Pinetum, Bedgebury. Kent. U.K.

- - 'Nigra' (2) Hort. Amer. A clone propagated for it's unusually dark green foliage. **O.** Probably the Rhode Island Nurs, Newport, R.I.

- - 'Nutley' Hort. Amer. 1985 A listed name.

- - 'Old Westbury' Hort. Amer.
  1985 A listed name. NOM.

- - 'Ovata' L.C. Chadwick 1951 See 'Vermeulen'. B

- - 'Payne's Spreading' Hort. Amer.
  1985 A listed name. NOM.

- - **'Prostrata'** L.C. Chadwick
  1951 A very strong-growing, widespreading, open clone. **O.** Evergreen Nurs, South Wilton. CT. c.1917. B,D,K U.S.A.

- - 'Pygmaea' Hornibrook 1923 A minute, oval bushling. NIC. B,H,W U.K.

- - 'Pyramidalis' L.L. Kumlein
  1946 In "Friendly Evergreens". NIC. but see *TAXUS* x *media* 'Pyramidalis'. B U.S.A.

- - 'Pyramidalis Grandifolium' Hort. Germany
  1986 Name illegit. **L.** Hachmann Nurs. Barmstedt in Holstein, (?*TAXUS* x *media* 'Grandifolia').

- - **'Robusta'** L.C. Chadwick
  1951 An early, strong-growing, fastigiate selection with dark green lvs. A female clone. **O.** Parsons Nurs, Flushing, L.Is, N.Y. B,K U.S.A.

- - 'Rustique' H.J. van de Laar
  1975 In "Dendroflora **11-12**". Large. spreading bush. **O.** Raised from seed of *TAXUS cuspidata* by F. G. Vroom, "Bonte Hoek" Nurs. Glissen, (1950) but may be a hybrid. At first distributed under the name 'Bonte Hoek'. K Holland

- - **'Sieboldii'** Chapman & Keen
     1976 A clone said to have been introduced to Leyden University in Holland by Von Siebold. NIC.   K   Japan

- - 'Silver Queen' Hort. Holland
     1992 New foliage white. Plant in Arboretum Trompenburg.

- - **'Stovekenii'** L.C. Chadwick
     1951 A dense, quick-growing column. Male. **O.** A seedling at the Pierson Nurs, Cromwell, CT.   B   U.S.A.

- - 'Stricta' Krüssmann   1972 An illegit. name. **I.** J.zu Jeddeloh Nurs, Oldenburg.   K   Germany

- - 'Taunton' Hort. Amer.   See *TAXUS* x *media*. 'Taunton'.

- - **'Thayerae'** Wilson   A flat-topped male clone. **O.** Raised by Wm. Anderson of the Bayard Thayer Estate, South Lancaster, MASS. (1917). ('Andersonii').   H   U.S.A.

- - 'Tsugifolia' Hort. Anglia   1985 Reported from Windsor Great Park, Berks.   U.K.

- - 'Umbraculifera' Hort. Anglia
     1985 An illegit. name reported from Windsor Great Park, Berks.

- - 'Vermeulen' Hort. Amer.   1933 In "Nurs. Cat". Now listed under *TAXUS* x *media*.

- - 'Viridis' Hort.   See *TAXUS* x *media* 'Viridis'.

- - 'Visseri' Hort. Amer.   1986 An illegit. listed name.

- - **'Wainui Petite'** Int. Con. Reg.
     1988

- - 'Wilsonii' Hort. Amer.   1986 An illegit. listed name for a compact, vase-shaped clone with dark green leaves.

- - 'Winter Jewel' Hort. Amer.
     1985 A listed name for an upright, conical form, said to be an improvement on 'Capitata'.

TAXUS disticha Henkel & Hochstetter
     1865 See *TAXUS baccata* 'Dovastoniana'.

TAXUS floridana Nuttall ex Chapman
     1860 Florida Yew.   8m,Z8   Florida, U.S.A.

TAXUS globosa Schlechtendal
     1838 Mexican Yew.   10m,Z8   Mexico.

TAXUS x *hunnewelliana* Rehder
     1925 A hybrid; intermediate between parents: *TAXUS cuspidata* x *TAXUS canadensis*. **O.** T.D.Hatfield, Hunnewell Pinetum, Wellesley, MASS. The cross has been repeated many times.   Z4,B   U.S.A.

- - 'Globosa' L.C. Chadwick 1976 A broadly spreading large bush. **O.** A plant on the Siebenthaler Co. Nurs, Dayton, Ohio, of unrecorded origin. NIC.

- - 'Richard Horsey' Int. Con. Reg.
     1975 A dense shrub, foliage dark green. **I.** U.S. Nat. Arb. Washington DC. **O.** R.F.Doren, (1976).   K   U.S.A.

TAXUS mairei (Lem. & Lev.) S. Y. Hu ex Liu
     1914 Maire Yew.   Z8   China

TAXUS x *media* Rehder   1923   Hybrid Yew.   B,K   U.S.A.

This is a very variable hybrid, intermediate between the parents: *TAXUS cuspidata* x *TAXUS baccata*. The cross was first made by T.D. Hatfield, Hunnewell Pinetum, Wellesley, Mass. (c. 1900). Note: Similarities make the correct listing of some cultivars uncertain.   B   U.S.A

- - **'Adams'** Chadwick & Keen
     1972   Columnar, foliage peculiar; variable. O. Adams Nurs, Springfield, Ohio. Other names are used. A male clone.   K   U.S.A.

- - 'Amersfoort' Hort. Amer.
       A mistake for *TAXUS baccata* 'Amersfoort'.   U.S.A.

- - **'Amherst'** Krüssmann   1972   Bright green. L. Laddie Mitiska Nurs, Amherst, Ohio. A seedling raised on the Hunnewell Estate.   K   U.S.A.

- - 'Andersonii' Hort. Amer.   1986   A name used for erect, free branching. Seedlings raised on the Bayard Thier Estate, South Lancaster. L. E.A. Cope. In "Native . . . Conifers . . . ".   U.S.A.

- - **'Andorra'** Chadwick & Keen
     1906   Fastigiate; free-fruiting. O. Andorra Nurs, Philadelphia, PA.   D,K   U.S.A.

- - **'Anthony Wayne'** Hess   1960   A handy columnar form; strong-growing; foliage yellowish-green. O. Hess Nurs. Wayne, N.J.   B,K   U.S.A.

- - 'Aristocrat' Hort. Amer.   1985   L. L.C. Hatch, in "Reference Guide". NOM.

- - 'Aurea' Hort. Amer.   1985   Name illegit. L. L.C. Hatch, in "Reference Guide". NOM.

- - **'Beanpole'** Vermeulen   1970   O. In "Nurs. Cat". Very slow-growing, narrow, dense column, berrying heavily. O. Vermeulen Nurs, Neshanic Station, N.J.   W2   U.S.A.

- - **'Berryhill'** L.C. Chadwick
     1950   A spreading female plant found at the Secrest Arboretum. I. Berryhill Nurs, Springfield, Ohio.   K   U.S.A.

- - 'Bonny Green Mound' Hort. Amer.
     1992   Tighter growing than 'Densiformis'.

- - **'Brevicata'** L.C. Chadwick
     1951   A loose name for a group of clones.   B,K   Hort. U.S.A.

- - 'Brevimedia' Hort. Amer.
     1986   An illegit. listed name. L. E.A. Cope. In "Native . . . Conifers

- - 'Broad Base' Hort. Amer.
     1985   An unacceptable name. See Art. 31.A (g) of the Cultivar Code. L. L.C. Hatch. In "Reference Guide".

- - **'Broad Beauty'** L.C. Chadwick
     1970   Low, spreading. I. Cole Nurs, Circleville, Ohio. NIC.   U.S.A.

- - 'Brownhelm' L.C. Chadwick
     1976   O. Laddie Mitiska Nurs. NIC.

- - **'Brownii'** L.L. Kumlien   1939   In "Hill's Book of Evergreens". An upright-vase shaped bush; heavy, waxy, dark green foliage. O. T.D. Hatfield, and named for Robert Brown, Cottage Gardens, Queens, L.Is., N.Y.   B,K   U.S.A.

- - 'Buffum' Hort. Amer.   Here listed under *TAXUS cuspidata*.

- - **'Burr'** Chadwick & Keen
     1976   I. C.R.Burr Nurs, Manchester, Conn.   U.S.A.

- - **'Cedar Hill'** D. Wyman   1964   A female clone, said to have originated on the Havemeyer Estate, L.Is., N.Y.   U.S.A.

- - 'Chadwick' Reg'd, Arn. Arb.
  1975 A dark-green spreading plant, berrying freely. **I.** Laddie
  Mitiska Nurs, Amherts, Ohio. **O.** A seedling on the
  Hunnewell Estate.   U.S.A.

- - 'Clifton' Hort.   A mistake for the following entry.

- - **'Cliftonii'** Reg'd, A.A.N.
  1949 **I.** H. Deverman Nurs. Cliftonville, N.J. (1939). The name
  'Wardii' is also in use for the same clone.   B,K   U.S.A.

- - 'Cole' Krüssmann   1972 A free-berrying clone, wider-spreading than 'Hicksii'. **I.** Cole
  Nurs, Painsville, Ohio. NIC.   D,K   U.S.A.

- - 'Coleana' Chadwick & Keen
  1976 An illegit. name. Now known as 'Cole'.   U.S.A.

- - 'Columnaris' Hort. Amer.   A mistake for *TAXUS cuspidata* 'Columnaris'.

- - 'Columnaris Corbit' Hort. Amer.
  An illegit. name. **L.** L.C. Hatch in "Reference Guide".

- - 'Columnaris Flushing' Hort.   A superfluous name for 'Flushing'.

- - **'Compacta'** Chadwick & Keen
  1976 **I.** Siebenthaler Nurs, Dayton, Ohio. NIC.   U.S.A.

- - **'Costich'** Chadwick & Keen
  1976 A male clone formerly known as 'Hick's No 2', selected by
  Professor C.S. Sargent as superior for hedging. **O.** Hick's
  Nurs, Westburg, N.Y.   D,K   U.S.A.

- - 'Cottage Garden' Hort. Amer.
  1985 Dense, compact. **L.** L.C. Hatch in "Reference Guide".   U.S.A.

- - 'Dark Green Spreader' Hort. Amer.
  1985 An unsatisfactory name that should be replaced. Spreading,
  dense; foliage very deep-green. **L.** L.C. Hatch in "Reference
  Guide".

- - **'Densiformis'** L. C. Chadwick
  1951 A dense, globose plant, spreading widely in age. Foliage
  bright green. **L.** C. Hoogendorm Nurs, Newport. R.I. B,K   U.S.A.

- - 'Densiformis Nana' Hort. Germany
  1983 A listed name. **L.** Horstmann Nurs, Schneverdingen.

- - **'Donewell'** Chadwick & Keen
  1976 Upright-spreading; glossy dark-green. **O.** Donewell Nurs,
  Painsville. Ohio. NIC.   U.S.A.

- - 'Dovermanii' Hort. Amer.
  1964 An illegit. listed name for a female clone.   U.S.A.

- - **'Drulia'** Chadwick & Keen
  1976 A vase shaped plant not recommended by D. Wyman. **O.**
  Drulia Nurs, Canfield, Ohio. NIC.   U.S.A.

- - **'Dutweiler'** L.C. Chadwick
  1951 A male clone **O.** Selected by Mr Dutweiler, foreman at Hicks
  Nurs, Westbury, L.I., N.Y. (Spelling varies).   B,K   U.S.A.

- - 'Earl Good' Hort. Amer.   1988 A listed name for an ovoid plant with an attractive dark
  colour **L.** L.C. Hatch in "Conifer Database".

- - **'Emerald'** Chadwick & Keen
  1976 A female plant; Upright, spreading bush; dark green **O.**
  Mitiska Nurs, Amherst, Ohio.   U.S.A.

- - **'Erecta'** Hort. Amer. 1986 An illegit. listed name. Both male and female clones are grown.

- - **'Everflow'** Hort. Amer. A mistake for the following entry.

- - **'Everlow'** Chadwick & Keen
  1976 A slow-growing, dark green spreader. **I.** Cole Nurs, Circleville, Ohio. U.S.A.

- - **'Fairview'** Chadwick & Keen
  1976 Vigorous globose to spreading; dark-green. **O.** Unknown. Formerly distributed by Fairview Nurs, Fairview, PA. as 'Hetz ALH'. U.S.A.

- - **'Farmen'** Thomsen 1956 A compact selection, lvs often sickle-shaped.**O.** Thomsen Nurs, Skalborg. B Denmark

- - **'Fastigiata'** Hort. Amer. 1986 An illegit. listed name. See 'Green Candle'.

- - **'Flemer'** Chadwick & Keen
  1976 Compact, dense female.**I.** F. & F. Nurs, Springfield, N.J. K U.S.A.

- - **'Flushing'** J. Vermeulen
  1952 In "Nurs. Cat". Fastigiate habit; large, shining dark green leaves; berries well. (See *TAXUS x media* 'Parade' Hort. Europe). W2 U.S.A.

- - **'Gem'** Hort. Amer. 1985 A listed name for globose clone with noticeably pale green foliage. **L.** L.C. Hatch in "Reference Guide".

- - **'Glauca'** Hort. Amer. 1985 An illegit. listed name. **L.** L.C. Hatch in "Reference Guide".

- - **'Globe'** Hort. ? Unacceptable name. See Art. 31A (g) of the Cultivar Code. Possibly a mistake for *TAXUS x hunnewelliana* 'Globosa'.

- - **'Grandifolia'** J. Vermeulen
  1976 In "Nurs. Cat". Stoutly compact, branched upright: widest at the top; dark green foliage. **O.** Vermeulen Nurs, Neshanic Station, N.J. K U.S.A.

- - **'Green Candle'** Chadwick & Keen
  1976 Slow, columnar; dark green foliage.**L** Laddie Mitiska Nurs, Amherst, Ohio. U.S.A.

- - **'Green Mountain'** Chadwick & Keen
  1976 Broadly globose, foliage chartreuse green. **L.** Bobbink and Atkins Nurs, East Rutherford, N.J. K U.S.A.

- - **'Groenland'** Hort. Holland
  1987 **L.** H.J. van de Laar in "Naamlijst . . .". NOM.

- - **'Halloran'** A mistake for 'Halloriana'. K

- - **'Halloriana'** L.C. Chadwick
  1951 A slow growing rounded bush. Female. **I.** Halloran Nurs, Boston. **O.** Obscure. B U.S.A.

- - **'Hatfieldii'** Rehder 1923 The Hatfield Yew. **O.** T.D. Hatfield of the Hunnewell Pinetum. (Formerly distributed as 'Hatfield No.2'). B,D,K,R U.S.A.

- - **'Heasleyi'** Hort. Amer. 1964 A listed name for a female clone.

- - **'Helleri'** Hort. Amer. 1964 A listed name for a quick-growing, erect male clone.

- - **'Henryi'** L.C. Chadwick 1951 Vigorous wide-spreading. **I.** Henry Verkade Nurs, New London, CT. B U.S.A.

- - **'Hetz'** D. Wyman 1964 A female vase-shaped plant not recommended by Wyman. NOM. U.S.A.

- - **'Hicksii'** Rehder 1923 A columnar clone with twisted shoots and dark green lvs. **O.** Hick's Nurs, Westbury, N.J., from seed of *TAXUS cuspidata* 'Nana'. B,D,G,K,R,W U.S.A.

- - 'Hick's No 2' Hort. Amer. Now known as 'New Hicks'.

- - **'Hillii'** Hill A name of uncertain application.

- - 'Hiti' Hort. Amer. Now considered indistinguishable from 'Stovekenii'.

- - 'H.M. Eddie' Hort.Amer. 1986 An unacceptable name for a conical tree; foliage dark green. **L.** E.A. Cope. In "Native . . . Conifers . . . ".

- - 'Hoogendorn' Chadwick & Keen
1976 Named for a female tree on the Hoogendorn Nurs, Newport, L.I. NIC. U.S.A.

- - 'Hoytii' D. Wyman 1964 Indistinguishable from the species: not recommended by Wyman. **O.** Stephen Hoyt & Sons, New Canaan, CT. U.S.A.

- - 'Hummeri' Hort. Amer. 1964 A listed name for a male clone. NOM.

- - 'Hunnewelliana' Hort. Amer. See *TAXUS x hunnewelliana.*

- - 'Jeffreyi' Kelsey 1960 Narrowly columnar. **L.** Kelsey's Nurs. Highlands, N.J. ('Jeffrey's pyramid'). U.S.A.

- - 'Kallay' Hort. Amer. Possibly a mistake for 'Kelseyi'.

- - **'Kelseyi'** J. Vermeulen 1915 In "Nurs. Cat." (As 'Kelsey's Upright'). Dense erect bush, leaves densely set, very dark green. Fruits freely, hence the popular name 'Kelsey Berrybush' **O.** Vermeulen Nurs, Neshanic Sta. N.J. and named in honour of F.W. Kelsey. B,D,K,W U.S.A.

- - 'Kelsey's' L.L. Kumlien 1946 In "Friendly Evergreens". (The Kelsey Yew) a bush form twists badly. U.S.A.

- - 'Kelsey's Upright'. Hort.Amer
1937 Raised from a sporting plant in a hedge of 'Kelseyi' by Vermeulen Nurs. but discontinued by them. U.S.A.

- - 'Kobel' Chadwick & Keen
1976 Spreading; open growth. **L.** Kobel's Nurs, West Lafayette, Ohio. U.S.A.

- - 'Kohli' Hort. Amer. 1986 A listed name for a rounded, upright clone; lvs very dark green. **L.** E.A. Cope. In "Native . . . Conifers . . . ". U.S.A.

- - 'L.C. Bobbink' Hort. Amer. See 'Bobbink'.

- - **'Lodi'** Chadwick & Keen
1976 A vase shaped clone, insufficiently distinctive to retain. **O.** Laddie Mitiska Nurs, Amherst, Ohio. U.S.A.

- - 'Matinecock' Hort. Amer.
1985 A listed name.

- - **'Maureen'** R.L. Fincham
1983 In "Amer. Conif. Soc. Bull. **1**". A dense, slow-growing column; foliage dark green.**O.** Joseph Reis. U.S.A.

- - 'Microphylla' D. Wyman 1964 In "Amer. Nurs". A female clone with unusually short leaves. Otherwise not distinguishable.

- - 'Midget' Hort. Amer. 1988 **L.** Mitsch Nurs, Oregon, PA.

- - 'Mioun' Hort. Amer. 1985 Possibly a mistake for 'Moon'.

- - 'Mitiska No.7' Hort. Amer. See 'Mitiska Upright'.

- - **'Mitiska Upright'** Chadwick & Keen
        1976   U.S.A.

- - **'Moon'** Krüssmann   1976   A clone with dark green, strongly fastigiate branches. **I.** Wm H, Moon Nurs, Yarley, PA. (1925) ('Moon's Fastigate').   K   U.S.A.

- - 'Nana Grand' L.C. Chadwick
        1940   In "Narrow-Leafed Conifer Evergreens". NIC.   B   U.S.A.

- - **'Natorp'** Krüssmann   1972   A widespreading, flat-topped female bush. **O.** W. A. Natorp Co. Cincinnati, Ohio.   K   U.S.A.

- - **'New Hicks'** L.C. Hatch   1985   In "Reference Guide". Denser and more branched than 'Hicksii'. (Formerly known as 'Hicks No. 2').   U.S.A.

- - **'Newport'** Chadwick & Keen
        1976   Slow-growing, dense, globose. A male clone.**O.** No record.   U.S.A.

- - **'Nidiformis'** F.J. Grootendorst.
        1953   In "Nurs. Cat". A low nest-forming plant.   B,D,G,K   U.S.A.

- - 'Nidiformis Nigra'   1953   A superfluous name for 'Nidiformis' or 'Nigra'?.   U.S.A.

- - **'Nigra'** L.C. Chadwick   1951   Widespreading; leaves black-green. **I.** Cottage Garden Nurs, N.Y.   B,K   U.S.A.

- - 'Nixe' (Buchtmann)   1992   A listed name.

- - **'Ohio Globe'** Chadwick & Keen
        1976   Globose, dense foliage blue-green. **O.** Laddie Mitiska Nurs, Amherst, Ohio. Formerly known as 'Mitiska No.5'.   U.S.A.

- - 'Orbiculata' Hort. Amer.   1985   An illegit. listed name. **L.** L.C. Hatch in "Reference Guide".

- - **'Ovata'** Krüssmann   1972   A hardy slow-growing, spreading bush. A female clone. **O.** No record; probably imported from Europe c 1920.   K

- - 'Parade' Hort. Europe   1967   A superfluous name for *TAXUS* x *media* 'Flushing'.   K

- - **'Peterson'** Chadwick & Keen
        1976   Widespreading bush; foliage dark green. **O.** C. J. Peterson of Xenia, Ohio. NIC?.   U.S.A.

- - **'Pilaris'** J. Vermeulen   1947   In "Nurs. Cat". Broadly columnar; darkish-green curled lvs. **O.** Vermeulen Nurs, Neshanic Station, N.J. ('Polaris').   W2   U.S.A.

- - 'Pilaris Grandfolia' J. Vermeulen
        1947   Name changed to 'Grandifolia' in 1948.   U.S.A.

- - **'Pyramidalis'** J. Vermeulen
        1946   In "Nurs. Cat". Sturdy, upright habit; foliage medium green. **O.** Vermeulen Nurs, Neshanic Station, N.J.   U.S.A.

- - 'Pyramidalis Robusta'   1946   Name changed to 'Robusta' in 1948.

- - 'Richard Horsey' Hort.   A mistake for *TAXUS* x *hunnewelliana* 'Richard Horsey'.

- - **'Robusta'** J. Vermeulen   1948   In "Nurs. Cat". **O.** Vermeulen Nurs, Neshanic Station, N.J.   U.S.A.

- - **'Roseco'** Chadwick & Keen
        1976   Vigorous, wide-spreading; foliage dense. **O.** No record.

- - **'Runyan'** Chadwick & Keen
        1976   Vigorous, globose shrub; very hardy. Originally listed as 'Hatfield No. 8'.   U.S.A.

- - **'Sargentii'** Rehder   Erect, dense; good for hedging.**O.** Selected at Arnold Arboretum.   K   U.S.A.

- - 'Sebian' L.C. Chadwick   A quick-growing plant,with narrow pale-green leaves. **O.** Mike Sebian Nurs, Painsville, Ohio.   K

- - 'Sentinalis' J. Vermeulen   1947 In "Nurs. Cat". Forms a very slim columnar plant with light-green foliage; curled leaves and bright red berries.**O.** Vermeulen Nurs, Neshanic Station, N.J.   K,G,W   U.S.A.

- - 'Sewelii'   1985 A listed name. No further information.

- - **'Skalborg'** Hort. Denmark
     1956 **L.** Thomsen Planteskole, Skalborg, Sweden.   B

- - 'Slavin' B. Harkness   1964 In "Phytologia **10 (4)**". A seedling raised in Rochester Parks Dept. N.Y.   U.S.A.

- - 'Smokestack' Hort. Amer.
     1988 A listed name for a narrowly columnar clone of medium vigour.

- - 'Stovekenii' Krüssmann   1972 A dense, conical male clone with dark-green foliage. **O.** The A.N. Pierson Nurs, Cromwell, CT, and named for the nursery foreman.   K   U.S.A.

- - **'Strait Hedge'** Krüssmann
     1979 A vigorous, well-furnished, upright clone with green needles. It fruits abundantly, even when young.   K

- - **'Stricta'** J. Vermeulen   1946 In "Nurs. Cat". Upright but broader and somewhat open at the top.   U.S.A.

- - 'Stricta Viridis' Hort. Amer.
     1946 Name changed to 'Viridis' in 1948.   K

- - **'Taunton'** D. Wyman   1964 Reported from Arnold Arboretum as a vase shaped plant of no great merit, and by Harrison in "Ornamental Conifers" from New Zealand as "outstanding. . . for its free-branching habit. . . and hardness".   U.S.A.

- - 'Thayerae' Hort. Amer.   D. Wyman lists it under *TAXUS cuspidata.* as 'Anderson'.   B,G,K

- - **'Totem'** Chadwick & Keen
     1976 An upright female clone, open in habit. **O.** Wilton Nurs, Wilton, CT.   U.S.A.

- - **'Vermeulen'** Chadwick & Keen
     1976 A dense columnar globose shrub with fastigiate branches: leaves closely set, deep glossy green. Often crops heavily. Berries late maturing. **I.** J. Vermeulen, Neshanic Station, N.J. One of the "Vermeulen Yews", but its origin is obscure.   D,K   U.S.A.

- - 'Verticalis' Hort. Amer.   A listed name. No further information.

- - **'Viridis'** J. Vermeulen   1948 In "Nurs. Cat". Dense, conical plant with stout, erect branches, a male clone. **O.** Vermeulen Nurs, Neshanic Station, N.J. (At first distributed as 'Stricta Viridis').   W   U.S.A.

- - 'Visseri' Hort. Amer.   1935 A selection made by Visser Nurs, Springfield Gardens, L. Is., N.Y. Locally popular.   U.S.A.

- - 'Ward' Hort.   See the following entry.

- - **'Wardii'** L.C. Chadwick   1950 Wide, irregularly spreading strong grower with dark lustrous green leaves; bearing heavy crops of late maturing seeds, often in pairs.**O.** R.T. Brown of Cottage Gar. Queens, L.Is., N.Y.   B,K   U.S.A.

- - **'Wellesleyana'** L.C. Chadwick
     1951 An upright-growing, male clone, foliage dark green.   B,G,K   U.S.A.

- - **'Wilsonii'** L.C. Chadwick
  1976 A male clone with dense lateral leaves. **O.** C.E. Wilson Nurs.   U.S.A.

- - 'Wiltonii' Hort. Canada   1982 **L.** T.J. Cole in "Woody Plants Source List".

- - 'Wymanii' Hort. Amer.   1982 An illegit. name. L. Weston Nurs, Hopkinton, WA.

TAXUS speciosa Florin   1948 Now known as *TAXUS mairei* (per Rushforth, 1987).   R

TAXUS sumatrana (Miguel) De Laubenfels
  1978 Here listed under *TAXUS mairei* (per Rushforth, 1987) but
       Silba proposes this name is the specific name, *TAXUS*
       chinensis is considered invalid.   Asia

TAXUS tardiva Lawson   1865 Now known as *TAXUS baccata* 'Adpressa'.

TAXUS wallichiana Zuccarini
  1843 Himalayan Yew.   15m,Z6   Himalayas

- - var. *chinensis* (Pilger) Florin   Not now distinguished from *TAXUS chinensis* (per Rushforth,
                                         1987).   G,R

TAXUS yunnanensis Cheng & L. K. Fu
  1975 Yunnan Yew. A newly described species, not distinguished by
       some authors from *TAXUS wallichiana*.

TETRACLINIS (Vahl) Masters (1892)

Cupressaceae

A monotypic genus allied to *Cupressus*, not hardy in cool, temperate regions.

TETRACLINIS articulata Masters
  1893   10m,Z9   Mediterranea

THUJA Linnaeus (1753)

Cupressaceae

The *THUJA*, first cousins of *CHAMAECYPARIS*, are a small genus containing five or six species, limited to North America and North-east Asia. They differ from their relatives mainly in the fruits. The foliage is in flat sprays with very different facing and lateral leaves and the foliage in most species is strongly scented. There are many cultivars, in some cases very similar.

A sixth species *THUJA orientalis* is now regarded as constituting a monotypic genus on its own and so is now listed by most authorities as *PLATYCLADUS orientalis*. But it having been so long listed under *THUJA* the cultivars are here still so listed to avoid confusion in the Nursery industry.

THUJA decussata Hort.	See *THUJA orientalis* 'Decussata' and 'Juniperoides'.		
THUJA dolabrata	See *THUJOPSIS dolabrata*.		
THUJA gigantea Nuttall	1834 Now known as *THUJA plicata*.		
THUJA koraiensis Nakai	1834 Korean Thuja.	8-10m, Z5	N.Korea
- - 'Pendula' Hort. Amer.	1992 In "Nurs. Cat". Rarafolia Nurs, Kintersville, PA.		
THUJA lobbii	Now known as *THUJA plicata*.		
THUJA nidifera	See under *CHAMAECYPARIS nootkatensis*.		
THUJA occidentalis Linnaeus	1753 Eastern Arborvitae, White Cedar.	20m, Z2	Canada
- - **'Ada'** J. Vermeulen	1973 Compact, rounded column; snow resistant. Foliage green throughout the year. L Vermeulen and Sons Nurs, Neshanic Station, N.J.		U.S.A.
- - 'Alba' Maxwell ex Gordon	1875 A vigorous form with the growing tips white especially so in Winter. Indistinguishable from 'Albospica'. O. Maxwell Nurs, Geneva, N.Y. ('Albospicata', 'Queen Victoria').	B,D,K,R	U.S.A.
- - 'Albospica' Hort. ex Beissner	1891 A superfluous name for 'Alba'. ('Albospicata').		
- - 'Albovariegata' Beissner	1909 A more or less stable form with whitish shoots.		Germany
- - 'Americana' Hort. Amer.	1986 An illegit. listed name for a clone with leaves on young shoots yellow. (? = 'Compacta Americana').		
- - 'Apicidia Alba' Hort. Amer.	1985 An illegit. listed name.		U.S.A.
- - **'Argentea'** Carrière	1855 An unstable white variegated form. NIC.	B,G	France
- - 'Arnprior' Hort. Amer.	1985 A listed name. NOM.		
- - 'Asplenifolia' Sénéclauze	1868 Leaves clustered at tips of branches. NIC.	B,K	France
- - 'Athrotaxoides' Beissner	1891 Form with abnormally thick and swollen branches.	B,D	France
- - **'Aurea'** (1) Carrière in Jacques and Her.	1857 A broadly conical tree with golden-yellow leaves. ('Mastersii Aurea').	B	France
- - 'Aurea' (2) Gordon	1875 A mistake for the G. Peabody Arborvitae. which is *THUJA occidentalis* 'Lutea'.	B	U.S.A.
- - 'Aurea' (3) Hort.	This name, alone or in combination, is loosely used for several clones.		

- - **'Aurea Americana'** Sargent
1859 Young shoots yellow, fading to green. **O.** Brinckerhoff Nurs,
Fishkill, Landing, N.Y.　　B　　U.S.A.

- - 'Aurea Nana' Hort. Canada
1986 An illegit. listed name.

- - **'Aureospicata'** Beissner 1896 An erect growing form. Young shoots yellow, deepening to
the colour of old gold by winter.　　D　　Germany

- - 'Aureovariegata' Henkel and Hochstetter
1865 Large coarse shrub, with yellow variegation.　　B　　Germany

- - 'Aurescens' Browicz and Bugala
1932 A conical shrub with leaves golden. **O.** Found in the
Korniekie Arboretum (1932).　　B,K,R　　Poland

- - 'Barabit's Gold' Hort. Holland
1989 H.J. van de Laar in "Naamlijst. . . ". NOM.

- - 'Batemanii' Bailey 1933 Probably a superfluous synonym for 'Bodmeri'.　　W　　U.S.A.

- - **'Beaufort'** F.G. Meyer 1963 In "Plant Explorations". Slow-growing upright form with
white variegation. **O.** Raised by W. Haalborn Nurs,
Driebergen.　　B,G,K,R　　Holland

- - 'Beteramsii' Schwerin 1910 Branchlets at first brownish red, turning to bronze and green
by winter. **O.** F. Beterams, Geldern. NIC.　　B,K,R　　Germany

- - 'Bluespire' Hort. Amer. 1986 A listed name.

- - **'Bodmeri'** Fröbel 1877 A monstrous form with thick congested foliage. More curious
than beautiful. ('Lycopodioides').　　B,D,K,W2　　Germany

- - **'Boisbriand'** Reg'd. C.O.P.F.
1981 Reg'd by W.H. Perron & Co, Chornedey, Laval, Quebec. An
upright oval habit. Foliage dense vivid green. A good hedge
plant.　　Canada

- - 'Bonita' Hort. Anglia 1964 In "Kew Handlist". See *THUJA orientalis* 'Bonita'.

- - 'Boothii' R. Smith 1867 A dwarf globose variety. Named in honour of James Booth of
Flotbeck Nursery, Hamburg.　　B,D,K　　Germany

- - **'Brabant'** H.J. van de Laar
1984 In "Naamlijst . . .". A compact, conical form with bright green
foliage. Possibly a hybrid: *THUJA occidentalis* x *THUJA
plicata*. **O.** and **I.** G.J.F. Rombouts, Steensel, North Brabant
province.　　Germany

- - **'Brandon'** R.H. Patmore
1940 In "Nurs. Cat". A densely foliaged columnar form. **I.**
Selection at Patmore Nurs, Brandon, Mantoba (1936).　　Canada

- - 'Brandon Pyramidal' Hort. A mistake for 'Brandon'?

- - 'Brans' P. den Ouden 1949 Dense conical habit; young leaves yellowish-white. **O.** Th.
Brans Nurs, Boskoop (1927).　　B　　Holland

- - 'Brendt' Den Ouden/Boom
1961 A hardy conical selection. **O.** and **I.** C. Brendt Nurs, Zislau.　　B　　Germany

- - 'Brewer' Hort. Amer. 1985 A listed name. **L.** L.C. Hatch in "Reference Guide". NOM.

- - 'Brewer's Hybrid' Hort. Amer.
1986 An illegit. listed name. Probably a superfluous name for
previous entry.

- - 'Brubaker' Hort. Amer. 1986 A listed name.

- - **'Buchananii'** Parsons   1887   O. In "Desc. Cat. Trees". Loose open, conical tree.   B,D,K,R   U.S.A.

- - 'Burrowii' Bailey   1933   Leaves yellow. No longer identifiable.   B

- - **'Caespitosa'** Hornibrook

     1923   Named for a dwarf cushion-shaped plant found in Glasnevin Botanic Garden.   B,D,H,K,W2   Ireland

- - 'Canadian Gold' Hort. Canada   Mistake for *THUJA plicata* 'Canadian Gold'.

- - 'Canadian Green' Hort. Canada

     1985   Globose selection, foliage bright green. **L.** L.C. Hatch in "Reference Guide".

- - **'Carman Columnar'** Reg'd. C.O.P.F.

     1974   A slow growing conical rather than columnar tree. Foliage medium green. **I.** Aubin Nurs, (1974); **O.** Imported during early 1960's. ('Carmen' is incorrect).   Canada

- - 'Carr's Dark Green' Hort. Amer.

     1990   A listed name for a vigorous dark green selection.

- - 'Caucasia' Hort. Amer.   1986   Reported from Longwood gardens, PA.

- - 'Cheshire' Hort. Amer.   1986   A listed name.

- - **'Cloth of Gold'** Späth   1891   In "Nurs. Cat". Open, slow-growing shrub with leaves and shoots golden-yellow.   B,K   Germany

- - 'Columbia' Parsons   1887   In "Nurs. Cat". A hardy columnar selection; foliage medium green, tipped white in summer, wholly white in winter. **O.** Parsons Nurs, Flushing, L.Is., N.Y.   B,K,R   U.S.A.

- - **'Columna'** Späth   1904   In "Nurs. Cat". A narrowly columnar form with leaves a shining dark green. **O.** Späth received it from Arnold Arboretum, unnamed.   B,K,R   Germany

- - 'Columnaris' Hort. Amer.

     1988   An unsatisfactory name. Unless a superfluous synonym of 'Columna', it is unacceptable under Article 31A (g) of the "Cultivar Code".

- - 'Compact American' Hort. Amer.

     1985   A name for a conical, compact selection with foliage dark green. **L.** L.C. Hatch. In "Reference Guide".

- - 'Compacta' Hort.   This name is loosely used for several compact clones. It should no longer be used, save as a group name. Other early clonal names no longer identifiable with any certainty are 'Globularis', Llaveana' and 'Spihlmannii'.   B,D,K,W2

- - 'Compacta Americana' Hort. Amer.

     1986   See 'Compact American'.

- - **'Compacta Erecta'** Reg'd. A.A.N.

     1949   Slow growing, compact upright habit, foliage dark green. **O.** and **I.** Westminster Nurs, Westminster, MD. (1947).   B   U.S.A.

- - 'Conica' Bailey   1933   A conical form, no longer distinguishable.   B   U.S.A.

- - **'Conica Densa'** Hetz   1952   In "Nurs. Cat". A globose form with erect branches; foliage dense. **O.** F.C. Hetz, Fairview Evergreen Nurs, Fairview, PA.   B   U.S.A.

- - **'Cristata'** R. Smith   1867   Foliage dense, drooping and crested at the tips; deep green.   B,H,K,W2   U.K.

- - **'Cristata Argenteovariegata'** Den Ouden

     1949   As previous entry, but white variegated. NIC.   B,K

- - 'Cristata Aurea' Beissner
1904 As previous entry, foliage yellowish or brown. **O.** F.J.
Grootendorst Nurs, Boskoop. (1900). B,G,H,K Holland

- - 'Cristata Variegata' Hort. Anglia
1985 Reported from Windsor Great Park, Berks. U.K.

- - 'Danica' G. Krüssmann 1973 In "Deutsche Barmschule 4". A globose, dwarf form, green
foliage, browning slightly in winter. **I.** Danslanex Nurs,
Rodekro, Denmark. Selected seedling on the Arne R. Jenson
Nurs, Orting, Denmark (1952). G,K,W2 Denmark

- - 'Dark American' Hort. Amer.
1986 A listed name. No further information.

- - 'Dart's Green' H.J. van de Laar
1986 A clone with upright habit. **O.** and **I.** Darthuiser Nurs,
Leersum (1972) but no longer in production. Holland

- - 'Dart's Wintergold' H.J. van de Laar
1986 A conical plant with leaves bronzy-yellow deepening in
winter. **O.** and **I.** Darthuiser Nurs, as above. No longer in
production.

- - 'De Beaufleur' Hort. Anglia
1985 Reported from Windsor Great Park, Berks. NOM. U.K.

- - 'Degroot's Emerald Spire' Hort. Amer.
1985 A listed name. Possibly the same as the following.

- - 'Degroot's Spire' Hort. Amer.
1985 A listed name for a slow-growing narrowly upright clone with
twisted foliage.

- - 'Densa' Gordon 1862 A compact, conical bush, with dense, globose green leaves. **O.**
Found in Bagshot Park, Surrey. NIC. U.K.

- - 'Densiforma' Bailey 1933 A very dense form. NIC. B U.S.A.

- - 'Denudata' Beissner 1891 An upright form, very open habit. **O.** Simon Louis Nurs. at
Metz. NIC. B France

- - 'Dicksonii' Nicholson 1901 Probably indistinguishable from 'Aureospicata' NIC. B U.K.

- - 'Dirigo Dwarf' Hort. Amer.
1986 A listed name. No further information.

- - 'Dorset Yellow' Hort. Amer.
1985 A listed name. NOM. ('Dorsett Yellow').

- - 'Douglasii' Hort. See 'Filiformis'.

- - 'Douglasii Aurea' Slavin
1932 A broadly conical tree; leaves. golden-yellow, bronzed in
winter. **O.** D. Hill Nurs, Dundee. B,G,K U.S.A.

- - 'Douglasii Pyramidalis' Späth
1891 In "Nurs. Cat". A slender columnar form; Foliage dense,
dark. Grows in twisted clusters. **O.** Probably Arnold
Arboretum. B,D,K Germany

- - 'Dumosa' Beissner 1933 In "Cultivated Conifers". **O.** Unrecorded. This is a name so
widely used "in the literature" as to be virtually useless. But
see the illustration in Welch (1966). K,W

- - 'Elegantissima' Den Ouden
1949 Narrowly conical foliage dark green, tips yellow, turning
brown. **O.** No record. B,G,K

- - **'Ellwangeriana'** Carrière
  1869 In "Revue Horticole". A juvenile form with foliage spreading. **O.** Ellwange and Barry, Rochester. N.Y. (It is not connected with the name 'Tom Thumb'). B,D,H,K U.S.A.

- - 'Ellwangeriana Aurea' Späth
  1895 A slow-growing sport on the previous item, with leaves golden to orange-yellow. **O.** Späth. B,D,H,K,W2 Germany

- - 'Ellwangeriana Erika' Barabits
  1965 In "Magyar Fenyóújdonságok". See 'Erika'. Hungary

- - 'Ellwangeriana Rheingold' See 'Rheingold'.

- - 'Emerald Green' Hort. Anglia See 'Smaragd'.

- - 'Emeraude' Hort. Europe Name unacceptable: now changed to 'Smaragd'.

- - 'Endean' Den Ouden
  1949 An open but sturdy, conical plant. Leaves light green. **O.** Endean Nurs, Ontario. B Canada

- - 'Ensata' Sénéclauze
  1868 A plant with a curious branch structure. **O.** Sénéclauze. B France

- - 'Erecta' Hesse
  1902 In "Nurs. Cat". A dense, regularly conical clone with erect branches and shiny dark green leaves. **O.** W.A. Hesse Nurs, Weener-on-Ems. B,K Germany

- - **'Ericoides'** R. Smith
  1867 A large, rounded bush with flexible branches and juvenile leaves, brown in winter. B,D,H,K,W2 U.S.A.

- - 'Ericoides Glauca' Hornibrook
  1939 Named for a similar plant at Rostrevor, Co. Down with glaucous summer foliage. NIC. B,H,K U.S.A.

- - **'Erika'** Barabits
  1965 In "Magyar Fenyóújdonságok". Large bush with entirely juvenile foliage. B Hungary

- - **'Europa Gold'** H.M. Grootendorst
  1977 In "Dendroflora 13". A slender, conical tree, with yellow foliage, brightest during the winter. **I.** Darthuiser Boomkwekerijen, Leesum. (1974). **O.** M. Schectema of Loosedrecht. K,G Holland

- - 'Europe Gold' Hort.
  1983 A hardy, erect, golden shrub. **O.** and **I.** Walter van Vliet Nurs, Pit Meadows, B.C. Canada

- - 'Fastigiata' Jaeger
  1865 A tall, conical tree, branchlets crowded, foliage light green. ('Stricta', 'Columnaris' and 'Pyramidalis' are similar clones difficult to differentiate). NIC. B,D,K Germany

- - 'Fastigiata Nova' Beissner
  1897 Similar to previous item, but more regularly columnar. NIC. B,K Germany

- - 'Fehnsilber' Hort. Holland
  1986 A variegated form, possibly not distinct from 'Wansdyke Silver'. Illustration in "Conifers". NOM. G

- - 'Filicoides' Beissner
  1891 Same as 'Spiralis'? NIC. B Germany

- - 'Filiformis' Beissner
  1901 A loose, dwarf, globose bush with recurving threadlike branches. B,D,G,H,K,W2 Germany

- - **'Frieslandia'** H.J. van de Laar
  1979 In "Dendroflora 15". A mutation from 'Elegantissima'. **O.** Gebr. Visser Nurs, Lippenhuisen. Holland

- - 'Fröbelii' Beissner
  1891 A clone similar to 'Globosa', but the foliage remains light green during the winter. B,H,K Germany

- - f. *gaspensis* Victorin and Rousseau
  1940 A regional variant found in the Gaspe Co.   B,K   Canada

- -'George Peabody' Hort. Amer.   See *THUJA occidentalis* 'Lutea'.

- - 'George Washington' Hort. Amer.
  1986 Bright golden form. A large, open, conical tree with yellow
  mottled foliage.

- - 'Giganteoides' Poulsen   1943 In "Nurs. Cat". A vigorous tree, possibly a hybrid. *THUJA
  occidentalis* x *THUJA plicata*. **O.** Found by Svend Poulsen,
  Copenhagen (1935).   B,G,K   Denmark

- - **'Globosa'** (1) Gordon   1875 A globose bush. growth dense and regular; foliage green,
  greyish-green in winter. See illustration in Welch (1966).   B,D,G,H,K,W2 U.K.

- - 'Globosa' (2) Hoopes   1868 The 'Tom Thumb' of American authors. "The smallest of it's
  class known, a tufted little plant rarely over nine inches".

- - 'Globosa Aurea' Hort.   1986 See 'Golden Globe'.

- - 'Globosa Nana' Hort. Amer.
  1986 An illegit. listed name. No further information.

- - **'Globosa Rheindiana'** Bergman
  1965 In "Plants and Gardens **21**". A globose to spreading mound
  with foliage in tufts. **L.** Hillside Nurs, Lehighton, PA. (as
  'Globosa Rhindiana') (1970).   W2   U.S.A.

- - 'Globosa Variegata' H.A. Hesse
  1985 A sport from 'Globosa' with variegated foliage.   B,W2   Germany

- - **'Globularis'** Beissner   1891 Another early globose selection difficult to identify today.
  But see Welch (1966).

- - 'Goldcrest' Hort. Amer.   1986 L. E.A. Cope. In "Native . . . Conifers". Growth conical; tips
  of young leaves yellow.

- - 'Gold Dust' Hort. Amer.   1986 A listed name. No further information.

- - 'Golden' Hort.   An unacceptable name. See Art. 31A (g) of the Cultivar
  Code.

- - 'Golden Champion' McConnell
  1969 In "Nurs. Cat". **I.** McConnell Nurs, Port Burwell, Ontario. **O.**
  George P. Blyth.   Canada

- - **'Golden Globe'** H.M. Grootendorst
  1965 In "Dendroflora **2**". A bright golden-yellow globose form
  (similar to and an alleged sport from 'Woodwardii') Imported
  as "unnamed" from the U.S.A. by Grootendorst.   .G,K,W2   Holland

- - 'Golden Harbor' Hort. Amer.
  1986 A listed name. No further information.

- - 'Gold Haze' Hort.   No information.

- - 'Gold Spot' Hort. Amer.   1985 A superfluous name for 'Aureovariegata'?

- - 'Goodwin' Hort. Amer.   1985 A listed name. No further information.

- - **'Gracilis'** Scott ex Gordon
  1875 Tall open tree, branches pendulous. **O.** Scott's Nurs. Merriott,
  Somerset. NIC.   B,K   U.K.

- - 'Green Midget' Hort. Amer.
  1985 A listed name. No further information.

- - 'Hancei' Hort. Amer.   1961 Reported from Arnold Arboretum as "not outstanding".   B   U.S.A.

- - 'Harrisonii' Rehder ... 1902 A neat little tree; foliage tipped with white. NIC. ... B ... U.S.A.

- - **'Hetz Junior'** Fairview ... 1942 In "Nurs. Cat". Conical; foliage juvenile. Indistinguishable from 'Ericoides'. **O.** Found by F.C. Hetz, founder of the Fairview Evergreen Nurs. Fairview. PA. ... B,K ... U.S.A.

- - **'Hetz Midget'** Hetz ... 1942 In "Nurs. Cat". A very slow-growing globose bush. **O.** A seedling on the same nursery. ... B,G,K,W2 ... U.S.A.

- - 'Hetz Midget Variegated' Hort. Amer. ... 1986 As last but patches of yellow foliage. **L.** E.A. Cope, in "Native . . . Conifers". ... U.S.A.

- - 'Hetz Wintergreen' Hetz ... 1950 In "Nurs. Cat". Vigorous; foliage remains green throughout the year. ... B,K,R

- - 'Hoersholmensis' Beissner ... 1897 A strong-growing, globose clone of uncertain identity. **O.** Nelson, Hoersholm Planteskole. ... B ... Denmark

- - 'Hollandica' Beissner ... 1904 A clone in the 'Wareana' group. Conical, dense, regular. **O.** Unrecorded. NIC. ... B,K ... Holland

- - **'Holmstrup'** A.M. Jensen ... 1951 In "Nurs. Cat". A compact, slow-growing clone with fine, dark green foliage. **O.** and **I** A.M. Jensen Nurs, Holmstrup. ('Holmstrupii'). ... B,D,G,K,W ... Denmark

- - 'Holmstrupensis' Hort. ... See 'Holmstrup'.

- - **'Holmstrup's Yellow'** A.M. Jensen ... 1965 In "Nurs. Cat". Growth dense; foliage golden-yellow. **O.** and **I.** A.M. Jensen Nurs, Holmstrup. (1951). ... B,G,K ... Denmark

- - 'Hookeriana' Waterer ... 1878 In "Nurs. Cat". A pygmy form. NIC. ... B,H ... U.K.

- - **'Hoopesii'** Slavin ... 1932 A plant with dense but coarse, light green foliage. Named to honour Josiah Hoopes, author of "The Book Of Evergreens". ... B ... U.S.A.

- - **'Hoseri'** Browicz and Bugala ... 1958 A dense, low, shrub. **O.** A seedling from 'Globosa' in the Körnickie Arboretum. ... B,K,W2 ... Poland

- - **'Hoveyi'** J. Hoopes ... 1868 A dwarf, globose to upright bush; leaves yellowish-green, turning brown in winter. ... B,D,H,K,W2 ... U.S.A.

- - 'Hoveyi Aureovariegata' Beissner ... 1907 Presumably a variegated sport on the previous entry. **O.** Jac. Beterams Nurs, Geldern. NIC. ... B ... Germany

- - 'Hudsonica' D. Wyman ... 1961 Possibly a superfluous name for 'Globosa'. **L.** Biltmore Nurs. (1902). ... B ... U.S.A.

- - 'Hugii' Olbrich ... 1917 A monstrous form with twisted foliage. **O.** Von Hug, Diedsdorf, near Zurich. ... B,K ... Switzerl.

- - 'Huron' Hort. Canada ... 1987 A listed name. No further information.

- - **'Indomitable'** Reg. Arn. Arb. ... 1963 In "Nurs. Cat". A strong-growing, spreading form; foliage dark green, a sport on 'Elegantissima'. **O.** and **I.** J. Konijn Nurs. then of Reeuwijk, Boskoop. ... B,K ... Holland

- - 'Intermedia' Rehder ... 1902 Described as a compact, dwarf form. NIC. ... B ... Germany

- - 'Intertexta' Schneider ... 1913 A monstrous form, branches widely spaced. NIC. ... B ... Germany

- - 'Iseli Golden Seedling' Hort. Amer.
        1992 Provisional name. ('Gelbbunt Iseli').

- - **'Iseli Weeping'** L.C. Hatch
        1988 In "Conifer Database". Broad-conical with pendulous
             branches; foliage yellow-green.   U.S.A.

- - **'Jessica'** Reg'd. C.O.P.F.
        1980 Reg'd by Wm. J. Intven of Canadale Nurs, St. Thomas,
             Ontario. A slow-growing, compact form; foliage bright green.   Canada

- - 'Kelleriis Viridis' Poulsen
        1945 In "Nurs. Cat". A compact, conical form with bright green
             leaves. **O.** D.F. Poulsen, Kelleriis.   B   Denmark

- - 'L'Haveana' Beissner
        1891 A small, columnar form no longer identifiable. Named for it's
             raiser.   Germany

- - **'Little Champion'** Reg'd. Arn. Arb.
        1956 In "Nurs. Cat". Dark, globose, foliage bright green. **O.**
             Seedling selected by G. Blythe, McConnell Nurs, Port
             Burwell, Ontario. Formerly distributed as 'McConnell's
             Globe'.   B,G,K,W2   Canada

- - **'Little Gem'** Beissner
        1891 A very slow-growing, dense, mounded dwarf with dark green,
             mostly adult foliage. **O.** Späth Nurs, Berlin.   B,D,G,H,K,W Germany

- - **'Little Giant'** Reg'd. C.O.P.F.
        1970 A very compact globose dwarf; dark green foliage. Reg'd by
             G. Blythe, McConnell Nurs, port Burwell, Ontario. **O.** The
             same.   Canada

- - **'Lombarts'** P. Lombarts 1912 In "Nurs. Cat". A medium-sized conical tree, with growing
             tips yellow. **O.** Pierre Lombarts Nurs, Zundert.   B   Holland

- - **'Lombarts Dwarf'** Den Ouden/Boom
        1965 Conical tree with persistent-green leaves. **O.** and **I.** Pierre
             Lombarts, Lombarts Nurs, Zundert.   B,K   Holland

- - **'Lombarts Wintergreen'** Den Ouden/Boom
        1965 Conical tree with persistent-green leaves. **O.** and **I.** As last
             entry.   B,K   Holland

- - 'Lori' L. Kordes
        1984 Columnar; leaves light green, maintained throughout the
             year. **I.** Kordes Nurs, Bilsen. **O.** Lohmann and Richter,
             Stuttgart.   Germany

- - **'Lutea'** Veitch
        1881 Slender-conical; foliage golden-yellow, light green beneath.
             The "George Peabody" Arborvitae. **O.** The Maxwell Nurs,
             Geneva, N.Y.   B,D,G,K   U.S.A.

- - 'Lutea Holmstrup' A. M. Jensen
        1951 In "Nurs. Cat". Name now changed to 'Holmstrup's Yellow'.

- - 'Lutea Humilis' Sudworth

        1927 Name only. NIC.

- - **'Lutea Nana'** Veitch   1881 A dwarf form of 'Lutea'.   B,H,K,W2   U.S.A.

- - 'Lutea Nova' G. Frahm   1911 As 'Lutea' but compact growth and leaves brighter colour. **O.**
             Seedling found by G. Frahm, Elmshorn.   B   Germany

- - 'Lutescens' Bailey   1892 See 'Wareana Lutescens'.   B,D,W   U.S.A.

- - 'Lycopodiodes' Hort. Canada
        1986 An illegit. listed name.

- - 'Macrocarpa' Jaeger   1865 Bushy habit and large cones. NIC.   B   Germany

- - 'Magnifica' Beissner   1884 A conical clone with thick brs; leaves dark green. NIC.   B   Germany

- - **'Malonyana'** Schneider   1913 A dense columnar tree. **O.** Found in the Park of Count Ambrosy-Migassi at Malonya.   B,G,K,R   Hungary

- - 'Mandy' Hort. Anglia   1991 A listed name. **L.** Treborth Nurs, Wales.

- - 'Marrisen's Sulphur' Hort. Holland
    1986 **L.** H.J. van de Laar in "Naamlijst . . .". NOM.

- - 'Martinius' Hort. Amer.   1986 An illegit. listed name. No further information.

- - 'Mastersii' Masters   1897 In "Gar. Chron". (as *THUJA occidentalis plicata*). A confused name. Here listed under *THUJA occidentalis* var. *sibirica* Hoopes (= The 'Wareana' group).   B,D,K,R   U.S.A.

- - 'McConnell's Globe' Hort. Holland
    A superfluous synonym for 'Little Champion'.

- - 'McConnell Golden Sport' Hort. Amer.
    1985 A listed name. No further information.

- -**'Meckii'** L. Kordes   1984 In "Nurs. Cat". A compact, globose form with bright green leaves. **O.** Heinrich Kordes Nurs, Bilsen, Holstein.   D,G,K   Germany

- - **'Meinecke's Dwarf'** Welch
    1979 A dwarf globose to upright form with a cream-white variegation.   G,K,W2   Germany

- - 'Menhir' Hort. Holland   1986 A narrowly columnar tree.   G   Holland

- - 'Miky' H. J. van de Laar   1990 In "Dendroflora **27**". A very compact narrowly conical dwarf plant with fine light-green leaves.   Hungary

- - **'Milleri'** Welch   1979 A very slow-growing, bun-forming or conical clone with upstanding branches.   G,W2   U.K.

- - 'Minima' (1) Hornibrook   1923 A name of uncertain application. NIC.   B,H,W2   Germany

- - 'Minima' (2) Hort. Amer.   A listed name for a dwarf form, similar to 'Hetz Midget'.   K

- - 'Monstrosa' Nelson   1866 "The rustic branched" form.   B

- - **'Nana'** (1) Gordon   1875 Probably the plant here listed as 'Wareana Lutescens'.

- - **'Nana'** (2) Bailey   1933 See *THUJA occidentalis* 'Hoopsii'.   U.S.A.

- - **'Nigra'** Bailey   1933 A conical tree with leaves persistently dark green.   B,K   U.S.A.

- - 'Nigra Arborescens' Hort. Amer.
    1985 A listed name.

- - 'Odra' Hort. Poland   1992 Reported from the Botanic Garden. Wroclaw.

- - **'Ohlendorffii'** Beissner   1887 **O.** Raised on the Ohlendorff Nurs, Hamburg. ('Ohlendorfii'). Juvenile foliage with four sided shoots of adult foliage protruding from the top.   B,G,K,W2   Germany

- - 'Parsons Compacta' Hort   See 'Compacta'.   K

- - **'Pendula'** Gordon   1862 A tree with ascending branches, pendulous branchlets. **O.** Raised on the Standich Nurs, Bagshot, Surrey. (1857).   B,D,not G,H,K   U.K.

- - 'Pendula Glauca' Beissner
    1891 A pendulous form with glaucous foliage. NIC.   B   Germany

- - 'Pendula Variegata' Nelson
    1866 Presumably a descriptive name. NIC.   B   U.K.

- - **'Perk Vlaanderen'** J. Konijn
1971 A good, slow-growing, compact, cream variegated form. **L.** Konijn Nurs, Pinetum, Templehof. Reeuwijk, Boskoop. **O.** Unrecorded; named for the Director of Parks, Utrecht.　　　G　　　Holland

- - var. *plicata* Loudon
1838 In "Arb. Frut. Brit". Now known as *THUJA plicata*. The word 'Plicata' as the third element in a name is always a mistake.

- - 'Polish Gold' Hort. Holland
A superfluous synonym for 'Aurescens'.

- - 'Prostrata' Victorin and Rousseau
1940 Named for a malformed tree found in Gaspe Co.　　　B　　　Canada

- - 'Pulcherrima' Schelle
1920 Similar to 'Lutea' but brighter colour. **O.** Hesse Nurs, Weener-on-Ems. ('Pulchella Aurea').　　　B　　　Germany

- - 'Pulverulenta' Hort. Anglia
1989 An illegit. listed name.

- - **'Pumila'** Otto
1867 A flat-topped, compact shrub, tending to become conical with age; foliage dark green.　　　B,H,K,W　　　Germany

- - **'Pumila Sudworth'** Hort. Amer.
1970 Dwarf, globose; gold, turning copper-bronze in winter. **L.** Hillside Nurs, Lehighton, PA. ('Sudsworth').

- - 'Pusilla' Sudworth
1927 NOM. Perhaps the origin of the preceding item.　　　U.S.A.

- - **'Pygmaea'** Welch
1966 A conical bush with irregular growth pattern and broad rich leaves. (Hence the name 'Plicata Pygmaea' of some authors).　　　H,K,W　　　U.S.A.

- - **'Pyramidalis'** (Endlicher) Zederb.
1907 A narrow and symmetrically conical clone.　　　B,K　　　Germany

- - **'Pyramidalis Compacta'** Beissner
1904 A compact, narrowly conical clone.　　　B,G,K　　　Germany

- - 'Pyramidalis Douglasii' Hort. Amer.
1986 A listed name.

- - 'Pyramidalis Hillii' Hort. Amer.
1972 An illegit. name listed by Sherwood Nurs, Portland, OR.

- - 'Queen Elizabeth' Hort. Anglia
1992 Plant in Windsor Great Park, Berks.

- - **'Queen Victoria'** Späth
1891 In "Nurs. Cat". A very bushy form with the tips of new growth white. It is possibly a superfluous synonym for 'Albospica'.　　　B　　　Canada

- - **'Recurva'** D. Wyman
1961 In "Amer. Nurs. **113**". Indistinguishable from 'Recurvata'.　　　B　　　U.S.A.

- - **'Recurva Nana'** Carrière
1867 A dense, dwarf, globose to conical form with the tips of the foliage recurved.　　　B,D,G,K,W　　　Belgium

- - **'Recurvata'** Beissner
1891 Similar to, perhaps identical with 'Recurva Nana'.　　　B　　　Germany

- - 'Recurvata Argenteovariegata' Beissner
1891 As previous item, but leaves white variegated.　　　B　　　Germany

- - 'Reevesii' Kammerer
1932 Similar to 'Hoveyii', but foliage denser and a brighter green.　　　B　　　U.S.A.

- - 'Reflexa' Carrière
1867 Differs from 'Pendula' by it's elongated branches and the few branchlets.　　　B　　　France

- - **'Reidii'** Rehder   1902   A broad, dwarf form with small leaves, retaining its colour well. Named for Wm. Reid of Elizabeth, N.J. (before 1871).   B,H   U.S.A.

- - 'Rheindiana Globosa' Hort. Amer.
     See 'Globosa Rheindiana'.

- - **'Rheingold'** Vollert ex Beissner
     1904   A dwarf with persistently juvenile leaves; colour as 'Ellwangeriana Aurea'. **O.** and **I.** From seed on Vollert Nurs, Lubeck.   B,D,G,H,K,W   Germany

- - 'Rheingold Beattie' Hort. Amer.
     1986   A listed name for a conical plant with yellow foliage, bronzing in winter. Presumably a mutation.

- - 'Riversii' Beissner   1891   A compact, conical form with yellowish-green foliage.   B,D,K   Germany

- - 'Robusta' Carrière   1855   A name of uncertain application. See *THUJA occidentalis* var. *sibirica*.   France

- - 'Robusta Argentea' Hort. Ireland
     1989   Reported from National Botanic Garden, Dublin.

- - 'Robusta Recurva' Hort. Amer.
     1986   An illegit. listed name.

- - 'Rogeri' Hort. Canada   1987   An illegit. listed name.

- - **'Rosenthalii'** Beissner   1884   A compact, columnar form with dark green, lustrous foliage.   B,G,K,R   Germany

- - 'Saundersii' A.R. Buckley
     1980   In "Trees and Shrubs of the Dominium Arboretum".   Canada

- - **'Semperaurea'** Rehder   1923   Dense, broadly conical tree; foliage shiny green, golden-yellow tipped.   B,K   U.S.A.

- - 'Semperaurescens' Hort.   A mistake for 'Semperaurea'.

- - **'Sherman'** Reg'd. Arn. Arb.
     1952   Reg'd by C.C. Smith, Sherman Nurs. Chester City, Iowa. A broad, erect tree with heavy, dark green foliage. **O.** Sherman Nurs, (1931). **I.** The same (1934).   B   U.S.A.

- - **'Sherwood Column'** Sherwood
     1972   In "Nurs. Cat". A dense, thick, heavy, dark green columnar tree. **I.** Sherwood Nurs, Portland, OR.   U.S.A.

- - **'Sherwood Frost'** Sherwood
     1972   In "Nurs. Cat". Growth upright; foliage spotted white. **O.** As 'Sherman'.   U.S.A.

- - 'Sherwood Frosty'   See previous entry.

- - **'Sherwood Moss'** Hort. Amer.   In "Nurs. Cat". A conical tree of informal outline and green juvenile foliage, bronzing in winter. **O.** and **I.** As previous items.   U.S.A.

- - 'Sherwood Plumespire' Hort. Amer.
     Possibly a mistake for 'Sherwood Column'.

- - var. *sibirica* Hoopes   1866   "The Siberian Thuja". This is a mistaken name for a supposed local variant found near the Niagara River, with thick stems and flattened leaves held in upright sprays, which some early authors confused with *THUJA plicata*. They are here listed as cultivars under 'Wareana'.

- - 'Silveriana Nana' R.L. Fincham
     1984   In "Amer. Conif. Soc. Bull". Name only. **O.** Jon Spaan.   U.S.A.

- - 'Silver Beauty' Hort. Anglia
1992 Slow-growing conical plant with good creamy white variegation. L. Marwood Gdns. Barnstaple. Devon.

- - 'Silver Queen' Beissner   1891 Growth rather slow, leaves uniformly variegated white.   B   Germany

- -'Skogholm' H. J. Grootendorst
1969 In "Dendroflora 6". A dense columnar tree; as 'Rosenthalii' but a brighter green. O. Skogholm Planteskole.   K,R   Sweden

- - 'Skybound' Boughen   1966 In "Nurs. Cat". A dense, narrowly conical tree. I. Morden Res. Sta. Manitoba. O. R.M. Boughen, Valley River Nurs, Manitoba.   Canada

- - 'Smaragd' Poulsen   1950 In "Nurs. Cat". A compact, conical form with mid green foliage. A sport from 'Kelleriis Viridis'. O. D.T. Poulsen Nurs, Kelleriis.   B,G,K   Denmark

- - 'Smithiana' Bailey   1933 A compact, conical dwarf, leaves dark green, purplish in winter.   B,H   U.S.A.

- - 'Snow Queen' Hort. N.Z.   No information.

- - 'Späthii' Hort.   A mistake for 'Ohlendorffii'? There is a completely stable juvenile foliage form in cultivation on the continent.

- - 'Sphaerica' Hornibrook   1939 Similar to 'Globosa' but smaller in every way.   B,H,K,W2   U.K.

- - 'Spicata Aurea' Hort. Canada
1987 An illegit. listed name.

- - 'Spihlmannii' P. Smith in Beissner
1891 A clone in the 'Compacta' group which retains it's fresh green colour during the winter. O. and I. P. Smith Nurs, Bergedorf, Hamburg. NIC.   H,W   Germany

- - 'Spiralis' Rehder   1923 A slender tree with branches arranged spirally. L. Bobbink and Atkins Nurs, Rutherford, N.J.   B,D,G,K,W2   U.S.A.

- - 'Steuberi' Hort. Holland   1987 Upright habit; foliage green; twigs yellow.   G

- - 'St.John' Hort. Canada   1987 An illegit. listed name.

- - 'Stolwijk' H.J. van de Laar
1986 In "Naamlijst . . .". A medium-size, compact, conical form with light-yellow early growth colour irridescent like mother of pearl in autumn. O. and I. G.C. Stolwijk Nurs, Boskoop. NOM.   Holland

- - 'Stricta Variegata' Den Ouden
1949 Similar to 'Erecta' with a white variegation. O. A sport on the J. Pels Nurs, Hazerwoude, near Boskoop.   B   Holland

- - 'Sudworthii' Hort. Amer.   See 'Pumila Sudworthii'.

- - 'Sudworth Gold' L.C. Hatch
1988 In "Conifer Database". A slow-growing conical bush with golden foliage.   U.S.A.

- - 'Sunburnproof' Hort. Amer.
1985 An unacceptable listed name.

- - 'Sunkist' Grootendorst'   1968 In "Dendroflora 4". A fast-growing, dense, conical plant of a good yellow. O. Gebr. Boer Nurs, Boskoop.   G,K   Holland

- - 'Suzie' Hort. Anglia   1991 A listed name. L. Treborth Nurs. Bangor, Wales.

- - 'Syracuse Juvenile' Hort. Amer.
1985 An unacceptable listed name.

- - 'Tatarica' Beissner   1891 An early mistake. See *THUJA orientalis* var. *tatarica*.

- - 'Techny' Krüssmann   1972 A compact, broadly conical form holding the deep-green
                                colour well in hard weather.   K   Germany

- - 'Ten Ham' H.J. van de Laar
                                1986 In "Naamlijst . . .". An upright conical plant. I. A.E.
                                Schiphorst Nurs, Wageningen (before 1975). O. Totenham?   Holland

- - 'Tetragona' Beissner   1891 A similarly biforme plant to 'Ohlendorffii', but a much coarser
                                and stronger-growing plant.   W   Germany

- - 'Theodonensis' Beissner   1891 A broad, upstanding form with dark green leaves.
                                ('Magnifica').   B   Germany

- - 'Thuyopsoides' Beissner   1894 In "Mitt. d.d.d. Ges". A large, loose form somewhat
                                resembling a *THUJOPSIS*. O. Christopher Neder Nurs,
                                Frankfurt on Main.   B,K   Germany

- - 'Tiny Tim' Grootendorst
                                1968 In "Dendroflora 2". A very slow-growing, bun-forming clone,
                                bronzing in winter. O. Little Tree Farm, London, Ontario.   G,K,W2   Canada

- - 'Tom Thumb' Bailey   1933 Not of Hoopes (1868), Beissner (1891), Bailey (1923) or
                                Welch (1979). Bailey (1933) states, "This is the smallest of
                                it's class (i.e. 'Globosa') known, a tufted little plant of very
                                low compact growth, rarely exceeding nine inches".   W2   U.S.A.

- - 'Trompenburg' Hort. Holland
                                1987 Dwarf upright bush of irregular growth pattern; foliage
                                flattened and a good light gold colour. O. Collected by J.R.P.
                                van Hoey Smith on his travels.   G

- - 'Umbraculifera' Beissner
                                1892 A slow-growing, umbrella-shape dense form with blue-green
                                foliage. O. Christopher Neder Nurs, Frankfurt-on-Main.   B,G,H,KW2   Germany

- - 'Unicorn' Reg'd. C.O.P.F.
                                1975 Reg'd. by H.H. Stensson. An erect, broadly conical tree;
                                heavy dark green foliage. I. Sheridan Nurs, Oakville,
                                Ontario. O. C. DeGroot (1964).   Canada

- - 'Van der Bom' Den Ouden
                                1949 An ovoid bush with ascending branches. O. and I. Jan G. van
                                der Bom Nurs, Oudenbosch.   B,K   Holland

- - 'Van Rhoon' H. J. van de Laar
                                1983 In "Dendroflora 20". A globose clone. O. and I. L. Konijn
                                Nurs, then of Reeuwijk. Probably named for the person who
                                introduced it.   Holland

- - 'Variegata' Loudon   1838 Some branches carry a bright golden variegation.   U.K.

- - 'Vervaeneana' Gordon   1862 An irregularly variegated form with slender branches. O.
                                Raised by M. Verveane of Ghent.   B,D,K   Belgium

- - 'Virescens' Hort. Amer.   1986 An illegit. listed name.

- - 'Viridis' Beissner   1891 A compact, conical clone with lustrous dark-green foliage.   B,D   Germany

- - 'Vroman's Hedger' Hort.   A listed name.

- - 'Wabernensis' Utess   1926 A selection near to 'Wareana'. O. Raised by Gosset, Wabern,
                                near Bern.   B   Switzerl.

- - 'Wagneri' Fröbel   1895 A narrowly conical tree with fine, green foliage. O. Karl
                                Wagner, Leipzig.   B,D,K   Germany

- - 'Wansdyke Silver' Den Ouden/Boom
    1965 Dwarf pyramid well variegated with silver white. Found by
       H. J. Welch and W. Archer in a deserted nursery in Surrey. B,G,K,R,W U.K.

- - 'Wareana' (1) (Booth) Gordon
    1839 In "Nurs. Cat". Tree with upright branches and sprays of
       dark-green coarse foliage held similar to *THUJA orientalis*.
       Tradition attributes the origin of this plant to a nurseryman
       named Ware of Coventry (1821). See *THUJA occidentalis*
       var. *sibirica*. B,K

- - 'Wareana' (2) Hort.   Several similar clones are in cultivation. See also 'Mastersii'.

- - 'Wareana Globosa' Beissner
    1891 A very dense, globose selection. NIC. B,W2 Germany?

- - 'Wareana Lutescens' Hesse
    1884 In "Nurs. Cat". Upright plant similar to Wareana but ends of
       foliage sprays yellow. O. H.A. Hesse Nurs, Weener-on-Ems. B,D,G,K,W Germany

- - 'Washingtonia Aurea' Hort. Amer.
    1986 An illegit. listed name. No information.

- - 'Watereri' Hornibrook 1923 A form similar to 'Ericoides' that seems lost to cultivation. B,H U.K.

- - 'Watnong Gold' Reg'd Arn. Arb.
    1972 Reg'd by Don Smith, Watnong Nurs, Morris Plains, N.J. A
       sport of 'Ellwangeriana Aurea', making a slender column. O.
       The same. (1964). W2 U.S.A.

- - 'Waxen' Späth 1891 In "Nurs. Cat". An elegant form with yellowish-green leaves
       of waxy appearance. O. The Arnold Arboretum. B,G,K U.S.A.

- - 'Westminster' Hort. Amer.
    1986 A listed name. No information.

- - 'Wiegneriana' Beissner 1896 Very similar to 'Riversii'. B

- - 'Winona' Hort. Amer. 1985 A listed name. No information.

- - 'Wintergreen'   See 'Lombart's Wintergreen'.

- - 'Wintergreen Pyramidal' Hort. Amer.
    1987 An unsatisfactory name that should be replaced.

- - 'Woodwardii' Woodward
    1874 A globose bush with green foliage in vertical sprays. O. Jacob
       Manning, Reading Nurs, Mass. and named for his son, J.
       Woodward Manning. (1872). B,D,H,K,W U.S.A.

- - 'Woodwardii Aurea' Hort. Canada
    1987 An illegit. name.

- - 'Yellow Ribbon' H.J. van de Laar
    1983 In "Dendroflora 20". A neat, slim plant with bright yellow
       foliage. I. G. E. F. Bolwijn, Putten. O. F.A. Ruizendal and
       Son, Waverveen. Holland

THUJA orientalis Linnaeus
    1753 Biota, Chinese Arborvitae, Platycladus. 15m,Z6 China

This Genus is now botanically recognised as *PLATYCLADUS orientalis*, but the more familiar name is retained here
for the convenience of users of the Checklist, since this change has not been widely adopted in the nursery trade. It is
widely cultivated throughout China and in the mid-19th century, numerous variants were imported. These were at
first considered as a distinct species, but are now regarded as cultivars.

- - 'Angulisans' Carrière 1867 A shrub with branches and branchlets erect and set sideways.
       NIC. B France

- - 'Archer's Gold' Hort. Anglia
        1985 Reported from Windsor Great Park, Berks.

- - 'Argentea' Carrière	1855 Foliage silvery variegated. NIC.	B	France
- - 'Aristata' P. Mouillefert	1898 Branches short and much twisted.	B	France
- - 'Articulata' Beissner	1896 A dense, globose form with long, thin branches. NIC.	B	Germany
- - 'Ascotensis' R. Smith	1867 A clone of f. *aurea* found at Ascot, Surrey. NIC.	B	U.K.

- - 'Athrotaxoides' (Carrière) Nicholson
        1887 Foliage as in *CHAMAECYPARIS obtusa* 'Athrotaxoides'.
              Named for a plant in Jardin des Plantes in Paris. (1897).
              ('Arthrotaxoides').   B,G,K,W2   U.K.

- - f. *aurea* (Carrière) Rehder
        1949 A botanical designation covering all clones with golden-
              yellow foliage. Not a clonal name.   W2

- - 'Aurea' Knight and Perry 1850 A clone of f. *aurea* no longer identifiable. So it is of value
              now only in a collective sense. NIC.

- - **'Aurea Nana'** Sénéclauze
        1868 "The Beehive Golden Biota". A dense, dwarf, ovoid bush with
              branches in vertical planes; foliage light golden-yellow, dull
              in winter. Similar seedlings turn up and 'Aurea Compacta',
              'Aurea Densa', 'Aurea Globosa', 'Millard's Gold' and ' Minima
              Aurea' are names used for clones that are difficult to separate.   B,D,G,H,K,W   France

- - 'Aureovariegata' Henkel and Hochstetter
        1865 The accepted name for a variegated clone raised from a
              seedling on the M. Dauvesse Nurs.   B   France

- - **'Aureus Nana'** Hort. Canada	A mistake. See 'Aurea Nana'.		
- - **'Bakeri'** Bailey	1933 A hardy clone with pale green leaves. NIC.	B	U.S.A.
- - **'Balaton'** Barabits	1965 In "Magyar Fenyóújdonságok".		Hungary

- - **'Berckmans Golden Biota'** Hort. Amer.
        See 'Conspicua'.   U.S.A.

- - **'Beverleyensis'** Rehder in Bailey
        1917 A columnar form, with young foliage golden-yellow. O. Hort.
              California.   B,K,W2   U.S.A.

- - **'Blijdenstein'** Den Ouden
        1949 A clone with yellowish-green foliage. O. Raised from seed on
              the Blijdenstein Pinetum, Hilversum.   B,G.K,W2   Holland

- - **'Blue Cone'** Monrovia
        Upright-oval plant with foliage bluish-purple in winter. L
        Monrovia Nurs, Azusa, CAL.   G,K   U.S.A.

- - **'Blue Spire'** L.C. Hatch 1988 In "Conifer Database". A conical tree; foliage blue-green.   U.S.A.

- - **'Bonita'** Slavin
        1932 A conical dwarf form; foliage bright green, yellow tips. L. D.
              Hill Nurs, Dundee, Ill. (1927).   B,H,K,W2   U.S.A.

- - **'Buchan'** Hort. Amer. 1987 L. Cedar Lodge Nurs.?   U.S.A.?

- - 'Caribbean Holiday' Hort. Anglia
        1985 A dwarf with a very bright golden colour. I. Wansdyke Nurs,
              Devizes, Wilts. O. Raised from a cutting brought to the
              nursery by an unrecorded customer.   U.K.

- - 'Cedar Lodge' Hort. N.Z. 1989 A listed name. L. Yamina Nurs, Monbulk, Australia.

- - 'Collens Gold' Hort. Anglia
  1983 Bright yellow columnar form.

- - 'Compacta' Hort. Amer.   See 'Sieboldii'.   K

- - 'Compacta Nana' Hornibrook
  1939 A slow-growing, formal, conical tree; foliage glaucous green,
        juvenile in parts, tipped mauve in winter.   B,H,K   U.K.

- - **'Conspicua'** Carrière   1902 A conical to columnar small tree with twigs vertically set;
        foliage pale yellow. O. Berckman, (before 1902).   B,K,W2   U.S.A.

- - 'Cristata' Carrière   1867 A slow-growing form with contorted foliage. O. Sénéclauze
        Nurs, Bourg Argental, Loires.   B   France

- - 'Cupressoides' R. Smith   1867 A synonym of 'Pyramidalis'.   B   France

- - 'Densa Glauca' Beissner   1891 A dense, dwarf, globose plant; leaves glaucous green. O. G.
        Jackman and Son, Woking, Surrey.   B,K,W2   U.K.

- - 'Dumosa' Beissner   1891 A mistake for *THUJA occidentalis* 'Dumosa'.

- - **'Dwarf Greenspike'** Ealy
  1988 In "Amer. Nurs. 113". O. Found by Dr. Ealy (1940). Conical
        growth dense.   B,K   U.S.A.

- - 'Elegans Aurea Nana' Krüssmann
  1983 An illegit. name. Probably a mistake for 'Aurea Nana'.   K   France

- - **'Elegantissima'** Rollisson ex Gordon
  1862 A narrow, conical tree; leaves golden-yellow, having a red-
        brown cast during the winter. O. Rollisson Nurs, Tooting,
        London (1858).   B,G,K   U.K.

- - 'Elegantissima Picta' De Vos
  1887 A silvery dwarf form.   B   Holland

- - 'Ensata' Carrière   1867 A curious tree with contorted foliage. NIC.   B   France

- - 'Ericoides' Dallimore and Jackson
  1923 Doubtfully distinct from *THUJA occidentalis* 'Ericoides'.   D   U.K.

- - 'Excelsa' Griffing   1929 In "Nurs. Cat". A tree of poor constitution. O. Griffing Nurs,
        Beaumont, Texas. NIC.   B   U.S.A.

- - 'Expansa' Lawson   1852 A tree with loose, spreading habit. NIC.   B   U.K.

- - 'Falcata' Lindley   1862 A dense upright form with large cones and long, sickle-like
        spines, said to be used for hedging in Japan? O. Found by
        J.G. Veitch and sent by him to the Veitch Nurs. NIC?   B   Hort. Japan

- - 'Falcata Lutea' Webster   1896 As previous entry but with golden-yellow foliage?   B   U.K.?

- - 'Falcata Nana' R. Smith   1867 A clone similar to but dwarfer than 'Falcata'.   B   U.K.?

- - 'Fastigiata' Hort. Ireland 1989 Reported from the National Botanic Garden, Dublin.   Ireland

- - 'Filifera' Hort.   A mistake, see 'Flagelliformis'.

- - **'Filiformis'** Loddiges ex Carrière
  1855 A threadleaf form no longer identifiable. NIC.   H   France

- - 'Filiformis Elegans' Sénéclauze
  1868 A curious plant found on the Sénéclauze Nurs, Bourg
        Argental, Loires. NIC.   B   France

  'Filiformis Erecta' Sénéclauze
  1868 A plant similar to 'Flagelliformis' but with erect branches. O.
        Same as previous entry.('Filiformis Stricta').   B,G,K,W2   France

- - 'Filiformis Nana' Sénéclauze
    1868 A very dwarf form also found on the same nursery. NIC.   B   France

- - 'Filiformis Pendula' Hort.
    1987 An unrecorded name for a pendulous, thread-like tree.   G

- - 'Filiformis Stricta' Beissner
    1891 Same as 'Filiformis Erecta'. NIC.   H

- - 'Flagelliformis' Jacques   1837 A pendulous threadleaf form that is no longer identifiable. Similar forms turn up in the seedbeds. NIC.   B,K,W2

- - 'Flame' Hort. Anglia   Columnar yellow turning red-brown in winter. O. and I. Spicer Nurs. Lutterworth, Leicestershire.   U.K.

- - 'Flash' Hort. Australia   1993 A listed name. O. Ferny Creek Nurs, Victoria. (Formerly distributed as 'J.W. Versteege').

- - 'Freneloides' R. Smith   1867 A superfluos synonym of 'Nepalensis'.

- - **'Fruitlandii'** Monrovia   1987 A compact, cone-shaped plant with rich-green foliage. L. Monrovia Nurs, Azusa, Cal.   U.S.A.

- - 'Funiculata' R. Smith   1867 A mere curiosity, apparently unstable. NIC.   B   U.K.

- - 'Glauca' Lawson   1852 A tall, widespreading tree. Foliage has a silvery-glaucous bloom. O. Raised by Lucombe and Pince Nurs, Exeter.   B   U.K.

- - 'Glauca Minima' R. Smith
    1872 See 'Minima Glauca'.

- - 'Globosa' H. Fraser   1875 A compact globose form with dark-green foliage. Probably not now true to name in cultivation.   B   U.K.

- - 'Gold Nugget' G. Haddow
    1991 Raised from seed. Very dwarf plant wider than high, good gold coloured form. L. Kenwith Nurs, Bideford, Devon.   U.K.

- - 'Gold Spire' Hort. Anglia   1985 Reported from Windsor Great Park. Berks.

- - **'Golden Ball'** Duncan & Davies
    1984 Forms an almost truly spherical plant, well furnished to the ground. L. Duncan & Davies Nurs, New Plymouth. O. Roly Barry, South Taranaki Nurs.   N.Z.

- - 'Golden Minaret' Hort. Anglia
    1985 Reported from Windsor Great Park. Berks.

- - **'Golden Pygmy'** H.J. van de Laar
    1986 In "Naamlijst . . .". A diminutive and very golden plant in the 'Aurea Nana' group. O. and I. L. Lulssen, Nuth.   Holland

- - **'Golden Rocket'** L. Konijn
    1968 In "Sortimentslijst". A stiffly upright form with several leaders.   Holland

- - 'Golden Septre' Hort. Anglia
    1993 A listed name. Windsor Great Park. Berks.

- - **'Golden Surprise'** H.J. van de Laar
    1977 In "Dendroflora 13". A cross between 'Aurea Nana' and 'Blijdenstein'. A dense pointed cone: foliage bright yellow becoming bronze-yellow in winter.   K   Holland

- - 'Golden Wonder' Hort. Ireland
    1985 Reported from Mount Congreave. Co. Wexford.   Ireland

- - 'Goodwin' D. Wyman   1961 In "American Nurseryman". A dense, symmetrical clone: deep green foliage. O. Paul M. Goodwin Nurs, Kingfisher, Okla.   B   U.S.A.

- - f. *gracilis* Carrière   1855 A superfluous synonym for 'Nepalensis'.   Nepal

- - 'Grasmere Gold' Hort. Anglia
                              1985 Slow-growing pillar, bright gold. O. and I. Hayes Nurs,
                                    Grasmere, Cumbria.

- - 'Grassington Gold' Hort. Anglia
                              1985 Reported from Windsor Great Park, Berks.

- - **'Greenangold'** John Emery
                              1989 In "Conif. Soc. Australian Newsletter 5". A narrow column.
                                    Both foliage and cones mixed green and gold. Will come true
                                    from seed.   N.Z.

- - **'Green Cone'** Hort. N.Z. 1985 A compact clone; foliage green, purple in winter. L. Cedar
                                    Lodge Conifer Nurs, New Plymouth.

- - 'Hillieri' Hornibrook   1923 An ovoid dwarf with foliage a soft yellow-green, green by
                                    winter. O. Hillier's Nurs, Winchester, (c. 1929).   B,H,K   U.K.

- - 'Hirose' Hort. Japan   1987 A dwarf variegated form. Inner foliage green, outer foliage
                                    gold variegated with white. Variegation more pronounced if
                                    planted in some slight shade. O. Y. Hirose, Iwakuni, Japan.
                                    L. Kenwith Castle Nurs, Bideford, Devon.

- - 'Hohman' D. Wyman   1961 In "Amer. Nurs, **113**". Named for a tree in Arnold Arboretum.
                                    O. An unrecorded nursery in Missouri.   B   U.S.A.

- - 'Howardii' Hort. Amer.   Now known as 'Blue Spire'.

- - 'Hybrida' Hoopes   1868 Possibly a compact clone of f. *gracilis*. NIC.

- - 'Incurvata' R. Smith   1867 Tall, densely branched; foliage very bright green. NIC.   B   U.K.

- - 'Intermedia' Carrière   1855 A form intermediate between 'Flagelliformis' and the norm.   B,K   U.K.

- - **'Juniperoides'** Carrière 1855 A rounded bush with juvenile foliage, green in summer,
                                    turning grey-purple in winter. ('Decussata').   B,G,K,W2   Hort. Japan

- - 'Kenwith' Hort. Anglia   1985 In "Nurs. Cat". Slender yellow pillar. O. and I. Kenwith
                                    Castle Nurs, Bideford, Devon.   U.K.

- - 'Kormend' Hort   1965 All as 'Balaton'.   Czechosl.

- - 'Laxenburgensis' Rosenthal
                              1888 A dense, slender cone. I. Rosenthal Nurs, Albern. O. Found
                                    by M. Chlupaty at the Castle Laxenburg, near Vienna.   B   Austria

- - 'Lisa' Hort. Amer.   1992 A slow-growing upright form, fresh green foliage slightly
                                    montrous as in 'Athrotaxoides'. Plant in Windsor Great Park,
                                    Berks.

- - 'Macrocarpa' R. Smith   1867 Clone with unusually large fruits. I. Ellwanger and Barry,
                                    Mt. Hope Nurs, N.Y. Now probably NIC.   B   U.S.A.

- - 'Madurodam' H.J. van de Laar
                              1986 In "Naamlijst . . .". A variety with creamy-yellow leaves,
                                    turning green. O. and I. J. Konijn, Lunteren, Ederveen.   Holland

- - 'Magnifica' Krüssmann   1979 A narrowly conical clone, similar to 'Elegantissima' O.
                                    unrecorded.   K

- - **'Meldensis'** (Quetier) Masters
                              1855 A rounded or upright bush with predominantly juvenile
                                    foliage.   B,G,.H,K,W2   France

- - 'Miller's Gold' Hort. Anglia   Doubtfully distinguishable from 'Aurea Nana'.

- - **'Minima'** Nicholson	1901 This is the earliest recorded name for this plant. See also the following entry.	B,G,W	U.K.
- - 'Minima Glauca' Beissner	1891 The accepted name for *BIOTA orientalis pygmaea* of Richard Smith (1867), changed by him to 'Glauca Minima' in 1872. A squat bush, leaves glaucous green, turning to yellowish-brown.	B,G	U.K.
- - 'Monstrosa' Carrière	1855 (In Index.) Clone with thick, short, congested leaves. NIC.	B,H	France
- - 'Monstruosa' Carrière	1855 A mis-spelling. See the previous entry.		
- - **'Morgan'** John Emery	1989 In "Conif. Soc. Australia Newsletter 5". Similar to 'Aurea Nana' but slower growing and with juvenile foliage.		Australia
- - f. *nana* Carrière	1855 A category no longer distinguished within the species. Useful only as a collective name.		
- - **'Nana Compacta'** Slavin	1932 A name of no clear application. It should not be used.		U.S.A.
- - 'Nepalensis' Endlicher	1847 Of graceful and ascending habit and regular growth. NIC.	B,K	France
- - 'Newarkii' Hort. Canada	1964 An illegit. listed name. L. McConnell Nurs, Canada.		
- - 'Pekinensis' Gordon	1875 A large, spreading tree. O. Found by R. Fortune near Peking and introduced into U.K. (1861).	B	Hort. China
- - var. *pendula* (Endlicher) Carrière	1855 A group of pendulous forms at one time treated as a separate species, *BIOTA pendula*.		
- - 'Pendula Variegata' Nelson	1866 Evidently a variegated 'sport' of the preceding entry. NIC.	B	U.K.
- - 'Picta' R. Smith	1872 A handsome form with cream coloured variegation. NIC.		U.K.
- - f. *pisifera* Carrière	1867 Not now distinguished within the species.	B	France
- - 'Pumila Argentea' Veitch ex Hornibrook	1923 Slow-growing form no longer identifiable. (Possibly = 'Summer Cream').	B	U.K.
- - **'Purple King'** Hort. Anglia	1979 L. Wansdyke Nurs, Devizes, Wilts.		U.K.
- - 'Pygmaea' R. Smith	1864 Name changed to 'Glauca Minima' in 1872. See 'Minima'.	B	U.K.
- - 'Pyramidalis' R. Smith	1867 A variant no longer identifiable. NIC		Hort. China
- - 'Pyramidalis Aurea' Hort. Germany	1972 An illegit. listed name. L. Kordes.	G,K	
- - **'Raffles'** Hort. Australia	1982 Dense, conical dwarf; foliage yellow in spring, bronze by winter. O. Yamina Rare Plants Nurs, Monbulk, Victoria.		Australia
- - 'Raket' H.J. van de Laar	1990 In "Dendroflora 27". A fastigiate form with threadleaf, light green leaves. I. A.M. Vergeer, Boskoop.		Holland
- - 'Rochester' D. Wyman	1961 In "American Nurseryman". A hardy clone selected by B. Slavin, Highland Park, Rochester, N.Y.	B	U.S.A.
- - 'Rosedale' Den Ouden/Boom	1965 A juvenile form yellow in spring, green in summer, purple in winter - wind tender. O. Rosedale Nurs, Washington Co., Texas. ('Rosedale hybrid').	B,K,W2	U.S.A.
- - **'Rosedalis'** Welch	1966 Name now in general use in place of 'Rosedalis Compacta'.	G,W2	

- - 'Rosedalis Compacta 'Hornibrook
          1923 See 'Rosedale'.   B,H,K   France

- - 'Rowneri' Hort. Anglia   1985 Reported from Windsor Great Park, Berks.

- - **'Sanderi'** Gough and Welch
          1978 In "Journal Linnean Soc. 77". Juvenile form. thick leaves,
                 blue in summer, purple in winter. Formerly listed as
                 CHAMAECYPARIS obtusa 'Sanderi'. and other names.   G,K,W2   Hort. Japan

- - **'Semperaurea'** Moore   1871 A sub-globose shrub with golden-yellow foliage maintained
                 throughout the year. **O.** V. Lemoine Nurs, Nancy.
                 ('Semperaurescens').   B,K   U.K.

- - 'Shirley Chilcott' Hort. Anglia
          1990 A listed name. No information. Wansdyke Nurs, Devizes,
                 Wilts.

- - 'Shirl's Supreme' J. Emery
          1989 In "Conif. Soc. Australia Newsletter 5".

- - **'Sieboldii'** (Endlicher) Lawson
          1851 A large, dense, beehive-shaped bush with creamish foliage in
                 spring then green. I. Into Leiden from Japan (1859).   B,H.K.W2   Hort. Japan

- - 'Skalbotg'

- - 'Southport' Hort. Anglia 1991 Shown at Southport Show, Southport, Lancs.

- - **'Spire'** Hort. N.Z.   1987 A clone allied to 'Beverleyensis', but a narrowly columnar
                 habit of growth. **L.** Cedar Lodge Nurs, New Plymouth.   N.Z.

- - 'Stricta' Loudon   1838 A tall, narrow columnar tree, fastigiate branches. NIC.
                 ('Pyramidalis').   B,K   U.K.

- - **'Summer Cream'** Welch
          1979 A small. round-topped little bush with it's young foliage
                 cream coloured. **O.** and **I.** Everton Nurs, Hants.   W2   U.K.

- - **'Tetragona'** (Beissner) Hornibrook
          1923 Similar to 'Filiformis Erecta', but with foliage noticeably
                 four-sided.   B,H,K   U.K.

- - 'Triangularis' (Carrière) Nicholson
          1867 A curious form with foliage in triangular sprays. NIC.   B,H   France

- - 'Trompenburg' Hort. Japan
          1988 Upright, pillar shaped plant, yellow foliage with white
                 variegation. Received by J.R.P. van Hoey Smith from Japan.
                 Much faster growing than 'Hirose'.

- - 'Ungeri' Boehmer   1903 In "Nurs. Cat". A dwarf globose clone; branchlets white-
                 tipped. **O.** Found by O. Unger in a Japanese garden (1904).
                 NIC.   B,H   Germany

- - 'Variegata' Dallimore and Jackson
          1855 A clone with mixed light-green and golden-yellow foliage.
                 NIC. ('Variegata Aurea').   D   France

- - 'Variegata Argentea' Carrière
          1855 As last entry, but the variegation is creamy-white. NIC.   France

- - 'Verschaffeltii' (Lemoine) Jaeger
          1865 A form with the tips of all branchlets golden-yellow. **O.** A
                 seedling raised by J. Makoy, a florist at Liege.   B   Belgium

- - **'Wainiui Petite'** Int. Con. Reg.
  1988 Dwarf ovoid bush; foliage pale lemon green, brighter in spring and summer. **I.** Cedar Lodge Nurs, New Plymouth. **O.** Seedling from 'Beverleyensis' on Bayley's Nurs, Gisborne.   N.Z.

- - **'Wang's Green'** H. J. van de Laar
  1983 In "Dendroflora 20". Dwarf globose plant; foliage dark green, deep purple-brown in winter. **I.** N. Rijlaarsdam Nurs, Boskoop. **O.** Wang's Nurs, Boskoop.   G   Holland

- - 'Weimerii' Beissner   1891 A compact form of 'Aurea'. **O.** Weimer Nurs, Bonn. NIC.   B,H   Switzerl.

- - **'Westmont'** Monrovia   1979 In "Nurs. Cat". An upright oval bush; foliage dark green tipped yellow. **I.** Monrovia Nurs, Azusa, Cal.   K   U.S.A.

- - 'Zuccariniana' R. Smith   1867 Dwarf globose bush; foliage persistent bright green. NIC.   U.K.

THUJA plicata Donn. ex D. Don
  1824 Western Red Cedar.   50m,Z5   West N. Amer.

This species was known by some early writers as *THUJA gigantea* or as *THUJA lobbii* and many names of variants now regarded as cultivars are listed under those names in older conifer books.

- - 'Argentea' Hort Australia   1989 An illegit name for a slow-growing form with the new growth white.

- - **'Atrovirens'** (R. Smith) Sudworth
  1897 Leaves shining dark green.   B,G,K,R   U.S.A.

- - **'Aurea'** Sénéclauze   1868 Leaves yellowish, with scattered patches of yellow.   D,K,R   France

- - 'Aureovariegata' Dallimore and Jackson
  1966 Probably identical with 'Zebrina', under which name it is now known in the trade.   D   U.K.

- - **'Aurescens'** Krüssmann   1960 Growth normal; growing shoots yellowish-green.   K   Germany

- - 'Balaton' Hort. Czechoslovakia
  1990 A listed name.

- - 'Bedgebury' Hort. Anglia   1992 A listed name. Plant in Windsor Great Park, Berks.

- - 'Bronze Darley Dale' Hort. Ireland
  1946 Reported from the National Arboretum, Dublin.

- - **'Bronze Prince'** Hort. N.Z.
  1987 Medium to large tree. Green in summer, turning a deep chocolate-brown. **L.** Cedar Lodge Nurs, New Plymouth.   N.Z.

- - 'Canadian Gold' R.L. Fincham
  1985 In "Coenosium Nurs. Cat". A fast-growing, broad, conical tree with bright yellow foliage.   U.S.A.

- - 'Cancan' Hort. N.Z.   A compact, conical form; leaves green with cream tips. **I.** Ross Stuart's Nurs. **O.** Blue Mountain Nurs, Tapuran, West Otaso. ('Can Can').   N.Z.

- - 'Cole's Variety' Hort. Anglia   A listed name. No information.

- - **'Collyer's Gold'** Welch   1976 In Wansdyke "Nurs. Cat". Slowly forms an upright bush; foliage green with rich golden growing tips.   W2   U.K.

- - 'Copper Gold' Hort. Holland
  1990 A dwarf form, descriptively named. **I.** van Dool, Boskoop.

- - **'Copper Kettle'** Welch   1978 In Wansdyke "Nurs. Cat". Slowly forms an upright bush with foliage golden-bronze - at it's best in Winter. **O.** E. Jenisch of Vienna.   Austria

- - 'Cristata' Webster   1896 A dwarf bush with foliage tufted at the tips. NIC.   B   U.K.

- - **'Cuprea'** Den Ouden   1949 A medium size ovoid bush; foliage dull yellow becoming bronze-yellow. O. and I. W.H. Rogers Nurs, Chandlers Ford. (c.1930).   B,G,K,W2   U.K.

- - 'December Gold' Hort. Anglia
    1992 A listed name. Plant in Windsor Great Park, Berks. ('Windsor Gold'?).

- - **'Doone Valley'** H.G. Hillier
    1970 In "Conifer Conference List". A slow-growing, conical bush; foliage golden-bronze. O. A selection by R.S. Corley of High Wycombe.   U.K.

- - **'Dura'** Timm   1948 In "Nurs. Cat". Narrowly conical with branches erect; foliage dark green, tender. I. J. Timm & Co. Nurs, Elmshorn, Near Hamburg. O. Found in a private garden in Oberbayerern. NIC.   B,K   Germany

- - 'Elegantissima' Hort. Amer.   An illegit. listed name. No information.

- - 'Erecta' R. Smith   1872 Upright, compact; foliage bright green. NIC.   B   U.K.

- - 'Euchlora' Krüssmann   1955 Narrowly conical but open habit. I. J. Timm & Co. Nurs, Elmshorn near Hamburg.   B,K   Germany

- - 'Excelsa' Timm   1947 In "Nurs. Cat". A tall, loose column - branches spreading; foliage dark glossy green. I. J. Timm and Co. O. Found in a cemetery in Berlin.   B,K   Germany

- - 'Extra Gold' Hort. Europe   Now to be 'Zebrina Extra Gold'.

- - 'Fastigiata' Carrière   1867 Habit as a Lombardy Poplar. ('Columnaris', 'Pyramidal').   B,K,R   Germany

- - 'Gelderland' Hort. Germany
    1992 A listed name. L. Horstmann Nurs. Schneverdingen.

- - 'Glauca' Henkel and Hochstetter
    1865 Foliage noticeably glaucous-green.   B   Germany

- - 'Globosa' Hort. Anglia   An illegit. and unacceptable listed name.

- - 'Gracilis' De Vos   1887 A loose bush of irregular growth. NIC.   B,D,K,W2   Holland

- - 'Gracilis Aurea' Den Ouden
    1949 Similar to previous item, but leaves tipped yellow.   B,G,K   Holland

- - **'Green Spire'** H. J. van de Laar
    1986 In "Naamlijst . . .". An upright, narrowly conical form; leaves light green. I. L. Poulsen, Nuth. (1982).   Holland

- - 'Green Sport' Hort. Amer.
    1968 A selection by Don Smith. Watnong Nurs, insufficiently distinctive to be worth retaining.

- - 'Green Survival' Krüssmann
    1983 A strong-growing, broadly conical form; foliage bright green. O. A seedling on the Darthuiser Nurs, Leesum, (1971).   K   Holland

- - **'Hillieri'** Hornibrook   1923 Globose shrub; dense green foliage. O. Mutation on Hillier's Nurs, Winchester (1880).   B,G,H,K,W2   U.K.

- - 'Hogan' Hort. Canada   1986 A listed name. ('Hoganii').

- - 'Incurva' Beissner   1894 Named for a tree in Villa Wendelstad, having incurved branches.   B   Germany

- - 'Irish Gold' Hort.   A listed name. Probably a mistake for 'Zebrina Extra Gold'.

- - 'J.Timm & Co' Hort. 1940 In "Nurs. Cat". Name later changed to 'Excelsa'.   B

- - 'Krauses Weeping' Hort. Amer.
           1982 L. Iseli Nurs, Boring, Oregon, PA.

- - 'Lobi' Hort. Canada   1986 A listed name. L. T.J. Cole in "Woody Plants Source List".
               NOM. Perhaps a mistake for 'Lobbii'?

- - 'Mendelii' Lombarts   1905 In "Nurs. Cat". A vigorous, dense tree: foliage tinged yellow.
               I. P. Lombarts Nurs, Zundert. O. Found in a local garden. B   Holland

- - 'Minima' R. Smith   1864 A mistake for *THUJA orientalis* 'Minima'.

- - 'Nana' Hort.   Now known as 'Sieboldii'.

- - **'Old Gold'** C.R. Harrison
           1975 In "Ornamental Conifers". A gold plant bronze in winter.
               Popular in N.Z. for hedges.O. Raised in Millichamps Nurs.   N.Z.

- - 'Pendula' Lieb ex Schneider
           1913 A conical tree with pendulous branches. O. E. Lieb, Partenit.
               NIC.   B   S.Russia

- - 'Pumila' R. Smith   1872 A dwarf bun-shaped plant; foliage bright green. NIC. B,G,W2 U.K.

- - 'Pygmaea' Hort. Amer. 1968 An illegit. listed name. No information.

- - 'Recurvata' Dallimore and Jackson
           1923 Branches much twisted.   B,D   U.K.

- - 'Roger's Golden Globe' Hort. Amer.
           1985 If distinguishable from 'Rogersii', then probably a mutation
               therefrom.

- - **'Rogersii'** Den Ouden/Boom
           1965 A globose to squatly conical dwarf; leaves very small, golden
               yellow. O. and I. W.H. Rogers Nurs, Chandler's Ford.
               (1928).   B,G,H,K,W2 U.K.

- - 'Rogersii Aurea' Hornibrook Now known in the trade as 'Rogersii'.   H

- - 'Saville Gardens' Hort. Anglia
           1985 A listed name. No information.

- - 'Semperaurescens' Dallimore and Jackson
           1923 Young shoots and leaves tinged with gold.   B,D   U.K.

- - **'Stoneham Gold'** W.H. Rogers
           1948 In "Nurs. Cat". An upright shrub; young leaves copper-gold,
               turning to dark green. O. Seedling from 'Aurea' raised by
               Gardner, foreman at W.H.Rogers Nurs, Chandler's Ford. B,G,K,R,W2 U.K.

- - 'Sunburst' Hort. Amer. 1986 A listed name for a tree form with golden foliage.

- - 'Sunshine' Hort. Amer. 1986 Another listed name for a similar plant. Possibly the same?

- - 'Threadleaf' Hort. Anglia 1992 A listed name. Plant in Windsor Great Park, Berks.

- - **'Theunissen'** J. Konijn 1968 In "Sortimentslijst". An upright, narrowly conical tree. O.
               Probably named for the finder - a visitor to the nursery. See
               'Green Spire' which may be it's present name in the trade?   Holland

- - 'Umbraculifera' Hort. Anglia
           1984 Reported from Royal Botanic Garden, Kew.

- - 'Variegata' Hort. Amer. 1986 An illegit. listed name.

- - 'Wareana' R. Smith   1864 (And other early authors). A mistake for *THUJA occidentalis*
               'Wareana'.

- - **'Watnong Green'** Mitsch

    1990 Broadly conical tree; foliage green, colour retained
throughout the year.   U.S.A.

- - **'Winter Pink'** G. Haddow

    1988 In "Nurs. Cat". A variegated clone which during winter has a
pink tinge. **I**. Kenwith Castle Nurs, Bideford, Devon.   U.K.

- - **'Zebrina'** Dallimore and Jackson

    1923 A vigorous tree with gold and green foliage in stripes, like a
zebra.   B,D,G,K,R   U.K.

- - **'Zebrina Extra Gold'** Hort. Europe

    1987 A listed name. Similar variegation but much greater area of
golden-yellow.   G   Ireland

THUJA sibirica   (Of some early authors). Now known as *THUJA occidentalis*
var. *sibirica*.

THUJA standishii (Gordon) Carrière

    1867 Japanese Thuja.   18m,Z7   Japan

THUJA standishii x *THUJA plicata*

    1985 In "Dendroflora 6". **I**. F.G. Grootendorst and Sons.   Denmark

THUJA sutchuensis Franchet

    1899 Szechuan Thuja. A rare species, probably not in cultivation.   5m,Z7   China

THUJOPSIS (Linnaeus) Siebold and Zuccarini (1844)

C u p r e s s a c e a e

A monotypic genus of tall, monoecious trees found only in Japan. It is related to *THUJA*, but the thick foliage is glaucous-white on the underside.

THUJOPSIS borealis Hort. ex Lindley
    1854 A mistake for *CHAMAECYPARIS nootkatensis*.

THUJOPSIS dolabrata Linnaeus (f.) Siebold and Zuccarini			
1844 Southern Japanese Thujopsis.		20m,Z5	S. Japan
- - 'Albovariegata'	1985 Reported from Windsor Great Park, Berks.		U.K.
- - 'Altissima' Ansorge	1902 Narrowly columnar. **O.** Seedling raised by Ansorge, nurseryman at Flottbeck, near Hamburg.	B,G,K	Germany
- - 'Atrovirens' ·	1866 "Leaves dark green".	B	U.K.
- - **'Aurea'** Nelson	1866 "Leaves golden variegated".	B	U.K.
- - 'Aurescens' Hort.	1987 Reported from Arboretum Trompenburg, Rotterdam, Holland.	G	
- - 'Cantab' Hort.	1977 Unpublished name for a variegated dwarf form. **I.** Ralph B. Sachs, The Dell Nurs, Woodham Mortimer, Essex. **O.** Said to have been found in the Cambridge Botanic Gardens.		U.K.
- - **'Cristata'** Ansorge	1902 A conical dwarf form with contorted growth. **O.** A seedling raised by Ansorge. (See above).	B,G,K	Germany
- - 'Decumbens' Beissner	1891 A normal tree save for the nodding branches. var. *dolabrata*.	B	Germany
- - var. *dolabrata* Henry	1907 The Southern Japanese Thujopsis. (The "type").	B,K	S. Japan
- - **'Glauca'** Nelson	1866 "Leaves very glaucous".	B	U.K.
- - **'Gracilis'** Nelson	1866 Slender branches and small leaves.	B,K	U.K.
- - **'Hondai'** Hort.	See var. *hondai*.		
- - var. *hondai* Makino	1901 The Northern Japanese Thujopsis.	B,K	Japan
- - 'Krugers Findling' Hort. Germany			
1992 A listed name. L. Horstmann Nurs, Schneverdingen.			
- - var. *laetevirens* Lindley	1861 In "Gardeners' Chronicle". Now known as 'Nana'.	R	Hort. Japan
- - 'Latifolia' Veitch ex Sénéclauze			
1868		B	France
- - **'Nana'** Siebold and Zuccarini			
1844 Formerly known as var. *laetevirens*, this name is in widespread use. **I.** Into U.K. by J.H. Veitch (1861).	B,G,H,K,W2	Hort. Japan
- - 'Plicata' Ansorge	1902 A semi-procumbent, dwarf form. **O.** A seedling raised by Ansorge. NIC.	B	Germany
- - 'Pygmaea' Hort. Amer.	An illegit. listed name.		
- - 'Robusta' Beissner	1891 A vigorous form with peculiar branch sructures.	B,K	Holland
- - 'Variegata' Von Siebold	1861 Irregular, creamy-white patches.	B,G,K,R	Hort. Japan

THUJOPSIS standishii Gordon
    1862 A mistake. See *THUJA standishii*.

TORREYA Arnott (1838)

cephalotaxaceae

The Nutmegs consisted of five species at one time classified under *Taxaceae*.

TORREYA californica Torrey			
1854	Californian nutmeg.	20m,Z8	California
- - 'Hergest Croft' Hort. Anglia			
1991	A dwarf plant raised from seed of 'Variegata' at Hergest Croft, Kington, Herefordshire. The plant is prostrate to low growing with creamy-white variegated leaves.		
- - 'Prostrata' Hort.	Probably a cultivariant. See 'Spread Eagle'.		
- - var. *radicans*	A bushy mountain form spreading by suckers.		
- - **'Spread Eagle'**	1970 A low-growing form with long, spreading branches. Probably a cultivariant. **O.** Hillier and Sons, Crook Hill Nurs. near Winchester.	R	U.K.
- - **'Variegata'** A.C. Mitchell			
1972	In "U.K. Forestry Comm. Booklet **33**". Named for a tree at Hergest Croft, Herefordshire.		U.K.
TORREYA californica x *TORREYA nucifera*		K	
TORREYA fargesii Franchet			
1899	Now treated as a variety of *TORREYA grandis* by some authorities (per Silba, 1984).	Z8	Szechuan
TORREYA grandis Fortune ex Lindley			
1857		15m	Szechuan
- - var. *fargesii* (Franchet) Silba			
1984	Formerly known as *TORREYA fargesu*.		
- - var. *merrillii* Hu	A local variant.	K	
- - var. *sargentii* Hu and Chun	A local variant.	K	China
TORREYA jackii Chun	1925 Cheklang Torreya.	12m,Z8	China
TORREYA nucifera Siebold and Zuccarini			
1846	Japanese Torreya.	15m,Z7	Japan
- - 'Aurea Variegata' Hort. Amer.			
1986	A listed name.		
- - var. *igaensis* Doi and Morikawa		K	
- - var. *macrosperma* (Miyoshi) Koidzumi		K	Japan
- - 'Prostrata' Hornibrook	1923 Named for a prostrate plant (A cultivariant?) at one time in the National Botanic Garden, Dublin.	B,G,H,K,W2	Ireland
- - f. *radicans*	Now listed under *TORREYA californica*.	B,K	
- - 'Spread Eagle' Hort.	A mistake. See *TORREYA californica*		
- - 'Variegata' Hort.	A listed name.		
TORREYA taxifolia Arnott			
1838	Florida Yew.	9m,Z8	U.S.A.
- - 'Argentea' Beissner	1904	B,K	Italy
TORREYA yunnanensis Cheng & Fu			
1975	Now known as *TORREYA grandis* var. *fargesu*.		

TSUGA Carriere (1855) Hemlock, Hemlock Spruce

P i n a c e a e

The Hemlocks form a Genus, related to the Spruces, of about 10 species of usually tall trees with thin stems, small leaves and a graceful habit. One species has given rise to a great variety of garden forms. But many of these, at first listed as dwarfs, develop into trees in time and so this distinctiveness is lost. But there is a plethora of new introductions to take their place in garden culture.

TSUGA ajanensis (1) Regel 1883 Now known as *PICEA jezoensis*.

TSUGA ajanensis (2) Sénéclauze
                     1868 Now known as *TSUGA heterophylla*.

TSUGA araragi (Siebold) Koehne
                     1893 Now known as *TSUGA sieboldii*.

TSUGA argyrophylla De Laubenfels and Silba
                     1984 Formerly known as *CATHAYA argyrophylla*.   20m,Z7   China

TSUGA blaringhemii Flous 1936 Not now distinguished within *TSUGA diversifolia*.

TSUGA brunoniana (Wallich) Carrière
                     1855 Now known as *TSUGA dumosa*.

TSUGA calcarea Downie   1923 Not now distinguished within *TSUGA canadensis*.

TSUGA canadensis (L.) Carrière
                     1855 Canadian or Eastern Hemlock.   30m,Z4   Canada, U.S.A.

- - 'Abbott's Cinnamomea' Hort. Amer.
                     1985 See 'Cinnamomea'.   S

- - 'Abbott's Dwarf' H.G. Hillier
                     1964 In "Dwarf Conifers". A globose shrublet with long very dark
                          green leaves, short leaves near tip of shoot and twisted.   S,W   U.S.A.

- - 'Abbott's Fountain' Hort. Amer.
                     A listed name for a large, spreading, open-centred bush.   S

- - **'Abbott's Pygmy'** Jenkins
                     1948 In "Hemlock Arb. Bull. **62**". Possibly the smallest form in
                          cultivation. **O.** Found by Frank L. Abbott, near Richmond,
                          Vermont, (1933).   S,W   U.S.A.

- - **'Abbott Weeping'** Krüssmann
                     1972 Named for a tree with irregularly pendulous branches similar
                          to 'Kelsey's Weeping'. **O.** Found in a field near Athens,
                          Vermont. (1933).   K,S   U.S.A.

- - 'Albopicta' Hort. Amer.   1986 A mistake for 'Albo-spica'.   S

- - 'Albo-spica' Jaeger and Beissner
                     1884 An early selection with whitish branch tips, most intense
                        during the summer. NIC. The clone 'LaBar White Tip has
                        taken it's place.   B,G,K,S

- - 'Albo-spicata' Hort. Amer.   A mistake for 'Albo-spica'.   S,W

- - 'Amawalk' Hort. Amer.   A listed name. Probably NIC.   S

- - **'Ammerland'** Hort. Germany
                     1986 The picture in "Conifers" shows a widespreading bush with its
                        young growth white. **I.** Heinrich Bruns, Westerstede,
                        Oldenburg.   G   Germany

- - 'Andréws' Welch in Swartley
                     1984 Named for a small plant received by Jenkins at Hemlock
                        Arboretum from H.S. Andréws Nurs. at Seattle, Washington.
                        ('Minuta Nana').   S   U.S.A.

- - **'Angustifolia'** Swartley ex Den Ouden/Boom
  1965 A clone of medium growth rate with tufted branches. **O.**
  George L. Erle of Clifton, N.J. B,K,S

- - f. *argentea* Nelson
  1866 A botanical designation, if one is required, to cover all forms
  with white young foliage. S

- - 'Argentea' Nelson
  1866 "The Silver Variegated Form". No longer identifiable, so
  should not be used as a cultivar name. S

- - 'Argenteovariegata' Hort. ex Beissner
  1909 See 'Variegata'. S

- - **'Armistice'** Warner ex Spingarn
  1965 In "Amer. Hort. Mag. **44**". Broadly conical; glossy dark green
  foliage, very dense. (See 'Muttontown' in Swartley). K,S,W U.S.A.

- - 'Armistice Dwarf' Hort. Amer.
  1971 An unsatisfactory name possibly the same as the previous
  entry or 'Muttontown'.

- - **'Ashfield Weeper'** Welch in Swartley
  1984 Weeping form of irregular outline when young. **O.** Found in
  the wild by O. Hamilton at Ashfield, Mass. (1964). **I.**
  Watnong Nurs, Morris Plains, N.J. S U.S.A.

- - 'Atrovirens' Beissner
  1897 The name is now loosely used for several selections with
  noticeably dark green leaves. B,K,S Germany

- - 'Aurea' Nelson
  1855 "The Golden Variegated". No clone can be identified from
  such a description, so its use should be discouraged. S U.K.

- - 'Aurea Compacta' Hort. Amer.
  1986 Indistinguishable from 'Everitt Golden'. B,S

- - 'Aurescens' Hort. Amer.
  See 'Silvery Gold'. S

- - **'Bacon Cristate'** Reg.'d Arn. Arb.
  1972 An upright dwarf. Dark green foliage, more cristate than in
  'Jervis'. **O.** Found by Ralph Bacon near Newton, N.J. (1925).
  I. Don Smith, Watnong Nurs, Morris Plains, N.J. (Formerly
  'Bacon No. I'). S,W U.S.A.

- - 'Bacon Dwarf' Don Smith
  1984 In "Amer. Conif. Soc. Bull. **L (3)**". Illus. (Formerly' Bacon
  No. 2'). U.S.A.

- - **'Bagatelle'** Welch in Swartley
  1984 A multi-stemmed clone that develops into a compact globose
  plant. **O.** The Bagatelle Nurs, Centre Moriches, L.I., N.Y. U.S.A.

- - 'Baldwin Dwarf Globe' Hort. Amer.
  A listed name.

- - **'Baldwin Dwarf Pyramid'** Welch in Swartley
  1984 A listed name. Upright dwarf with somewhat twisted
  branches, needles noticeably vary in size. **O.** Found by J.W.
  Swartley in a nursery. **I.** The same. S U.S.A.

- - **'Barrie Bergman'** Welch in Swartley
  1984 A flat-topped plant raised by Fred Bergman of Feasterville,
  PA, from a mutation on 'Cole's Prostrate' (1970). S U.S.A.

- - **'Beaujean'** H.G. Hillier
  1964 Compact, symmetrical plant; branches spreading out, from a
  nest-like, hollow centre. **O.** Found by A.C. Beaujean of
  Yonkers Nurs, N.Y. (1926). Formerly 'Saratoga Broom'. K,S U.S.A.

- - **'Beehive'** Welch in Swartley
        1984 Upright-oval, multi-stemmed bush with dense habit; leaves small. **I.** Mitsch Nurs, Aurora, OR. (1982).   S   U.S.A.

- - **'Bennett'** Swartley ex Den Ouden/ Boom
        1965 Compact habit. Arched ascending brs with pendulous tips. Probably several undistinguishable clones are now in cultivation. **O.** Mr. Bennett of Atlantic Highlands, N.J. (Distributed mistakenly at first as 'Minima').   B,K,S,R   U.S.A.

- - 'Bennett's Minima' Hort. Amer.   The original 'Bennett', if it can be traced.

- - 'Bergman' Hort. Amer.   Not itself a valid cultivar name. See Swartley p.92 for an explanation of the following names (and others that are listed).   S

- - 'Bergman's Aurescens Nana' Hort. Amer.
        1970 See 'Silvery Gold'.

- - 'Bergman's Cascade' Hort. Amer.
        A listed name.

- - 'Bergman's Cinnamon Dwarf' Hort. Amer.
        1970 In "Nurs. Cat". Raraflora Nurs, Feasterville, PA. Provisional name.   U.S.A.

- - 'Bergman's Contorta Spicata' Hort. Amer.
        1970 See 'Contorted'.

- - 'Bergman's Frosty' Hort. Amer.   Now known as 'Frosty'.

- - 'Bergman's Gem' Welch in Swartley
        1984 A small globose plant with 'Cinnamomea' type buds and foliage found in the wild in Vermont.   U.S.A.

- - 'Bergman's Heli'   Now known as 'Heli'.

- - **'Betty Rose'** Welch in Swartley
        1984 A very diminutive form, with leaves irregularly arranged, new growth flushes white twice a year. **O.** Found in Vanceboro, Maine by Francis J. Heckman of Ambler, PA.   S   U.S.A.

- - 'Biltmore Weeping' Hort. Amer.
        A listed name. (Possibly = 'Bergman's Cinnamon Dwarf').

- - **'Bonnie Bergman'** Welch in Swartley
        1984 A slow-growing open dwarf. **O.** Raised from a witch's broom found on a tree at Stroudsberg, PA.   S   U.S.A.

- - **'Boulevard'** Swartley in Den Ouden/Boom
        1965 A conical plant with very dense dark green foliage. **O.** A seedling in the Boulevard Nurs, Newport, R.I.   B,K,S,R   U.S.A.

- - 'Bowman' Hort. Amer.   A listed name. NIC.

- - **'Bradshaw'** Reg'd. A.A.N.
        1946 Good compact pyramid; branches spreading, with tips upturned. **O.** Raised from seed by H. Hohman, Kingsville Nurs, MD. (1936). **I.** The same (1946).   B,K,S   U.S.A.

- - **'Brandley'** Dawson ex Jenkins
        1936 In "Hemlock Arb. Bull. **15**". Dense and broad with crowded, ascending branches. **O.** Selected as a seedling by J. Brandley, nurseryman at Walpole, Mass. ('Brandleyi').   B,K,S   U.S.A.

- - 'Branklyn' Haddow   1993 See 'Prostrata' (1). In view of the fact that this is now considered to be a clone of f. 'Pendula' of the 'Brookline' type but not proven to be the same as 'Brookline' the above new name has been given this to this clone which is very low-growing and in it's earlier years completely prostrate.

- - 'Brevifolia' Headfort   1932   In "Roy. Hort. Soc. Conifer Conf. Rep". Named for a plant at Headfort, Kells, Co. Meath. Probably NIC.   S   Ireland

- - 'Brimfield Golden' Hort. Amer.
    1984   A listed name for a loose, strong-growing clone with yellowish leaves. NIC.

- - **'Bristol'** Swartley ex Den Ouden/Boom
    1965   A compact, bushy shrub. **O.** The Bristol Nurs, Bristol, Conn. NIC.   B,K,S   U.S.A.

- - 'Bristol Short-leaf' Hort. Amer.
    1984   A listed name. No information. NIC.   S

- - 'Broad Globe' Hort. Amer.
    1984   A listed name. No information.

- - **'Brookline'** Welch   1966   One of the four original seedlings of the "Sargent Hemlocks". See 'Pendula'.   S,W

- - **'Broughton'** Swartley ex Den Ouden/Boom
    1965   An irregular conical form, slow-growing but eventually rather open. **O.** Leslie M. Broughton Nurs, Madison, Ohio.   B,K,S   U.S.A.

- - 'Buck Estate' Hort. Amer.
    1986   A listed name.

- - **'Callicoon'** Swartley ex Den Ouden/Boom
    1965   A vigorous, broadly-spreading selection. **O.** Seedling on the Curtis Nurs, Callicoon, N.Y. Formerly known as 'Curtis Spreader'.   B,K,S,W   U.S.A.

- - 'Calvert' Hort. Amer.   1984   A listed name.   S

- - **'Cappy's Choice'** Mitsch
    1974   In "Nurs. Cat". A compact low bush, with fine textured leaves, light green with hint of gold. **O.** Selected seedling by James Caperci, Rainiers Mount Alpine Gardens, Seattle, Washington.   U.S.A.

- - 'Christie' Hort. Amer.   Now known as 'Muttontown'.

- - **'Cinnamomea'** Hort. ex Jenkins
    1934   In "Hemlock Arb. Bull. 6". Globose bush, cinnamon-brown twigs and buds. **O.** Found by Frank L. Abbott, near Athens, Vermont.   B,K,S   U.S.A.

- - 'Classic' Hort. Amer.   1986   A listed name. No information.

- - **'Cloud Prune'** Reg.'d Arn. Arb.
    1972   Slow-growing; spreading;foliage develops in dense clumps. **O.** Found by Wm. D. Wallbridge of Short Hills, in Sussex Co., N.J. (1938). **I.** Watnong Nurs, Morris Plains, N.J.   S   U.S.A.

- - **'Coffin'** Welch in Swartley
    1984   A small bush with twiggy congested foliage. **O.** Unrecorded. **I.** Eastern Nurs, Holliston, Mass.   S   U.S.A.

- - 'Cole' Hort. Amer.   Now to be 'Cole's Prostrate'

- - **'Cole's Prostrate'** Wm.T. Gotelli
    1960   In "Amer. Hort. Mag. 39". The smallest of the mat-forming spreaders. **O.** Collected by H.R. Cole in 1929 near Mt. Madison, Coos County Nurs, Hampshire. **I.** Gray and Cole Nurs, Ward Hill, Haverhill, Mass.   G,S,W   U.S.A.

- - 'Columnaris' Bolle ex Beissner
    1891   Named for a columnar plant found by Dr. Bolle. NIC.   B,S

- - 'Compacta' Sénéclauze   1868 Named for a plant on the Sénéclauze Nurs, Bourg Argental, Loires. NIC, but the name is loosely applied to several compact clones, so should no longer by used.   B,G,S   France

- - 'Compacta Aurea' Hort. Amer.
   1986 A superfluous name for 'Everitt Golden'.

- - 'Compacta Nana' Beissner
   1891 Another early selection no longer identifiable.   B,H,S   Germany

- - 'Conica Nana' Young ex Hornibrook
   1939 A conical dwarf form. O. M. Young Nurs, Guildford, Surrey. No longer identifiable. NIC.   B,H,S   U.K.

- - 'Connecticut Turnpike' Hort. Amer.
   A listed name for a dense dwarf with crested foliage. O. A plant found by Greg Williams and Lagne Zeigenfuss along the Connecticut Turnpike, Exit 55.   S   U.S.A.

- - 'Contorted' Helene Bergman
   1965 In "Plants and Gardens 2." An unsatisfactory name. See Art. 31A (g) of the "Cultivar Code".   S   U.S.A.

- - 'Coplen' Swartley ex Den Ouden/Boom
   1965 A compact, conical plant of medium vigour. O. Found by Mylo D. Coplen, Rockville, MD. in the vicinity of Mount Storm, West Virginia (1921) NIC.   B,S   U.S.A.

- - 'Corbit' Welch in Swartley
   1984 A slow-growing clone similar to 'Bennett' but slower. I. Joe Cesarini of Sayville. O. Joséph Popeleski, Green Lawn, N.Y.   S   U.S.A.

- - 'Cotton Candy' S. Waxman
   1990 In "Int. Pl. Prop. Soc. Bull". A broad, conical bush with dense foliage and twisted leaves. O. S. Waxman at the University of Connecticut, Storrs, CT.   U.S.A.

- - 'Creamey' Welch in Swartley
   1984 Similar to but more compact than 'Gentsch White' and with cream-coloured growth tips. O. Otto Gentsch, West Merrick, L.I., N.Y.   S   U.S.A.

- - 'Curley' Epstein ex Spingarn
   1969 In "Amer. Rock. Gar. Soc. Bull. 27". ('Curly'). An upright, compact bush with leaves slightly curled. O. Found by Harold Epstein of Larchmont, N.Y.   S   U.S.A.

- - 'Curtis' Hort. Amer.   This name standing alone is of uncertain application, so should not be used. The following are names used by Dr. J.C. Swartley in his Thesis in 1939, only some of which were distributed.

- - 'Curtis Compact' Hort. Amer.
   1985 Name given to a seedling in the Curtis Nurs, Callicoon with dense, dark green foliage that has quite out-grown it's name.   U.K.

- - 'Curtis Denseleaf' Welch in Swartley
   1984 Another of several selections on the same nursery.   S   U.S.A.

- - 'Curtis Ideal' Swartley in Den Ouden/Boom
   1965 Similar to the previous entry. A clone with very long, bright green leaves, openly set.   B,K,S,W2   U.S.A.

- - 'Curtis Largeleaf' Hort. Amer.   A listed name.

- - 'Curtis Spreader' Hort. Amer.
   1984 Now known as 'Callicoon'.   B,S,W2   U.S.A.

- - **'Cushion'** Welch in Swartley
1984   S   U.S.A.

- - **'David Verkade'** Welch in Swartley
1984 A strong growing, mat-forming plant. **I.** Verkade's Nurs, Wayne, N.J.   S   U.S.A.

- - **'Dawsoniana'** Hatfield ex Bailey
1933 A tree with conspicuously attractive foliage. **O.** Found by Harry S. Dawson owner of the Eastern Nurs. Holliston, Mass. ('Dawsonia').   B,K,H   U.S.A.

- - **'Densifolia'** Jenkins   1934 This name has been loosely applied to several clones. so should no longer be used.   B,K   U.S.A.

- - **'Detmer's Weeper'** Don Smith
1972 In "Nurs. Cat". A strong-growing prostrate spreader. **O.** A tree in Detmer's Nurs, Tarrytown, N.Y. **I.** Joséph Cesarini, Johnson's Rare Plant Nurs, Sayville. N.Y. ('Ditmar's Weeper').   S   U.S.A.

- - 'Devil's Fork' Hort. Amer.   A listed name for a dwarf form with several upright stems, tips pendulous.**O.** Found in the wild.

- - 'Diversifolia' Hort. Amer.
1986 An illegit. listed name. Probably a mistake for *THUJA diversifolia.*

- - **'Doc's Choice'** Int. Con. Reg.
1977 A very dense, conical tree with leaves darker than the normal. Reg'd. by R.F. Doren of U.S. Nat. Arb. Washington DC. **O.** Seedling selected by Floyd Smith of Bear Garden Nurs.   S   U.S.A.

- - 'Doran' Helene Bergman   1965 In "Plants and Gardens **21**". An irregular conical tree with tight, light-green foliage. ('Doran's Dwarf'?)   S,W   U.S.A.

- - 'Doran's Prostrate' Hort. Amer.   A listed name. No information.

- - **'Dover'** Welch in Swartley
1984 A compact, broad plant with large leaves. **O.** A seedling selected by Dirk van Heiningen, of the Van Heiningen Nurs.   S   U.S.A.

- - 'Drake' Palette   1978 In "Nurs. Cat". A low bush with cinnamomea-type twigs. Palette Gardens Nurs, Quakertown, PA. ('Drake's Spreader').   S   U.S.A.

- - 'Dr. Corbit' Hort. Amer.   1984 An illegit. listed name, changed to 'Corbit' to comply with I.C.N.C.P. rules.

- - 'Dr.Hornbeck' Hort. Amer.   Now to be 'Hornbeck'. See previous entry.

- - 'Dr Swartley' Hort. Amer.   Now to be 'John Swartley'. See prevous entry.

- - 'Droop Tip' Hort. Amer.   An unacceptable name (Art. 31A(g) of the "Cultivar Code").

- - 'Dwarf Pyramid' Hort. Anglia
1984 See 'Baldwin Dwarf Pyramid'.

- - **'Dwarf Whitetip'** Swartley in Den Ouden/Boom
1965 A graceful, spreading shrub with growth tips white. fading to green by the winter. **O.** Presumed to be a plant in the Morris Arboretum, Philadelphia, PA.   B,K,S,W2   U.S.A.

- - **'Elm City'** Swartley in Den Ouden/Boom
1965 A semi-weeping bush of irregular wide-spreading habit. **O.** A selected seedling in The Elm City Nurs. Elm City, Conn. (1932).   B,K,S,W2   U.S.A.

- - 'Erich Winkler' Hort. Germany
1991 A listed name. L. Gert. Bohme.

- - **'Essex'** Welch in Swartley
>1984 A very dwarf plant that forms an irregular upright cone. Foliage as 'Pygmaea' but smaller leaves. **O.** Found by Greg Williams at Essex, Vermont.   S   U.S.A.

- - 'Everitt Dense Leaf' Hort. Amer.
>Indistinguishable from 'Hussii'.

- - **'Everitt Golden'** Swartley ex Den Ouden/Boom
>1965 A stiff, coarse-textured plant, with ascending branches. Foliage light golden-yellow at first, darkening later. **O.** Found in the wild near Eaton, New Hampshire by Samuel A. Everitt (1918). ('Everitt's Golden').   B,G,S,W   U.S.A.

- - 'Everitt's Gold' Hort. Amer.   A mistake for the previous item.

- - **'Fantana'** Swartley ex Den Ouden/Boom
>1965 A broad bushy plant similar to 'Bennett'. **O.** Selected by P.F. Avogadro, nurseryman of Bellmore, L.I., N.Y.   B,G,K,S,W   U.S.A.

- - **'Far Country'** Welch in Swartley
>1984 A multi-stemmed plant like 'Innisfree', named to commemorate Charles Jenkins, founder of the "Far Country" Hemlock Arboretum and who supplied the Mother plant to the Swarthmore College, Swarthmore, PA. For years it was distributed as 'J210'.   S   U.S.A.

- - 'Fastigiata' Beissner
>1891 Another early selection. No longer identifiable. The name should not be used save in a collective sense.   B

- - **'Feasterville'** Welch in Swartley
>1984 A conical plant with foliage suggestive of a juniper. **O.** A seedling raised by F.W. Bergman at Raraflora, Feasterville, PA.   S   U.S.A.

- - 'Femii' Hort. Amer.   An illegit. name, perhaps a mistake for 'Fremdii'.

- - **'Florence'** S. Waxman
>1981 In "Int. Pl. Prop. Soc. Bull". A broad, multi-layered shrub with pendent branch-tips. **O.** Raised by S. Waxman at Univ. of Connecticut, Storrs, CT.   U.S.A.

- - var *formosana* (Hayata) Li et Keng.
>In "Journal of Chinese Forestry **8**".

- - 'Freiburg' Hort. Amer.
>1992 A dwarf selection from the Stupka Nurs. Shape perfectly conical. **I.** Rarafolia Nurs, Kintersville, P.A.

- - **'Fremdii'** Jenkins
>1932 In "Hemlock Arboretum **2**". One of the earliest selections. It makes a small rounded tree with closely set, dark-green leaves. **O.** Found by Charles Fremd (1887). **I.** Koster Nurs. Boskoop, Holland. ('Fremdii').   B,G,K,S   U.S.A.

- - **'Frosty'** Welch in Swartley
>1984 A bush-form with the foliage silvery-white, turning green (unless grown in complete shade).   S   U.S.A.

- - "Gable" Hort. Amer.   Not valid as a cultivar name.   K,S

- - 'Gable Cinnamon' Hort. Amer.
>1970 A listed name for a rounded bush-like plant seen in the Arnold Arboretum. (Formerly known as 'Gable No. 8').

- - **'Gable Weeping'** Swartley in Den Ouden/Boom
>1965 A compact, weeping form. **O.** A selection in the Joseph B. Gable Nurs, Stewartstown, PA.   B,K,S,W   U.S.A.

- - **'Geneva'** Swartley in Den Ouden/Boom
>1965 Dwarf, globose bush, branches closely set, dark green. Named for a plant at the Trinity Church Home, Geneva, N.Y.   B,K,S   U.S.A.

- - "Gentsch" Hort. Amer.   Not valid as a cultivar name.

- - 'Gentsch Dwarf' Hort. Amer. See next entry.

- - 'Gentsch Dwarf Globe' Hort. Amer.
          Now known as 'Palomino'.

- - 'Gentsch Globe' Hort. Amer. See previous entry.

- - 'Gentsch Snowflake' Hort. Amer.
          Possibly a mistake for 'Snowflake'.

- - 'Gentsch Variegated' Hort. Amer.
          A mistake for 'Gentsch White'.   W2

- - **'Gentsch White'** Welch in Swartley
    1984 A globose bush with the young foliage bright creamy-white at
       it's best in the autumn. **O.** Found by Otto Gentsch,
       nurseryman of L.I., N.Y. ('Gentsch White Tip').   S   U.S.A.

- - f. *globosa* Beissner   1887 A botanical designation that would cover all the globose
       forms.

- - 'Globosa' Beissner.   1887 An early globose clone. NIC. The name is now loosely
       applied to several such selections.   B,H,K,S Germany

- - 'Globularis Erecta' Kunkler
    1884 Another early selection no longer identifiable in cultivation.
       ('Globosa Erecta').   B,K,S   U.S.A.

- - **'Golden Splendor'** Mitsch
    1979 In "Nurs. Cat". An upright, fast-growing clone that resists
       sun-scorch. **O.** Unrecorded. **I.** Mitsch Nurs, Aurora, OR.   U.S.A.

- - **'Gracilis'** (1) Waterer ex Gordon
    1862 A graceful small bush with drooping growth tips. Probably
       several very similar clones are now in cultivation.   B,G,K,S U.K.

- - 'Gracilis' (2) H. Hohman 1970 In "Nurs. Cat". The upright clone distributed by H. Hohman,
       Kingsville Nurs, MD. is now known as 'Henry Hohman'.   U.S.A.

- - 'Gracilis Droop-tip' Hort. Amer An illegit. listed name. Possibly a mistake for 'Gracilis' (1),
       above.

- - 'Gracilis Nana' Hort. Amer. An illegit. and superfluous name for 'Gracilis'. ('Nana
       Gracilis').

- - 'Gracilis Oldenburg' Krüssmann
    1972 An illegit. listed name. Now to be 'Oldenburg'.   K,S

- - **'Great Lakes'** Welch in Swartley
    1984 Named for a multi-stemmed. open. conical specimen in U.S.
       Nat. Arboretum, Washington, DC. **O.** Ralph M. Warner,
       Milford, Conn.   S   U.S.A.

- - **'Green Cascade'** J. Vermeulen
    1972 In "Nurs. Cat". Strong-growing but very dense and closely
       clothed with small leaves. **O.** Selected seedling in Baier
       Lustgarten Nurs, Middle Village, L.I., N.Y. **I.** Vermeulen
       Nurs, Neshanic Station, N.J. (1972).   S,W U.S.A.

- - 'Green Mountains' Hort. Amer.
    1984 A listed name. NIC.

- - **'Greenspray'** Reg'd. Arn. Arb.
    1963 A rather open form where new spring growth overlaps older
       growth. Hence the name. **O.** H.J. Homan, Kingsville Nurs,
       MD. (1942).   S,W U.S.A.

- - **'Greenwood Lake'** Swartley in Den Ouden/Boom
  1965 A dwarf form similar to 'Hussii' but more open. **O.** Found by an unrecorded customer and given to George L. Ehrle, Clifton, N.J. B,K,S,W2 U.S.A.

- - **'Guldemond's Dwarf'** J. Vermeulen
  1964 In "Nurs. Cat". A dense, irregular pyramid. **O.** Found by D. Guldemond, Longlestown, PA. **I.** J. Vermeulen Nurs, Neshanic Station, N.J. S U.S.A.

- - 'Gulden' New Name 1993 A conical shaped tree with heavy dark green foliage. **O.** Raised by Francis V. Gulden of Suncrest Gardens, Mt. Holly Springs, PA. (1968). It is difficult to propagate. ('FVG').

- - **'Hahn'** Welch in Swartley
  1984 Named for a plant on the rock garden at Petschau, Bohemia. (at first the illegit name 'Nana' was used). S Czechosl.

- - **'Hancock'** Welch in Swartley
  1984 Name suggested for a clone raised by Joe Cesarini from a witch's broom found near Hancock. N.Y. **I.** James Cross, Cutchogue, L.I., N.Y. U.S.A.

- - **'Harmon'** Harmon ex Den Ouden/ Boom
  1965 A tree, at first columnar but widening with age. **O.** Found on the La Bar Rhododendron Nurs, Stroudsberg, PA. and named by Henry Hohman in honour of Russell Harmon, manager at La Bar. B,K,S U.S.A.

- - 'Heckman' Hort. Amer. A listed name.

- - **'Helene Bergman'** Welch in Swartley
  1984 A diminutive little plant that originated as a mutation on 'Cole's Prostrate' (Bergman called it 'Cole's Sport' in 1965, but there are other such sports in cultivation). U.S.A.

- - **'Heli'** Welch in Swartley 1984 An irregular, semi-dwarf plant with very broad leaves and curious buds.('Bergman's Heli'). S U.S.A

- - **'Henry Hohman'** Welch in Swartley
  1984 Formerly known as 'Gracilis'. Which see for details. S U.S.A.

- - **'Hicks'** Swartley in Den Ouden/Boom
  1965 A conical tree with spreading branches and leaves a distinctly yellowish green. L. Hicks Nurs, Westbourg, N.Y. (1947). B,K,S U.S.A.

- - 'Hiti' D. Wyman 1960 In "Amer. Nurs. 112". A conical tree with ascending branches, the blue undersides of the leaves exposed. **O.** Found in Pomfret, Conn. by Ellery B. Baker then manager of the Hiti Nurs, Pomfret, Conn. ('Pomfret', 'Compacta'). S U.S.A.

- - 'Hohman Spreader' Hort. Amer.
  1984 Now renamed 'Kingsville Spreader'.

- - 'Hoods Variety' Hort. Amer. An illegit. listed name. See 'Albospica'. K

- - **'Hornbeck'** Don Smith 1972 In Watnong "Nurs. Cat". Similar to 'Hussii' but slower growing. **O.** Found by Dr. Peter Hornbeck in Petersham, Mass. S U.S.A.

- - **'Horsford'** Helene Bergman
  1965 In "Plants and Gardens 21". A dense, squat little plant that in time becomes open. W2 U.S.A.

- - 'Horsford Compact' A listed name for a compact mutation found by Fred Bergman on 'Horsford'. ('Horsford Dwarf'). K

- - **'Horsford Contorted'** L. Zeigenfuss
1970 In Hillside "Nurs. Cat". A curious plant with twisted
branches. **O.** Found by Wm. Horsford. **I.** Layne Zeigenfuss,
Hillside Gdns. ('Horsford Contorta', 'Pigtail'). NOM.   U.S.A.

- - 'Horsford Youngcone' Hort. Amer.
Now known as 'Youngcone'.

- - 'Horstmann' Hort. Germany
1986 A group of clones raised from witch's brooms by G.
Horstmann, Schneverdingen. Offered as Nos. 1 to 6.   G?   Germany

- - **'Horton'** Stout
1939 In "Journ. New York Bot. Gar. **40**". One of the five clones
that constitute the 'Sargent Hemlocks'.   S   U.S.A.

- - 'Howard Waxman' S. Waxman
1986 In "Int. Pl. Prop. Soc. Bull". A dense upright-spreading shrub,
leaves twisted, showing white undersides. **O.** S. Waxman at
Univ. of Connecticut, Storrs, CT.   U.S.A.

- - **'Howe'** Welch in Swartley
1984 A compact, conical plant, found in Everton, New Hampshire.
I. Herr Hawkins, Wayne, N.J. ('Howei').   S   U.S.A.

- - 'Hubble' Hort. Amer.   1984 A listed name. NIC.

- - 'Huffman' Welch in Swartley
1984 A provisional name. ('Huffman's Compact')   S   U.S.A.

- - 'Humphrey Welch' Hort. Amer.
1991 A listed name. In "Nurs. Cat". Rich's Foxwillow Pines,
Woodstock PA. More information required.

- - **'Hunnewell'** Welch in Swartley
1984 See under 'Sargentii'.   S   U.S.A.

- - **'Hussii'** Jenkins
1932 In "Hemlock Arb. Bull. **1**". A very slow-growing upright
shrub with dense, congested foliage. **O.** Found by John F.
Huss, Supt. of Parks at Hartford, Conn. (1900).   B,K.   U.S.A.

- - 'Ideal' Hort. Amer.   See 'Curtis Ideal'.

- - **'Imperial'** Welch in Swartley
1984 A compact form with white growth tips fading to a cream
colour. **I.** Brimfield Garden Nurs, Wethersfield, Conn.
('Imperial White-tip').   U.S.A.

- - **'Innisfree'** Welch in Swartley
1984 A multi-stemmed globose shrub. **O.** Found by Alfred J.
Fordham in the town Innisfree. Mass.   S   U.S.A.

- - **'Jacqueline Verkade'** Reg'd. Arn. Arb.
1969? An upright to ovoid bush with regular, short green leaves. **O.**
and **I.** Verkade's Nurs, Wayne, N.J.   S,W   U.S.A.

- - **'Jan Verkade'** Welch in Swartley
1984 A fast-growing sprawling clone that does not form a leader,
somewhat similar to 'Kelsey's Weeper'. **O.** and **I.** Verkade's
Nurs, Wayne, N.J.   S   U.S.A.

- - **'Jeddeloh'** H. M. Grootendorst
1965 In "Dendroflora **2**". Forms a dense, hemispherical plant of the
'Gracilis' type with fresh light-green foliage. **O.** Raised from
seed on the J.zu Jeddeloh Nurs, Oldenburg. **I.** The same.   G,K,S,w   Germany

- - **'Jenkinsii'** Bailey
1933 A fast-growing tree with an open, ascending branch structure
and very short, fine leaves. **O.** Raised from seed on the
Towson Nurs, Towson, MD.   B,K,S   U.S.A.

- - **'Jenning's Yewlike'** Welch in Swartley
1984 Fast-growing, upright form, but with long leaves and a neat, compact habit. **O.** Selected on the F. and F. Nurs, Princeton, N.J. | S | U.S.A.

- - **'Jervis'** Helene Bergman
1965 In "Plants and Gardens 21". A dense, conical slow-growing shrub. **O.** Found by G.C. Nearing of Metuchen, N.J. It was at first distributed as 'Nearing' but the name 'Jervis' is now in general use. | K,S | U.S.A.

- - 'J. Lee Edwards' Hort. Amer.
1981 **O.** Bacon. **L.** Watnong Nurs, Morris Plains, N.J. ('T.L. Edwards').

- - **'John Swartley'** Welch in Swartley
1984 A slow-growing spreader with short leaves, yellowish during the winter. **O.** Found by Greg Williams near Weissport, PA. Formerly distributed as Dr. Swartley which is unacceptable under the "Cultivar Code". | S | U.S.A.

- - **'Julianne'** S. Waxman 1989 In "Int. Pl. Prop. Soc. Bull". A regular, conical, many-branched shrub. **O.** S. Waxman at the Univ. of Connecticut, Storrs, CT. | U.S.A.

- - 'Julians' Welch in Swartley
1984 See 'Slenderella'. | S | U.S.A.

- - 'Juniperoides' Hort. Amer. Now known as 'Feasterville'. ('Juniperlike').

- - **'Kathryn Verkade'** J.W. Spingarn
1969 In "Amer. Rock Gar. Soc. Bull. 27". A slow-growing clone resembling a miniature version of 'Bennett'. **O.** Raised from a witch's broom by Verkade's Nurs, Wayne, N.J. | S | U.S.A.

- - 'Kelseyi' Hort. Amer. Same as 'Kelsey's Weeping'.

- - **'Kelsey's Weeping'** Swartley ex Den Ouden/Boom
1965 A curious, strong-growing plant with a strongly asymetrical habit. **O.** Found on the H.P. Kelsey Nurs, East Boxford, Mass. | B,K,S | U.S.A.

- - **'Kingston Hollow'** Welch in Swartley
1984 A bushy little tree with curiously contorted foliage. **O.** Found on the Mayfair Nurs, Nichols, N.Y. by Walter Kolaga (1970). | S | U.S.A.

- - 'Kingsville' H. Hohman 1946 In "Nurs. Cat". Named for a plant of no particular distinction on the Kingsville Nurs, Kingsville, MD. | B,S | U.S.A.

- - 'Kingsville Fastigiate' Reg'd. A. A. N.
1949 In "Woody Plant Reg. 1". A narrowly, fastigiate clone. **O.** and I. H.J. Hohman, Kingsville Nurs, Kingsville, MD. | U.S.A.

- - **'Kingsville Spreader'** Formerly known as 'Hohman Spreader'. | U.S.A.

- - "Labar" Hort. Amer. Not a valid cultivar name. See the next two entries.

- - **'LaBar Gem'** Swartley 1946 In "Amer. Nurs. 133". A compact but irregular conical, rather stiff clone with dark green foliage. **O.** Found in West Virginia (1936) and introduced by the La Bar Rhododendron Nurs, Stroudsberg, PA. | B,S | U.S.A.

- - **'LaBar White Tip'** Swartley
1946 In "Amer. Nurs. 133". A free-growing open, bushy tree showing conspicuous whiteness in the young foliage. **O.** Found in the above Nursery (1945) | S | U.S.A.

- - 'Lantz' Hort. Amer. 1992 Produces white cones which gives it a most unusual contrast. **O.** Stupka Nurs. **I.** Rarafolia Nurs, Kintersville, PA.

- - 'Latifolia' Sénéclauze   1868   An early clone no longer identifiable, but similar clones can be found.   B,K,S   France

- - **'Laurie'** Swartley   1946   In "Amer. Nurs. **133**". A globose form with a dense branching system. **O.** Selected by Robert Laurie, owner of the Stoughton Nurs, Stoughton, Mass. **I.** The same.   U.S.A.

- - 'Layne's Variegated' Hort. Amer.
    1988   A listed name. More information required.

- - **'Lewis'** Helene Bergman
    1965   In "Plants and Gardens **21**". A slow-growing, irregularly conical plant with a stiff, open branch-system. **O.** Selected by Clarence McKinley Lewis of Skyland, Sterlington, N.Y. **I.** Carl Starker of Aurora, OR. ('Lewisii', 'Dwarf Upright').   S   U.S.A.

- - 'Lincoln White Tip' Hort. Amer.
    1986   A listed name. NIC.

- - **'Little Joe'** Welch in Swartley
    1984   A diminutive seedling with leaves slightly smaller than in 'Minuta'.   S   U.S.A.

- - 'Little Snow' Hort. Germany
    1986   A listed name.

- - 'Longwood' Hort. Amer.   See 'Slenderella'.

- - 'Loudon' Hort. Amer.   1986   A listed name. ('Loudon Dwarf'). NIC?

- - **'Lustgarten Creeping'** J. Vermeulen
    1971   In "Nurs. Cat". A slow-growing, pendulous clone. **O.** The Baier Lustgarten Nurs, Middle Village, L.I., N.Y. **I.** Vermeulen & Sons Nurs, Neshanic Station, N.J.   U.S.A.

- - 'Lutea' Hort. Amer.   1967   An illegit. listed name for a clone with "brilliant golden" leaves.   G,S

- - 'Macrophylla' Fitschen in Beissner
    1930   The name has been loosely applied to several clones with large leaves.   B,K,S

- - **'Mansfield'** Swartley   1946   In "Amer. Nurs. **134**". A tall-globose multi-stemmed clone. **O.** Found by Dr. Raymond Wallace in Mansfield, Conn.   B,K,S   U.S.A.

- - "Many Cones" and "Many Stems" are treated by Swartley as descriptive nick-names of no clear application.   U.S.A.

- - **'Marilyn'** R.L. Fincham   1983   In "Amer. Conif. Soc. Bull. **2**". Dwarf, stubby, downward arching branches; light green foliage. **O.** Joséph Reis.   U.S.A.

- - **'Matthews'** Jenkins   1935   In "Hemlock Arb. Bull. **11**". A globose clone eventually forms a normal tree, distinctive only for it's longer than normal leaves. **O.** Found by Edwin Matthews of the outdoor Gdns Nurs, Philadelphia, PA.   B,S   U.S.A.

- - **'Meyers'** Swartley in Den Ouden/Boom
    1965   A compact conical form with very dense, dark green foliage. **O.** Found by E.W. Meyers, nurseryman at Hatboro, PA.   B,K,S   U.S.A.

- - 'Microphylla' Lindley   1864   A name now loosely used for several selections with small leaves.   B,H,K

- - 'Milfordensis' Young ex Gordon
    1875   An early selection, long since lost sight of. ('Milfordiensis').   B,K

- - 'Milleri' Hort. Amer.   1990   An illegit. listed name for a dwarf with irregularly ascending branches and very small needles. ('Miller').

- - **'Minima'** Hesse ex Schelle
1909 A very slow-growing clone, similar to but less vigorous than
'Bennett', Not the smallest!   B,G,H,K   Germany

- - **'Minuta'** Teuscher   1935 In "New Flora and Silva". A dwarf, compact plant wider than
high of somewhat irregular shape. See the history in Swartley.   B,K,S,W   U.S.A.

- - 'Mitsch Upright' Mitsch   1990 In "Nurs. Cat". A dense, fast-growing, broadly-upright form
useful for large hedges.   U.S.A.

- - **'Möll'** Krüssmann   1955 A compact, bushy selection named after it's finder, Peter Möll
of Heisterbacherrot.   B,K   Germany

- - 'Moon's Columnar' Jenkins
1936 In "Hemlock Arb. Bull.". Named for a fastigiate tree in the
Hunnewell Arboretum. NIC.   S   U.S.A.

- - **'Muttontown'** Welch in Swartley
1984 See under 'Armistice' in Swartley.   S   U.S.A.

- - 'Myers' Den Ouden/Boom
1965 A compact selection by E.W. Meyers, nurseryman at Hatboro,
PA. NIC.   B   U.S.A.

- - 'Nana' Carrière   1855 This early selection can no longer be identified, so the name
should not be used. (Save in a collective sense).   B,H,K,S   U.S.A.

- - 'Nana Compacta' Hort. Anglia
1985 An illegit. listed name.

- - 'Nana Gracilis' Hort. Amer.   An illegit. and superfluous name for 'Gracilis'.

- - 'Nana Pyramidalis' Hort. Anglia
1985 An illegit. listed name.

- - 'Narragansett' Reg'd. Arn. Arb
1972 A variable little plant similar to 'Beaujean'. O. A witch's
broom found by James W. Brandley of Pawtucket, Rhode Is,
(1928). ('Brandley Broom').   S   U.S.A.

- - 'Nearing' Swartley in Den Ouden/Boom
1965 Now known as 'Jervis'. See Swartley.   B,W2

- - 'New Gold' Hort. Amer.   1992 Upright habit. Spring growth bright gold. I. Buchholz Nurs,
Gaston, Oregon.

- - 'Newport' Hort. Amer. 1967   A listed name. No further information.

- - **'Oldenburg'** Welch in Swartley
1984 Name to replace 'Gracilis Oldenburg'.   Germany

- - **'Outpost'** Swartley   1946 In "Amer. Nurs. **83**". A quick-growing pendulous tree with
completely pendulous branchlets. The origin is unclear.   B   U.S.A.

- - **'Palomino'** J.W. Spingarn
1969 In "Amer. Rock Gar. Soc. Bull. **27**" A very slow-growing
bush with irregular, congested growth. ('Gentsch Dwarf
Globe' is the same). Cinnamomea group.   W   U.S.A.

- - 'Parkeri' Hort. Amer.   1986 A listed name. No further information.

- - 'Parson's Little Leaf' Hort. Amer.
1986 A listed name. No further information.

- - 'Parvifolia' Veitch   1881 Another early selection. The name is merely descriptive and
no longer identifiable, so the name should not be used.   B,G,H,K,S   U.K.

- - **'Parvula'** Victorin and Rousseau
1940 The remarks in the previous entry also apply to this entry.   S   U.S.A.

- - f. *pendula* Beissner	1887 A botanical category covering all pendulous tree-forms.	S,W	N. America
- - **'Pendula'** (1) Hort. in Beissner	1891 The earliest use of this as the name of a cultivar can no longer be identified, so must be regarded as NIC.	B,H,K,S	Germany
- - 'Pendula' (2) Bean	1914 A hemispherical mass of hanging branches and a thatch of foliage.	B,G	U.K.
- - 'Pendula' (3) Hort.	The Sargent Hemlocks are spreading forms on a framework of heavy branches.	S,W	U.K.
- - 'Pendula Argentea' Masters	1903 Named for a tree in the Royal Botanic Gardens at Kew, a tree with pendent branches with the growth tips whitish. NIC.	B	U.K.
- - 'Perfecta Nana' Hort. Amer.	1989 An illegit. listed name for a globose form with brown-tipped buds.		
- - 'Picta Alba' Hort. Amer.	An illegit. listed name, probably a mistake for 'Albospica'.		
- - 'Pigtail' Hort. Amer.	Name widely in use in the trade for 'Horsford Contorted'.		
- - 'Pincushion' Hort. Amer.	A listed name. No further information.		
- - 'Plainview' Hort. Amer.	1984 A listed name. No further information.		
- - 'Pomfret' Swartley in Den Ouden/Boom	1965 A superfluous synonym for 'Hiti'.	B,S	
- - **'Popeleski'** Welch in Swartley	1984 A dwarf with an irregular habit and crowded leaves and branches. Named for a plant in the possession of Josph Popeleski, Greenlawn, L.I., N.Y. I. Joe Cesarini, nurseryman of Sayville, L.I., N.Y.	S	U.S.A.
- - 'Prostrata' (1) Bean	1914 Named for a plant in the garden of Mr. Renton, Branklyn, Perth that turned out to be in the 'Sargentii' group. The name should not be used. New name to be 'Branklyn'.	B,G,K,S	Scotland
- - 'Prostrata' (2) Jenkins	1941 In "Hemlock Arb. Bull. **35**". Now known as 'Cole's Prostrate'.		
- - 'Pumila' Ordnung ex Beissner	1909 A selection that can no longer be identified.	B,H,K,S	Czechosl.
- - 'Pygmaea' Hort. Amer.	A superfluous name for 'Abbott's Pygmy'.		
- - 'Pyramidalis' Vermeulen	1942 In "Nurs. Cat". Since 1959 listed as 'Vermeulen's Pyramid'.	S	U.S.A.
- - 'Raraflora Snowflake' Hort. Amer.	1986 See 'Snowflake'.	S	
- - 'Recurva' Hort. Amer.	Early name for 'Verkade's Recurved'.	S	
- - 'Redding' Stout	1939 In "N. Y. Bot. Gard. Journal **40**". Named for a tree with extremely dense foliage, near Redding, Conn. O. and I. The (one time) Outpost Nurs. Redgefield, Conn.	S	U.S.A.
- - 'R.F. Watson' Hort. Anglia	1985 An illegit. listed name. No further information.		
- - 'Rhode Island' Hort. Amer.	See 'Stewart's Gem'. ('Rhode Island University').	S	
- - **'Rock Creek'** Welch in Swartley	1984 A compact globe with multiple trunks and foliage in flexible, fan-like sprays. O. and I. Rock Creek Nurs. Rockville, MD.	S	U.S.A.

- - **'Rockland'** Reg'd. Arn. Arb.

    1963 In "Arnoldia 23". Reg'd as **O.** Herman Brandt. **I.** Robert W. Pugh of Spring Valley, N.Y.   S   U.S.A.

- - **'Rockport'** Heistad   1930 In "Florist Exchange" (as *Compacta Nana*). Named for a tree found by H. Heistad of Rockport, Maine on Haystalk Mountain. NIC.   B,S

- - **'Ruggs Washington Dwarf'** H.G. Hillier

    1964 In "Dwarf Conifers". A globular dwarf with cinnamon shoots and hairy buds. Named for a plant in the U. S. Nat. Arb., Washington DC. The origin is not on record? ('Ruggii', 'Washingon Dwarf' and other names are found).   K,S,W2   U.S.A.

- - **'Salicifolia'** Verkade   In "Nurs. Cat". Named for a small tree on the Detmer Nurs, Torrytown, N.Y. and **I.** by them.   S   U.S.A.

- - 'Saratoga Broom' Hort. Amer.   Now known as 'Beaujean'.   B

- - **'Sargentii'** F.J. Scott   1870 See article on this group of pendulous forms in Swartley.   S   U.S.A.

- - 'Sargentii Pendula' Hort.   A mistake for 'Sargentii'.   H

- - **'Schramm'** Welch in Swartley

    1984 A narrowly fastigiate tree. **O.** Named for a tree found by Dr. J.R. Schramm near Compass, PA. but possibly never brought into cultivation.   S   U.S.A.

- - 'Sherwood' Hort. Amer.   See the following entry.

- - **'Sherwood Compact'** Welch in Swartley

    1984 A slow-growing mound with twisted branches and dark green leaves. **O.** Sherwood Nurs, Portland, OR.   S   U.S.A.

- - **'Silver Tip'** Helene Bergman

    1965 In "Plants and Gardens 21". A free-growing shrub with short white-tipped branchlets. **O.** A seedling at the Bergman Nurs, Raraflora, Feasterville, PA.   U.S.A.

- - **'Silvery Gold'** Welch in Swartley

    1984 A plant similar to 'Everitt Golden' but with silvery-white growth tips. Listed by Raraflora Nurs, (1970) under the illegit name 'Bergman's Aurescens Nana'.   S   U.S.A.

- - **'Slenderella'** Welch in Swartley

    1984 A quick-growing clone with small, light green leaves. Named for a plant at Longwood Gardens, Kennet Square, PA. ('Julians').   S   U.S.A.

- - **'Snowflake'** Welch in Swartley

    1984 A free-growing bush with a good white colour. **I.** Raraflora Nurs, Feasterville, PA. (as 'Raraflora Snowflake').   G?,S   U.S.A.

- - 'Sparsifolia' Beissner   1891 NIC.   B,K

- - 'Sport of Coles' Hort. Amer.   Now known as 'Helene Bergman.'   K

- - 'Sport of Jervis' Hort. Amer.   Said to have been found by Fred Bergman as a vigorous mutation on 'Jervis', but the distinction does not seem to have been established.

- - **'Starker'** Welch in Swartley

    1984 Probably a seedling of 'Sargentii' type but slower-growing. (Minuta Pendula', 'West Coast Creeper', 'West Coast Spreader'. **O.** Carl Starker of Jennings Lodge, OR. **I.** Bergman's Raraflora Nurs, Feasterville, PA.   W2   U.S.A.

- - **'Stewart's Gem'** Welch in Swartley
  1984 A compact form with cinnamon tips. ('Stewartii'. 'Stewart's
  Dwarf', 'Stewart's Dwarf Globe').   S   U.S.A.

- - **'Stockman's Compact'** J.Vermeulen ex Lewis
  1961 In "Amer. Nurs. **114**". A slow-growing compact form,
  eventually belying it's name. **I.** Vermeulen and Sons Nurs,
  Neshanic Station, N.J. (1960). Previously listed as
  ('Compacta Mk 2') (1941).   B,S   U.S.A.

- - **'Stockman's Dwarf'** J.Vermeulen ex Lewis
  1961 In "Amer. Nurs. **114**". Grows in tight mounds of prune-type
  growth. **I.** As previous item. ('Compacta Mk 1') (1941-1960).   B,K,S   U.S.A.

- - **'Stranger'** Swartley in Den Ouden/Boom
  1965 A compact tree-form named for a tree in the Cherry Hill Nurs,
  Newbury. Mass. ('Strangeri').   B,K,S   U.S.A.

- - 'Summer Snow' Hort. Amer.   A listed name for a conical clone intermediate in all respects
  between 'Albo-spica' and 'Gentsch White'.   S   U.S.A.

- - 'Suncrest' Hort. Amer.   1993 A listed name.

- - 'Swain' Hort. Canada   1986 A listed name. No information.

- - **'Taxifolia'** Abbott ex Jenkins
  1935 In "Hemlock Arb. Bull. **11**". A slow-growing form with yewlike foliage. Found by Frank L. Abbott near Athens, Vermont.
  NIC.   B,K,S   U.S.A.

- - **'Thurlow'** Welch in Swartley
  1984 A fast-growing clone of the 'Hussii' type. **O.** Found by Greg
  Williams and Layne Ziegenfuss in the Cherry Hill Nurs, and
  named in honour of M. Thurlow, part owner of that nursery.   S   U.S.A.

- - **'Towson'** Helene Bergman
  1965 In "Plants and Gardens **21**". A slow-growing upright compact
  tree with very dark leaves. **I.** Rock Creek Nurs, Rockville,
  MD. (1930). NIC. **O.** Found on the Towson Nurs,
  Cockeysville, MD. (1930).   B,S   U.S.A.

- - 'Trebnitz' Hort. Germany
  1991 Plant in Windsor Great Park, Berks. More inf. required.

- - 'Tristate' Hort. Amer.   A listed name for a dense. narrowly conical plant raised from
  a witch's broom.

- - 'Tucker's Selection' Hort. Amer.
  An unacceptable listed name.

- - **'Unique'** Welch in Swartley
  1984 A dense, flat, bun-shaped plant. **O.** A seedling in the South
  Wilton Nurs. Wilton, Conn.   S   U.S.A.

- - **'Upper Bank'** Welch in Swartley
  1984 A slow-growing conical form found by Greg Williams and
  Layne Zeigenfuss on the Upper Bank Nurs. Media. PA. **I.**
  Layne Zeigenfuss. Hillside Nurs. Lehighton, PA.   S   U.S.A.

- - **'Valentine'** Welch in Swartley
  1984 Named for a wide-spreading tree lacking a leader found by
  the Valentine Nurs, Cosby, Tenn.   S   U.S.A.

- - **'Van Dyne'** Welch in Swartley
  1984 A selection in the 'Cinnamomea' group   S   U.S.A.

- - 'Variegata' Jaeger in Beissner
  1884 An early selection no longer distinguishable in cultivation   S

- - **'Variegata Gentsch'** Hort. Amer.
    1984 Now to be 'Gentsch White'.

- - **'Verkade Petite'** Reg'd. Arn. Arb.
    1969 In "Arnoldia **29**". A diminutive plant with a crowded branch
          system and fresh-green young foliage, but a rather poor
          constitution. **O.** Found by John Verkade (1930).   S,W   U.S.A.

- - **'Verkade Recurved'** Reg'd. Arn. Arb.
    1968 In "Arnoldia **29**". An open-growing clone with irregular
          growth habit and recurved leaves. It was registered by W.
          John Verkade who found the plant in a private collection.   G,R,S,W   U.S.A.
- - **'Verkade's Pincushion'** Hort. Amer
          Now known as 'Pincushion'.

- - **'Verkade's Witch's Broom'** Hort. Amer.
    1984 Now known as 'Kathryn Verkade'.

- - **'Vermeulen's Pyramid'** J.Vermeulen
    1960 In "Nurs. Cat". A narrow columnar tree with dense foliage.
          O. Collected by Wm. C. Horsford of Charlotte, Vermont
          (1915). **L.** Vermeulen and Sons Nurs. Neshanic Station, N.J.
          (1960).   B,K,S,W   U.S.A.

- - **'Von Helms'** Helene Bergman
    1965 In "Plants and Gardens **21**". A dense irregular cone with large
          dark green leaves. ('Von Helms' Dwarf'). **O.** A seedling on the
          Wm. von Helms Nurs. Monsey, N.Y.   B,K,W   U.S.A.

- - **'Warner's Armistice'** Hort. Amer.
          Now known as 'Armistice'.

- - **'Warner's Globe'** Welch in Swartley
    1984 A large, rather open, globose bush with foliage in tufts. **I.**
          Ralph M. Warner of Milford, Conn.   K,R,S,W   U.S.A.

- - **'Warnham'** D.W. Hatch   1985 In "Nurs. Cat". **O.** Raised from a witch's broom found at
          Warnham Court, Surrey. It forms quite a vigorous carpet
          plant. **I.** Chantry Nurs, Honiton, Devon.

- - **'Watnong Star'** Reg'd. Arn. Arb.
    1970 In "Arnoldia **30**". Forms a globose plant. The very soft
          foliage is almost white. **I.** Watnong Nurs, Morris Plains N.J.
          O. Found in a wood in New Hampshire.by Robert Clark.   G,W2   U.S.A.

- - **'Waverly'** Jenkins   1948 In "Hemlock Arb. Bull. **61**". Named for a large tree found by
          Francis J. Stokes of Germanstown, Philadelphia. PA.   S   U.S.A.

- - 'Wellesleiana' Hornibrook
    1939 Named for a plant said to have at one time to have existed in
          the Hunnewell Pinetum, Wellesly, Mass., but not now
          traceable. NIC.   H,S   U.S.A.

- - 'West Coast Creeper' Hort. Amer.
          Now known as 'Starker'.

- - **'Westonigra'** Den Ouden/Boom
    1965 A compact clone of exceptionally dark green. **O.** and **I.** The
          Weston Nurs. Weston, Mass. (1940).   B,S   U.S.A.

- - 'Wheelerville' Swartley in Den Ouden/Boom
    1965 Probably NIC. Makes a dense, slow cone.   B,S   U.S.A.

- - 'White Tips' Hort. Anglia
    1985 A listed name. No further information.

- - 'Will's Dwarf' Hort. Anglia
    1985 A listed name. No further information.

- - **'Wilton'** Swartley in Den Ouden/Boom
      1965 A graceful. well-clothed tree; leaves bright glossy green. **O.**
           Raised by C. van Heiningen of the Wilton Nurs, Wilton,
           Conn.   B,S   U.S.A.

- - 'Wilton Globe' Hort. Amer.
      1986 An old name probably no longer in use.   S

- - **'Wind's Way'** S. Waxman
      1990 In "Int. Pl. Prop. Soc. Bull". **O.** S. Waxman at Univ. of
           Connecticut, Storrs, CT.

- - **'Wodenethe'** Welch in Swartley
      1984 One of the four original plants in the 'Sargentii' group.   S   U.S.A.

- - 'Yellow Tip' Hort. Amer.   1986 An unacceptable listed name.

- - **'Youngcone'** Greg Williams in Swartley
      1984 A bushy clone that regularly bears cones when only 5/6 years
          old. **O.** Found by Greg Williams in a pasture in Vermont.   S   U.S.A.

- - 'Youngs Coning' C. R. Harrison
      1975 In "Ornamental Conifers". A mistake for previous entry.

TSUGA caroliniana Engelmann
      1881 The Carolina Hemlock.   15-20m,Z6   S.E. U.S.A.

- - **'Adams Weeping'** Welch in Swartley
      1984 An upright unsymmetrical tree with pendulous branches. **O.**
          Selected by Percy Adams of the Rothswald Estate in
          Jenkintown, PA. **I.** Raraflora, Feasterville, PA.   U.S.A.

- - **'Arnold Pyramid'** Reg'd. A. A. N.
      1949 Slow-growing, densely conical tree. **I.** Arnold Arboretum,
          Jamaica Plains, Mass. **O.** Kelsey Nurs, East Boxford, Mass.
          (1931).   B,K   U.S.A.

- - **'Ashford'** Welch in Swartley
      1984 Named for a tree in the Hemlock Arboretum with unusual
          foliage pattern and dark green foliage. It was supplied by the
          Gardens of the Blue Ridge, Ashford, N. Carolina (1938).   S   U.S.A.

- - 'Compacta' Hornibrook
      1939 At first described as a dwarf, dense shrub in the Arnold
          Arboretum, the plant eventually became fully arboreal. The
          name should not now be recognised or re-used for a different
          clone.   B,H,S,W2   U.K.

- - **'Elizabeth Swartley'** Welch in Swartley
      1984 Named for a pendulous tree with the habit of *Cedrus deodara*
          on the Joséph B. Gable property near Stewartstown, PA. This
          very elite selection was named by Dr. Swartley in honour of
          his wife.   S   U.S.A.

- - 'Frick Estate' Hort. Amer.
      1988 A listed name without description. **L.** Mitsch Nurs, Boring,
          OR.

- - **'LaBar Bushy'** Welch in Swartley
      1984 A large, loose-growing shrub with mutiple stems. **O.** The La
          Bar Rhododendron Nurs, Stroudsberg, PA.   S   U.S.A.

- - **'LaBar Weeping'** L. Zeigenfuss
      1967 **L.** Hillside Nurs. A plant that is slow-growing and prostrate
          unless stem trained. **O.** A selected seedling in the same
          nursery as the previous item.   G,R,S,W   U.S.A.

- - **'Warner Weeping'** Welch in Swartley

        1984 A tree similar to 'Adam Weeping' but less strongly pendulous.
             O. Ralph M. Warner, Conn.   U.S.A.

- - 'Zwerg' Horstmann   1986 Dwarf. broad, upright plant with picturesque outline. New
                              name required. **O.** Horstmann Nurs. Schneverdingen.

TSUGA chinensis (Franchet) Pritzel

        1900 Chinese Hemlock.   15m,Z6   China

- - var. *daibuensis* Ying   1974 See *TSUGA chinensis* var. *formosana.*

- - var. *formosana* (Hayata) Li ex Keng

        1954 Formosan Hemlock. Here listed as a distinct species.

- - var. *oblongi squamata* Cheng et Fu

        1978 A local variant differing in its scales.

- - var. *robusta* Cheng et Fu

        1936 Description as last entry.

- - var. *tchekiangensis* (Flous) Cheng et Fu

        1978 Another local variant similarly distinguished. (per Rushforth,
                1987).   R

TSUGA crassifolia Flous   1936 A species close to *TSUGA blaringhemii*, q.v.

TSUGA diversifolia (Maximowicz) Masters

        1881 Northern Japanese Hemlock.   15m,Z5   N. Japan

- - **'Gotelli'** Welch in Swartley

        1984 Named for a dense, irregular dwarf plant in the Wm. Gotelli
                collection in the U.S. Nat. Arb. Washington D.C. that had
                come from the Thompson Nurs, in New Zealand.   R,S,W   U.S.A.

- - 'Hedergott' Hort. Germany

        1983 Cushion shaped dwarf form. **O.** Horstmann Nurs.
                Schneverdingen.

- - **'Manifold'** Welch in Swartley

        1984 Named for another tree in the same collection. A small, flat-
                topped tree with an open branch system but very dense
                foliage.   S   U.S.A.

- - 'Medford Lake' Welch in Swartley

        1986 A small tree found in the Medford Nurs. Medford, N.J. **I.**
                Edward Harbaugh, Taunton Lake. Medford, N.J.

- - 'Nana' Hort. Amer.   Now to be 'Gotelli'.

- - 'Thompson' Welch in Swartley

        1964 Named for a small plant in the Arnold Arboretum, received
                from the Thompson Nurs, Kinderhook, N.Y.

TSUGA douglasii Carrière   1855 Now known as *PSEUDOTSUGA menziesii*.

TSUGA dumosa (D. Don) Eichler

        1889? Himalayan Hemlock. Formerly known as *ABIES brunoniana*,
                and under other names.   20-40m,Z7   N. India

TSUGA dura Downie   1923 Not now distinguished within *TSUGA dumosa.*

TSUGA formosana Hayata 1908 Taiwan Hemlock. Allied to *TSUGA chinensis*, of which it is
                         treated as a variety by some authorities.   20-50m   Taiwan

TSUGA forrestii Hayata   1923 Forrest Hemlock. By some authorities now merged in *TSUGA*
                        chinensis.   15m,Z7   China

TSUGA hanburyana   A superfluous name for *TSUGA sieboldii*.

TSUGA x *henryi*	See *TSUGA* x *jeffreyi*.	30m,Z6	W. U.S.A.

TSUGA heterophylla (Rafinesque) Sargent
1832 Western Hemlock. — 50m,Z6 — W. Canada

- - 'Argenteo-variegata' (Beissner) Silva Tarouca
1923 Branches silvery-white at first. NIC? — B,K,R,S — Germany

- - 'Belvedere' Hort. Anglia — 1985 A listed name. No further information.

- - 'Conica' P. den Ouden — 1949 A dense conical to ovoid shrub. O. Raised from seed collected in the Gimborn Arboretum, Doorn. — B,G,K,R — Holland

- - 'Dumosa' P. den Ouden — 1949 An unacceptable name. See Art. 31A of the "Cultivar Code". — B,K,R

- - 'Epstein Dwarf' Hort. Amer.
1986 A listed name. No further information.

- - **'Green Mantle'** H.G. Hillier
1971 In "Hillier's Manual". Named for a tall, graceful narrow tree with pendulous branches in Windsor Great Park, Berks. **I.** Hillier's Nurs, Winchester. — U.K.

- - **'Iron Springs'** Reg'd. Arn. Arb.
1972 Slow-growing, irregular, dwarf form with dark green leaves, I. University of Washington. O. Found by Mrs Blogg of Seattle, near Iron Springs, Washington. — R,W2 — U.S.A.

- - 'June Morley' Int. Con. Reg.
1978 Registered by A.L. Lowry. Navan, Co. Meath. (13 Nov. 1978). A slow-growing, densely pendulous tree. O. Found by Pubble Nurs, Pubble, Co. Fermanagh. — Ireland

- - **'Laursen's Column'** H. G. Hillier
1971 In "Hilliers' Manual". A striking tree of loosely columnar habit. I. Hillier's Nurs, Winchester. O. A seedling found by Mr. Asger Laursen (1968) on the Hillier Nurs. — R,S — U.K.

- - 'Morris's Weeper' Hort. Amer.
1984 Named for a pendulous tree 10m high, found by R.D. Morris, whilst taking photographs on the Willapa Bay Game Estate, Washington. It is available in the trade. — U.S.A.

- - 'Nana' Hort. Canada — An illegit. listed name.

- - **'Sixes River'** Welch in Swartley
1984 A curious mutation on one twisted branch of a 25m tree, found by Ronald Gourley of Blue Diamond Nurs, Wington, OR. — S — U.S.A.

- - 'Variegata' Hort. Germany
1986 An illegit. name.

TSUGA hookeriana Carrière
Now known as *TSUGA mertensiana*.

TSUGA intermedia Handel-Mazzetti
1924 Intermediate between *TSUGA chinensis* and *TSUGA yunnanensis*.

TSUGA x *jeffreyi* (Henry) — 1919 A natural hybrid: *TSUGA heterophylla* x *TSUGA mertensiana*. — N. America

TSUGA leptophylla Handel-Mazzetti
1924 Not distinguished within *TSUGA dumosa*.

TSUGA lindleyana Roezl

TSUGA longibracteata Cheng
    1932 Bristlecone Hemlock.   30m,Z7   China

TSUGA mertensiana (Bongard) Carrière
    1867 Mountain Hemlock   20-30m,Z5   West N. Amer.

- - f. *argentea* (Beissner) Rehder
    1949 A botanical designation covering all glaucous blue, white or
    grey forms. (See Swartley p.168).   B,K,S   Sporadic

- - 'Argenteovariegata' Beissner
    1909 A descriptively named selection no longer distinguishable.   Germany

- - **'Blue Cloud'** Poulsen ex Krüssmann
    1979 A selection with intensely blue leaves. O. Raised by D.T.
    Poulsen Nurs, Kelleriis.   G,S   Denmark

- - **'Blue Star'**.H.J. Grootendorst
    1965 In "Dendroflora 2". A clone of an outstanding blue colour.
    O. and I. J. Konijn Nurs, then of Heemstede.   G,K,R,S   Holland

- - **'Cascade'** Welch in Swartley
    1984 A very compact, slow-growing conical plant. O. Found by
    J.D. Vertrees of Oregon on the Cascade Mountains, Douglas
    Co. OR. and distributed by him in the trade.   R,S,W2   U.S.A.

- - **'Columnaris'** Krüssmann
    1955 Named for a compact, columnar tree in the Arboretum at
    Drafle.   K,S   Sweden

- - **'Elizabeth'** Welch in Swartley
    1984 A spreading dwarf form, twice as wide as high. O. Found on
    Mount Rainier by Mrs. Elsie Fry's daughter, Elizabeth. I.
    Caperci's Alpine Garden at Mount Rainier, Seattle.   R,S,W2   U.S.A.

- - 'Emile's Select' Hort. Amer.
    1986 A listed name. No further information.

- - **'Glauca'** Hesse
    1940 This was the first glaucous-blue clone to be named. Seedlings
    of various shades of blue and silvery-grey turn up.   B,K,S,W2   Germany

- - **'Glauca Fastigiata'** Krüssmann
    1983 Name only.   K   Germany

- - 'Glauca Nana' Hort Amer.
    1980 An illigit. name for a slow-growing plant with good pale blue
    colour. L. Watnong Nurs, Morris Plains, N.J.

- - 'Glauca Prostrata' Hort. Anglia
    1985 A listed name. No further information.

- - **'Mount Arrowsmith'** Welch in Swartley
    1984 A slow-growing conical plant. O. A plant found in the wild
    by Ed. Lohbrunner of Victoria, B.C.   Canada

- - **'Mount Hood'** Welch in Swartley
    1984 A slow-growing plant originally found "in the wild".
    (Formerly distributed as 'Sherwood Compacta').   U.S.A.

- - **'Murthly Castle'** Welch in Swartley
    1984 Named for a large pendulous tree at Murthly Castle, Perth,
    evidently one of the earliest introductions of this species into
    Britain.   S   Scotland

- - **'Nana'** Welch
    1966 Named for a dwarf plant in Mr. Gotelli's collection which
    does not seem to have survived. The name must not be re-
    used.   G,W   Scotland

- - 'Nana Pendula' Hort. Anglia
          1985 A listed name. No further information.

- - **'Quartz Mountain'** Welch in Swartley
          1984 A very slow-growing conical form collected on Quartz Mountain by George Scheuk of the Wild Garden, Kirkland, Washington.   S   U.S.A.

- - 'Sherwood Compacta' Hort. Amer.
          Now known as 'Mount Hood'.   W2

- - 'Van's Prostrate' Hort. Amer.
          1986 A very tight-growing, spreading form, found at Wells Creek, Mount Baker, Washington by Lewis van Winkle (1966) as a plant 6 ft spread by 18" high. **I.** Very difficult to propagate but now in limited production.

TSUGA patens Downie   1923 Not know distinguished within *TSUGA chinensis.*

TSUGA pattoniana Sénéclauze
          1868 Not now distinguished within *TSUGA mertensiana.*

- - var. *jeffreyi* Henry   1907 Now known as *TSUGA* x *jeffreyi.*

- - 'Foliis Variegatis' Beissner
          1891 A form with coloured foliage. **O.** Raised from seed by Hesse.

TSUGA sieboldii Carrière 1855 Southern Japanese Hemlock.   20m,Z6   Japan

- - 'Nana' (1) Carrière   1855 A cultivated dwarf form with short leaves rarely over lm high.   Hort. Japan

- - 'Nana' (2) Welch   1966 A dwarf tree listed in the Gotelli collection (1962) which had grown only 2 ft in 20 years. This, together with plants labelled 'Compacta' and 'Fastigiata' were supplied to him by Thompson Nurs, (1961).   G,W   U.S.A.

- - **'National'** Welch in Swartley
          1984 Named for a picturesque. fast-growing tree in the U.S. Nat. Arb., Washington, DC, selected by Robert F. Doren.   S   U.S.A.

- - 'Variegata' Hort. Japan 1987 A yellow variegated form for which a new name is required. **O.** Y. Hirose. Iwakuni, Japan.

TSUGA stairi Hort.   Now known as *PSEUDOTSUGA menziesii* 'Stairi'.

TSUGA taxifolia Juntze   Now known as *PSEUDOTSUGA menziesii.*

TSUGA tschekiangensis Flous
          1936 Now known as *TSUGA chinensis.*

TSUGA tsuja Murray   See *TSUGA sieboldii.*

TSUGA wardii Downie   1923 See *TSUGA chinensis*

TSUGA yunnanensis (Franchet) Pritzel
          1900 Not now distinguished within *TSUGA chinensis* by some authorities.

WIDDRINGTONIA Endlicher (1842)

Cupressaceae

The Widdringtonias comprise three species of evergreen trees allied to *Callitris* from southern and eastern Africa. They can only be grown in the mildest areas in Britain. There have been several name changes.

WIDDRINGTONIA cedarbergensis Marsh
          1966 Clanwilliam Cedar.   5-10m,Z9   S. Africa

WIDDRINGTONIA cupressoides (L.) Endlicher
          1847 See *WIDDRINGTONIA nodiflora.*

WIDDRINGTONIA dracomontana Stapf.
          1916 See *WIDDRINGTONIA nodiflora.*

WIDDRINGTONIA juniperoides (L.) Endlicher
          1847 See *WIDDRINGTONIA cedarbergensis.*

WIDDRINGTONIA nodiflora (L.) Powrie
          1972 Sapree-Wood.   10-40m, Z9   S. Africa

WIDDRINGTONIA schwarzii (Marloth) Masters
          1905 Willowmore Cedar.   15-25m,Z9   S. Africa

WIDDRINGTONIA whytei Rendle
          1884   B